MERRILL

Focus On Physical Science

AUTHORS
Charles H. Heimler
California State University—Northridge, California
Jack Price
Palos Verdes Peninsula Unified School District—Palos Verdes, California

CONSULTANT
Paul W. Zitzewitz
University of Michigan-Dearborn—Dearborn, Michigan

CONTENT CONSULTANTS
Jack T. Ballinger, Department of Chemistry
St. Louis Community College at Florissant Valley, St. Louis, Missouri
Gordon J. Aubrecht, Department of Physics
The Ohio State University, Columbus, Ohio

MERRILL
PUBLISHING COMPANY
A Bell & Howell Information Company
Columbus, Ohio
Toronto • London • Sydney

A MERRILL SCIENCE PROGRAM

Focus on Physical Science: Student Edition
Focus on Physical Science: Teacher Edition
Focus on Physical Science: Teacher Resource Book
Focus on Physical Science: Review and Reinforcement Guide
Focus on Physical Science: Review and Reinforcement Guide, Teacher Annotated Edition
Focus on Physical Science: A Learning Strategy for the Laboratory
Focus on Physical Science: A Learning Strategy for the Laboratory, Teacher Annotated Edition
Focus on Physical Science: Overhead Transparency Package
Focus on Physical Science: Chapter Review Software
Focus on Physical Science: Test Generator Software
Physical Science Skillcards
Safety Card Package
Focus on Life Science Program
Focus on Earth Science Program

Charles H. Heimler is Professor of Science Education at California State University at Northridge, California. He received his B.S. degree from Cornell University and his M.A. and Ed.D. degrees from Columbia University and New York University. In his 36 years in education, Dr. Heimler has taught general science, biology, chemistry, and physics at the secondary school level as well as chemistry and biology at the university level. He currently supervises student teachers in science and teaches a course in computer education.

Jack Price taught chemistry and mathematics for 13 years in Detroit before assuming administrative positions. He is presently Superintendent of Schools in Palos Verdes, California. He earned his B.A. degree at Eastern Michigan University and M.Ed. and Ed.D. degrees at Wayne State University. Dr. Price has participated in NSF summer institutes at New Mexico State University and the University of Colorado and has done original research in organometallic compounds at Wayne State University.

Paul W. Zitzewitz is Professor of Physics at The University of Michigan-Dearborn. He received his B.A. at Carleton College and his M.A. and Ph.D at Harvard University, all in physics. Dr. Zitzewitz has 17 years teaching experience and has served as Chair of the Department of Natural Science. He has published more than 50 research papers in the field of atomic physics, and is an author of Merrill's *Physics: Principles & Problems.*

Reading Consultant
David R. Urbanski, Reference Librarian, Dublin Branch Library, Dublin, Ohio

Special Features Consultants
Julie Herold, Science Teacher, Westerville North High School, Westerville, Ohio
John E. Roeder, Teacher's Clearinghouse for Science and Society Education, New York, New York
Laurel Sherman, Affiliate Scholar, Oberlin College, Oberlin, Ohio

Reviewers
Betty B. Humphreys, Physical Science Teacher
Irmo Middle School, Columbia, South Carolina
Eva Kirkpatrick, Physical Science Teacher
Seckman Junior High School, Imperial, Missouri
William E. Myers, Math/Science Curriculum Coordinator
Wheeling District 21, Wheeling, Illinois
Linda Noland, Physical Science Teacher
Edmond North Mid-High, Edmond, Oklahoma
Judith A. Oliver, Physical Science Teacher
Jarrett Junior High, Springfield, Missouri
William H. Rodgers, Science Supervisor
Williamsport School District, Williamsport, Pennsylvania
Clifton H. Smith, Physical Science Teacher
Millburn Junior High School, Millburn, New Jersey
Charles L. Wachs, Physical Science Teacher
Crestwood High School, Atlanta, Georgia
Christine B. Wilde, Chemistry/Physics Teacher
Central Catholic High School, Modesto, California

Series Editor: Joyce T. Spangler; *Project Editor:* Madelaine Meek; *Editor:* Teresa Anne McCowen; *Book Designer:* Kip M. Frankenberry; *Project Artist:* David L. Gossell; *Illustrators:* Dick Smith, Charles Passarelli, Jim Shough; *Photo Editor:* David Dennison; *Production Editor:* Helen C. Mischka

Cover Photograph: Robotic Arm: T. J. Florian from Rainbow

ISBN 0-675-03164-8

Published by
MERRILL PUBLISHING COMPANY
A BELL & HOWELL COMPANY
Columbus, Ohio 43216

To the Student

You will probably enjoy your study of physical science because you are curious about the world around you. Solar energy, machines, chemical changes, radiation, electricity, and many other aspects of your environment are all part of physical science. ***Focus on Physical Science*** will help you to understand many phenomena that occur in your everyday life.

Many jobs and careers require a background in physical science. Careers in chemistry, physics, health services, home economics, engineering, mechanics, and environmental protection make use of physical science principles. As you read ***Focus on Physical Science,*** *Career* features and *Biographies* will help you explore your interests in these fields and in many others.

Scientists use many methods to attack problems and find answers. In this textbook, you will learn some scientific problem solving strategies methods and how to use them. *Investigation, Skill,* and *Problem-Solving* activities will help you discover how you can use these same strategies in your own life. Their use will increase your success in solving everyday problems and accomplishing tasks.

Focus on Physical Science contains many features that will help you learn. Each unit begins with a photograph and a brief introduction to the theme of the unit. A *Timeline* points out important scientific events and their relationships to other historical events. The photograph and introductory paragraph at the beginning of each chapter describe the major theme of the chapter and relate it to your everyday life.

Each chapter has several major divisions. At the beginning of each major division, a list of *Goals* identifies what you will learn as you study the short, numbered sections. *Margin questions* printed in blue emphasize the important ideas in each section. Use these questions as self-checks to evaluate your progress. Major terms are highlighted in boldface type. At the end of each major division, *Review* questions provide another means of self-evaluation.

At the end of each chapter are study and review materials. The *Summary* provides a list of major points and ideas presented within the chapter. *Vocabulary* lists important new terms and contains a ten question vocabulary review. *Main Ideas* contains questions that are useful as a review of the chapter's concepts and questions that require you to apply what you have learned. *Skill Review* includes questions about and applications of the skills learned in this chapter and previous chapters. *Projects* provides thought-provoking problems and ideas for further exploration. Sources of more information are listed under *Readings*.

Several special features have been included to make your study of physical science more interesting. *Technology* features provide exciting information on new technological developments in physical science. A *Science and Society* feature located at the end of each unit offers you the opportunity to explore the interactions and effects of physical science on society.

At the end of the textbook are the *Appendices, Glossary,* and *Index*. The Appendices contain tables, charts, and safety information. The Glossary contains definitions of the major terms presented in the textbook. The complete Index will help you quickly locate specific topics within the textbook.

This textbook has been written and organized to help you learn physical science. As you do your classwork and complete your assignments, you will gain the satisfaction of understanding physical science and its applications to everyday life.

Table of Contents

UNIT 1

PHYSICAL SCIENCE FUNDAMENTALS

Chapter 1 The Nature of Science... 4

SCIENCE ACTIVITIES
- 1:1 A Case History 5
- **SKILL 1-1** 6
- **TECHNOLOGY:** APPLICATIONS 7
- 1:2 Scientific Methods 8
- 1:3 Theories and Laws 9
- **BIOGRAPHY:** Rosalind Franklin 9
- 1:4 Scientific Models 10

PROBLEM SOLVING
- 1:5 What is a Problem 11
- 1:6 Problem Solving Strategies 12
- **CAREER:** Technical Writer 12
- **SKILL 1-2** 13

SCIENCE AND YOU
- 1:7 Science and Technology 15
- 1:8 Physical Science 16
- 1:9 Experimentation 17
- **PROBLEM SOLVING** 19
- **SKILL 1-3** 20

Chapter 2 Physical Science Methods 24

MEASUREMENT
- 2:1 Units and Standards 25
- 2:2 International System of Units 26
- 2:3 Uncertainty in Measurement 26

USING SI
- 2:4 Length 29
- 2:5 Mass 31
- 2:6 Volume 32
- 2:7 Density 33
- **SKILL 2-1** 34
- **SKILL 2-2** 36
- 2:8 Time and Temperature 37

MORE PHYSICAL SCIENCE SKILLS
- 2:9 Laboratory Safety 39
- **TECHNOLOGY:** APPLICATIONS 39
- 2:10 Solving Equations 41
- **CAREER:** Carpenter 41
- **BIOGRAPHY:** Luis W. Alvarez 42
- 2:11 Graphing 43
- PROBLEM SOLVING 45
- **SKILL 2-3** 46
- **SCIENCE AND SOCIETY** 50

UNIT 2

FORCE AND ENERGY

Chapter 3 Motion 54

DESCRIBING MOTION IN A STRAIGHT LINE
- 3:1 Position and Distance 55
- 3:2 Speed and Velocity 56
- 3:3 Determining Speed 57
- **INVESTIGATION 3-1** 59
- 3:4 Acceleration 60
- **CAREER:** Sports Medicine Technician 61
- **SKILL** 64

FORCES AND MOTION
- 3:5 Inertia 65
- 3:6 Forces on Bodies 66
- 3:7 Newton's First Law of Motion 66
- **TECHNOLOGY:** ADVANCES 68

FORCES
- 3:8 Examples of Forces 69
- 3:9 Gravity and Weight 70
- **INVESTIGATION 3-2** 72
- 3:10 Measuring Forces 73
- **BIOGRAPHY** Galileo Galilei 73
- **PROBLEM SOLVING** 74

Chapter 4 The Laws of Motion....78

ACCELERATED MOTION
- 4:1 Newton's Second Law....79
- CAREER: Stunt Car Driver....80
- 4:2 Falling Objects....82
- INVESTIGATION 4-1....84

MOTION IN TWO DIRECTIONS
- 4:3 Projectiles....86
- 4:4 Motion in Circles....87
- SKILL....89
- 4:5 Weightlessness and Freefall....90
- TECHNOLOGY: ADVANCES....90

MOMENTUM
- 4:6 Newton's Third Law....91
- INVESTIGATION 4-2....94
- 4:7 Momentum and its Conservation....95
- 4:8 Rockets....95
- BIOGRAPHY: Isaac Newton....95
- PROBLEM SOLVING....96

Chapter 5 Energy....100

MECHANICAL ENERGY AND WORK
- 5:1 Energy of Motion....102
- 5:2 Potential Energy....102
- 5:3 Work and Energy Transfer....103
- 5:4 Energy Conservation....104
- BIOGRAPHY: Walter Massey....104
- INVESTIGATION 5-1....107
- CAREER: Biophysicist....108

THERMAL ENERGY AND HEAT
- SKILL....109
- 5:5 Temperature....110
- 5:6 Thermal Energy....110
- 5:7 Heat and Work....111
- TECHNOLOGY: APPLICATIONS....112
- 5:8 Measuring Thermal Energy....112
- 5:9 Using Calorimeters....114
- PROBLEM SOLVING....114
- INVESTIGATION 5-2....116

Chapter 6 Heat in our World....120

KEEPING COMFORTABLE IN THE COLD
- 6:1 Thermal Energy Transfer....121
- TECHNOLOGY: ADVANCES....123
- 6:2 Preventing Loss of Thermal Energy....124
- BIOGRAPHY: Mary Somerville....124
- INVESTIGATION 6-1....127
- 6:3 Heating Systems....128

PUTTING HEAT TO WORK
- SKILL....131
- CAREER: Heating, Ventilation, and Air Conditioning Technician....132
- 6:4 Heat Engines....132
- 6:5 Heat Movers....135
- PROBLEM SOLVING....136
- 6:6 Thermal Pollution....136
- INVESTIGATION 6-2....138

Chapter 7 Machines....142

SIMPLE MACHINES
- 7:1 What is a Simple Machine?....143
- 7:2 Mechanical Advantage....144
- CAREER: Metallurgical Engineer....145
- INVESTIGATION 7-1....147
- 7:3 The Lever....148
- 7:4 Pulleys....150
- TECHNOLOGY: APPLICATIONS....150
- 7:5 The Wheel and Axle....151
- 7:6 Inclined Plane, Screw, and Wedge....152
- INVESTIGATION 7-2....153

USING MACHINES
- 7:7 Combining Simple Machines....155
- 7:8 Efficiency....156
- 7:9 Power....157
- BIOGRAPHY: Lillian Gilbreth....157
- PROBLEM SOLVING....159
- SKILL....160
- SCIENCE AND SOCIETY....164

UNIT 3

THE NATURE OF MATTER

Chapter 8 Solids, Liquids, and Gases....168

THE FORMS OF MATTER
8:1 The States of Matter 169
8:2 The Kinetic Theory of Matter 170
INVESTIGATION 8-1 172
8:3 Thermal Expansion 173
CAREER: Hydraulic Engineer 174
THE NATURE OF A GAS
8:4 Pressure 175
8:5 Boyle's Law 176
8:6 Charles' Law 176
SKILL 178
FLUIDS
8:7 Archimedes' Principle 179
8:8 Pascal's Principle 180
BIOGRAPHY: Mary Ross 180
8:9 Bernoulli's Principle 181
TECHNOLOGY: APPLICATIONS 182
CHANGING STATES OF MATTER
8:10 Changes of State 184
8:11 Heats of Fusion and Vaporization . 185
8:12 Refrigerators and Heat Pumps 187
PROBLEM SOLVING 189
INVESTIGATION 8-2 190

Chapter 9 Classification of Matter 194
COMPOSITION OF MATTER
9:1 Substances 195
CAREER: Science Textbook Editor 196
9:2 Mixtures 197
9:3 Solutions, Suspensions, and Colloids 198
SKILL 199
INVESTIGATION 9-1 201
PROPERTIES OF MATTER
9:4 Physical Properties 202
TECHNOLOGY: APPLICATIONS 204
9:5 Physical Changes 204
9:6 Chemical Properties 204
9:7 Chemical Changes 206
BIOGRAPHY: Agnes Pockels 206
INVESTIGATION 9-2 207
PROBLEM SOLVING 210

Chapter 10 Atomic Structure and the Periodic Table 214
STRUCTURE OF THE ATOM
10:1 Elements 215
10:2 Models of the Atom 216
10:3 Parts of the Atom 217
10:4 Electron Cloud 218
BIOGRAPHY: Homer Neal 218
TECHNOLOGY: ADVANCES 219
10:5 Atomic Mass 220
10:6 Isotopes 221
CAREER: Electron Microscopist 222
SKILL 223
INVESTIGATION 10-1 224
THE PERIODIC TABLE
10:7 Structure of the Periodic Table 225
10:8 Groups of Elements 227
10:9 Periods of Elements 230
10:10 Chemical Activity 231
PROBLEM SOLVING 233
INVESTIGATION 10-2 234

Chapter 11 Chemical Bonds 238
HOW ATOMS COMBINE
11:1 Compounds 239
11:2 Which Elements Combine? 241
KINDS OF BONDS
11:3 Electron Loss and Gain 242
PROBLEM SOLVING 243
INVESTIGATION 11-1 244
11:4 Electron Sharing 245
11:5 Bonding in Solids 245
11:6 Hydrated Crystals 248
WRITING FORMULAS
11:7 Oxidation Numbers 249
TECHNOLOGY: APPLICATIONS 250
BIOGRAPHY: Emma Carr 251
INVESTIGATION 11-2 252
11:8 Naming Binary Compounds 253
11:9 Polyatomic Ions 253
CAREER: Chemistry Teacher 255
SKILL 256
SCIENCE AND SOCIETY 260

UNIT 4

PATTERNS OF MATTER

Chapter 12 Elements in Groups 1 Through 12

Chapter 12 Elements in Groups 1 Through 12 264

METALS

12:1 Properties of Metals 265
12:2 The Metallic Bond 265
INVESTIGATION 12-1 266
12:3 Flame Tests 267

GROUPS 1 AND 2

12:4 Alkali Metals 268
12:5 Alkaline Earth Metals 269
CAREER: Chemical Engineer 270

TRANSITION ELEMENTS

12:6 Properties of Transition Elements 273
12:7 Iron, Cobalt, and Nickel 274
12:8 Copper, Silver, and Gold 275
INVESTIGATION 12-2 276
12:9 Zinc, Cadmium, and Mercury 277
12:10 Lanthanoids and Actinoids 278
BIOGRAPHY: Chien-Shiung Wu 279

METALLURGY

12:11 Ores 280
12:12 Metal Alloys 281
TECHNOLOGY: ADVANCES 282
PROBLEM SOLVING 283
SKILL 284

Chapter 13 Elements in Groups 13 Through 18 288

NONMETAL GROUPS

13:1 Hydrogen 289
13:2 Halogens 290
CAREER: Cosmetologist 292
13:3 Noble Gases 293

MIXED GROUPS

13:4 The Boron Group 294
13:5 Nitrogen Group 296
INVESTIGATION 13-1 298
13:6 Oxygen Group 299
INVESTIGATION 13-2 303

THE CARBON GROUP

13:7 Carbon 304
13:8 Silicon and Its Compounds 307
TECHNOLOGY: ADVANCES 307
13:9 Germanium, Tin, and Lead 310
BIOGRAPHY: Mario Molina 310
PROBLEM SOLVING 311
SKILL 312

Chapter 14 Carbon and Organic Chemistry 316

ORGANIC COMPOUNDS

14:1 Organic Compounds 317
TECHNOLOGY: ADVANCES 318
14:2 Formulas for Hydrocarbons 318
BIOGRAPHY: Benjamin Alexander 319
INVESTIGATION 14-1 321
14:3 Isomers 322
14:4 Additional Compounds 323
SKILL 325
14:5 Polymers 326

BIOLOGICAL MOLECULES

14:6 Amino Acids and Proteins 328
PROBLEM SOLVING 329
INVESTIGATION 14-2 330
14:7 Carbohydrates, Lipids, and Vitamins 331
CAREER: Nutritionist 334
SCIENCE AND SOCIETY 338

UNIT 5

INTERACTIONS OF MATTER

Chapter 15 Solutions 342

SOLUTION THEORY
- 15:1 Types of Solutions 343
- 15:2 Solution Process 344
- 15:3 Rate of Solution 345
- TECHNOLOGY: APPLICATIONS 345
- SKILL 348

PARTICLES IN SOLUTION
- 15:4 Solvents 349
- 15:5 Polar Molecules 349
- CAREER: Dry Cleaning Operator 350
- 15:6 Solutions as Conductors 351

SOLUBILITY AND CONCENTRATION
- 15:7 Solubility Rules 353
- 15:8 Determining Concentration 354
- BIOGRAPHY: Ellen Richards 355
- 15:9 Saturated Solutions 356
- PROBLEM SOLVING 357
- INVESTIGATION 15-1 358
- 15:10 Effects of Solute Particles 359
- INVESTIGATION 15-2 360

Chapter 16 Chemical Reactions .. 364

CHEMICAL EQUATIONS
- 16:1 Writing Equations for Reactions... 365
- CAREER: Water Treatment Technician 366
- 16:2 Balancing Equations 367
- BIOGRAPHY: Jane Marcet 369

KINDS OF CHEMICAL REACTIONS
- 16:3 Synthesis Reactions 370
- 16:4 Decomposition Reactions 371
- 16:5 Displacement Reactions 371
- INVESTIGATION 16-1 372
- INVESTIGATION 16-2 374
- 16:6 Catalysts and Inhibitors 375
- TECHNOLOGY: APPLICATIONS 375
- SKILL 376

MASS AND ENERGY IN CHEMICAL REACTIONS
- 16:7 Conservation of Mass 378
- 16:8 Molecular and Formula Mass 379
- 16:9 Mass Relationships in Equations .. 380
- 16:10 Energy and Reactions 381
- PROBLEM SOLVING 382

Chapter 17 Acids, Bases, and Salts 386

ACIDS AND BASES
- 17:1 Common Acids 387
- TECHNOLOGY: APPLICATIONS 388
- 17:2 Common Bases 390
- 17:3 Ions in Acids and Bases 392
- 17:4 Anhydrides 394
- CAREER: Research Chemist 395

MEASURING ACIDITY
- 17:5 pH of a Solution 395
- 17:6 Determining pH 396
- 17:7 Neutralization and Salts 397
- SKILL 398
- 17:8 Titration 400
- BIOGRAPHY: Gerty Cori 401
- INVESTIGATION 17-1 402

REACTIONS OF ORGANIC ACIDS
- 17:9 Esters 403
- 17:10 Soaps and Detergents 404
- PROBLEM SOLVING 405
- INVESTIGATION 17-2 406
- SCIENCE AND SOCIETY 410

UNIT 6

WAVES, LIGHT, AND SOUND

Chapter 18 Waves and Sound ... 414

DESCRIBING A WAVE
- 18:1 Wave Characteristics ... 415
- 18:2 Frequency of a Wave ... 416
- 18:3 Velocity of a Wave ... 417
- **INVESTIGATION 18-1** ... 418

WHAT IS SOUND?
- **TECHNOLOGY:** ADVANCES ... 420
- 18:4 Compressional Waves ... 420
- 18:5 Velocity of Sound ... 422
- 18:6 Loudness and Pitch ... 422
- **SKILL** ... 423
- 18:7 The Doppler Effect ... 425
- **BIOGRAPHY:** Philip Morrison ... 425
- **CAREER:** Recording Engineer ... 426

MUSIC
- 18:8 Musical Sounds ... 427
- **INVESTIGATION 18-2** ... 428
- 18:9 Musical Instruments ... 429
- 18:10 Interference ... 430

CONTROLLING SOUND
- 18:11 Acoustics ... 432
- 18:12 Noise Pollution ... 433
- **PROBLEM SOLVING** ... 434

Chapter 19 Light ... 438

ELECTROMAGNETIC RADIATION
- 19:1 The Electromagnetic Spectrum ... 439
- **INVESTIGATION 19-1** ... 440
- 19:2 Radio and Microwaves ... 442
- **TECHNOLOGY:** APPLICATIONS ... 443
- 19:3 Infrared Radiation ... 444
- 19:4 Visible Radiation ... 445
- 19:5 Ultraviolet Radiation ... 445
- **BIOGRAPHY:** Ignacio Tinoco, Jr. ... 445
- 19:6 X Rays and Gamma Rays ... 446
- **SKILL** ... 447

LIGHT AND COLOR
- 19:7 Light and Matter ... 449
- 19:8 Colors ... 449
- **CAREER:** Commercial Artist ... 450
- 19:9 Pigment Colors ... 451

WAVE PROPERTIES OF LIGHT
- **INVESTIGATION 19-2** ... 454
- 19:10 Reflection ... 455
- 19:11 Refraction ... 455
- **PROBLEM SOLVING** ... 456
- 19:12 Diffraction and Interference ... 457

Chapter 20 Mirrors and Lenses ... 464

MIRRORS AND REFLECTION
- 20:1 Reflection in Plane Mirrors ... 465
- 20:2 Curved Mirrors ... 466
- **INVESTIGATION 20-1** ... 468
- **CAREER:** Photographer ... 470

LENSES AND REFRACTION
- 20:3 Lenses ... 471
- 20:4 Lenses and Vision ... 473
- 20:5 Telescopes and Microscopes ... 474
- **BIOGRAPHY:** George Carruthers ... 474
- 20:6 Cameras ... 476
- **SKILL** ... 478

SPECIAL APPLICATIONS OF LIGHT
- 20:7 Polarized Light ... 479
- 20:8 Lasers ... 480
- **PROBLEM SOLVING** ... 480
- 20:9 Optical Fibers ... 481
- **TECHNOLOGY:** APPLICATIONS ... 483
- **INVESTIGATION 20-2** ... 484
- **SCIENCE AND SOCIETY** ... 488

UNIT 7
ENERGY RESOURCES

Chapter 21 Electricity ... 492

STATIC ELECTRICITY
- 21:1 Electric Charge ... 493
- **INVESTIGATION 21-1** ... 495
- 21:2 Conductors and Insulators ... 496
- 21:3 The Electroscope ... 497
- **TECHNOLOGY:** ADVANCES ... 498

CURRENT ELECTRICITY
- 21:4 An Electric Current ... 499
- 21:5 Electric Potential ... 501
- 21:6 Resistance and Ohm's Law ... 501
- **CAREER:** Electrician ... 502
- **BIOGRAPHY:** Meredith Gourdine ... 503
- **SKILL** ... 504

ELECTRICAL CIRCUITS
21:7 Series Circuits 505
21:8 Parallel Circuits 506
INVESTIGATION 21-2 507
21:9 A Complex Circuit 508
ELECTRICAL ENERGY AND POWER
21:10 Electric Power 510
21:11 Calculating Electric Energy 511
PROBLEM SOLVING 512

Chapter 22 Electricity and Magnetism 516
MAGNETIC FIELDS AND FORCES
22:1 Magnets 517
22:2 Magnetic Fields 518
22:3 Effect of Magnetic Fields on Electric Charges 519
INVESTIGATION 22-1 520
22:4 Meters 521
22:5 Motors 521
TECHNOLOGY: APPLICATIONS 522
INVESTIGATION 22-2 524
PRODUCTION OF ELECTRIC CURRENTS
22:6 Generators 525
CAREER: Microwave Communications Engineer ... 525
22:7 Direct and Alternating Current 527
22:8 Transformers 527
BIOGRAPHY: Adriana Ocampo 527
ELECTRONICS
22:9 Diodes and Transistors 529
SKILL 531
22:10 Integrated Circuits 532
22:11 Radio and Television Transmission 533
22:12 Computers 534
PROBLEM SOLVING 535

Chapter 23 Radioactivity and Nuclear Reactions 540
RADIOACTIVITY
23:1 Radioactive Elements 541
23:2 Nuclides 542
CAREER: Nuclear Medicine Technician 543
TECHNOLOGY: APPLICATIONS 545
RADIOACTIVE DECAY
23:3 Nuclear Radiation 546
23:4 Decay and Half-Life 547
BIOGRAPHY: Irene Joliot-Curie 547
INVESTIGATION 23-1 548
SKILL 551
DETECTING RADIOACTIVITY
23:5 Radiation Detectors 552
23:6 Radiation Counters 553
INVESTIGATION 23-2 554
NUCLEAR REACTIONS
23:7 Fission 555
23:8 Fusion 556
PROBLEM SOLVING 558

Chapter 24 Energy Alternatives .. 562
ENERGY USE TODAY
24:1 Fossil Fuels 563
CAREER: Environmental Health Technician 565
24:2 Energy Conservation 566
BIOGRAPHY: Jose Martinez 566
SKILL 567
24:3 The Need for Alternatives 568
TECHNOLOGY: ADVANCES 568
RENEWABLE ENERGY SOURCES
24:4 Solar Energy 570
24:5 Hydroelectricity 571
24:6 Wind Energy 572
INVESTIGATION 24-1 573
24:7 Tidal Energy 574
24:8 Geothermal Energy 574
INVESTIGATION 24-2 575
NUCLEAR ENERGY
24:9 Nuclear Reactors 576
24:10 Nuclear Waste Disposal 578
24:11 Thermonuclear Energy 579
PROBLEM SOLVING 580
SCIENCE AND SOCIETY 584

APPENDICES 586
Appendix A: SI Units of Measurement . 587
Appendix B: Laboratory Safety and Techniques 587
GLOSSARY 592
INDEX 605
PHOTO CREDITS 613

Skills and Investigations

SKILL 1-1 Observing and Inferring.. 6
SKILL 1-2 Solving a Problem....... 13
SKILL 1-3 Identifying Variables and Constants............... 20

SKILL 2-1 Measuring Volume 34
SKILL 2-2 Comparing Densities..... 36
SKILL 2-3 Graphing................ 46

INVESTIGATION 3-1 A Distance Versus Time Graph 59
SKILL Analysis................. 64
INVESTIGATION 3-2 Measuring Force 72

INVESTIGATION 4-1 Change in Velocity 84
SKILL Studying Science Assignments............. 89
INVESTIGATION 4-2 Centripetal Force 94

INVESTIGATION 5-1 Mechanical Energy and Work.................... 107
SKILL Using a Calculator....... 109
INVESTIGATION 5-2 Work and Thermal Energy.................. 116

INVESTIGATION 6-1 Absorbing Radiation..... 127
SKILL Determining Cause and Effect 131
INVESTIGATION 6-2 Conduction and Convection.............. 138

INVESTIGATION 7-1 Pulleys.................. 147
INVESTIGATION 7-2 The Inclined Plane....... 153
SKILL Determining Constants and Variables 160

INVESTIGATION 8-1 All About Air............. 172
SKILL Asking the Right Question 178
INVESTIGATION 8-2 Change of State 190

SKILL Separating a Mixture.... 199
INVESTIGATION 9-1 Mixtures 201
INVESTIGATION 9-2 Chemical Properties...... 207

SKILL Predicting............... 223
INVESTIGATION 10-1 Atomic Models 224
INVESTIGATION 10-2 Metals and Nonmetals .. 234

INVESTIGATION 11-1 Ionic and Covalent Bonds 244
INVESTIGATION 11-2 Hydrated Crystals 252
SKILL Writing Chemical Formulas................ 256

INVESTIGATION 12-1 Flame Tests............. 266
INVESTIGATION 12-2 Transition Metal Compounds............. 276
SKILL Using Flow Charts 284
INVESTIGATION 13-1 Metals and Alloys....... 298
INVESTIGATION 13-2 Oxygen in Air........... 303
SKILL Classifying 312

INVESTIGATION 14-1 Organic Molecules 321
SKILL Making Models 325
INVESTIGATION 14-2 Textiles 330

SKILL Designing an Experiment.............. 348
INVESTIGATION 15-1 Solubility of a Salt....... 358
INVESTIGATION 15-2 Distillation............... 360

INVESTIGATION 16-1 Reactions That Produce Gases 372
INVESTIGATION 16-2 Displacement Reactions.. 374
SKILL Writing Balanced Chemical Equations............... 376

SKILL Using Various Indicators.. 398
INVESTIGATION 17-1 An Acid-Base Titration.... 402
INVESTIGATION 17-2 Soap and Detergent 406

INVESTIGATION 18-1 Frequency of Vibration .. 418
SKILL Interpreting Diagrams.... 423
INVESTIGATION 18-2 Musical Pitch 428

INVESTIGATION 19-1 Compressional and Transverse Waves 440
SKILL Drawing Conclusions 447
INVESTIGATION 19-2 The Spectrum of Light ... 454

INVESTIGATION 20-1 Concave Mirrors 468
SKILL Making Scale Drawings .. 478
INVESTIGATION 20-2 Convex Lenses.......... 484

INVESTIGATION 21-1 Electrostatics 495
SKILL Understanding Statistics.. 504
INVESTIGATION 21-2 Electric Circuits 507

INVESTIGATION 22-1 Electromagnets.......... 520
INVESTIGATION 22-2 Generating Current 524
SKILL Reading a Meter........ 531

INVESTIGATION 23-1 Half-Life Simulation 548
SKILL Carbon-14 Dating........ 551
INVESTIGATION 23-2 Radiation Protection 554

SKILL Evaluating Scientific Literature 567
INVESTIGATION 24-1 Solar Energy............ 573
INVESTIGATION 24-2 Energy Uses 575

UNIT 1

The history of science is one of discovery and invention. New knowledge, new materials, and new processes have come about sometimes by chance but most often through careful, well-planned research. All the discoveries of science, however, have resulted from a new way of looking at the very ordinary world around us.

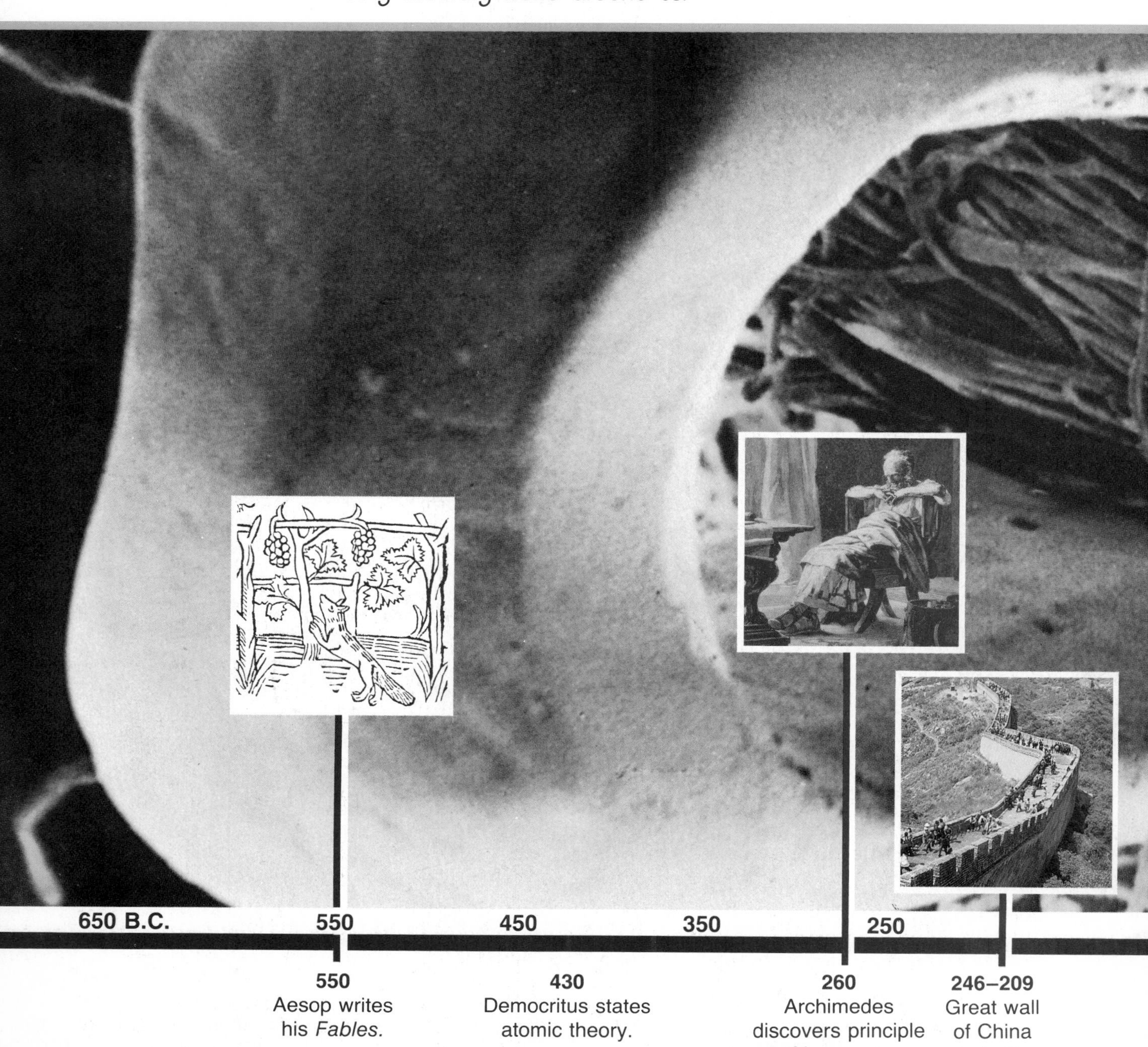

550
Aesop writes his *Fables*.

430
Democritus states atomic theory.

260
Archimedes discovers principle of buoyancy.

246–209
Great wall of China is built.

PHYSICAL SCIENCE FUNDAMENTALS

150 50 50 A.D. 1150 1250 1350

100
Cai Lun invents paper.

1260
Marco Polo travels to China.

1350
Black plague hits Europe.

SCIENCE ACTIVITIES
PROBLEM SOLVING
SCIENCE AND YOU

The Nature of Science

The earliest records of history have shown that humans have always tried to understand the world around them. Over the years we have organized much of what we know and tried to build on it. Science means "having knowledge." It is a process for observing, studying, and attempting to explain our world. Science is creative. Science is learning and doing. In this course you will be learning, explaining, and doing science through many science activities.

SCIENCE ACTIVITIES

How are scientific discoveries made? How are problems solved? Do all scientists use the same process? What part do "experiments" play? In the following sections, you will learn about many methods of problem solving used in science and in everyday life.

GOALS

1. You will learn scientific methods of problem solving.
2. You will learn about scientific laws, theories, and models.

1:1 A Case History

Not all scientists follow the same path in solving problems, nor does the same person solve problems in the same way each time. There are, however, methods that are common to most problem solving. This is true even if the problems are everyday rather than scientific.

In December 1984, an engineer who worked at a nuclear power plant in Pennsylvania ran into just such an "everyday" problem. The first time the engineer stepped into the plant's radiation detector, it buzzed and its red light went on. This meant he was contaminated with radiation. Day after day he would set off the alarm. Each time he would have to sit in the decontamination room. After four to six hours, the radiation would decrease to safe levels, and he could leave.

F.Y.I. Isaac Newton was once asked how he happened to make all his important scientific discoveries. He answered, "By thinking night and day."

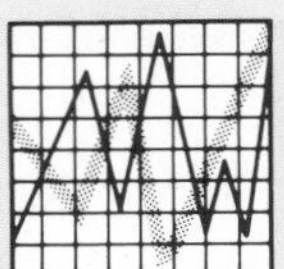

SKILL 1–1

Observing and Inferring

Problem: How can you determine the inside structure of a box?

Materials

a sealed box

paper and pencil

Background

Scientists must often make models of things that they cannot actually see. A model for the structure of an atom is but one example. How do scientists form models? Generally, they gather as much information as possible through various experiments. Then they make inferences based on their results. Scientists use these inferences as the basis for making models.

You can use this process to make a model of something you cannot see. Your teacher will give you a box that is fitted with slats in a maze-like arrangement. The box also contains a marble. Your "problem" is to describe a model for the inside structure of the box.

Procedure

1. Record the number of the box you are given. Lift, tilt, and gently shake the box. Do not open the lid or look inside the box.
2. Record all your observations. You may want to make a sketch of the way you think the marble in the box is rolling.
3. From your observations, infer what the inside structure of the box is like.
4. Compare your inferences with those of other students using the same box. You may wish to make additional observations and revise your inferences after making comparisons.
5. When you have finished making observations, sketch your model on a piece of paper.
6. When all students have completed their sketches, compare your model with the actual inside structure of the box you used.

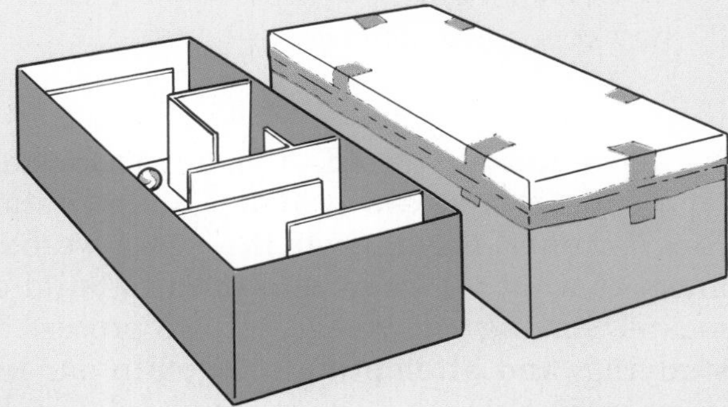

FIGURE 1–1.

Questions and Conclusions

1. How is an observation different from an inference?
2. How can you determine the inside structure of a box?

Decide whether each of the following is an inference or an observation.

3. a. The child is smiling.
   b. The child is happy.
4. a. A marble cannot roll to the lower left corner of the sealed box.
   b. There is a slat across the lower left corner of the sealed box.
5. a. I think there is someone at the door.
   b. The dog is barking at the door.
6. a. The air conditioner ran continuously through the night.
   b. It must be hot outside.

Listed below are several observations. Make an inference based on each of these observations.

7. The ice cream in the freezer was melted. (make an inference about the freezer.)
8. The lights in the house go out during a thunderstorm.
9. Water is splashing down the window.
10. Explain why your inferences for Questions 7–9 might be incorrect.

TECHNOLOGY: APPLICATIONS

Radon in Homes

In parts of Pennsylvania, New York, and New Jersey, radon is called "the cancer-causing time bomb." As many as 10% of all homes in the United States may contain unsafe levels of this radioactive gas.

Special equipment is needed to detect radon because you cannot see or smell it. The most widely used detectors are the charcoal canister and the alpha track detector (see Figure 1–2).

Radon usually enters houses through cracks or openings in basements. Thus, it is important to seal the floor and walls. A waterproofing sealant is good for this. Ventilation is also important. Opening windows, especially in the basement, and using fans will help to get rid of radon in indoor air. A more costly approach is the use of an air-to-air heat exchanger.

The methods used to reduce the amount of radon in a house will depend on the characteristics of that particular house. The United States Environmental Protection Agency publishes a homeowner's guide to radon reduction.

The engineer tried to figure out the source of the radiation. He thought about where he had been in the plant each day. The location did not seem to matter. Each time he walked into the radiation detector, the alarm went off. After this had gone on for about two weeks, he had an idea. Perhaps the contamination was not from the power plant at all. He tested this idea by going directly from his car to the detection device when he reported to work. It buzzed. He was not getting the radiation at work.

Only half the problem was solved, however. Where was he getting the radiation? His first guess was his house. Experts in radiation measurement went to his house and found extremely high levels of radon, a radioactive gas. This finding led the experts to further questions. What was the source of the radon? Was the source inside or outside the house? The experts decided to test other homes in the area. They tested over 2000 houses. More than 800 were found to have high levels of radioactivity. These results led them to suspect an outside source.

The experts studied the area further and found the radiation source. The houses were located over rocks containing uranium. Radon is produced when atoms of uranium break down. It was radon in the air of his home that caused the engineer's problem with radiation.

FIGURE 1–2. A radiation detector is used to check nuclear power plant workers for contamination.

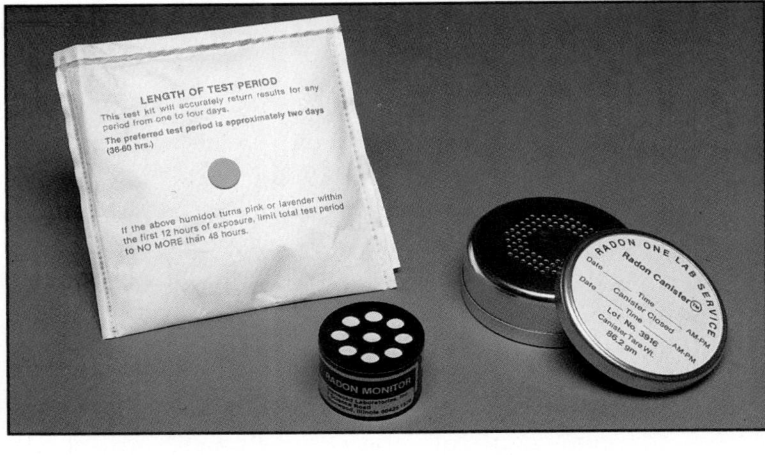

FIGURE 1–3. Several types of detectors can be used to test a home for radon. The detectors are exposed to the air in the house for a period of time and then sent for analysis.

1:2 Scientific Methods

In the radiation problem, the engineer's guess was right. Often guesses are not. Scientists often make wrong guesses, but they learn from them. They make observations. They propose and test ideas and then form conclusions. Observation is basic to science. **Observation** is the process of gathering information using the senses. When you observe something, you note facts about it. The buzzer sounded, and the red light flashed. These were observations. Tools are often used to make observations. Rulers, thermometers, microscopes, and clocks are but a few of these tools.

What is a hypothesis?

A scientist uses observation to help form a guess to solve a problem. This educated guess is called a **hypothesis.** The engineer guessed that his home was the source of radiation. A hypothesis can be tested. To test the guess, a scientist may set up an experiment. The experiment could help prove or disprove the hypothesis. The radiation experts tested the engineer's house. They found radiation in his house.

What is a conclusion?

A **conclusion** is a judgment based on interpreting observations. The conclusion may or may not support the hypothesis. The radiation experts saw their radiation detectors respond. They concluded that the engineer's radiation came from his house. In this case, the conclusion was correct. However, scientists do not usually base a conclusion on only one experiment. Nor do they use only one set of data. Experiments are often repeated. This is done to find out if the same results occur each time. The more often the results support the hypothesis, the more certain the scientist is that the hypothesis is correct.

How do scientists arrive at conclusions?

From experiments, scientists may infer more than one conclusion. An inference is a judgment based on reasoning from evidence. For example, from finding high radon levels in over 800 homes, scientists inferred that it came from an outside source. Further tests showed this inference to be correct.

Scientists may not always use these same methods. The work of successful scientists is not always the same step-by-step process. However, all scientists will study a problem or question in an organized manner. Skill, luck, trial and error, and intelligent guessing all play a part. Sometimes a scientist's mind is so well prepared that he or she can jump to the correct conclusion simply from asking the right questions.

BIOGRAPHY

Rosalind Franklin

1920–1958

Rosalind Franklin was a British physical chemist. She used X-ray analysis in her study of the properties of coal. Later she made DNA crystals and took X-ray pictures of this complex molecule. Her work was important in constructing a model of DNA.

1:3 Theories and Laws

A scientific **theory** is an explanation based on many observations during repeated experiments. All the data gathered by the scientists about the radiation in the Pennsylvania homes led to one explanation. Their theory was that the high radon concentration in the homes came from the ground on which the homes were built. Rocks in that area contain uranium. Uranium is a radioactive substance. Some of the uranium atoms break down and radon is formed in the process. Once the radon got into the homes, its concentration built up, and the people living there picked up the radiation.

What does a scientific law describe?

A scientific **law** is a "rule of nature" that describes the behavior of something in nature. Laws are also based on many observations. The following is a law. When a hot object is placed in a cold area, the object becomes cooler while its surroundings become warmer. Scientists have developed theories to explain why this

FIGURE 1–4. In modern laboratories, complex instruments aid scientists in making observations.

FIGURE 1–5. An early model for the atom was the solar system.

energy transfer occurs. When ice is heated, it melts. That is a law. The kinetic theory explains why ice melts.

Theories and laws can be changed. If new observations show a theory or law to be wrong, it is changed or discarded. For example, at one time there was a law that stated, matter can neither be created nor destroyed. New observations have shown that this law is not correct. Under certain conditions, matter changes to energy. The law was changed to account for the new observations. It now states, the total amount of matter and energy does not change.

1:4 Scientific Models

How do scientists use models?

Scientists often use models to explain something not easy to see or understand. A **model** is an idea, system, or mathematical expression that is similar to what a scientist is trying to explain. For example, an early model for the atom was the solar system. The center of the atom was compared to the sun. Electrons were like planets revolving around the sun. A model is not exactly like what is being described. However, it helps us understand. It does not have all the properties of the idea it describes, but it is a good fit.

Models may change. When more information was gained about the atom, the model was changed to that of an electron cloud. Because the electrons seem to cover all of the space around a nucleus, a cloud was a better model. The electron cloud appears to fill all the space around the center or nucleus.

Review

1. Label each of the following as an observation or an inference.
   a. The pencil is yellow.
   b. Water is a liquid.
   c. I did not study hard enough before the test.
   d. Copper(II) sulfate is blue.
   e. The dog is scratching because it has fleas.

2. How are data related to observations?

3. A window has light blue glass in it. Plants placed in this window either die or grow poorly. Suggest a hypothesis based on this observation.

4. What is the difference between a theory and a law?

★ **5.** Determine how the blood circulation system is a model for the refrigeration cycle in a refrigerator.

PROBLEM SOLVING

Every day people are faced with problems to solve. What can we do with nuclear waste? Where will we put our trash? What foods are most helpful to good health? How can we find a cure for AIDS? How can I get enough money together for the concert next month and still go to the movies this weekend? While these questions certainly vary in importance, each requires some degree of problem solving skill. In these sections, you will learn the differences between problems and exercises, and some ways to solve problems.

GOALS

1. You will learn to distinguish problems and exercises.
2. You will learn to use various problem solving strategies.

1:5 What Is a Problem?

The questions above are problems because someone wants to know the answers and does not yet know how to go about finding them. There is a gap between the present knowledge and the knowledge one wants to have. If there is no gap, and the person with the question can go directly to the solution, the "problem" is really an exercise. One can usually solve an exercise easily or, at least, have a good idea of how to solve it. With problems, however, the solutions are not clear.

How does an exercise differ from a problem?

What is a problem for one person may not be a problem for another. Finding the sum of 2 and 3 may be a problem for a first grader, but not for you. Solving for pH in pH $= -\log [H^+]$ is more likely a problem for you. But, in turn, it is just an exercise for someone who has studied chemistry.

FIGURE 1–6. To solve this problem, a line must be drawn from the center of one maze to the center of the other without crossing any lines.

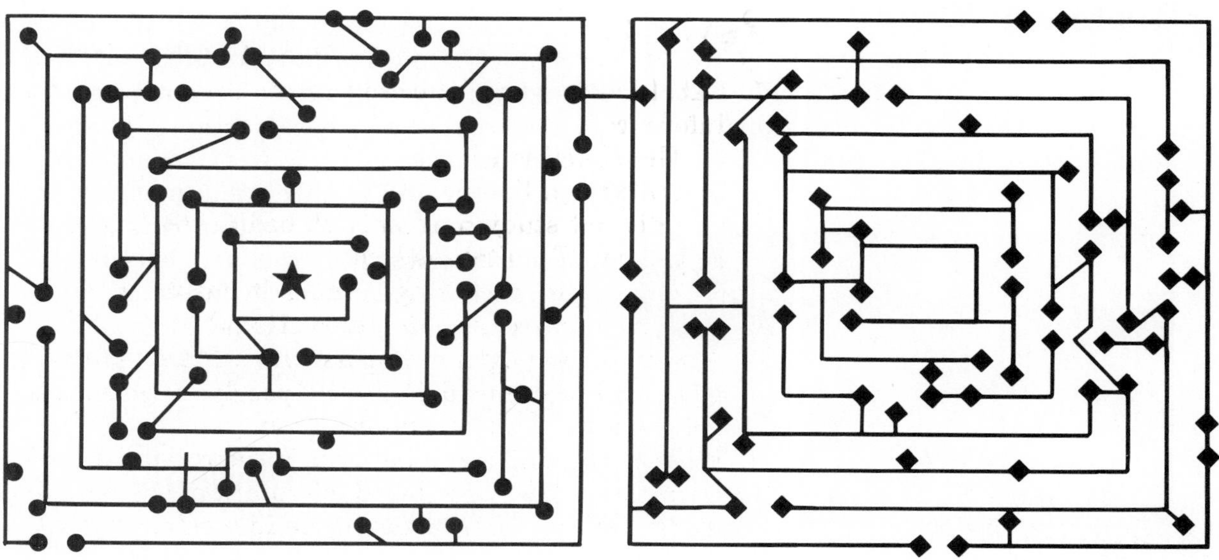

Problems always present new ideas or situations. Therefore, it is normal that one is not sure how or where to begin. Even the greatest scientists and inventors have traveled down paths that seemed to lead them nowhere. They learned from their mistakes. Thomas Edison found out that more than one hundred materials would not work as a light bulb filament before he finally tried carbonized thread.

Usually there are several ways to solve a problem, not just one right way. Fortunately, it is possible to learn many ways to go about solving problems. These ways are called problem solving strategies.

1:6 Problem Solving Strategies

In solving problems, it is important to want to solve them. You need to begin somewhere. Think about what you want to do, choose a strategy, and then try it. Be systematic in your approach. What you are trying to do is move from what you know to what you do not know.

How can you begin to solve a problem?

There are some good ways to get started. One is to make a guess, check it out, and, if it does not work, make another guess. The engineer first thought the radiation was from the plant. That idea proved wrong. He then guessed that the radiation was from his home, and he was right. If he had been wrong again, he might have checked his car, stores, restaurants, or any number of other places.

CAREER

Technical Writer

As a student, Rosa Pérez found science terms easy to understand. She was also good at giving directions. Now Rosa is a technical writer.

Technical writers put scientific and technical information into easy to understand language. Rosa prepares manuals, catalogs, and instructional guides that are used to sell, assemble, and use machinery and scientific equipment.

If you have good writing and communications skills, you can become a technical writer. You can work in publishing, radio, TV, or advertising.

For career information, write
Society for Technical Communications, Inc.
815 15th Street NW, Suite 516
Washington, DC 20005

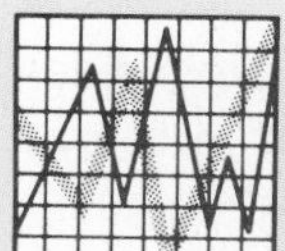

SKILL 1–2

Solving a Problem

Problem: Can you use problem solving strategies?

Materials

8 pennies   paper and pencil

Background

There are many ways to solve problems. Several problem solving methods are discussed in Section 1:6. When you analyze a problem, you should try to think about what methods will help you solve the problem efficiently. Often more than one method will work. Sometimes one method will solve part of the problem, but a different method must be used to solve the rest of the problem. Here are some examples of how problem solving methods can be used.

Problem Solving Example 1

Problem: Arrange 8 pennies as shown below.

H H H H __ T T T T

Move the pennies to form the following arrangement.

T T T T __ H H H H

Restrictions:

1. A penny cannot move more than one space at a time.
2. A penny cannot jump over more than one penny at a time, either heads or tails.
3. When moving a penny by jumping, tails can move left only and heads can move right only. Pennies may not be stacked.

You may decide that the best way to attack this problem is simply trial and error. Try it. If you are unsuccessful after several trials, you may want to consider other methods. Try breaking the problem into simpler problems.

1. Try to solve this problem: H __ T.
2. Next solve this problem: H H __ T T.
3. Then solve this problem: H H H __ T T T.
4. Finally solve the original problem.

Each time you solve one of the simpler problems, think about the steps you used. Try to use these steps to solve the large problem.

If you still cannot solve the problem, consider this series of steps for problem 2.

a.	H H __ T T	b.	H H T __ T
c.	H __ T H T	d.	H T __ H T
e.	H T T H __	f.	H T T __ H
g.	H T __ T H	h.	__ T H T H
i.	T __ H T H	j.	T T H __ H
k.	T T __ H H		

Now try to solve the original problem with all eight pennies. Before we leave this example, consider one other problem solving method: creative thinking. Reread the problem. Are there any restrictions on simply turning the pennies over? Sometimes we overlook simple answers to problems because of some preconceived ideas. Always read the problem carefully before trying to solve it.

Problem Solving Example 2

Problem: You have 5 large boxes. Inside each box are 3 smaller boxes. Inside each smaller box are 2 more boxes. How many boxes are there?

This problem can be solved easily by drawing a diagram.

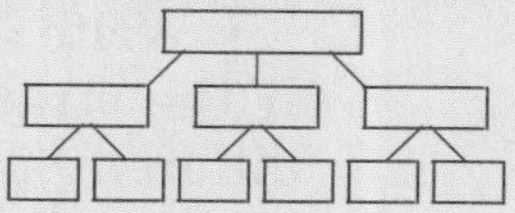

$$\frac{10 \text{ boxes}}{\text{set}} \times 5 \text{ sets} = 50 \text{ boxes}$$

Can you suggest another way to solve the problem?

Questions

1. Arrange four pennies in three rows of two. The rows must be at right angles to each other.
2. There are only two rectangles whose sides are whole numbers and whose area and perimeter are the same. What are they?

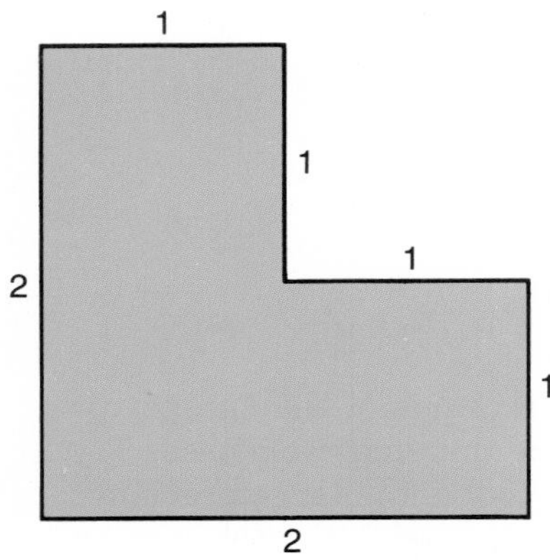

FIGURE 1–7. The drawing represents a piece of land in a new subdivision. It must be divided into four lots that are the same size and shape. How can this be done?

If a chosen strategy does not solve a problem, what should be done?

F.Y.I. Science is nothing but trained and organized common sense. —Thomas H. Huxley, *Collected Essays*

Another possibility is to look for a pattern, then predict what will happen next and check your prediction. As you will see in Chapter 10, Mendeleev did exactly this in classifying the chemical elements into a table. Another method is to make and use a drawing. One of the greatest aids to understanding a problem is to make a picture of it. It may help to construct a table or a graph. As we have seen in Section 1:4, models often help us understand unfamiliar ideas.

Thomas Edison used an excellent strategy for solving problems in his search for a filament for a light bulb. He eliminated possibilities. Sometimes it is easier to solve a problem by knowing what does not work. Sometimes you can work backwards from what is given. You might solve a simpler, related problem. You may write a mathematical expression. What works best depends upon the problem, your attitude, and your experience.

To be a successful problem solver in science, you must understand the problem. Restate it in your own words. Then set a goal. Once you know what you are looking for, be sure you have the facts you need. The best problem solver on Earth could not analyze a complex electrical circuit without knowing Ohm's law.

Now you are ready to choose a likely strategy and try it. Here is a list of problem solving strategies already discussed.

- Guess and check.
- Look for a pattern.
- Make a drawing or model.
- Construct a table or chart.
- Eliminate possibilities.
- Work backwards.
- Solve a simpler, related problem.
- Identify what is wanted, given, and needed.
- Write a mathematical expression.

If the strategy you chose does not work, then choose a different one. Keep trying until you find a solution. When you have found a solution, check it against the problem to see if it is reasonable.

Review

6. What is a problem?
7. How is an exercise different from a problem?
8. Find the next three numbers in each of these series. (Strategy: find a pattern.)
a. 3, 6, 9, _, _, _ b. 2, 4, 3, 5, _, _, _

9. If at the bookstore erasers cost thirty-three cents and pencils cost fourteen cents, how could you spend exactly $1.50 (no sales tax) on these two items? (Strategy: construct a table.)

★ 10. A neighborhood group spent $26.55 for 16 packets of marigold and zinnia seeds. If zinnias cost $1.55 and marigolds cost $1.80, how many packages of each did the group buy? (Strategy: guess and check.)

SCIENCE AND YOU

Antibiotics were developed to keep soldiers healthy. The space program has given us new fabrics. It has also given us different ways to serve food. Small electronic devices have advanced the practice of medicine. These products come from science and technology. In these sections, you will learn how physical science fits into both.

GOALS

1. You will increase your understanding of the nature of physical science.
2. You will learn how to carry out experiments and organize the records of these experiments.

1:7 Science and Technology

Science and technology are two sides of the same coin. They depend on each other. There is no sharp dividing line between them. In general, however, science relates to discovery and technology to invention. Often inventions lead to other discoveries. For example, through scientific knowledge electron microscopes and space rockets were developed. In turn, scientists use them to learn more about the microscopic world and the universe.

How may science and technology be distinguished?

FIGURE 1–8. With an electron microscope, scientists can view a white blood cell destroying bacteria (a). With newer microscopes, even atoms become visible (b).

a

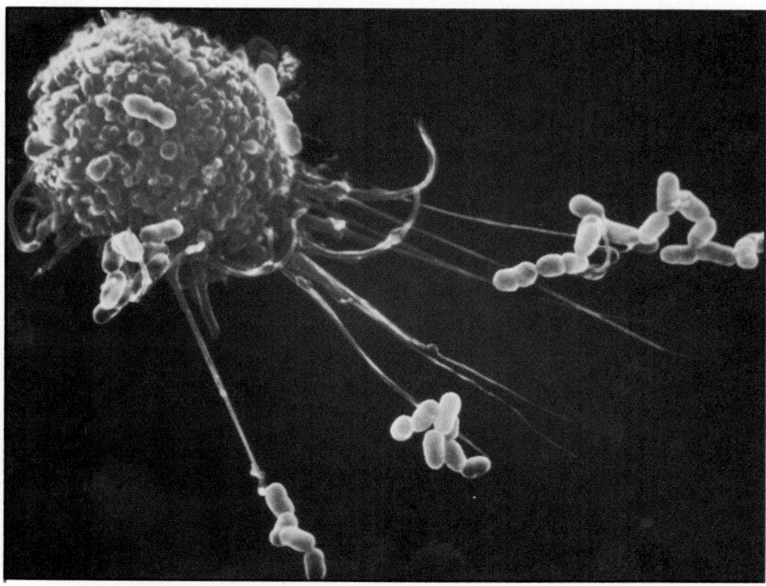

b

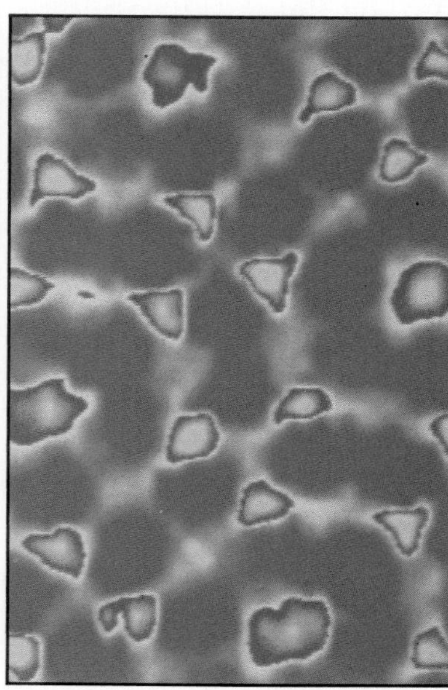

F.Y.I. The English chemist, John Walker, did not patent his invention. He felt that something as important as matches should be public property.

In the past, science was called "pure science" or "applied science." This difference implied that "pure" scientists did not care if their discoveries were useful. People supposed that applied scientists were concerned only with results. They assumed that applied scientists made no important discoveries. Today applied science is called **technology.** Technologists are applied scientists, as are engineers. It is true that there may be no immediate use for some scientific discovery. Technologists, however, may look at the discovery in a different way and may develop a use for it. Scientists discovered radiation. Technologists developed the radiation detector. There is a need for both science and technology, and both will be studied here.

1:8 Physical Science

What is physical science?

What is a property of matter?

Physical science is the study of matter and energy. The universe is composed of matter. Your body, this book, and your desk are matter. In physical science, you will learn the properties of metals, water, air, and many other kinds of matter. A **property** is a feature of matter or the way it acts. Extreme hardness is a property of diamonds. They are difficult to scratch. A black color is a property of coal. A sour taste is a property of lemon juice. Perfume evaporates easily. Wood will burn in air. These examples are all properties of matter.

FIGURE 1–9. Architects and builders must know the properties of many kinds of matter (a). An understanding of energy is needed to produce entertaining shows (b).

a

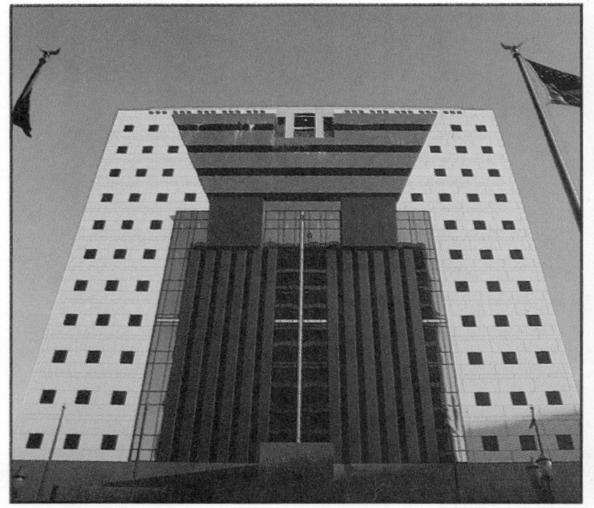

b

You will also learn about force and motion. You will study electricity, sound, thermal energy, and light. You will see how energy is related to matter. You will learn about energy transfer. For example, electric current can move through matter. Heat can move between objects. You may use a thermometer to measure your body temperature. Heat is transferred from your body to the cooler thermometer. You will find out why this happens and why the liquid in the thermometer rises as it warms. You will discover that energy can do useful work. The chemicals in a battery can change to release energy as electric current. This current can be used to run a radio or cassette player. It may be used to power a heart pacemaker.

1:9 Experimentation

What is an experiment?

An **experiment** is an organized process used to test a hypothesis. Scientists usually design experiments to learn new information. They use them to solve particular problems. In your study of physical science, you will also do experiments. Many of these are processes already used by others. They are new to you, however, and will give you a great deal of information.

What is the purpose of observation in experiments?

In your experiments, you will make observations in order to form conclusions. To do this well, you should keep accurate records of your work. Here is one way you might organize the records of your experiments.

Problem: What question do you hope to answer?

Hypothesis: What is the scientific "guess" that the experiment will test?

Procedure: What methods will you use to carry out the experiment?

Observations and Data: What do you see, hear, touch, taste, or smell? What changes occur? What measurements do you make?

Analysis and Conclusion: Based on your observations, is your hypothesis correct? If so, what is your answer to the question? If not, what changes should you make in your hypothesis or your procedure?

What is the purpose of a control in an experiment?

A **control** is used to show that the result of an experiment is really due to the condition you are testing. A control is a standard for comparison. For example, a scientist wants to know how a certain fertilizer affects plants. Two groups of plants are exposed to exactly the same conditions of light, heat, and moisture. Only one

FIGURE 1–10. Scientists keep careful records of their experiments in bound notebooks.

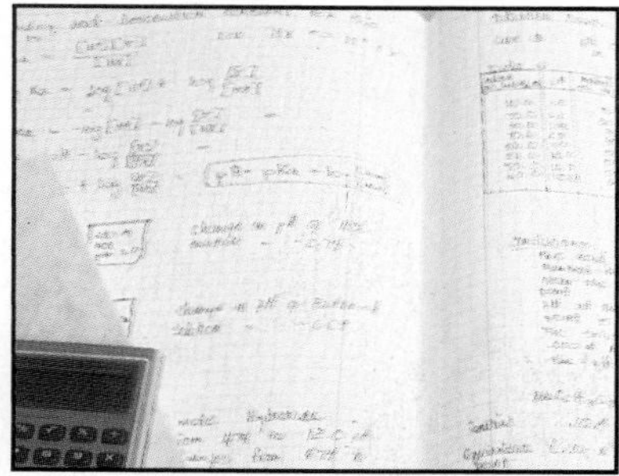

of the conditions is changed. Group A plants are given the fertilizer and Group B plants are not. Group B is the control. It shows how the plants would have grown without the fertilizer. The scientist compares the fertilizer-treated group to the control.

Define independent variable.

What is a dependent variable?

What is a constant?

In another experiment, the scientist wants to determine whether the amount of fertilizer affects the growth of the plants. The scientist uses a different amount of fertilizer on each group of plants. One group of plants, the control, has no fertilizer. The amount of fertilizer is the independent variable. The **independent variable** is the factor adjusted by the experimenter. The amount of growth of each plant depends on the amount of fertilizer added, and is the dependent variable. A **dependent variable** results from the action of the independent variable. The amounts of light, water, and heat are constant factors in this experiment. A **constant** is a factor that does not change throughout an experiment. Table 1–1 shows some data that the experimenter might observe. What conclusions could you draw from these numbers?

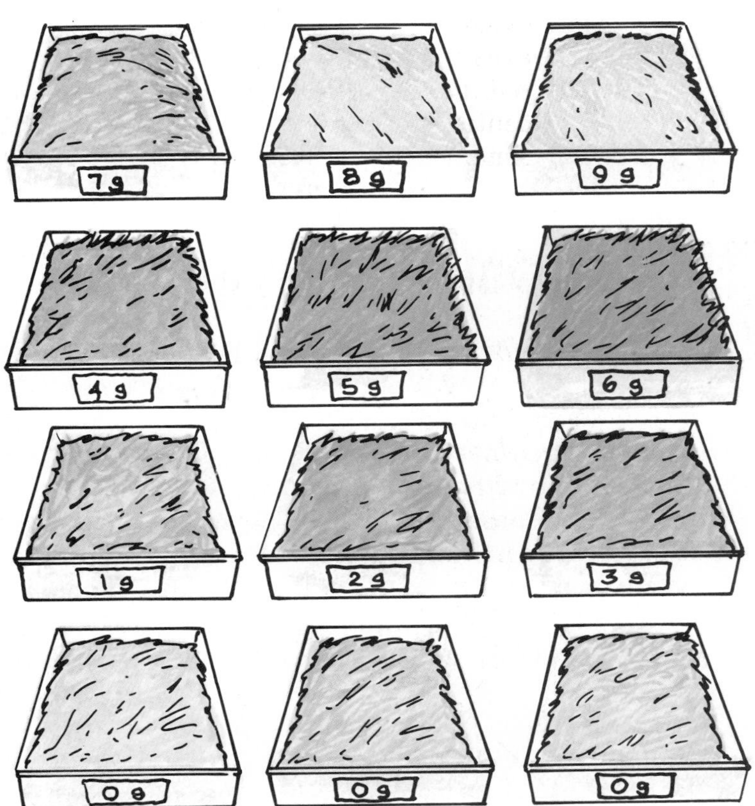

FIGURE 1–11. The results of the fertilizer experiment might look like those shown here. Note the control group that received no fertilizer.

Table 1–1

Table of Experimental Data			
Quantity of fertilizer applied	**Increase in height after 2 weeks**	**Quantity of fertilizer applied**	**Increase in height after 2 weeks**
0.0 g	15 mm	5.0 g	34 mm
1.0 g	17 mm	6.0 g	32 mm
2.0 g	24 mm	7.0 g	26 mm
3.0 g	30 mm	8.0 g	14 mm
4.0 g	33 mm	9.0 g	2 mm

Review

11. List two properties of each of these materials.
a. iron b. gold c. window glass d. air

12. Give two examples of energy transfer.

13. A medical scientist tests a new drug intended to treat a certain disease. Two groups of people are selected who have the disease. One group is given the drug. The other is not. What is the purpose of the second group?

14. Explain the difference between dependent and independent variables. Give an example of each.

★ **15.** A scientist develops a new outdoor house paint. The scientist believes the paint will last longer than any other house paint. What experiment could be done to test the scientist's hypothesis? Describe a control for this experiment.

PROBLEM SOLVING

A Chinese Puzzle

An ancient Chinese puzzle called a tangram is shown below. The tangram consists of five triangles, a square, and a rhomboid. These shapes can be arranged to make more than 300 different figures. The figures may resemble people, animals, letters, and various other objects. Forming the figures involves problem-solving skills such as trial and error and the ability to rearrange shapes.

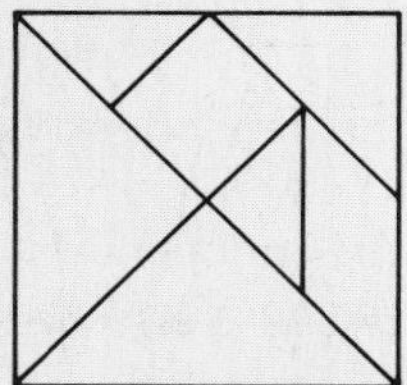

Make the puzzle from a material such as cardboard, wood, or plastic. Cut it apart on the lines. Test your problem-solving ability and try to construct a kangaroo, a dog, a bird, a polar bear, a cat, and some letters of the alphabet.

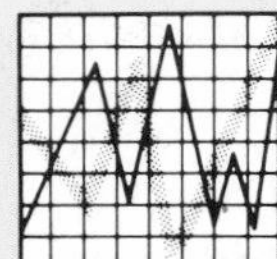

SKILL 1–3

Identifying Variables and Constants

Problem: What are the variables and constants in an experiment?

Materials

paper and pencil

Experiment 1

Rachel purchased some "super sand" at a toy store and was amazed at the way it acted when poured into a glass of water. She set up an experiment to see how it might differ from beach sand and sandy soil. The equipment she prepared is shown in Figure 1–12.

FIGURE 1–12.

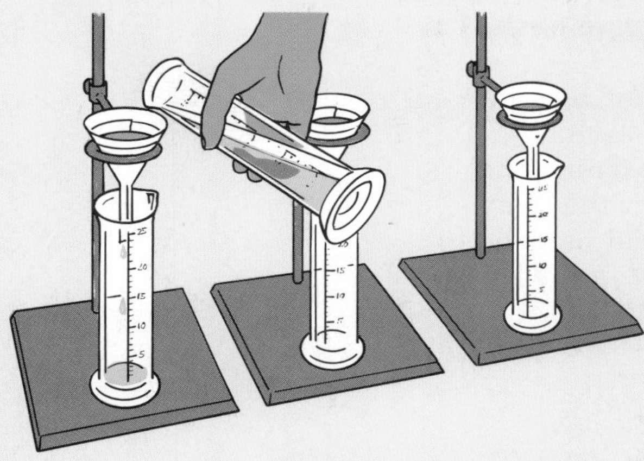

Rachel poured exactly 25 mL of water into each funnel and measured the amount of water that filtered into each graduated cylinder.

What was the independent variable? Recall that the independent variable is something you can change in an experiment. If you answered that the type of sand was the independent variable, you are right. Rachel can select however many types of sand she wants to test. What is the dependent variable? The dependent variable will vary in response to the independent variable. The amount of water that filters into each graduated cylinder will vary, depending on the type of sand. The amount of water in the graduated cylinder is the dependent variable.

Constants are those factors that are the same for each trial. There are several constants in this experiment. The size of the funnels, the size of graduated cylinders, the type of filter paper, and the amounts of sand and water used are all constant.

Experiment 2

Leroy noticed that windstorms seemed to follow a drop in temperature during the summer. He wanted to find out if his observations were accurate. He decided to collect and analyze weather data for the months of June and July. What independent and dependent variables should he analyze? You are correct if you think that temperature change is the independent variable. Leroy will need to determine the time period for measuring temperature change. The dependent variable could be wind speed during the storm. Can you name some factors that should be constants? Time between temperature readings, time of temperature readings before the storm's onset, or time of day might all be constants. Leroy should also use the same thermometer for his temperature readings.

Questions

Juan's math teacher gives the class a quiz everyday. Juan wants to improve his grades. He thinks that he might study better at a certain time of day. He decides to study math at different times of the day for the next three weeks. He chooses these times for study: before school, after school, after dinner, and before bedtime.

1. What are the dependent variables in Juan's experiment?
2. What are the independent variables?
3. What are some constants that he should consider?

Chapter 1 Review

SUMMARY

1. Scientists define a problem by asking questions. 1:1
2. Observations are facts. 1:2
3. Experiments test hypotheses and lead to conclusions. 1:2
4. An inference is a judgment based on reasoning. 1:2
5. Laws describe events; theories explain laws. 1:3
6. Models are used to help in understanding an idea or a system. 1:4
7. A problem is a situation in which there is a gap between present knowledge and the knowledge one wants to have. 1:5
8. There are many strategies to use in solving a problem such as looking for a pattern and eliminating possibilities. 1:5, 1:6
9. Technology is applied science. 1:7
10. Physical science is the study of matter and energy. 1:8
11. An experiment is an organized way of testing a hypothesis. 1:9
12. A control is a standard for comparison in an experiment. 1:9
13. An independent variable is adjusted by the experimenter; a dependent variable changes based on the independent variable. 1:9

VOCABULARY

a. conclusion
b. constant
c. control
d. dependent variable
e. experiment
f. hypothesis
g. independent variable
h. law
i. model
j. observation
k. physical science
l. property
m. technology
n. theory

Matching

Match each description with the correct vocabulary word from the list above. Not all vocabulary words will be used.

1. adjusted by the experimenter
2. an educated guess
3. a fact
4. explains a law
5. a feature of matter
6. applied science
7. a description of an event in nature
8. used to explain something not easily understood
9. judgment based on interpreting observations
10. a standard used for comparison in an experiment

Chapter 1 Review

MAIN IDEAS

A. Reviewing Concepts

Choose the word or phrase that correctly completes each of the following sentences.

1. A hypothesis is tested by a(n) *(inference, conclusion, experiment).*
2. The standard for comparison in an experiment is called a(n) *(control, independent variable, dependent variable).*
3. The engineer's guess that the radiation came from his house was a *(model, hypothesis, conclusion).*
4. All of the following are examples of matter except *(light, air, water, iron).*

Complete each of the following sentences with the correct word or phrase.

5. A guess based on observations is a(n) ________________.
6. Physical science is the study of ________________.
7. Technology is thought of as ________________ science.
8. The conclusion of an experiment is based on the interpretation of ________________.
9. Taste, color, hardness, and ability to burn or rust are ________________ of matter.
10. When there is a gap between what you know and what you need to know, you have a(n) ________________.
11. The factor adjusted by the experimenter is the ________________.
12. A hard-to-understand idea may be represented or described by a(n) ________________.
13. A factor that does not change in an experiment is a(n) ________________.
14. A "rule of nature" is a scientific ________________.
15. From the conclusion of an experiment, other events may be ________________.

B. Understanding Concepts

Answer the following questions using complete sentences when possible.

16. What is the purpose of any experiment?
17. Does a conclusion always support a hypothesis? Why or why not?
18. What is the value of a control in an experiment?
19. How do science and technology differ?
20. List two properties of coal.
21. Label the following as inferences or observations.
    a. The carpet is green.
    b. Ice is a solid.
    c. The sun will shine tomorrow.
    d. Grapefruit tastes sour.
22. What is physical science?
23. Find the next three numbers: 2, 4, 8, —, —, —.
24. Name four different problem solving strategies.
25. Explain the difference between a problem and an exercise.

C. Applying Concepts

Answer the following questions using complete sentences when possible.

26. How is a theory related to a law?
27. When air or helium is added to a balloon, the balloon expands. Suggest a model that might help to explain why this happens.
28. A scientist wants to test the effect of changing the amount of vitamin E in the diet of laboratory rats. Describe a control that could be used.
29. Explain how technology can advance science and how science can advance technology.
30. You have \$30.00. You buy a radio for \$15.00. You then decide to sell the radio for \$20.00. Later you buy it back for \$30.00. Finally, you sell it again

for $40.00. How much money did you make or lose? Use one or more of the problem solving strategies discussed in this chapter.

SKILL REVIEW

1. How can the technique of breaking a problem into simpler problems make problem solving easier?

2. Which of the following are inferences and which are observations?
  a. It is snowing.
  b. The sky is getting dark, so it must be going to rain.
  c. The baby must be hurt, since it is crying.
  d. The car is traveling faster than the speed limit.

3. A ferry carried 35 cars across a lake. Each car had an average of 3 passengers. On the average, each passenger had 2 suitcases. The crew of 12 each had 1 suitcase, except for the captain who had 2 suitcases. How many suitcases were on the ferry? What problem-solving method would be useful for this problem?

4. Five boys were walking home from school together on the Monday of exam week. The boys appeared to be about the same age. Four of the boys were carrying math and health books, while the fifth boy carried only a math book. Which of the following is a reasonable inference to make based on the information given?
  a. All boys have a difficult time with math.
  b. The fifth boy is healthier than the other four boys.
  c. The five boys are going to have a math exam on Tuesday.
  d. The five boys are going to have a health exam on Tuesday.

5. A teacher decided to see if the number of homework problems assigned from a chapter had an effect on chapter test scores. Identify the dependent and independent variables in the teacher's experiment.

PROJECTS

1. Look up the word *placebo* and determine its use in medical experiments.

2. Set up an experiment to find out what colors of light are most favorable to plant growth. State your hypothesis.

READINGS

1. Goldberg, Joan Rachel. "The Eureka Moment: Paul Kohl." *Science Digest.* February, 1986, pp. 34–35, 75.

2. Hassan, Aftab. *Preparation for Problem Solving in Science and Mathematics.* Bethesda, MD: Betz Publishing, 1986.

3. Weiss, Ann E. *Seers and Scientists.* San Diego, CA: Harcourt Brace Jovanovich, 1986.

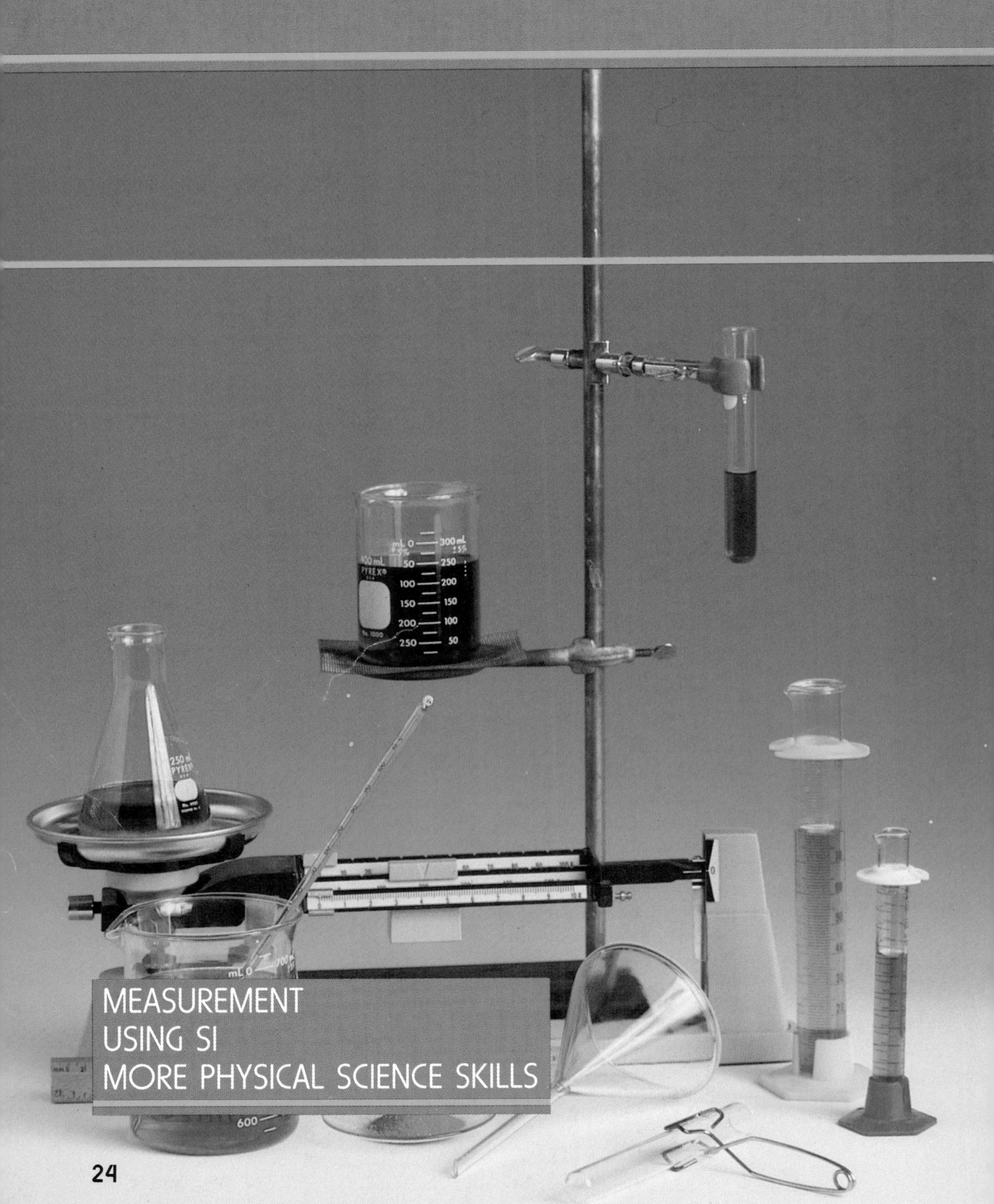

MEASUREMENT
USING SI
MORE PHYSICAL SCIENCE SKILLS

Chapter 2

Physical Science Methods

Learning physical science requires many kinds of skills. You need laboratory techniques such as measuring. You must be able to use some simple mathematics. In addition, you must collect data and draw conclusions from them. Probably the most important skills you will need are those for problem solving. You will learn procedures for attacking and finding solutions to problems.

MEASUREMENT

GOALS

1. You will learn about standards of measurement and the System of International Units.
2. You will increase your understanding of uncertainty in measurement.

Measurement is basic to science. When we measure, we compare an object to some standard quantity. Standards are needed so that people can understand and use each other's measurements. Measurements can never be exact. The amount of uncertainty in a measurement depends on the measuring device. It also depends on your ability to make the comparison.

2:1 Units and Standards

Think about measuring length. You can use the length of another object, such as your shoe, as your standard. You could measure the distance from your seat to the teacher's desk, by walking with one foot directly in front of the other and counting the number of steps. You are comparing the distance to the length of your shoe. Your unit of measurement is a shoe length.

The distance from your desk to your teacher's may be 25.5 shoe lengths. If others in your class measured the same distance, would they get the same measurement? Probably not. Shoe sizes may vary a great deal. Your measurement unit, shoe length, is usable but not practical. Others cannot duplicate your result. Even you might have trouble if you wore other shoes. To make useful measurements, a measurement standard must be used. A **standard** is an exact quantity people agree to use for comparison. Standards are used to define units of measurement. Using the same standard means that two people measuring the same object should get close to the same result.

FIGURE 2–1. Measurements of mass are compared to the standard kilogram. The standard is a platinum-iridium alloy kept at the International Bureau of Weights and Measures in France.

2:2 International System of Units

What is the meaning of a measurement standard?

Every measurement has a unit and a number. The foot, quart, and pound are measuring units used in the United States. However, other countries use another system of units. In 1795, a group of scientists met to create a uniform system of measurement. They adopted the meter, 1/10 000 000 of the distance between the North Pole and the Equator, as the standard unit of length. From this unit, the metric system took its name. Today Le Système International d'Unités (**SI**), a modern form of the metric system, is used. All of the SI units and standards are agreed upon and understood around the world.

In SI, prefixes are used to make the base units larger or smaller by multiples of ten. Instead of memorizing many different units, all you have to remember are the meanings of the main prefixes. The prefixes most often used in science are shown in Table 2–1.

Table 2–1

Important SI Prefixes

Prefix	Symbol	Multiplying factor
kilo-	k	1000
deci-	d	0.1
centi-	c	0.01
milli-	m	0.001
micro	μ	0.000 001
nano-	n	0.000 000 001

What is accuracy?

FIGURE 2–2. SI units are used by scientists around the world.

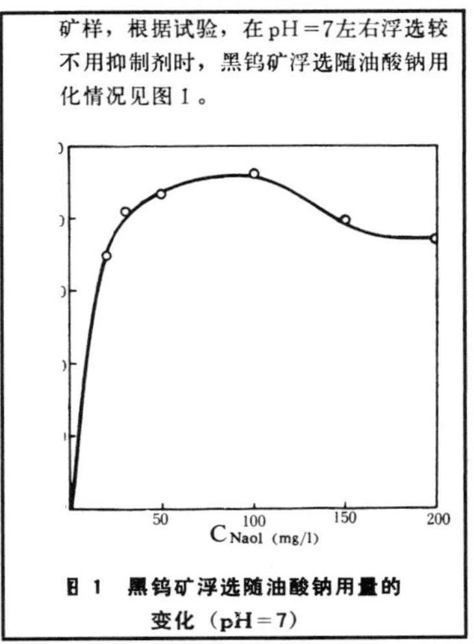

矿样，根据试验，在pH＝7左右浮选较不用抑制剂时，黑钨矿浮选随油酸钠用化情况见图1。

图1 黑钨矿浮选随油酸钠用量的变化（pH＝7）

2:3 Uncertainty in Measurement

You will soon be making actual measurements in the laboratory. Before you do, you should understand that your measurements have limitations.

Assume that you are using a reliable measuring instrument. The **accuracy** of your measurement is how close your value is to the actual or accepted value. Accuracy depends on how carefully you are able to com-

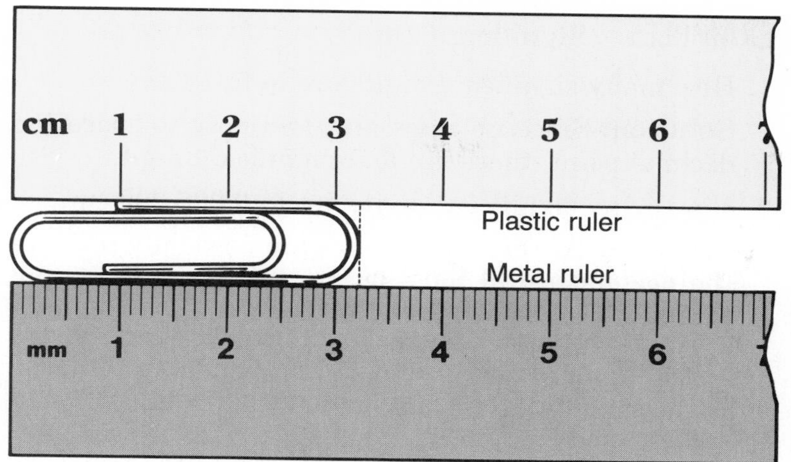

FIGURE 2–3. The graduations on the measuring instrument determine the precision of a single measurement. What are the small divisions on the metal ruler?

pare the object being measured to your standard. Accuracy usually improves with practice.

How precise your measurement is also depends on the measuring instrument. A measurement can only be as precise as the measuring instrument will allow it to be. No amount of practice will improve precision. Being precise does not guarantee accuracy.

Figure 2–3 should help you understand precision and accuracy. Suppose you want to measure the length of the paper clip. The plastic ruler is marked in centimeters, and the metal ruler is marked in millimeters. With the plastic ruler, you can estimate that the length is 2/10 of the way from 3 cm to 4 cm. You should record the measurement as 3.2 centimeters. This measurement contains one digit (3) that you know for certain. It also has a second digit (0.2) that is estimated. With the metal ruler, you can estimate that the length is 3/10 of the way from 3.2 cm to 3.3 cm. You should record the length as 3.23 cm. This value is more precise than the 3.2 cm value measured with the plastic ruler, because a more precise tool was used in measuring.

How is the precision of a measurement shown?

The precision of a measurement is indicated by the number of significant digits. Numbers that result from measurement are called **significant digits.** When a measurement is written down, zeros must sometimes be added only to space the decimal point. For example, a certain length was measured as 53/1000 m. In decimal form, this is 0.053 m. Only the 5 and 3 were read from the meter stick and are significant. The zeros are place holders. However, the value 5.037 g has four significant digits. Here the zero is part of the measurement. The value 520.05 cm^3 has five significant digits; 5000.0 g has five; and 72.600 mL also has five.

F.Y.I. In 1975, the United States Congress passed the Metric Conversion Act. This act called for a voluntary changeover to the metric system throughout the country.

EXAMPLES Significant Digits

1. How many significant digits are in 53.01 m?

   Solution: Since no zeros are used only to space the decimal point, there are four significant digits.

2. How many significant digits are in 0.005 900 cm?

   Solution: The first three zeros are used only to space the decimal point, but the last two were read from the measuring instrument. Therefore, there are four significant digits.

Note that spaces, instead of commas, are used to group digits in long numbers.

$$198{,}623 = 198\ 623$$

This is done because many countries use a comma in place of a decimal point.

We often use measurements to calculate other values. Nothing calculated from measurements can be more precise than the least precise measurement. If the length and width of a rectangle are measured to three significant digits, the area should have only three significant digits.

EXAMPLE Using Significant Digits

What is the area of a rectangle whose length is 1.23 cm and whose width is 5.13 cm?

Solution:
$$\begin{aligned} A &= l \times w \\ &= 1.23\text{ cm} \times 5.13\text{ cm} \\ &= 6.3099\text{ cm}^2 \end{aligned}$$

However, the measurements were precise to only three significant digits. Therefore, you must round off to three significant digits.

$$A = 6.31\text{ cm}^2$$

PRACTICE PROBLEMS

1. How many significant digits are in each of the following measurements?
   a. 25.03 g
   b. 0.0593 m
   c. 520.0 cm^3
   d. 15 kg
   e. 8.090 cm
   f. 0.5090 mL
2. What is the floor area of a room 3.1 m by 3.65 m?
3. What is the volume of a rectangular block with length 5.02 cm, width 3.71 cm, and height 10.03 cm? Remember that $V = l \times w \times h$.

Review

1. What is a standard?
2. What is SI?
3. What is the difference between 5 mL of water and 5.0 mL of water? Give an example of a situation where this difference might be important.
4. Which measurement is more precise, 4.3 cm or 4.89 cm?
5. ★ Explain why greater precision does not guarantee greater accuracy.

USING SI

The use of the SI system makes it easy to change from one unit to another. Once you learn the metric prefixes, changing units involves only moving the decimal point. Using SI is as simple as using the United States money system.

GOALS

1. You will learn the SI units for length, mass, time, and temperature.
2. You will gain skills in changing units of measure to larger or smaller units.

2:4 Length

What is the SI unit of length?

The **meter** (m) is the SI unit of length. The distance from a doorknob to the floor is about a meter. The high hurdles in a boys' track event are about a meter high. Meter sticks and metric rulers are tools used to measure length.

The meter is divided into 100 equal parts called centimeters (cm). The prefix *centi-* means 1/100 (one hundredth). There are 100 centimeters in a meter.

$$100 \text{ cm} = 1 \text{ m}$$

Deci- means 1/10. A decimeter (dm) is one-tenth of a meter and is equal to 10 cm.

$$10 \text{ dm} = 1 \text{ m}; 1 \text{ dm} = 10 \text{ cm}$$

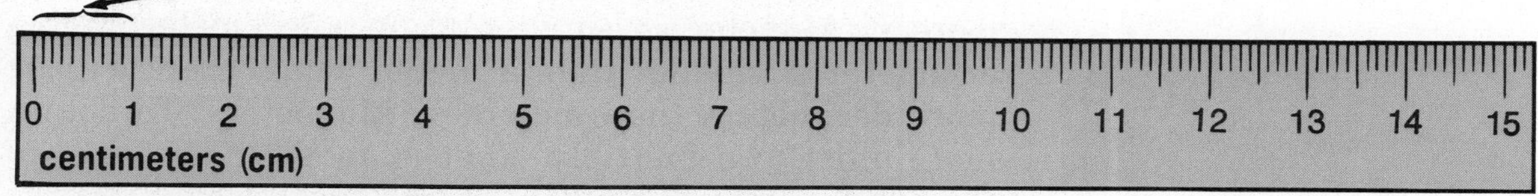

FIGURE 2–4. The relationships of units of length are shown on the ruler.

An even smaller unit is a millimeter (mm). There are 1000 millimeters in a meter. The prefix *milli-* means 1/1000 (one thousandth). There are 10 millimeters in 1 centimeter.

$$1000 \text{ mm} = 1 \text{ m}; 10 \text{ mm} = 1 \text{ cm}$$

What is the meaning of *kilo-*?

Long distances are measured in kilometers (km). A kilometer is 1000 meters. The prefix *kilo-* means 1000. A kilometer is about 5 city blocks in length.

$$1 \text{ km} = 1000 \text{ m}$$

F.Y.I. The factor-label method is useful in the conversion of units. In this method, you multiply by unit fractions, that is, a factor equal to 1. As you know, when a quantity is multiplied by 1, its value does not change. Suppose you want to convert 80 mm to meters. Since 1000 mm = 1 m, then

$$\frac{1 \text{ m}}{1000 \text{ mm}} = 1.$$

In this method, we multiply by a factor or series of factors to cancel the unwanted units. Since the unit fraction above contains both "mm" and "m," we multiply 80 mm by it.

$$80 \cancel{\text{mm}} \times \frac{1 \text{ m}}{1000 \cancel{\text{mm}}} = 0.080 \text{ m}$$

The "mm" unit cancels and "m" remains.

To change from one unit to another, just multiply or divide by multiples of 10. A quick way to do this is to move the decimal point to the right or left. Move the decimal point as many places as there are zeros in the multiple of 10 you are using. When you go from a large unit to a small unit, move the decimal point to the right. When you go from a small unit to a large unit, move the decimal point to the left. Suppose you want to change 0.932 m to cm. Since 1 m = 100 cm, and meters are larger than centimeters, move the decimal two places to the right.

$$0.932 \text{ m} = 93.2 \text{ cm}$$

To change 245 mm to centimeters, you need to know that 10 mm = 1 cm and millimeters are smaller than centimeters. Move the decimal 1 place to the left.

$$245 \text{ mm} = 24.5 \text{ cm}$$

EXAMPLES Length Conversion

1. Change 353 millimeters to centimeters.

Solution: 1 cm = 10 mm
Since a centimeter is larger than a millimeter, divide by 10. Simply move the decimal one place to the left.

$$353 \text{ mm} = 35.3 \text{ cm}$$

2. How many decimeters are in 539.6 kilometers?

Solution: 1000 m = 1 km and 10 dm = 1 m
First, change kilometers to meters, then meters to decimeters. A meter is smaller than a kilometer and a decimeter is smaller than a meter. Thus, there will be more decimeters than meters or kilometers. To obtain more units, you multiply. That is, move the decimal to the right.

$$539.600 \text{ km} = 539\ 600.0 \text{ m} = 5\ 396\ 000 \text{ dm}$$

PRACTICE PROBLEMS

4. Change each of the following.
   a. 0.759 m to cm   b. 9569 mm to km
5. A playing field is 50.3 m wide. How many dm is this? How many mm?

2:5 Mass

Mass is the amount of matter in an object. Mass is measured with a balance. The **kilogram** (kg) is the SI unit of mass. Your book has a mass of about 1.2 kilograms. The mass of a paper clip is about 0.5 gram. What is the mass of your book in grams?

What is mass?

EXAMPLES Mass Conversions

1. A book has a mass of 527 g. How many kilograms is that?

   Solution: 1 kg = 1000 g
   Since the kilogram is a larger unit, divide 527 by 1000. Simply move the decimal three places to the left.

   $$.527 \text{ g} = 0.527 \text{ kg}$$

2. A stone has a mass of 2.24 kg. What is its mass in grams?

   Solution: 1000 g = 1 kg
   Since a gram is a smaller unit than a kilogram, multiply by 1000. To do this, move the decimal three places to the right.

   $$2.240 \text{ kg} = 2240 \text{ g}$$

FIGURE 2–5. A double-pan balance compares the mass on the left pan with standard masses on the right (a). Some balances measure mass electronically (b).

a

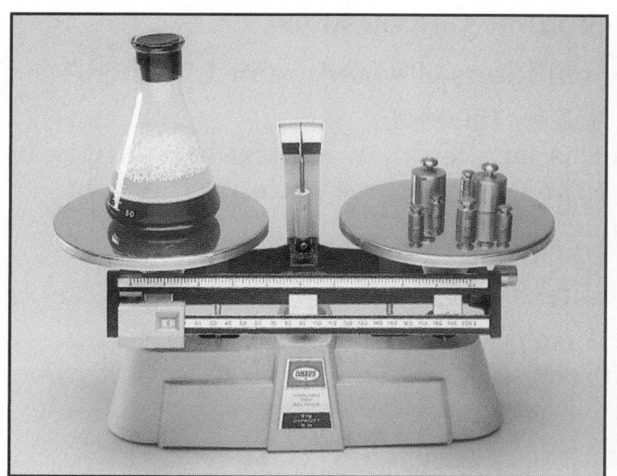

b

FIGURE 2–6. The cubic meter is a space one meter long by one meter wide by one meter high.

What is volume?

What is a cubic decimeter?

PRACTICE PROBLEM

6. Change each of the following.
 a. 329 g to kg
 b. 4.23 g to mg
 c. 5.03 kg to g

2:6 Volume

The amount of space occupied by an object is the object's **volume.** The units for volume are derived from units of length. A brick that has dimensions of 5 cm by 9 cm by 20 cm will have a volume of 900 cubic centimeters (cm^3). A cubic meter (m^3) is a very large unit. You can see in Figure 2–6 that each side of the cube is 1 meter long. It contains 1 000 000 cubic centimeters. Smaller volume units are often needed. The liter (L) is one such unit. Many soft drinks are available in two-liter bottles. A **liter** is the same size as a cubic decimeter (dm^3). This is the volume of a cube that is 1 dm (10 cm) on each side. The cubic decimeter is an SI derived unit. The liter, though not an SI unit, is used with the SI system. We will use liters in this book.

$$1\ L = 1\ dm^3 = 10\ cm \times 10\ cm \times 10\ cm = 1000\ cm^3$$

As you see, a liter is also the same as 1000 cm^3. For small volume measurements, most scientists use the milliliter (mL) or cubic centimeter (cm^3). One milliliter equals one cubic centimeter.

$$1\ mL = 1\ cm^3$$

One liter contains 1000 milliliters or 1000 cubic centimeters.

EXAMPLES Volume Conversions

1. How many milliliters of water are in 1.24 liters?

Solution: 1 L = 1000 mL
A milliliter is smaller than a liter, so multiply by 1000. Move the decimal three places to the right.

$$1.240\ L = 1240\ mL$$

2. How many liters of water are in 234 cm^3?

Solution: 1 cm^3 = 1 mL and 1000 mL = 1 L
Thus, 1000 cm^3 = 1 L. Since a liter is 1000 times larger than a cubic centimeter, divide by 1000. Move the decimal three places to the left.

$$234\ cm^3 = 0.234\ L$$

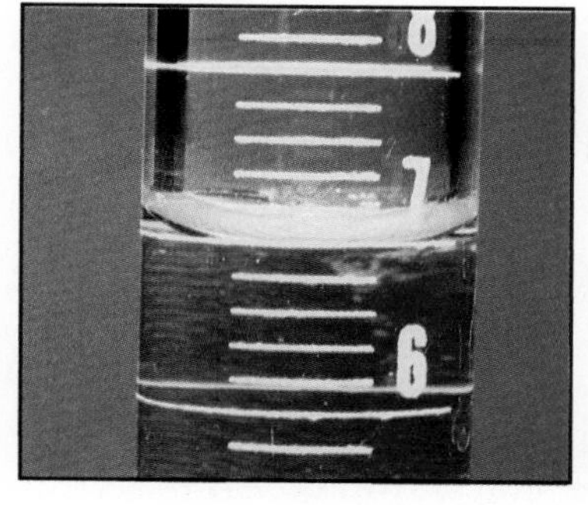

a

b

FIGURE 2–7. Water forms a downward curve in a graduated cylinder (a). Mercury curves upward in a glass cylinder (b). The mercury volume is about 7.1 milliliters.

PRACTICE PROBLEMS

7. Change the following.
  a. 0.356 L to mL
  b. 4.1 cm^3 to dm^3

8. A gasoline pump reads 42 dm^3. What is the volume in liters? In milliliters?

Graduated cylinders are tools used for measuring liquid volumes in the laboratory. In Figure 2–7 you see that the level of the liquid is curved. This curved surface of a liquid is called the **meniscus.** To read the volume of most liquids, you must note the level at the bottom of the curve. For some liquids, like mercury, the curve is up. Read that curve at the top.

2:7 Density

SI units can be combined to express other measurements. These units are called derived units. In Section 2:6, we saw that units for volume are derived from units of length. The unit for density is also a derived unit. **Density** is the mass of a material divided by its volume. It is often expressed in grams per cubic centimeter, g/cm^3. The density of a substance can be used to help identify the substance. Densities of some common substances are given in Table 2–2.

What is density?

Table 2–2.

Densities of Some Substances

Substance	Density (g/cm^3)	Substance	Density (g/cm^3)
hydrogen	0.000 09	aluminum	2.7
oxygen	0.0013	iron	7.9
water	1.0	copper	8.9
sugar	1.6	lead	11.3
table salt	2.2	mercury	13.6
quartz	2.6	gold	19.3

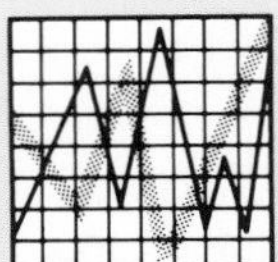

SKILL 2–1

Measuring Volume

Problem: How can you determine volume indirectly?

Materials 

250-mL beaker
600-mL beaker
small blocks of wood or metal
graduated cylinder
lead sinker
string
metric ruler
goggles

Procedure

Part A

1. Place a 250-mL beaker inside a 600-mL beaker. Fill the smaller beaker to the top with water.
2. Measure the length, width, and height of a block of wood or metal. Calculate the volume. Record this calculated value.
3. Gently place the block in the 250-mL beaker. You may have to push the wood block under the water with a pencil point.
4. Remove the 250-mL beaker and pour the overflow water from the larger beaker into the graduated cylinder.
5. Record the volume of the overflow in the data table.
6. Repeat Steps 1 through 5 with other blocks.

Part B

1. Fill a graduated cylinder about ⅓ full with water. Read the volume carefully and record in the data table.

FIGURE 2–8.

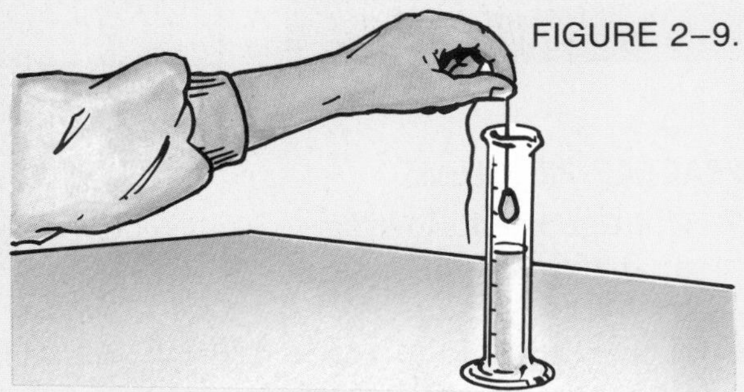

FIGURE 2–9.

2. Tie a string to a small lead sinker.
3. Lower the sinker into the cylinder until it is completely submerged.
4. Read the level of the water. Record the amount the water level rises.
5. Record the volume of the sinker.

Data and Observations

Part A		
volume of block ($l \times w \times h$)	______	cm^3
volume of overflow	______	mL
Part B		
original volume	______	mL
volume with sinker added	______	mL
volume of sinker	______	mL

Analysis and Conclusions

1. In Part A, how does the volume of the block compare with the volume of the overflow? Should they be the same? Why might they be different?
2. In Part B, how does the volume of the sinker compare with the rise in the water level? Should they be the same? Why might they be different?
3. How can you determine volume indirectly?

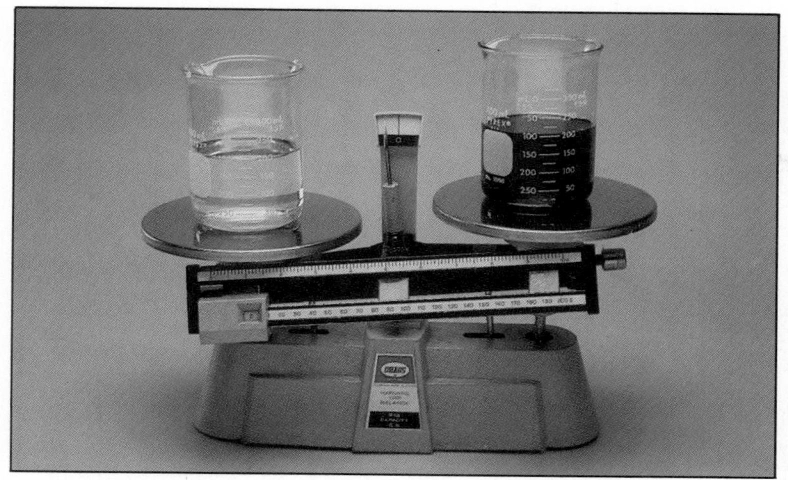

FIGURE 2–10. The motor oil and water occupy equal volumes. The balance shows that the water has greater mass. Thus, water is more dense than motor oil.

Silver and polished aluminum may look alike, but they have different densities. How can you tell them apart? You could measure their densities. The density of silver is greater than the density of aluminum. The density of a material does not depend on how much of it you have. One gram of silver has the same density as one hundred kilograms of silver.

How does the density of silver compare with the density of aluminum?

The density of a material is found by dividing the mass of a sample by its volume. The equation is

$$density = \frac{mass}{volume} \qquad D = \frac{m}{V}$$

EXAMPLE Determining Density

A rectangular object is 3.0 cm long, 2.0 cm wide, and 1.0 cm deep, Figure 2–11. The object has a mass of 4.0 g. What is its density?

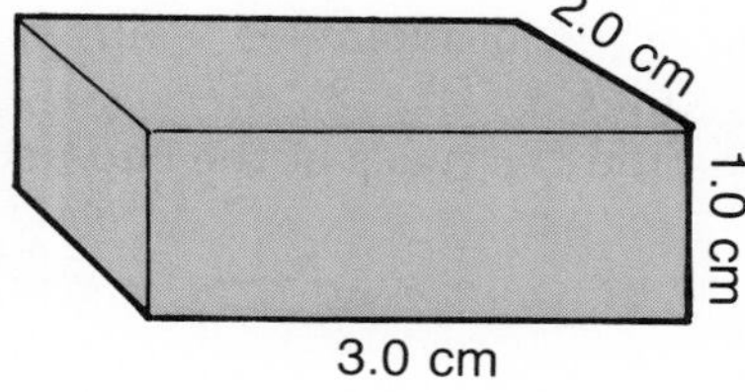

FIGURE 2–11.

Given: $m = 4.0$ g
$l = 3.0$ cm
$w = 2.0$ cm
$h = 1.0$ cm

Unknown: density of object (D)

Basic Equations: $D = \frac{m}{V}$
$V = l \times w \times h$

Solution: $V = l \times w \times h$
$= 3.0 \text{ cm} \times 2.0 \text{ cm} \times 1.0 \text{ cm} = 6.0 \text{ cm}^3$

$D = \frac{m}{V}$

$= \frac{4.0 \text{ g}}{6.0 \text{ cm}^3} = 0.67 \text{ g/cm}^3$

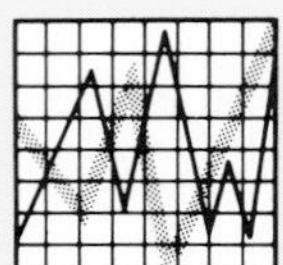

SKILL 2–2

Comparing Densities

Problem: How can you compare the densities of different liquids?

Materials

balance
100-mL beaker or clear container
graduated cylinder
3 small paper or plastic drinking cups
cooking oil
molasses
water
goggles
apron

Procedure

1. Label the cups **A**, **B**, and **C**. Use the balance to find the mass of each cup. Record these values in a table.
3. Use a clean graduated cylinder to measure 25 mL of water. Pour the water into cup **A**.
3. Find the mass of the cup and water.
4. Use the graduated cylinder to measure 25 mL of cooking oil. Pour the oil into cup **B**.
5. Find the mass of the cup and oil.
6. Use a clean graduated cylinder to measure 25 mL of molasses. Pour the molasses into cup **C**.
7. Find the mass of the cup and molasses.

Data and Observations

Measurements	A	B	C
mass of cup of liquid (g)			
mass of cup (g)			
mass of liquid (g)			
volume of liquid (cm^3)			
density of liquid (g/cm^3)			

Questions and Conclusions

1. Which liquid has the greatest density?
2. If you carefully poured all of the liquids into a beaker, which liquid would be on top? Which liquid would be on the bottom? Try it to see.
3. How do the densities of the liquids compare with their positions in the beaker?
4. What measurements must be made to determine the density of a material?
5. How can you compare the densities of different liquids?
6. Compared to the liquids tested, how dense would you expect gasoline to be?

FIGURE 2–12.

FIGURE 2–13. A hydrometer is used to test the density (specific gravity) of battery acid and radiator coolant.

PRACTICE PROBLEMS

9. Find the density of a rectangular block of wood 4.0 cm by 3.0 cm by 2.0 cm if its mass is 4.5 g.
10. What is the density of acid in a car battery if 200 mL of the acid has a mass of 240 g?

2:8 Time and Temperature

What is the SI unit of time?

Time is the interval between two events. The SI unit for time is the second (s). In the laboratory, time is generally measured with a stopwatch or a clock. Some very special clocks can measure time to hundredths of a microsecond (μs).

In science, temperature is usually measured using the Celsius temperature scale. Temperatures in weather reports are often given in degrees Celsius. This temperature scale is based on the freezing and boiling points of water. The freezing point of water is 0°C. The boiling point of water is 100°C. There are then 100 Celsius degrees between freezing and boiling. On the Celsius scale, room temperature is about 25°C. The normal temperature of the human body is about 37°C. In the International System of Units (SI), temperature is measured

F.Y.I. Some atomic clocks do not gain or lose more than a second over 3000 centuries. Atomic clocks measure time by counting the number of vibrations of atoms of cesium. The atoms vibrate 9 192 631 770 times each second. Very accurate atomic clocks are maintained at the National Bureau of Standards in Washington, DC.

FIGURE 2–14. Atomic clocks provide the most accurate measure of time.

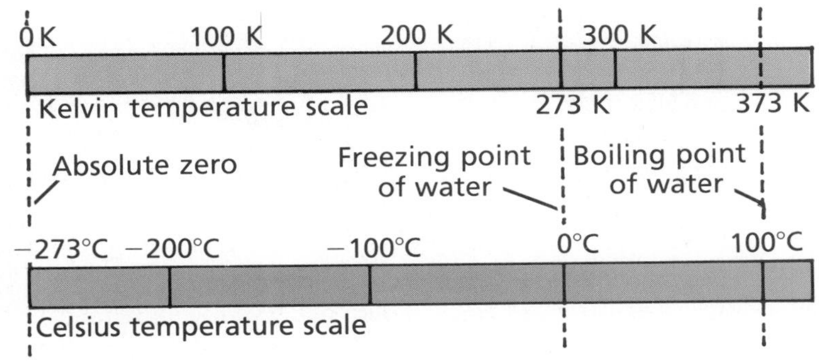

FIGURE 2–15. Zero on the Kelvin scale is absolute zero. Zero degrees on the Celsius scale is the same as 273 K.

0 K | 100 K | 200 K | 300 K
Kelvin temperature scale | 273 K | 373 K
Absolute zero | Freezing point of water | Boiling point of water
−273°C | −200°C | −100°C | 0°C | 100°C
Celsius temperature scale

What is absolute zero?

in a different unit. The SI unit of temperature is the **kelvin** (K). On the Kelvin scale, zero is the same as absolute zero, the coldest possible temperature. Absolute zero, 0 K, is −273°C.

$$0°C = 273 \text{ K}$$

Most laboratory thermometers are read in Celsius units. Celsius degrees can be changed to kelvins by adding 273, because the degree size is the same on the two scales.

$$\text{degrees Celsius} + 273 = \text{kelvins}$$

Therefore, there are 100 degrees between the freezing point and the boiling point of water on the Kelvin scale. Water freezes at 273 K and boils at 373 K.

PRACTICE PROBLEM

11. Change each of the following.
a. 27°C to K b. 420 K to °C

Review

6. Why are standards needed in measuring systems?

7. A glass beaker has a mass of 140 grams. After some water is added to the beaker, the mass of the beaker and water is 380 grams. Calculate the mass of the water. What is the volume of the water?

8. What volume of water will be needed to fill a rectangular aquarium 32.0 cm wide, 45.0 cm long, and 30.0 cm deep? How many liters is this?

9. What is the density of 25 cm^3 of salad oil that has a mass of 23 grams?

★ **10.** A rectangular block of stone is 2.0 cm wide, 3.1 cm long, and 5.4 cm deep. The stone has a density of 8.5 g/cm^3. What is the mass of the stone?

MORE PHYSICAL SCIENCE SKILLS

Do you know how to work safely in a laboratory? Are you able to use simple equations to calculate physical quantities? Can you observe and record data and then display them on a graph? These are some of the skills you will need during your study of physical science. The following sections will give you a chance to practice these skills.

GOALS

1. You will learn some simple rules of laboratory safety.
2. You will review and extend your ability to solve equations.
3. You will acquire skills in graphing experimental data.

2:9 Laboratory Safety

The first rule of laboratory safety is know what you are doing. Before beginning an activity, read the directions carefully and study the cautions.

What are the causes of most laboratory accidents?

Think safety at all times. Most injuries or accidents in a laboratory are due to broken glass, hot objects, and spatters. Always treat glass objects with care, treat all equipment as if it were hot, and wear safety glasses and a protective apron.

TECHNOLOGY: APPLICATIONS

Labeling and Safety

The National Fire Protection Association (NFPA) has been a leader in the area of safety. The group has developed a labeling technique that decreases the risk of handling hazardous materials. Perhaps you have seen their labels, like the one at the right, on chemical containers. You may also have seen them on railroad cars or trucks. These NFPA labels provide important information.

Each diamond-shaped label is divided into four smaller, colored diamonds. Each color stands for a particular hazard: blue, health; red, fire; yellow, reactivity; white, special problem. Numbers from 0 to 4 represent the degree of danger: 4 = extreme, 3 = serious, 2 = moderate, 1 = slight, 0 = minimal. The ₩ means the material will react if mixed with water. Other items that might be in the white area on the label are ACID and the symbol for radioactive material.

This textbook uses several safety symbols to alert you to possible laboratory dangers. These symbols are explained in Table 2–3. Be sure you understand each symbol before you begin an investigation.

Table 2–3

Safety Symbols	
DISPOSAL ALERT This symbol appears when care must be taken to dispose of materials properly.	**ANIMAL SAFETY** This symbol appears whenever live animals are studied and the safety of the animals and the students must be ensured.
BIOLOGICAL HAZARD This symbol appears when there is danger involving bacteria, fungi, or protists.	**RADIOACTIVE SAFETY** This symbol appears when radioactive materials are used.
OPEN FLAME ALERT This symbol appears when use of an open flame could cause a fire or an explosion.	**CLOTHING PROTECTION SAFETY** This symbol appears when substances used could stain or burn clothing.
THERMAL SAFETY This symbol appears as a reminder to use caution when handling hot objects.	**FIRE SAFETY** This symbol appears when care should be taken around open flames.
SHARP OBJECT SAFETY This symbol appears when a danger of cuts or punctures caused by the use of sharp objects exists.	**EXPLOSION SAFETY** This symbol appears when the misuse of chemicals could cause an explosion.
FUME SAFETY This symbol appears when chemicals or chemical reactions could cause dangerous fumes.	**EYE SAFETY** This symbol appears when a danger to the eyes exists. Safety goggles should be worn when this symbol appears.
ELECTRICAL SAFETY This symbol appears when care should be taken when using electrical equipment.	**POISON SAFETY** This symbol appears when poisonous substances are used.
PLANT SAFETY This symbol appears when poisonous plants or plants with thorns are handled.	**CHEMICAL SAFETY** This symbol appears when chemicals used can cause burns or are poisonous if absorbed through the skin.

Keep your workspace clean and uncluttered. Know how to wipe up spills and do so immediately. Arrange your equipment so you are not reaching over burners or dragging your sleeve over a lab setup. Above all, pay attention to your teacher. He or she will demonstrate the correct techniques for the use and disposal of materials and the handling of equipment, as well as other safety practices in the laboratory. Lists of safety rules and first aid procedures are given in Section B–1 of the Appendix.

2:10 Solving Equations

Many of the relationships in physical science are expressed most clearly as simple mathematical equations. Remember, an equation tells you that two quantities are equal. Sentences like $4 + 3 = 7$ and $3 \times 6 = a$ are equations. Equations in this course will generally be easy to solve. Many of them will be exercises rather than problems.

What does an equation state?

CAREER

Carpenter

As a child, Darren Young would tag along with his dad while he fixed the kitchen sink, painted a bedroom, or put in a brick patio. Building and fixing things became almost second nature to Darren.

In high school, he took industrial technology. He learned the value of careful measurement. He made a mailbox for his house, a kitchen table, and a wooden cabinet for his books and stereo. Darren began working for a construction company as an apprentice carpenter. His duties included installing windows and doors, changing locks, putting up drywall, and adding trim inside and outside new homes.

After four years, Darren had learned how to determine which materials were necessary for a job and how to estimate the costs involved. With this knowledge, he started his own business, and now has five people working for him.

For career information, write
Associated General Contractors of America, Inc.
1957 E Street NW
Washington, DC 20006

BIOGRAPHY

Luis W. Alvarez

1911–88

Luis Alvarez helped to develop the "bubble chamber," an instrument he used to identify many new elementary particles. For this research, he was awarded the Nobel Prize in 1966. In the past few years, he had proposed a theory about why dinosaurs became extinct.

From your work in mathematics you have learned that all simple equations can be solved using addition, subtraction, multiplication, division, or a combination of two or more of these operations. An equation that involves addition, for example, can be solved by subtraction. In general you use the operation or operations that undo what the equation shows.

EXAMPLES Solving for a Variable

1. Solve for x: $x + 3 = 8$

Solution: Because 3 is added to the variable x, the equation can be solved by subtracting 3 from both sides.

$$x + 3 - 3 = 8 - 3$$
$$x = 5$$

2. Solve for m: $3m = 9$

Solution: Because m is multiplied by 3, solve for m by dividing each side by 3.

$$\frac{3m}{3} = \frac{9}{3}$$
$$m = 3$$

3. Solve for r: $\frac{r}{2} - 5 = 2$

Solution: Because r is divided by 2, and 5 is subtracted, undo the process by adding 5 to each side. Then multiply each side by 2.

Add 5. $$\frac{r}{2} - 5 + 5 = 2 + 5$$

$$\frac{r}{2} = 7$$

Multiply by 2. $$\frac{r}{2} \times 2 = 7 \times 2$$

$$r = 14$$

F.Y.I. The formulation of the problem is often more essential than its solution.

—Albert Einstein

Equations can be solved for any variable. You often need to rewrite an equation when you want to fit the data you have available.

EXAMPLE Solving for Mass

The density of gold is 19.3 g/cm^3. What is the mass of a 3.6-cm^3 sample?

Solution: The density equation in Section 2:7 can be used to find mass if the density and volume are known.

$$D = \frac{m}{V}$$

Multiply each side by V. $$D \times V = \frac{m}{V} \times V$$

$$D \times V = m$$

$$m = (19.3 \text{ g/cm}^3)(3.6 \text{ cm}^3) = 69 \text{ g}$$

PRACTICE PROBLEMS

12. Solve for the variable.

a. $5x = 7$ b. $7 = \frac{R}{3}$

13. Solve for x.

a. $2x + 3 = 9$ b. $\frac{x}{3} - 5 = 2$

14. Solve for t.

a. $M = at + 5$ b. $\frac{k}{t} = f$

15. What is the mass of 4.7 cm^3 of iron? Refer to Table 2–2 for density.

2:11 Graphing

In many experiments, scientists want to know how changing one quantity affects the value of another. Suppose you have made a pendulum and want to investigate the relationship between the length of the pendulum and its period. The period of a pendulum is the time it takes to swing from one side to the other and back again. In your investigation, the length of the pendulum is the independent variable, that is, the experimental condition changed by the investigator. The time of the period is the dependent variable. The dependent variable is the quantity that changes because of the change in the independent variable. It is sometimes called the responding variable. Table 2–4 shows some data you might gather during your investigation. What conclusions can you draw from the table? Can you make any predictions as to what the period would be at a length of 200 cm? At 310 cm?

What is the responding variable in an experiment?

Often it is easier to see how a pair of variables are related by plotting a graph. The following steps will help you plot graphs for your lab activities.

Why plot data on a graph?

1. Identify the independent and dependent variables. The independent variable is plotted on the horizontal (x) axis. The dependent variable is plotted on the vertical (y) axis.
2. Subtract the lowest value of the independent variable from the highest value. This gives you the range of the independent variable.

Table 2–4

Table of Experimental Data			
Length of Pendulum	**Period**	**Length of Pendulum**	**Period**
30 cm	1.0 s	180 cm	2.4 s
60 cm	1.4 s	210 cm	2.6 s
90 cm	1.7 s	240 cm	2.8 s
120 cm	2.0 s	270 cm	3.0 s
150 cm	2.2 s	300 cm	3.2 s

3. Mark off the horizontal axis in a way that best fits the range of the independent variable. Spread out the data as much as possible. Let each space stand for a convenient amount. Choosing three or six spaces equal to 10 units is not convenient. How would you find where to plot 1.4? Rather, choose 2, 5, or 10 spaces to represent 10 units.
4. Number and label the horizontal axis. Do not forget to include zero if your data begin at zero.
5. Repeat Steps 2 through 4 for the dependent variable on the vertical axis.
6. Plot your data values on the graph. Make each point a small, dark dot with a small circle around it.
7. Draw the best straight line or curve that comes closest to connecting the data points.
8. Title the graph. Make sure the title clearly tells what the graph represents.

On what axis of a graph is the dependent variable plotted?

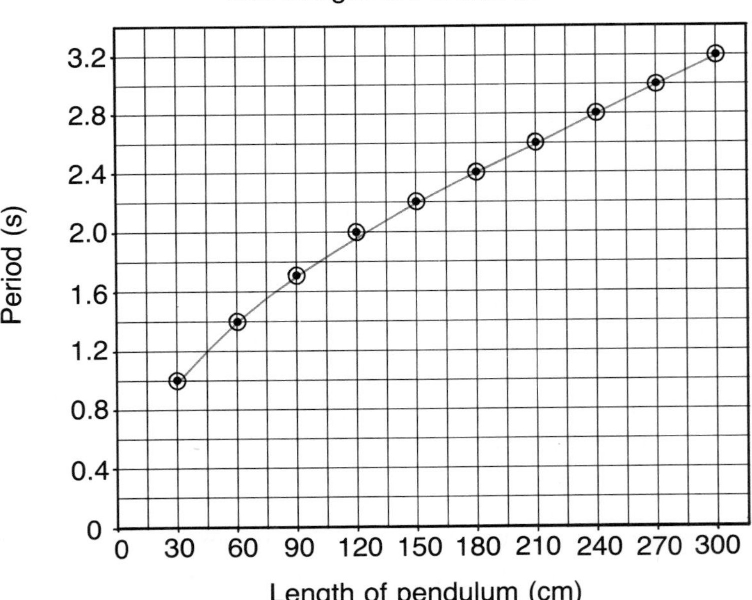

FIGURE 2–16. The pendulum data is shown on a graph. Note that the curve follows the data points smoothly, but does not "connect the dots."

Notice in Figure 2–16 how these steps were applied. From the graph, it is now easier to see a relationship. Doubling the length of the pendulum, for example, does not double the period. When does it double? When would you expect it to triple? Now give the period for 200 cm and 310 cm.

Review

11. Give three simple rules for laboratory safety.

12. Solve for the variable in each equation.

a. $3x - 2 = 7$

b. $5 = \frac{v}{2} - 4$

13. Why are graphs a useful way of displaying data?

14. A student measured the temperature every two hours during a day. The data are shown below.

a. Plot the data on a graph.

b. Make a note of any relationship you find between time of day and temperature.

Time	Temp. (°C)	Time	Temp. (°C)
8:00 A.M.	19	2:00 P.M.	35
10:00	24	4:00	34
12:00 Noon	31	6:00	30
		8:00	26

★ **15.** Solve for m: $4 = 3m - t$

PROBLEM SOLVING

Making a Hydrometer

In Skill 2–2, you used one method to find the densities of liquids. Another way is to use a hydrometer. When placed into a liquid, a hydrometer will sink to a certain depth. The density of the liquid can then be read on a standardized, built-in scale. The divisions on this scale were determined by testing several different liquids. You may have seen a hydrometer. One type is used to test battery acid, another to check antifreeze in car radiators.

Use a plastic straw and a disposable eyedropper to make your own hydrometer. A plastic vial and one-hole stopper can be used in place of the eyedropper. You may wish to use other materials. Use different liquids and their densities to determine the scale for your hydrometer. Then test it for accuracy.

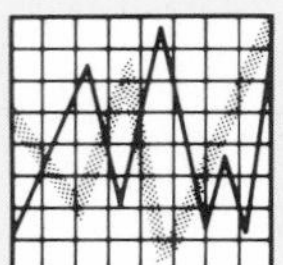

SKILL 2–3

Graphing

Problem: How do you construct a graph of scientific data?

Materials

graph paper

paper and pencil

Background

Experimental data provide information about the variables from specific measurements. Graphs are prepared from the data. A straight line or curve is drawn using the data points as a guide. The data points are not connected in a "dot-to-dot" manner. Rather, the line that best fits the data is drawn.

Often scientists need to know what the value of a variable will be at a point that was not measured. *Interpolation* is a method used to approximate values that are between points on a graph. *Extrapolation* is a method for approximating values that are beyond the range of the data. Data must be extrapolated when values needed are not in the range of the measurements obtained.

The data in the table were obtained from an experiment conducted to find out how the volume of a gas changes when its temperature changes. Use this data to construct and interpret a graph.

Procedure

1. Draw a graph on a piece of graph paper like the one shown. Use the steps on pages 43–45.
2. Mark off the x-axis for the independent variable.
3. Mark off the y-axis for the dependent variable.
4. Plot a point for each temperature/volume set of data in the table. Draw the line that best fits the data points.
5. Extrapolate the line to obtain approximate values from 0 K to 600 K.

Data and Observations

Temperature (K)	Volume (cm^3)
0	
100	71
140	
210	155
273	
280	195
360	257
400	
600	

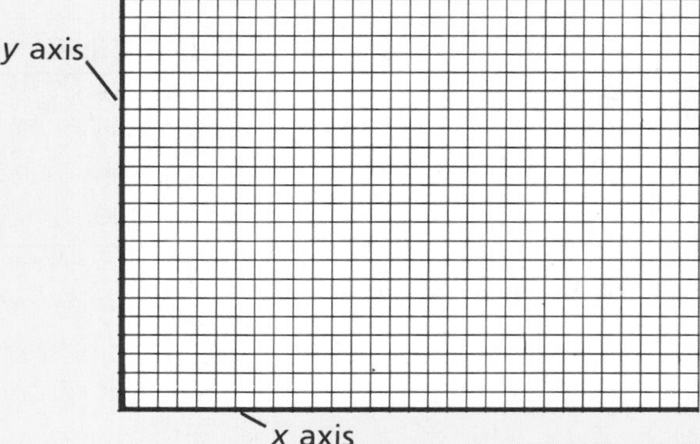

Analysis and Conclusions

1. Write a sentence that describes the relationship between the temperature and the volume of a gas.
2. Copy the data table on a sheet of paper. Use your graph to predict values for the volume of a gas at 0 K, 140 K, 273 K, 400 K, and 600 K.
3. What Celsius temperature corresponds to 273 K?
4. Why is the extrapolated value for the volume of a gas at 0 K not reasonable?
5. How do you construct a graph of scientific data?

Chapter 2 Review

SUMMARY

1. A standard is a fixed quantity used for comparison in measurement. 2:1
2. People all over the world use standard SI units. 2:2
3. Metric units larger or smaller than the base units are indicated by prefixes and differ by factors of 10. 2:2
4. Significant digits are numbers that result from measurement. 2:3
5. The standard SI unit for length is the meter. 2:4
6. Mass is the amount of matter in an object. In SI, the basic unit of mass is the kilogram. 2:5
7. Volume is the space occupied by an object and is measured in units of length cubed. 2:6
8. Density is a derived unit that is equal to mass per unit of volume. 2:7
9. The standard SI unit of time is the second. 2:8
10. The kelvin is the standard SI unit of temperature. 2:8
11. To avoid accidents and injuries, know and follow the rules for laboratory safety. 2:9
12. Physical science relations are often expressed as equations. It is sometimes necessary to rewrite an equation to use available data. 2:10
13. Scientists graph data so they can better see the relationship between two variables. 2:11

VOCABULARY

a. accuracy
b. density
c. kelvin
d. kilogram
e. liter
f. mass
g. meniscus
h. meter
i. SI
j. significant digits
k. standard
l. volume

MATCHING

Match each description with the correct vocabulary word from the list above. Not all vocabulary words will be used.

1. SI unit for mass
2. the space an object occupies
3. mass per unit of volume
4. a system of units used worldwide
5. numbers that result from measurement
6. how close a measurement is to an accepted value
7. one cubic decimeter
8. exact quantity used for comparison
9. SI unit of length
10. amount of matter in an object

Chapter 2 Review

MAIN IDEAS

A. Reviewing Concepts

Choose the word or phrase that correctly completes each of the following sentences.

1. ______________ are fixed quantities used by everyone when measuring.
2. A balance is used to measure ______________.
3. An SI unit for volume, equal to a liter, is the ______________.
4. Density is defined as ______________.
5. Thermometers in laboratories use the ______________ scale.
6. The SI unit of temperature is the ______________.
7. A milliliter of water has a mass of ______________.
8. The variable that is changed by the experimenter is called the ______________.
9. The kilogram is the basic unit of ______________ in SI.
10. The precision of a measurement is related to the number of ______________.
11. The prefix in SI that means 1/100 is ______________.
12. To change meters to kilometers, ______________.
13. Liters, dm^3, and mL are units of ______________.
14. A ______________ is used to measure liquid volume.
15. The ______________ is the SI unit of time.

B. Understanding Concepts

Answer the following questions using complete sentences when possible.

16. How many significant digits are in the following measurements?
   a. 50.3 g b. 74.00 m c. 0.0593 kg
17. Convert 628 g to kilograms.
18. A stone dropped in a graduated cylinder causes the water level to rise from 18 mL to 22 mL. What is the volume of the stone?
19. A temperature of 798 K is how many Celsius degrees?
20. In 12.5 cm^3 of water, how many milliliters are there?
21. If a beaker has a mass of 25 g and 150 mL of water are added to it, what is the total mass of the filled beaker?
22. How are SI units like the United States money system?
23. What is the density of a material that has a mass of 32.0 g and a volume of 1.60 cm^3?
24. A measurement of 47.5 dm^3 is how many liters?
25. You want to know if the milk served in your cafeteria is skim, 2%, or whole milk. How could you use the differences in density to find out?

C. Applying Concepts

Answer the following questions using complete sentences when possible.

26. The vertical axis of a graph is 120 squares high. You have to plot data that ranges from 0 meters to 400 meters. What is the best way to mark off the scale?
27. A rock has a mass of 17.28 g. When it is dropped into a graduated cylinder, the water level rises from 15.3 mL to 26.5 mL. What is the density of the rock?
28. What are the advantages of using standard units of measurement? of using SI?
29. A block of iron measures 5.32 cm by 6.25 cm by 4.03 cm. If the block has a mass of 2.2 kg, what is its density in g/cm^3?
30. Convert 50 km/h to m/s.

SKILL REVIEW

1. Two students want to compare their relative lung capacities. Their teacher gives them each a large, stretch balloon, a bucket of water, and a dishpan. How can the students use these materials to compare the relative volumes of their lungs?
2. If you had two cans of green beans that were alike except that one was low in salt, how could you tell the cans apart?
3. On which axis of a graph should the independent variable be placed?
4. Refer to Question 1 above. List two variables the students should keep constant when determining their relative lung capacity.
5. Graph the following experimental data.

Stretching of a Spring	
Mass	**Distance**
100 g	3 cm
200 g	6 cm
300 g	9 cm
400 g	12 cm
500 g	15 cm

What type of line does the graph appear to be? How far would you expect a one kilogram mass to stretch the spring? Could it happen?

PROJECTS

1. Write to the National Bureau of Standards in Gaithersburg, Maryland 20899, for information on the agency. Make a report to your class about the functions of this agency.
2. Observe and list the food packages in your cupboards that use SI base units or derived units. Discover whether there is a pattern in the types of foods that use SI. Report your findings to the class.

READINGS

1. Arnold, Carolyn. *Measurements: Fun, Facts, & Activities*. New York: Franklin Watts, 1984.
2. Hopkin, Robert A. *The International SI System & How It Works*. 3rd ed. Tarzana, CA: American Metric Journal, 1983.
3. *Measuring and Computing*. New York: Arco Publishing, 1984.

SCIENCE AND SOCIETY

ARE SI UNITS IN AMERICA'S FUTURE?

How old are you? Most of you would respond to this question with a single number—say, "thirteen," "fourteen," or "fifteen." But fifteen what? Fifteen seconds? "No," you'd probably answer, "fifteen years!"

The point here is that all measurements such as how old you are, how far you have to come to school, or how much electricity you used last month require *units* as well as numbers. Fortunately, the whole world agrees to measure time with the same units: seconds, minutes, hours, weeks, months, and years. Of these units to measure time, the basic unit is the *second*.

Background

By agreement among all the nations of the world, the second is now defined in terms of the frequency of a particular vibration of cesium atoms. All clocks are calibrated to operate according to this standard.

The nations of the world have also agreed on units to measure other things. These units are reviewed on a regular basis by an international committee. Because they have come about by international agreement, these units are known as the International System of Units, or SI.

Some of these units have been described in Chapter 2. One of these units is the *meter,* which is the international standard for measuring length. Although people in most nations use meters to measure distances in their everyday lives, most Americans use inches, feet, yards, and miles.

The meter has been a legally valid unit to measure length in the United States since 1866, and in 1893 the foot was defined in terms of the meter. In 1975 the Metric Conversion Act asked Americans to switch to measuring distances in meters voluntarily and established a Metric Board to help to accomplish this. In 1982 this board was replaced by the Office of Metric Programs with a 90% reduction in budget.

Many have considered this budget reduction to result from a lack of interest in switching to using SI units. The general population is reluctant to change. Distances to nearby towns are measured in miles and the speeds to drive there in miles per hour. Food in supermarkets is bought by the pound instead of the kilogram. Some changes to SI units *have* been

FIGURE 1. A road sign along an interstate highway shows distance in SI and English-system units.

made, however. Some soft drinks and juices are sold by the liter and many food packages give gram equivalents.

Case Studies

1. Industries that sell goods to other nations have had to use SI units in order to keep their customers. This has been particularly true for chemicals, computers, business machines, and automobiles. As of 1985, General Motors used SI units for almost all its auto parts, Chrysler for 70%, and Ford for 50%. Because of European and Japanese contributions to NASA's space station, all the engineering will be done with SI units.

2. When it comes to electricity, Americans do use SI units and probably don't even realize it. The electrical appliances we use measure electric current in *amperes,* potential difference in *volts,* and power in *watts*. You will find in Chapter 22 that these are SI units. The *kilowatt-hour,* used to measure how much electric energy you use, is directly related to the *joule,* which is the SI unit for energy.

3. The United States differs from most other nations in its units for measuring distance, mass, and temperature. How would you feel about measuring your height in meters and your mass in kilograms? If the temperatures on your weather report were given in degrees Celsius or Kelvin, would you understand what they mean? Meters, kilograms, and degrees Celsius and Kelvin may seem foreign to you. This is probably because you are used to inches, pounds, and degrees Fahrenheit. Yet many students your age in other parts of the world have grown up knowing nothing but meters, kilograms, and degrees Celsius.

4. In recent years, United States farmers have traveled to Taiwan, Korea, and other countries to discuss farming methods and results. Farmers from these countries have also visited the United States. The use of different units to describe crop yields and measure livestock production has made communication difficult.

Developing a Viewpoint

Come to class prepared to discuss these issues.

1. Because we often need to measure things, the units in which we measure them have a definite impact on our daily lives. What do you feel Americans should do about their units of measurement, keep things as they are or change to SI units?

2. Survey ten people about changing to SI. Ask the question: "Why do you think we should or should not change to SI units of measurement?" Based on the information you obtain from your survey, defend the majority opinion.

3. In local industries like building construction, SI units have not been widely accepted. In fact, some people in building construction have even objected to using SI units. If you were a carpenter who has measured boards in feet and inches for years, would you see a reason to make a change?

Suggested Readings

Michael D. Lemonick. "What Ever Happened to Metric?" *Time*. July 6, 1987, pp. 80–81.

J. Walsh. "Metrically the U.S. Doesn't Measure Up." *Science*. April 8, 1983, p. 175.

"Shift to Metrics Moving Ahead by Millimeters." *U.S. News and World Report*. June 7, 1982, p. 77.

M. M. Waldrop. "NASA Unveils Space Station Concept." *Science*. May 30, 1986, p. 1089.

UNIT 2

Imagine what it feels like to be in the cockpit of this jet plane as it is catapulted off the end of the aircraft carrier. A force several times greater than the normal force of gravity must be exerted on the plane to give it the speed it needs to fly. Force and motion are related; neither could exist without energy.

1429
Joan of Arc frees French city of Orleans.

1454
Gutenberg designs printing press.

1492
Columbus sails to the Americas.

FORCE AND ENERGY

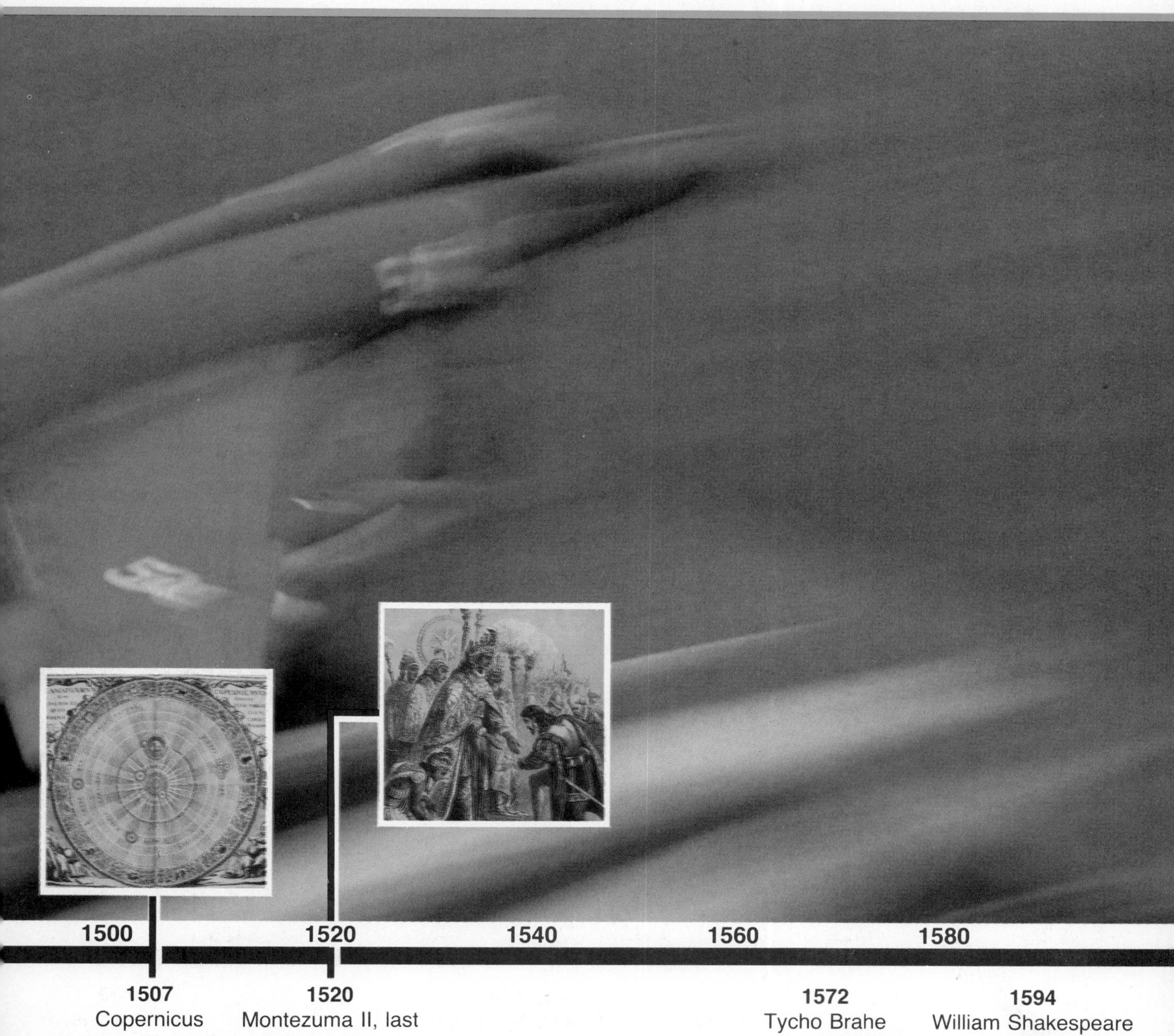

1500 | 1520 | 1540 | 1560 | 1580

1507
Copernicus says sun is center of solar system.

1520
Montezuma II, last Aztec emperor of Mexico, dies.

1572
Tycho Brahe records birth of new star in Cassiopeia.

1594
William Shakespeare writes *Romeo and Juliet.*

DESCRIBING MOTION IN A STRAIGHT LINE
FORCES AND MOTION
FORCES

Chapter 3

Motion

Motion is all around us. People walk, run, ride bicycles and skateboards, and travel from place to place in automobiles and airplanes. At an amusement park they speed up and down, soar in vertical circles, or spin round and round on many rides. One of the earliest goals of scientists was to explain motion. In this chapter, you will learn to describe simple forms of motion. You will also learn some causes of this motion.

DESCRIBING MOTION IN A STRAIGHT LINE

You already know some ways to describe motion. For instance, you can find the speed of a car by reading its speedometer. To understand the relationship between motion and its causes you will learn about acceleration and how to calculate it.

GOALS

1. You will know how to find the distance an object has moved.
2. You will be able to calculate speed and know how speed and velocity differ.
3. You will know how to calculate the acceleration of a body from knowledge of its velocity at two different times.

3:1 Position and Distance

In order to describe motion, you have to know where an object is. The location of any object is its position. A position is always described by choosing a reference point. For example, think of a knot in a rope. You might describe the knot by saying it is four meters from one end. The end of the rope is the reference point. A distance is the separation of two positions. In this example, the distance between the knot and the end of the rope is four meters.

How is position described?

Describe the distance between your school and your home. When you ride on a school bus, what is your distance from the driver?

F.Y.I. "In questions of science the authority of a thousand is not worth the humble reasoning of a single individual."
Galileo

a

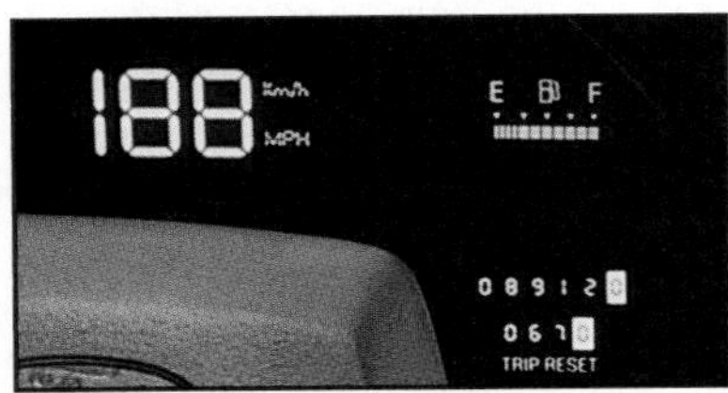

b

FIGURE 3–1. The speedometers in most cars register the instantaneous speed of the cars (a). Some new speedometers contain microcomputers that calculate the average speed for the trip as well (b).

What is a rate?

What is the difference between constant speed and average speed?

How are velocity and speed different?

3:2 Speed and Velocity

When a school bus drives you to school, the bus is in motion. How fast an object moves is called its speed. The bus has a speedometer that registers the speed of the bus at each instant.

Speed is the rate of change of the position of an object. As a shorthand, we will refer to speed as rate of motion. **Rates** are ratios between two different quantities. To find the rate of motion, or speed, you measure the distance an object travels. You then divide it by the time needed to travel that distance. For example, if you walk 12 km in two hours, then your speed is six kilometers per hour, 6 km/h. Speed is always measured in units formed from a distance unit (km) divided by a time unit (h). Another example of a speed unit is meters per second (m/s).

If the school bus is driven on a highway, its speedometer may always read the same value, such as 90 km/h. A speed that does not change is called a constant speed.

A school bus seldom travels at a constant speed very long. Especially in heavy traffic or when picking up riders, its speed is always increasing or decreasing. When the speed of an object varies, it may be easier to talk about its average speed. **Average speed** is total distance traveled divided by the total time of travel.

$$\textit{average speed} = \frac{\textit{total distance}}{\textit{total time taken}}$$

For example, the speed of the bus may vary from 0 km/h to 50 km/h, but if the bus travels a total of 10 km in 1/2 hour, then its average speed is 10 km divided by 1/2 hour, or 20 km/h.

So far we have talked only about the speed of motion. The direction of a motion may also be important. In describing car travel, you often say you traveled at a certain speed in a certain direction. For example: 90 km/h due west, or 50 km/h northwest. While speed describes how fast an object is moving, **velocity** describes both the speed and its direction. If one car travels 85 km/h west and a second car 85 km/h east, they have the same speed but different velocities. For two objects to have the same velocity, they must be moving at the same speed and in the same direction.

All speeds are relative. Suppose you walk toward the front of a bus at a speed of 5 km/h. If the bus is at rest, passengers on the bus and people on the sidewalk would both agree that you were moving at 5 km/h. What if the bus was not at rest, but was moving at 20 km/h? The

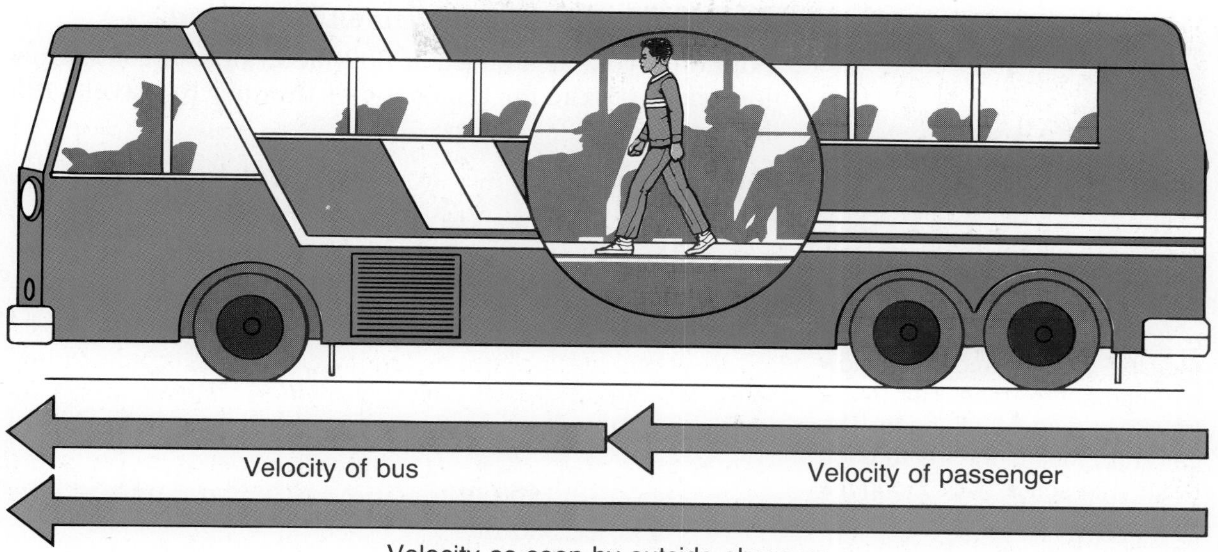

FIGURE 3–2. To a person on the sidewalk, the speed of the passenger is his walking speed plus the speed of the bus.

passengers in the bus would still measure your speed as 5 km/h. People standing on the sidewalk, however, would find that you traveled a larger distance in the same amount of time. They would find your speed to be 20 km/h + 5 km/h = 25 km/h.

3:3 Determining Speed

Speed can be calculated from the values of distance and time, using the formula below.

$$speed\ (v) = \frac{distance\ (d)}{time\ (t)}$$

$$v = \frac{d}{t}$$

EXAMPLE **Calculating Speed**

What is the speed, in km/h, of a truck that travels 15 kilometers in 15 minutes at a constant speed?

Given: distance

$d = 15$ km

time

$t = 15$ min $= 0.25$ h

Unknown: speed (v)

Basic Equation: $v = \dfrac{d}{t}$

Solution: $v = \dfrac{d}{t}$

$$= \frac{15\text{ km}}{0.25\text{ h}} = \frac{60\text{ km}}{\text{h}}$$

EXAMPLE Calculating Time from Speed

Sound travels at a speed of 330 meters per second. How long does it take for the sound of thunder to travel 1485 meters?

Given: speed

$v = 330$ m/s

distance

$d = 1485$ m

Unknown: time (t)

Basic Equation: $v = \frac{d}{t}$ or

$$t = \frac{d}{v}$$

Solution: $t = \dfrac{d}{v}$

$$= \frac{1485 \text{ m}}{330 \text{ m/s}} = 4.5 \text{ s}$$

How can speed be found from a graph?

FIGURE 3–3. Both graphs show the same trip. The car in (a) travels at a constant speed. The car in (b) makes the trip through traffic with some stops along the way.

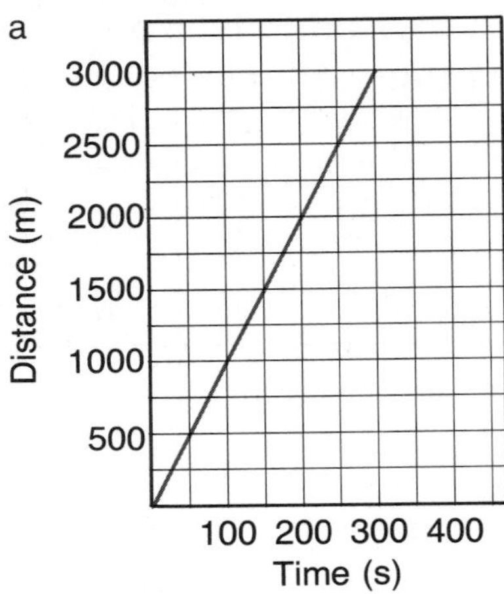

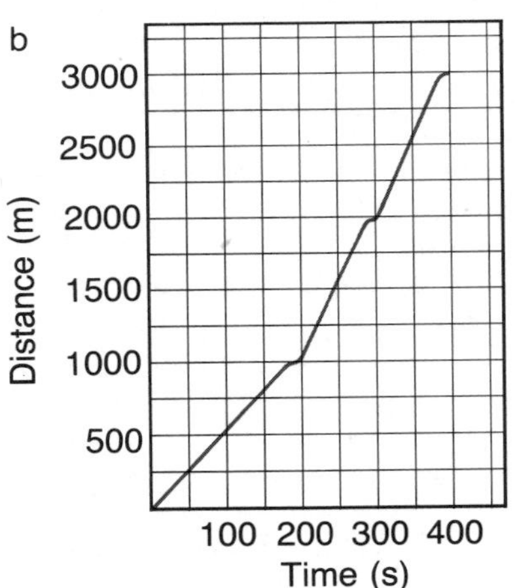

PRACTICE PROBLEMS

1. A sprinter can run 100 m in 10 seconds. Find the speed of the runner.
2. A train on which you are traveling is moving at 150 km/h. You are running toward the front of the train at a speed of 8 km/h, as measured by people on the train. What is your speed as measured by people standing next to the tracks?

Speed can also be found by using a graph on which distance is plotted at various times. The graph in Figure 3–3a shows that the car traveled 1000 m in the first 100 seconds. It continued to cover a distance of 1000 m in each 100 seconds. Therefore, its speed was constant. The speed of the car is 1000 m divided by 100 seconds or 10 m/s.

A graph of a car moving with changing speeds is shown in Figure 3–3b. In the first 50 seconds the car travels 250 m. The car continues to travel at this speed for 175 seconds. During the next 25 seconds its distance does not change. Its speed during this time is zero; it is at rest. During the 50 seconds between 200 and 250 seconds the car travels 550 meters. Thus its speed is faster than it was before it stopped. The faster the speed, the greater the slope of the line on the graph. Notice that the car stops two more times in its trip. When the car is stopped, the line on the graph is horizontal. Its average speed for the whole trip is the total distance, 3000 m, divided by the total time, 400 seconds, or 7.5 m/s.

INVESTIGATION 3–1

A Distance Versus Time Graph

Problem: What can you learn from a distance versus time graph?

Materials

pencil
graph paper with large squares

Procedure

1. Allow 3-square margins on paper.
2. Decide which is the independent variable and which is the dependent variable. Label the x-axis with the name of the independent variable, and the y-axis with the name of the dependent variable. Title your graph.
3. Determine the range of the independent and dependent variables. Number the squares along the x and y axes.
4. Use the data provided to plot the distances the skateboarder has traveled in the times indicated. For example, in 5 s the skateboarder has gone 9 m. In 10 s, the skateboarder has traveled 15.5 m. Do this by marking a dot at each point where a time and distance line cross. Circle each point.
5. Draw a *smooth* line that connects all the dots. The slope of the line shows the speed. The steeper the line, the greater the speed.

FIGURE 3–4.

Data and Observations

The following data show the distance from the starting position a skateboarder has traveled in the given time interval.

Total time (s)	Total distance (m)	Total time (s)	Total distance (m)
0.0	0.0	8.0	14.0
1.0	0.5	9.0	15.0
2.0	1.0	10.0	15.5
3.0	4.0	11.0	16.0
4.0	7.0	12.0	17.0
5.0	9.0	13.0	18.0
6.0	11.0	14.0	19.0
7.0	13.0	15.0	20.0

Analysis

1. What values are plotted on the y-axis? On the x-axis?
2. During what time period is the skateboarder traveling fastest?
3. During what time period is the skateboarder traveling slowest?
4. How far does the skateboarder travel between 10 s and 15 s?
5. What is the skateboarder's average speed for (a) the entire trip? (b) during the first 5 seconds? (c) during the third second?
6. Suppose the distance for 16 s were 19 m. Describe the motion of the skateboarder during that time.

Conclusions

7. What can you learn from a distance versus time graph?
8. Why might you prefer to show the data on a graph rather than in a table?

3:4 Acceleration

When an automobile is stopped at a red light, it is at rest. The speed of the car is zero. When the light turns green, the driver steps on the gas pedal. The car moves forward and the speedometer shows an increasing speed. Suppose that after 5 seconds the speed is 20 km/h. After 10 seconds it is 40 km/h, and after 15 seconds it is 60 km/h. Twenty seconds after it started, it reaches a speed of 80 km/h. The driver then puts less pressure on the gas pedal and drives at a constant 80 km/h.

The graph in Figure 3–5a shows the speed of a car versus time after a traffic light turns green. The line starts at zero and slopes upward. The upward slope shows that the speed is increasing. The car is accelerating.

What is acceleration?

Acceleration is the rate of change of velocity. An object's velocity is described by its speed and direction. If the direction of motion does not change, then the acceleration is the rate of change of speed.

To find the acceleration for an object, divide the change in velocity by the interval of time over which the velocity changed. The change in velocity is the difference between the final velocity and the initial velocity.

The size of the acceleration depends on both the change in velocity and the time intervals. A body can have a large acceleration if the change in velocity is very large. Acceleration will also be large if a velocity change takes place very quickly.

FIGURE 3–5. The car in (a) shows constant acceleration. The acceleration of the car in (b) is zero. This car is traveling at a constant velocity.

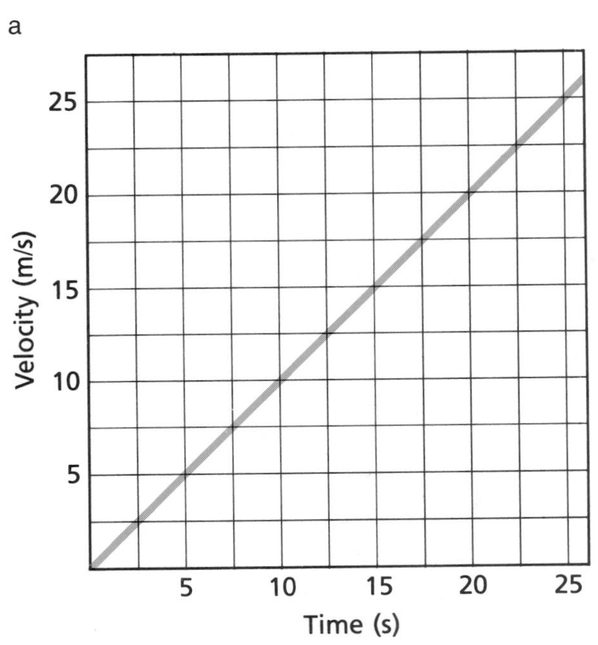

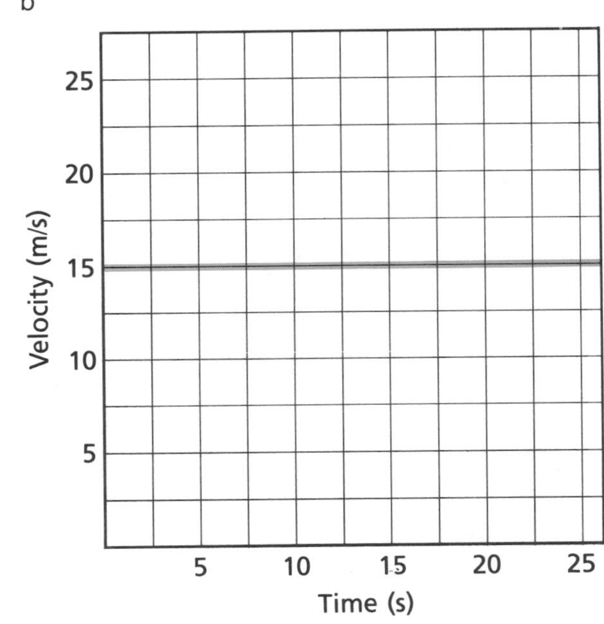

CAREER

Sports Medicine Technician

Julie Lang always loved sports. When she couldn't take part, she was not content just to sit on the sidelines and cheer. She became an athletic trainer in the ninth grade for the soccer and wrestling teams.

When Julie graduated from high school, she took a job as a sports medicine technician with the local professional football team. She learned how to prevent and treat injuries, how to select proper equipment, and how to identify possible safety hazards. She took courses in first aid and physiology in adult education classes to better equip her to treat injured players.

Julie is quite successful today. She develops rehabilitation programs and teaches athletes how to prevent and treat their injuries. She has also developed a training program for the families of the players.

For career information, write

American College of Sports Medicine
1 Virginia Ave. Suite 340
P.O. Box 1440
Indianapolis, Indiana 46206

The equation used to calculate the average acceleration is

$$\text{average acceleration} = \frac{\text{final velocity} - \text{initial velocity}}{\text{time over which velocity changed}}$$

How is acceleration calculated?

$$a = \frac{v_f - v_i}{t} = \frac{\Delta v}{t}$$

The symbol Δ is the Greek letter delta and means *change in.*

Velocity is measured in meters/second, m/s, so acceleration is measured in $\frac{\text{meters/second}}{\text{second}}$. The unit for acceleration is usually written as m/s^2 and read "meters per second squared" or "meters per second per second."

Look at the change in speed over a 5 second interval in Figure 3–5a. You will see that the speed increases by 5 m/s in a 5 second interval. That is, $\Delta v = 5$ m/s and $t = 5$ s. The direction does not change. The acceleration is (5 m/s)/(5 s) = 1 m/s^2. The change in speed is the same each and every 5 second interval. Thus, the acceleration is constant. A constant acceleration is shown by a straight line on a velocity versus time graph, Figure 3–5b.

EXAMPLE Calculating Acceleration

From rest, a bicyclist accelerates to a velocity of 12 meters per second in some direction over 25 seconds. What is the acceleration of the bicyclist?

FIGURE 3–6. The bike riders will accelerate from rest until they reach their desired velocity.

What do the velocity-time graphs for positive, negative, and zero acceleration look like?

Given: initial velocity
$v_i = 0$ m/s
final velocity
$v_f = 12$ m/s
time
$t = 25$ s

Unknown: acceleration (a)

Basic Equation: $a = \frac{v_f - v_i}{t}$

Solution:

$$a = \frac{v_f - v_i}{t} = \frac{12 \text{ m/s} - 0 \text{ m/s}}{25 \text{ s}} = 0.48 \text{ m/s}^2$$

The direction of a is the same as that of velocity.

When velocity increases, the change in velocity is a number greater than zero. The change is a positive number, and the acceleration is positive. The slope on a velocity versus time graph is upward. When velocity is constant, the change in velocity is zero and the acceleration is also zero. The line on a velocity versus time graph is horizontal.

Suppose a car slows down. Its velocity decreases over a period of time. In this case its final velocity is smaller than its initial velocity. The change is a number less than zero. The acceleration is also a negative number. This means that the acceleration is in the direction opposite to the velocity. The line representing slowing down on a velocity versus time graph slopes downward.

EXAMPLE Calculating Acceleration

When traveling westward along a highway, a driver slows down from 24 meters per second to 15 meters per second in 12 seconds. What is the driver's acceleration?

Given: initial velocity
$v_i = 24$ m/s
final velocity
$v_f = 15$ m/s
time
$t = 12$ s

Unknown: acceleration (a)

Basic Equation: $a = \frac{v_f - v_i}{t}$

Solution:

$$a = \frac{v_f - v_i}{t} = \frac{15 \text{ m/s} - 24 \text{ m/s}}{12 \text{ s}} = -0.75 \text{ m/s}^2$$

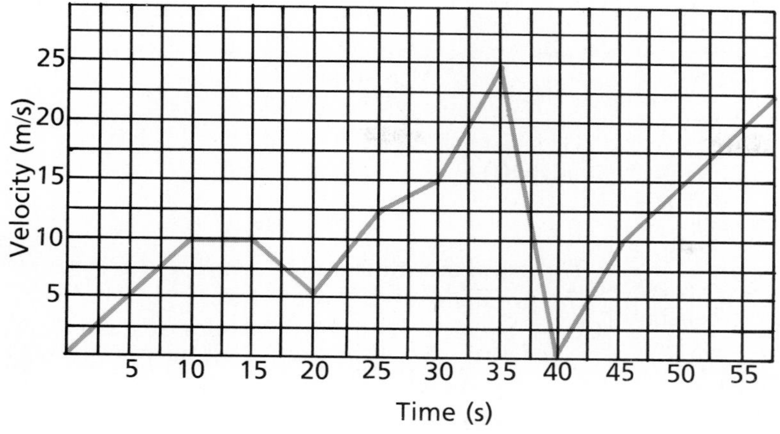

FIGURE 3–7. This graph shows the positive and negative accelerations of a car over time. From the change in direction of the line, you can tell if the car is speeding up or slowing down.

The acceleration of an object slowing is negative.

PRACTICE PROBLEMS

3. An automobile accelerates from 15 m/s to 30 m/s in 3.0 s. Find its acceleration.

4. A parachute on a drag-race car opens and changes the velocity of the car from 75 m/s to 45 m/s in a period of 4.0 s. Calculate the average acceleration of the car.

Review

1. How long does it take sound, with speed 330 m/s, to travel 2475 m?

2. a. What is the velocity of the car in Figure 3–7 after 10 seconds? After 15 seconds?

b. Study the figure. Identify the time intervals where the acceleration is positive, where it is zero, and where it is negative.

3. a. Sketch the position vs time graph and a velocity vs time graph of a car with constant velocity.

b. Sketch the same two graphs for a car with constant acceleration.

4. One car accelerates from rest to 50 km/h in 4 s. A second car accelerates from rest to 80 km/h in 8 s. Does the faster car have the larger acceleration?

★ **5.** The data on the right describes the motion of an object over a period of 5 seconds.

a. Make a position vs time graph.

b. Make a velocity vs time graph.

c. Describe the motion of the object and sketch an acceleration vs time graph.

Time (s)	Distance (m)
0.0	0.0
1.0	2.0
2.0	8.0
3.0	18.0
4.0	32.0
5.0	50.0

SKILL
Analysis

Problem: How do you solve a word problem?

Background

Being able to analyze a problem and to reason through a solution is one of the most sophisticated of all skills in science. The steps below provide a logical plan for attacking work problems. Very carefully work through the sample problem at the bottom of the page. Note how each step is applied in solving the problem. After you have studied the Sample Problem, look at the Examples on page 58. Identify each step in the model procedure.

When you understand how to do each step, do the Practice Problems on page 63, using the model format. Do not skip any steps. It might surprise you to know that *Step 1 is the most important step.*

Procedure

Step 1. Read the problem carefully. As you read, form a picture of the action in your mind. Be sure you understand all the terms used. Restate the problem in your own words.

Step 2. Identify the quantities that are given in the problem.

Step 3. Identify the quantity to be found.

Step 4. Examine the problem carefully to see the relationship between what is given and what you are asked to find. Identify the equation that contains these quantities.

Step 5. If necessary, solve the equation for the unknown quantity.

Step 6. Substitute the given values into the equation, along with their proper units.

Step 7. Check to see if the answer will be in the proper units.

Step 8. Solve the equation.

Step 9. Check your answer to see if it is reasonable.

The numbers indicate the appropriate steps in the problem-solving procedure.

1. A hiker walked for 2.0 hours at a speed of 6.5 kilometers per hour. How far did the hiker walk?
2. **Given:** $time = 2.0\ \text{h}$

   $$speed = 6.5\ \frac{\text{km}}{\text{h}}$$
3. **Unknown:** *distance*
4. **Basic Equation:** $speed = \dfrac{distance}{time}$
5. **Solution:** $distance = speed \times time$
6. $$distance = 6.5\ \frac{\text{km}}{\text{h}} \times 2.0\ \text{h}$$
7. $$distance\ (\text{km}) = \frac{\text{km}}{\text{h}} \times \text{h} = \text{km}$$
8. $$6.5\ \frac{\text{km}}{\text{h}} \times 2.0\ \text{h} = 13\ \text{km}$$
9. It is reasonable for a hiker to cover 13 kilometers, walking for 2 hours at 6.5 kilometers per hour.

Practice Problems

1. An ant moves 30.1 mm in 72 s. How fast is it moving?
2. A car goes 25 km in 0.60 h and then travels 39 km in the next 1.5 h. What is the average speed for the entire trip?
3. A girl rushes out of her house and hurries toward school at 9.0 km/h. Five minutes later her father discovers that she has forgotten her lunch and starts out, at 15 km/h, to catch her.
   a. How far does she get in 5.0 min?
   b. How long, in minutes, does it take her father to catch her?
   c. How far from home are they when they meet?

FORCES AND MOTION

GOALS

1. You will know the definitions of force and inertia.
2. You will explain what happens to the velocity of a body that moves without a net force acting on it.

The early Greeks thought that all matter was a mixture of four elements, earth, water, air, and fire. Each element had its "natural place." Earth was at the bottom and fire at the top. They explained motion as the desire of the elements to return to their natural places. By the year 1400, European scientists knew that these explanations were not correct. Galileo Galilei, born in Pisa, Italy, in 1564, made careful studies of motion. He was the first to define and study acceleration. His experiments led to our modern understanding of the causes of motion.

3:5 Inertia

F.Y.I. Newton's first law of motion is a restatement of Galileo's principle of inertia.

A hockey puck slides across a rink with hardly any change in velocity until it strikes the wall, net, or another stick. A bowling ball continues down the alley until it hits the pins or the gutter. In both these cases, the velocity of the body is constant until it hits another body. Its acceleration is zero until it strikes something. The property of a body that resists any change in velocity is called **inertia** (ihn UR shuh). Rest is a special case of motion with a velocity equal to zero. Therefore, inertia is also the property of an object at rest that causes it to remain at rest. The amount of **mass** an object has is a measure of its inertia. The more mass a body has, the greater its inertia.

How is inertia related to the motion of an object?

How is inertia related to the mass of an object?

FIGURE 3–8. When the car suddenly stops, inertia keeps the dummy moving forward through the windshield. Seat belts supply the opposing force necessary to stop motion and reduce injury from accidents.

FIGURE 3–9. When the dogs pull with equal force in opposite directions, the forces on the toy are balanced and the toy does not move. The toy moves when one dog pulls harder than the other. There is a net force.

3:6 Forces on Bodies

What changes the velocity of a body? In other words, what gives it an acceleration? A hockey puck is struck by a hockey stick to start its motion. Its motion is changed by contact with the wall, the net, or another stick. The bowler gives the bowling ball its initial motion. Contact with the gutter or pins changes its motion. In both cases one object puts a force on another object. A **force** is a push or a pull one body exerts on another.

How is the motion of a body changed?

Does a force always change velocity? Have you ever watched two dogs pulling on the opposite ends of a toy? Look at Figure 3–9. The force exerted by one dog opposes the force exerted by the other. If the two opposing forces are balanced, the toy will not move. Two **forces** are **balanced** when they are equal in size but opposite in direction. Unbalanced forces occur when one force is greater than the other. When forces on an object are unbalanced, there is a **net force.** A net force always changes the velocity of a body. If one of the dogs in the picture pulls harder than the other, the toy will accelerate in the direction of the greater force. Recall that acceleration also occurs if the direction of motion changes. Thus a net force is also needed to change the direction of the velocity, even if the speed does not change.

3:7 Newton's First Law of Motion

The laws that describe how forces change the motion of an object were stated by Sir Isaac Newton (1642–

1727). **Newton's first law of motion** states that *an object that is moving at a constant velocity continues at that velocity unless a net force acts on it.* Objects at rest remain at rest unless a net force acts on them. An object in motion continues moving at the same speed and in the same direction unless a net force acts on it. This law is sometimes referred to as the law of inertia. The following cases illustrate Newton's first law of motion.

Case I

Have you ever pulled a sled along behind you through the snow? If you stopped suddenly, you may have known the pain of being hit in the back of the legs by the sled. No net force acted on the sled. Due to inertia, it continued its straight line motion until it met a net force, that of your legs. If you had stepped aside, the sled would have continued on until friction or some other force stopped it.

Case II

Imagine you are standing still in a motionless bus when it suddenly lurches forward. Your body has inertia. Therefore a force is needed to change its velocity. The bus floor accelerates your feet, but your body may fall backwards. As you grab onto a handle or strap, the force exerted by the bus through the strap gives your body forward velocity. What will happen if the bus stops suddenly? Due to inertia, your body continues in motion

a

b

FIGURE 3–10. If the person pulling the sled stops suddenly, the sled will continue its forward motion until it is stopped by some force (a) Holding on to the strap on a crowded bus helps the upper part of your body accelerate forward at the same time as your feet (b).

TECHNOLOGY: ADVANCES

Smart Cars

Since 1983, scientists and engineers in Germany have been developing a system that uses a microcomputer to direct people driving automobiles in unfamiliar towns. A detailed map of a region is stored as a set of computer instructions on a compact disc (CD). The driver starts the CD and tells the computer his present location and the house number to which he wants to go. The computer then finds the shortest path to that address.

Special sensors in the wheels tell the computer how far the car has gone, and even report its turns. Meanwhile, a computerized voice gives directions like "turn left at the next corner." In addition, a map of the neighborhood is displayed on a television-like screen. The driver does not have to fumble with maps or make sudden decisions. In this way, computers will be making cars more pleasant to drive as well as safer.

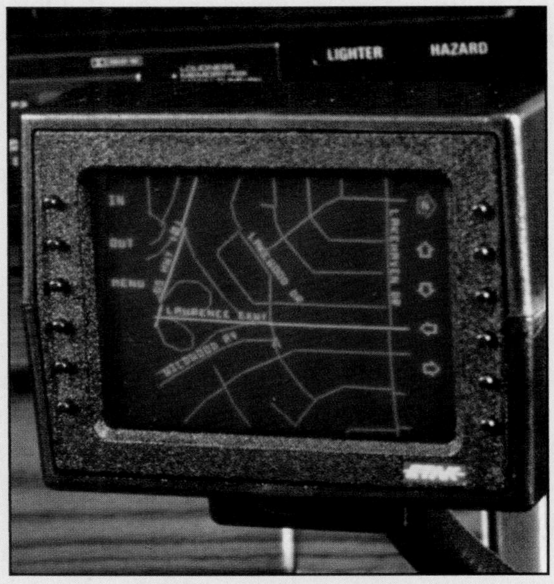

until something stops it. Why might you fall if you are standing in a bus that makes a sudden sharp turn around a corner?

Review

6. Which object has greater inertia, a bowling ball at rest or a pitched baseball?
7. a. When will two opposing forces not change motion?
   b. What are balanced forces and a net force?
8. Suppose you tie a rope to a doorknob and pull on the other end of the rope. Your hand does not move. Identify the two opposing forces on your hand.
9. What forces stop or change the motion of a bicycle? of a surfboard?
10. ★ To demonstrate inertia, put a piece of smooth stiff cardboard on the top of a glass and lay a coin on the cardboard. Then snap your finger against the cardboard to give it a sudden motion. Explain your

results. Suppose you glue corduroy on the top of the cardboard. Will the demonstration still work? If not, does the coin no longer have inertia?

FORCES

Forces are all around us. Earth, floors, and walls all exert forces on us. Thanks to the force of friction we can walk, write with a pencil, and drive.

GOALS

1. You will understand the nature of several forces that act on us.
2. You will know what weight is and how it differs from mass.
3. You will be able to measure forces.

3:8 Examples of Forces

Forces arise when two bodies collide. A force is also required to stretch an elastic material like a rubber band. The force of the stretched rubber band in a slingshot can be used to accelerate a stone. A bowling ball slows as it rolls down the alley. The ball presses on the alley, creating a small dent in the wood. The bottom of the ball also becomes slightly flatter. The forces that cause these changes in shape are the forces that change the velocity of the ball. In all these cases, forces are the result of squeezing, stretching, or bending matter. Can you think of other examples of this type of force?

How does friction affect motion?

If you give your book a shove, it will slide across your desk. However, the speed of the book quickly decreases. The force between the surfaces of the book and desk is friction. **Friction** is the force that opposes the motion

a

b

FIGURE 3–11. The sticky pine tar rag increases friction so the batter can get a better grip on the bat (a). In skiing, skis are waxed to reduce the force of friction (b).

between two surfaces that are touching each other. The amount of friction depends on the types of surfaces and the force pressing them together. It does not depend on how large an area is in contact.

There are many examples of friction in your daily life. When you walk, there is friction between the soles of your shoes and the floor. Have you ever tried to walk on ice or on a floor covered with water or oil? Your feet slip, and walking is more difficult because there is less friction. As you write with a pencil, friction rubs the black graphite from the pencil tip onto the paper. When you use a rubber eraser, friction between the eraser and the paper causes a pencil mark to be rubbed away. Scouring abrasives are used to clean pots and pans. These increase the frictional force and wipe away dried foods and stains.

FIGURE 3–12. The weight of a medium-sized apple is about one newton.

3:9 Gravity and Weight

Not all forces are exerted by bodies touching one another. If you drop a book, it falls to the ground. Its velocity when it leaves your hand is zero, but its velocity is not zero when it hits the ground. Objects fall because Earth exerts a force on them, even when they do not touch Earth. The force of gravity pulls objects to Earth.

What are the units of mass and weight?

The force of gravity that Earth exerts on an object depends on the mass of the object. Remember that inertia is the measure of the mass of a body. The greater the mass, the more difficult it is to change its motion. Mass is also the amount of matter in an object. Mass is measured in kilograms (kg) or grams (g).

FIGURE 3–13. This map shows the variations in the force of gravity throughout the United States and Canada.

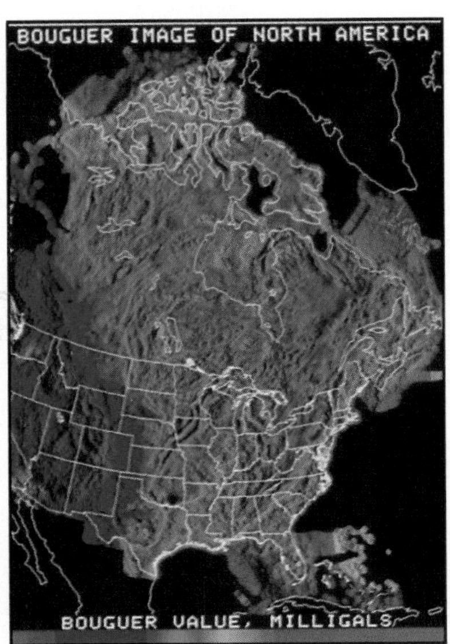

The force of gravity that Earth exerts on an object resting on its surface is called its **weight.** The unit of weight, or any other force, is the newton (N). A medium-sized apple weighs about one newton. A person with a mass of 60 kg weighs about 600 N. The amount of gravitational force Earth exerts on an object depends on the mass of the object. As mass increases, so does weight. Each kilogram of mass has a weight of 9.8 N on the surface of Earth. When a person goes on a diet, the body loses mass. Therefore, there is also a decrease in weight. The force of gravity on a person decreases due to the decrease in mass.

Gravity is a property not only of Earth but of all matter. Every object in the universe pulls on every other object. Every object exerts a force on other objects. This force is **gravity.** The pull between most objects is very

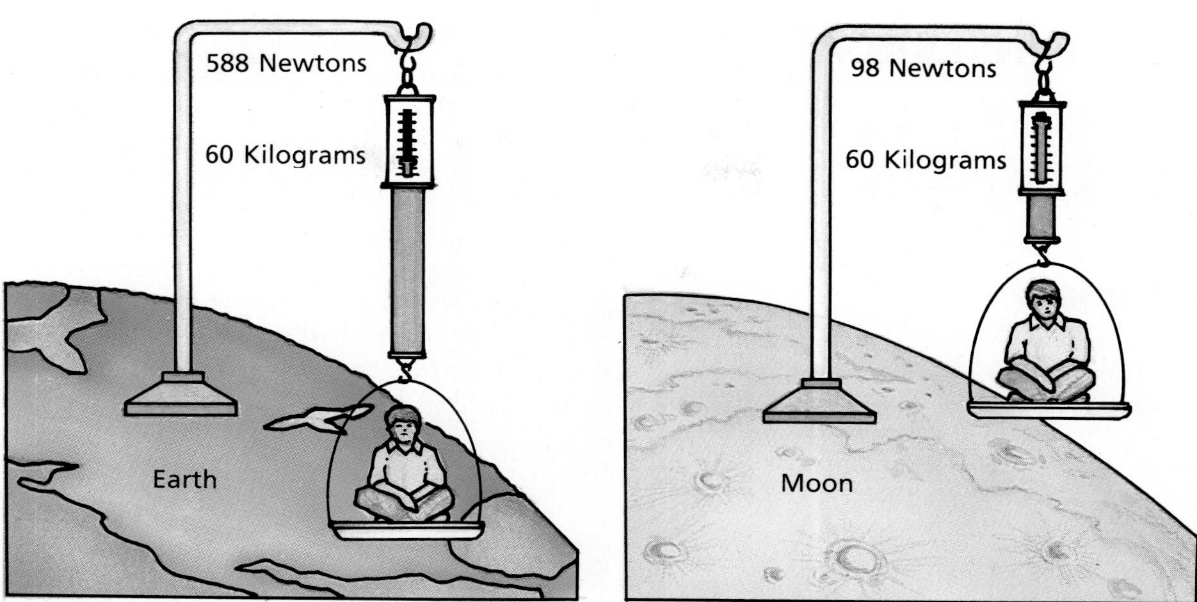

FIGURE 3–14. A scale measures the force of gravity pulling on your body. Since the gravity of the moon is less than that of Earth, your weight would be less on the moon; however, your mass would remain the same.

small. For example, a rock one meter in diameter might have a mass of 5000 kg. The force of gravitational attraction between this rock and a baseball is less than the weight of a mosquito.

How is mass related to gravity?

The more mass an object has, the greater the force of gravity it exerts. For example, Earth has a greater mass than the moon. Therefore, Earth exerts a greater force on objects than does the moon. Your weight on the moon would be 1/6 of your weight on Earth. The pull of gravity on the moon is only 1/6 as great as the pull of gravity on Earth. Your mass, however, would be exactly the same on the moon as it is on Earth. The quantity of matter in your body is not changed by moving it to the moon. It is just as difficult to change the velocity of your body on the moon as it is on Earth. Your body has the same inertia on Earth and on the moon.

How is weight different from mass?

How does the distance between objects affect the force of gravity between them?

The force of gravity also depends on the distance between two objects. For example, as the distance between a rocket and Earth increases, the pull of gravity decreases. Suppose the force of Earth on a rocket is 36 000 N when the rocket is 10 000 km from the center of Earth. When the rocket is 20 000 km from the center of Earth, the force of gravity is reduced to 9000 N. That is, when the distance is doubled, the force of gravity becomes 1/4 of what it was originally. When the rocket is 30 000 km away, the force is only 4000 N. When the distance is tripled, the force becomes 1/9 of its original size.

INVESTIGATION 3–2

Measuring Force

Problem: How can you use a spring scale to measure force?

Materials

ring stand
extension clamp
spring
paper clip
paper cup
string
cardboard
10 metal washers
marble
pencil
eraser
graph paper
ruler

Procedure

1. Set up the ring stand and extension clamp as shown in Figure 3–15.
2. Use string to tie the spring to the extension clamp. Make sure the spring can rotate one or two turns.
3. Bend a paper clip to form a pointer and attach it to the bottom end of the spring.

FIGURE 3–15.

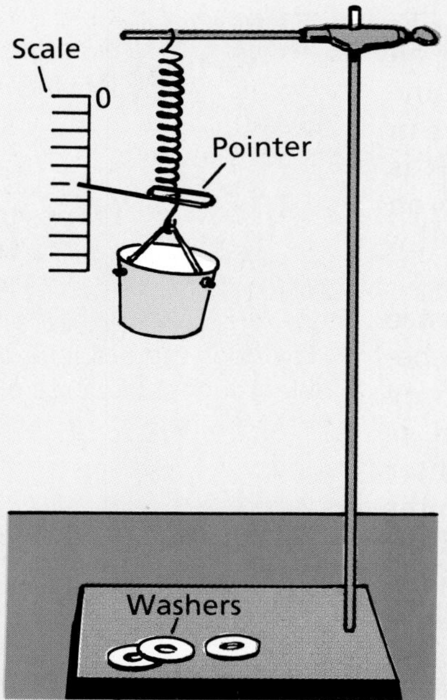

4. Use the bottom half of a paper cup. Use string to attach the bottom of the cup to the spring.
5. Set up a piece of cardboard behind your apparatus as in Figure 3–15. Mark the position of the pointer and label it 0.
6. Add a metal washer to the cup. Mark the new position of the pointer on the cardboard.
7. Repeat Step 6, adding another washer each time, until you have 10 washers in the cup. If adding a washer increases the length of the spring much more than adding the previous washer did, you may have overstretched the spring. Remove all washers and recheck the zero. Repeat Step 6 to make sure the marks are all correct.
8. Remove the washers.
9. Place the marble in the cup of your scale and find the force it exerts on the spring. Lightly mark the position of the pointer on the cardboard scale.
10. Record the force (weight) in terms of your washer-force scale.
11. Repeat Steps 9 and 10 for the pencil and eraser.
12. Remove the cardboard scale and measure and record the distance from the zero mark to the pointer position of each object you weighed.
13. Make a graph placing the number of washers on the x-axis and the distances from the zero mark on the y-axis.
14. Determine the weight of the objects you weighed from your graph.

Conclusions and Applications

1. What do the distances between the zero mark and the scale marks represent?
2. Why are washers not used as standard units of force measure?
3. How is a spring used to measure force?

3:10 Measuring Forces

A bathroom scale measures the force of gravity on your body; it measures your weight. Scales use the principle of balanced forces. When your body is at rest there is no net force acting on it. Gravity exerts a downward force, weight, on your body. The floor or the bathroom scale exerts an equal upward force. The scale measures the force needed to balance your weight.

How does a scale do this? The scale contains a spring that is bent by the force of your body on the scale. A bent spring pushes back until its force balances the force of your body. The amount of bending is shown on the dial. The dial is calibrated to convert the bending into units of weight.

A simple scale can be made by hanging an elastic band on a paper clip. When a piece of metal is hung on the other end, the elastic band stretches until the weight of the metal equals the force the elastic band exerts. The length of the elastic band is a measure of the force on it. Figure 3–16 is a graph showing how the length depends on force. From the graph you can tell that the elastic band will be 16 mm long when a force of 2.5 N pulls on it.

The elastic band scale that was just calibrated can now be used to measure other forces. Hook it on a wooden block and pull the block across your desk using the elastic band. The length of the elastic band now measures the force of friction between a block and your desk.

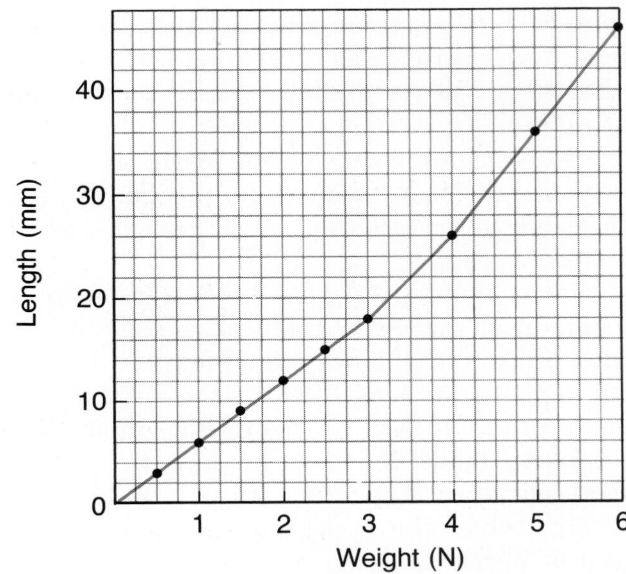

BIOGRAPHY

Galileo Galilei
(1564–1642)

Born in Pisa, Italy, Galileo showed that all objects are affected equally by gravity and fall with the same acceleration.

Remembered for introducing the telescope, his observations of the sky showed that Earth was not the center of the universe. He was brought before the Inquisition in 1632, refused to retract his writings about a sun-centered universe, and was confined to his villa for the rest of his life.

FIGURE 3–16. This is the graph of the length of the rubber band plotted against the number of washers.

PROBLEM SOLVING

A Weighty Subject

Eric, a student now in ninth grade, is the next American to land on the moon.

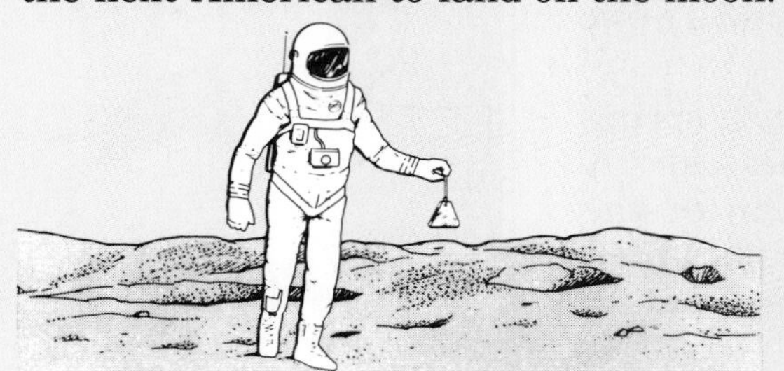

He had read that the gravity on the moon is 1/6 that on Earth, but he wanted to test it for himself. He could not convince NASA to build a spring scale, so he secretly took an elastic band and metal piece with him.

On Earth, the metal piece stretched the band by 46 mm. How long would Eric expect to find the elastic stretched on the moon?

Rubber bands are not very good scales. If you pull on one for a while then let go, it may not return to its original length. If you pull too hard, it breaks. Better scales are made with metal springs.

Review

11. a. Define force.
   b. List three examples of forces that involve contacts between bodies.
   c. Give three examples of forces that are the result of bending or stretching objects.

12. A planet is discovered that is the same size as Earth, but has twice as much mass. If your weight on Earth is 750 N, what would be your weight on that planet?

13. Suppose you hung an object with an unknown weight on the elastic band used in Figure 3–16. The band's length was 21 mm. What was the weight of the object?

14. The elastic band in Figure 3–16 is used to pull a wooden block across a table at a constant speed. While pulling the block you measure the elastic band to be 22 mm long. What is the force of friction?

★ **15.** Make a graph of force on the rocket versus distance from Earth using the data in Section 3:9. Draw a smooth curve through the data points. Now predict the force when the rocket is 15 000 km from the center of Earth.

Chapter 3 Review

SUMMARY

1. Distance is the separation between two positions. 3:1
2. Speed is the rate at which a body changes its position; average speed describes the motion of objects even if they are not moving at constant speed. Velocity is speed in a given direction. 3:2
3. Speed equals distance/time required to cover the distance. 3:3
4. Acceleration is the change in velocity divided by the time over which the change took place; a body accelerates if its direction changes, even if its speed is constant. 3:4
5. Inertia is the property of a body that resists any change in velocity. 3:5
6. A force is a push or pull on a body. An unbalanced force changes the motion of a body. 3:6
7. A body with no net force on it maintains constant velocity. 3:7
8. Friction opposes motion between two surfaces in contact. 3:8
9. Gravity is the force exerted on one body by another; weight is the force of gravity on objects on Earth. 3:9
10. An elastic band or spring can be calibrated as a scale to measure forces. 3:10

VOCABULARY

a. acceleration
b. average speed
c. balanced forces
d. force
e. friction
f. gravity
g. inertia
h. mass
i. net force
j. Newton's first law of motion
k. position
l. rate
m. speed
n. velocity
o. weight

Matching

Match each description with the correct vocabulary word from the list above. Some words will not be used.

1. rate of change of position
2. required to change velocity of object
3. location of an object
4. force between two surfaces in relative motion
5. a push or a pull that can change motion
6. state of forces on body with constant velocity
7. the property of a body that measures its resistance to a change in motion
8. rate of change in velocity
9. summary of observations that bodies with no net force have constant velocity
10. force of gravity on an object

Chapter 3 Review

MAIN IDEAS

A. Reviewing Concepts

Choose the word or phrase that correctly completes each of the following sentences.

1. Acceleration is the rate of change of velocity with *(distance, time, space, weight)*.
2. Acceleration is measured in *(m/s^2, m/kg, m/s, m/s/N)*.
3. According to Newton's first law every object has *(acceleration, inertia, motion, force)*.
4. The object with the largest inertia is *(a truck at rest, a pitched baseball, a baseball at rest, an automobile traveling 90 km/h)*.
5. A bowling ball slows down before striking the pins because of *(inertia, gravity, friction, balanced forces)*.

Complete each sentence with the correct word or phrase.

6. Velocity has information on both speed and ____________.
7. The ____________ of an object is the same on Earth and far away from it.
8. Velocity on a distance versus time graph is greatest where the slope of the plotted curve is ____________.
9. On a velocity versus time graph the slope of a graph showing the motion of an object acted on by no net force is ___zero___.
10. When a runner leaves the starting line and increases speed, the runner ___accelerates___.

Determine whether each of the following sentences is true or false. If it is false, change the underlined word to make the sentence true.

11. <u>Inertia</u> stops a moving object.
12. The <u>mass</u> of an astronaut is smaller on the moon than on Earth.
13. The acceleration of an object is shown by the slope on a <u>distance</u> versus time graph.
14. Acceleration <u>may</u> have a negative value.
15. A car rounding a curve at 50 km/h <u>is</u> accelerating.

B. Understanding Concepts

Answer the following questions using complete sentences when possible.

16. A bicycle speeds up from 7 m/s to 19 m/s in 4 seconds. What is the bicycle's acceleration?
17. An automobile travels 530 km in 6 hours. Find its average speed.
18. A coasting car slows from 27 m/s to 24 m/s in 6 seconds. Calculate its acceleration.
19. A jogger covers a distance of 10 km at an average speed of 6 km/h. Find the time the jogger took.
20. Under what conditions can a car traveling at a constant 70 km/h have a net force acting on it?
21. If you are in a spacecraft moving away from Earth, describe how your weight changes as your distance from Earth increases.
22. Find the acceleration of the car in Figure 3–7 between 20 seconds and 25 seconds.
23. Calculate the acceleration of the car in Figure 3–7 between 35 and 40 seconds.
24. You hang a 5-N weight from a rubber band. Suddenly the band breaks. Describe the force(s) on the weight before and after the band broke. In each case, tell whether there is a net force or balanced forces.
25. In a science fiction movie, a spaceship far from any planet or star shuts off

its rocket engine. It immediately stops moving. Does this obey the laws of physics? If so, which law?

C. Applying Concepts

Answer the following questions using complete sentences when possible.

26. You are standing on a bus. Describe how you would brace yourself when the bus is (a) turning to the right, (b) moving at constant speed, and (c) slowing down.

27. An automobile moving at 15 m/s starts to accelerate at a rate of 3 m/s^2. Find its velocity 5 seconds later.

28. A race car put on the brakes when it had a speed of 40 m/s. Its acceleration was -10 m/s^2. How long did it take to come to rest?

29. A superball is moving downward at a speed of 2 m/s just before it hits the floor. After bouncing from the floor, it rises at a speed of 2 m/s. If it took just 0.001 seconds to change velocity, what was its acceleration?

30. Sketch the motion of the superball of Problem 29 on both distance vs time and velocity vs time graphs.

SKILL REVIEW

1. What is the difference between an observation and an inference?

2. How do you read a meniscus?

3. In an experiment, what is the difference between a constant factor and a variable factor?

4. When graphing experimental data, which quantity goes on the y-axis?

5. What is the last step in solving a science word problem?

PROJECTS

1. Calculate the highest speed with which you can ride your bicycle by measuring the time it takes you to ride a known distance, after you have reached your maximum constant speed. To calculate your acceleration, ask a friend with a watch with a second hand to measure the time it takes you to reach your maximum speed. Then use the acceleration formula.

2. Prepare a poster that shows 10 different forces you observe every day. Make a drawing that illustrates each force. Use arrows to show the directions of the forces.

READINGS

1. Brancazio, P. J. "Sir Isaac and the Rising Fast Ball." *Discover*. July, 1984, pp. 44–45.

2. Fishman, Lew. "Physics of Golf." *Science Digest*. June, 1986, pp. 46–49, 78.

3. Laithwarte, Eric. *Force: The Power Behind Movement*. New York: Franklin Watts, 1986.

4. Watson, Philip. *Super Motion*. New York: Lothrop, 1982.

5. Whyman, Kathryn. *Forces in Action*. New York: Franklin Watts.

ACCELERATED MOTION
MOTION IN TWO DIRECTIONS
MOMENTUM

Chapter 4

The Laws of Motion

You have described motion by means of distance, velocity, and acceleration. You also have learned that without a net force, an object moves at a constant velocity. How, then, does an object get that velocity in the first place? The relationship between force and acceleration was first described by Isaac Newton.

ACCELERATED MOTION

How does the velocity of an object change if there is a net force acting on it? Sir Isaac Newton described the effects of forces on motion in his second law.

GOALS

1. You will learn that the acceleration of an object increases with increasing external force and decreases with increasing mass.
2. You will learn that all bodies near the surface of Earth, neglecting air resistance, fall with an acceleration 9.8 m/s^2.
3. You will learn that air resistance reduces the acceleration of falling bodies and that if the net force becomes zero the body falls at a constant, terminal velocity.

4:1 Newton's Second Law

Newton's first law of motion states that if no net force acts on an object, the velocity of the object does not change. Just how does the velocity change when there is a net force? Suppose your family car runs out of gas and stops. You need to get it to the side of the road. You get out and start pushing. The greater the force you apply, the faster it will accelerate. So, if two people push, it will reach the same velocity faster. The acceleration is in the direction of the force. If you want the car to move forward, you push forward. Finally, the acceleration is greater if the mass is smaller. It is easier to accelerate a compact car than a truck.

How is the acceleration of an object related to the force that causes the acceleration?

Newton's second law of motion states that *the acceleration of an object increases as the amount of net force applied from outside the object increases.* For the same force, a small mass will have a greater acceleration than a larger mass. In equation form, Newton's second law is $F = ma$. The equation shows that a force is required to produce a certain acceleration.

CAREER

Stunt Car Driver

Bobby James' childhood memories are of soapbox derbies. His interest in motion was endless. In school he learned how the laws of motion applied to car design. One year, after attending the Indianapolis 500, he was able to take a class in race-car physics. He knew then that his career would be in cars, so he became a test driver for a local car racing team. Many years and thousands of test runs later, Bobby was ready to become a stunt car driver. Today he travels around the country doing shows with stunt cars, and also works for television as a stunt car driver. Bobby takes his job seriously and hopes to design his own race course someday.

For career information, write

American Society for Engineering Education
11 Dupont Circle, NW
Washington, DC 20036

F.Y.I. Most of the fundamental ideas of science are essentially simple, and may, as a rule, be expressed in a language comprehensible to everyone.

Albert Einstein

We have been using newtons as the units for measuring force. The newton is a derived unit, which means it is made by combining other units. The equation for Newton's second law shows how the unit was derived.

$$\textit{Force}\ (1\ \text{N}) = \textit{mass}\ (1\ \text{kg}) \times \textit{acceleration}\ (1\ \text{m/s}^2)$$
$$1\ \text{N} = 1\ \text{kg} \times 1\ \text{m/s}^2$$

Therefore, one newton is the force needed to give a mass of one kilogram an acceleration of 1 meter/second^2.

Case I

A team of horses pulls an empty wagon. The harder the horses pull, the more rapidly the wagon gains speed. That is, the greater the force, the larger is the wagon's acceleration. If the wagon is loaded, the horses must pull harder to make the wagon change velocity at the same rate.

FIGURE 4–1. The horse must exert a greater force to accelerate this loaded wagon than to accelerate an empty wagon.

FIGURE 4–2. This dragster has the power of a locomotive but less mass than a passenger car.

Case II

In a drag race a car must be able to accelerate to high speeds very quickly. Drag racers have huge, wide tires with soft rubber surfaces to get the greatest friction with the road, very powerful engines to supply a large force, and bodies with very little mass.

EXAMPLE Calculating Force

The maximum acceleration of a fist in a karate blow has been measured to be 3500 m/s^2. The mass of the fist is 0.70 kg. If the fist hits a wooden block, what force does the wood place on the fist?

Given: mass

$m = 0.70$ kg

acceleration

$a = 3500$ m/s^2

Unknown: force (F)

Basic Equation: $F = m \times a$

Solution:

$$F = m \times a$$
$$= 0.70 \text{ kg} \times 3500 \text{ m/s}^2$$
$$= 2450 \text{ kg m/s}^2 = 2450 \text{ N}$$

PRACTICE PROBLEMS

1. How much force is needed to accelerate a bicycle and rider with mass 60 kg at 1.5 m/s^2?
2. What is the acceleration of a 4000 kg airplane that has a force on it of 24 000 N?
3. An 80-N force will accelerate a 20-kg mass at 4 m/s^2.
   a. What force will be required to maintain the same acceleration if the mass is doubled?
   b. If the mass is doubled and the force remains the same what is the acceleration?

What is the rate of acceleration of a falling object on Earth?

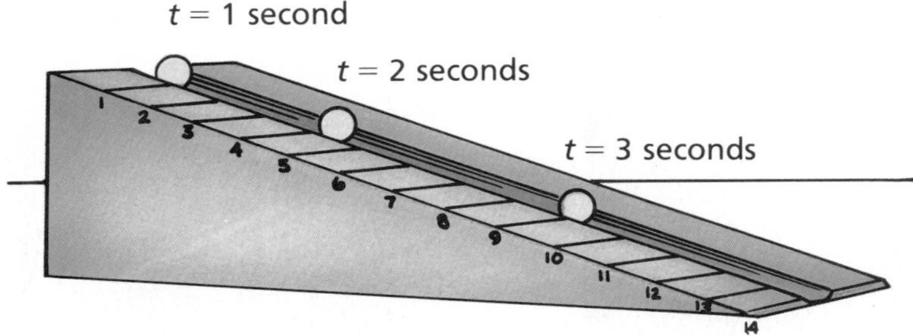

FIGURE 4–3. Galileo's experiment showed that all objects fall at the same rate. He timed the motion of the ball rolling down the inclined plane.

FIGURE 4–4. Though the white object is larger and more massive than the red object, both fall at the same rate.

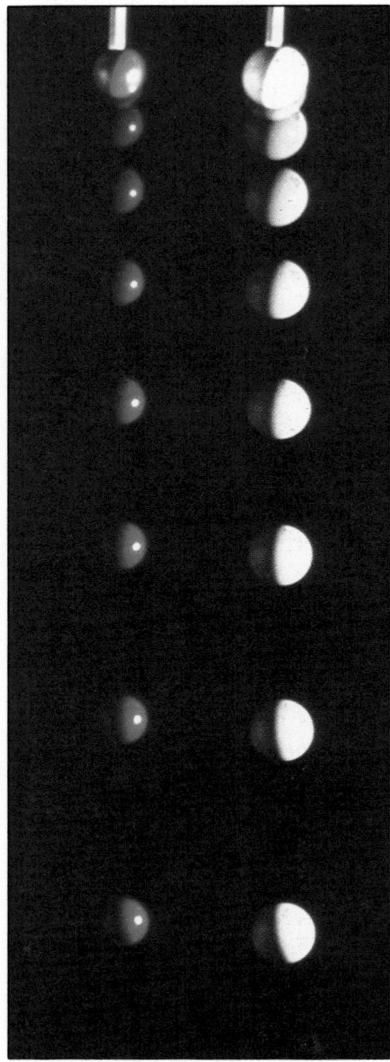

4:2 Falling Objects

A bowling ball and a golf ball are dropped from a tenth-story window. Which ball strikes the ground first? Would the bowling ball fall faster because it is heavier?

Galileo studied the motion of objects by rolling a ball down a ramp, Figure 4–3. He found that the speed of a ball increased an equal amount in each time interval. That is, the acceleration of the ball is a constant value. His experiments showed that the acceleration was the same for any ball, no matter what its mass. The increase in velocity would be the same for a bowling ball and a golf ball.

Figure 4–4 shows a photograph of two falling objects. Thirty flash pictures were taken each second. You can easily see that both objects fall at the same rate. You can also see that the distance the balls move between two flashes increases as they fall. If you calculated the acceleration of a ball falling in a vacuum, you would find it to be 9.8 m/s^2. That is, the downward velocity of the ball would increase 9.8 m/s for each second it falls. All objects near the surface of Earth fall with the same acceleration. If the object started from rest, it would be traveling 9.8 m/s at the end of one second. At the end of the next second, its velocity would be 19.6 m/s (2 × 9.8 m/s). How fast would it be falling after three seconds?

According to Newton's second law, an object accelerates only if it has a net force on it. The force on a falling object is the gravitational attraction of Earth. Because $F = m \times a$, weight, W, $= m \times 9.8$ m/s^2. To find the weight of an object in newtons, multiply its mass in kilograms by the acceleration due to gravity, 9.8 m/s^2.

An object moving in Earth's atmosphere has a second force acting on it, air resistance. **Air resistance** is the force exerted by air on a moving object. Air resistance acts in a direction opposite to the motion, and depends

FIGURE 4–5. The structure of the dandelion seed allows it to reach terminal velocity quickly.

on the speed, size, and shape of the falling object. As an object falls in air, the air resistance increases as the speed increases. When the upward force of air against the object is equal to the downward force of gravity, the object no longer accelerates. It has a constant velocity. **Terminal velocity** is the largest velocity reached by a falling object. An object falling at this speed has no net force acting on it. It keeps falling at a constant velocity.

Why does a falling object reach terminal velocity?

In a vacuum there is no air, and, therefore, no air resistance. Such is the case on the moon, which lacks an atmosphere. The acceleration of an object on the moon is the same throughout its fall because there is no air resistance. An object like a stone or a feather falling on the moon does not reach a terminal velocity. It continues to accelerate until it strikes the moon's surface.

F.Y.I. Small insects have large surface areas and low weights. They quickly reach terminal velocities of only a few centimeters a second. An ant can fall from a fifty-story building and walk away unharmed after hitting the sidewalk.

In Earth's atmosphere, objects such as feathers, table tennis balls, and open tissues fall more slowly than heavy, solid objects. An open tissue very quickly reaches terminal velocity when it falls. Thus, the terminal velocity of the open tissue will be lower than that of a compact object such as the same tissue wadded up into a tiny ball. It will also be less than that of a heavier object, such as a golf ball.

Automobile designers try to reduce air resistance to make cars more efficient. There are cases, however, when air resistance is useful. The resistance of air on a parachute reduces the terminal velocity of a person attached to the parachute. Thus, a parachutist can land without injury.

FIGURE 4–6. Engineers test automobiles in wind tunnels to find the designs with the least air resistance.

INVESTIGATION 4–1

Change in Velocity

Problem: How does the velocity of a ball change during flight?

Materials

thin, centimeter-ruled graph paper
metric ruler
pencil

Procedure

1. Figure 4–7 shows a ball in motion. The time interval between each position of the ball is 1/30 of a second.
2. Place a piece of graph paper on top of the drawing.
3. Mark each position of the ball with a dot.
4. Remove the graph paper. Draw straight lines connecting every fourth position of the ball (3 intervals). The time between 3 intervals of the ball is 0.1 second. Why?
5. Measure and record the length of each straight line. The length of each line can be used to show the distance traveled during each 0.1 second of flight.

Data and Analysis

Interval	Distance	Speed (mm/s)	Direction
1–4	22	220	
4–7	17	170	

Conclusions

1. The distance divided by time can be used to calculate an average velocity for each interval. Calculate and record the average velocity for each interval.
2. At what interval is the velocity smallest?
3. When does the vertical velocity of the ball have a positive value?
4. When does the vertical velocity of the ball have a negative value?
5. How does the velocity of a ball change in flight?

FIGURE 4–7.

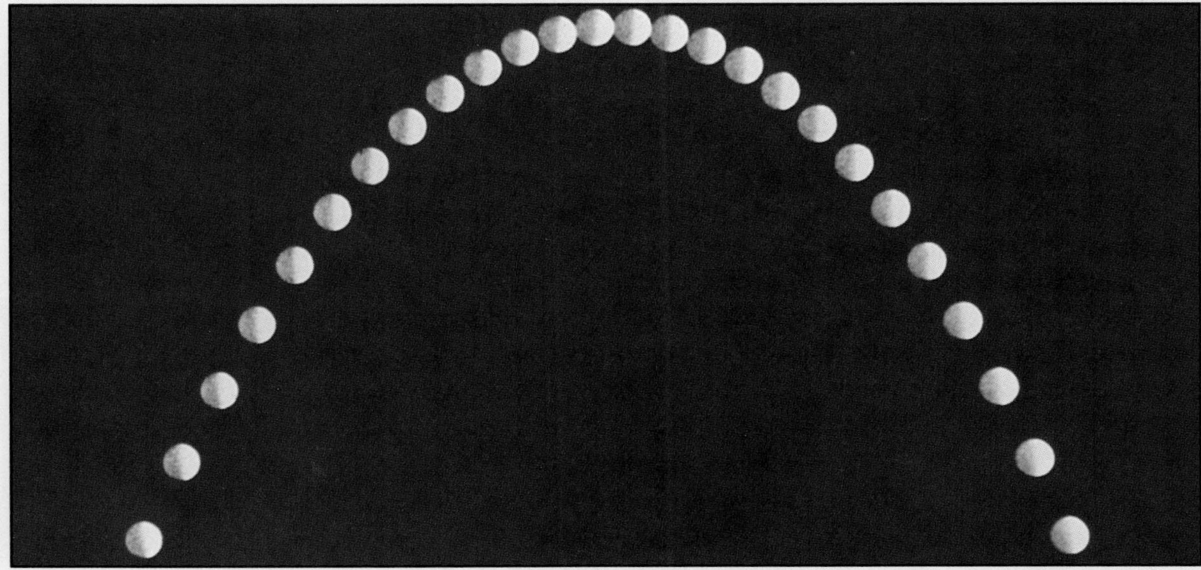

EXAMPLE **Acceleration of Gravity**

An acorn falls from the top of an oak tree to the ground in 1.5 seconds. What is the velocity of the acorn when it hits the ground?

Given: time
$t = 1.5$ s
acceleration
$a = g = 9.8\ \text{m/s}^2$

Unknown: velocity (v)

Basic Equation: $v = a \times t$

Solution: $v = g \times t$
$= 9.8\ \text{m/s}^2 \times 1.5\ \text{s} = 14.7\ \text{m/s} = 15\ \text{m/s}$

PRACTICE PROBLEMS

4. An object dropped from a 20-story building takes about 4 seconds to fall. How fast is it going when it strikes the ground?
5. Between the last two pictures of the large ball in Figure 4–4, the ball has been falling 0.55 s. Find its speed. Then find the distance it would fall in 0.33 s, the time between flashes. Check your answer by measuring.

For most small, heavy objects, air resistance is small enough so that it can be ignored. Galileo's genius was that he recognized that the study of motion would be possible by explaining the simpler case of motion without air resistance. The answers obtained this way would be close to the actual values for many cases. The work of considering the effects of the atmosphere could be left to later scientists.

F.Y.I. The acceleration of gravity equals $9.8\ \text{m/s}^2$, and is symbolized by the letter *g*.

Review

1. A sports car and a moving van are traveling at a speed of 30 km/h. If the same force is applied to both, which vehicle will stop first? Why?
2. List three examples of the second law of motion not mentioned in this section.
3. Why does it take more force to push a car at rest than to keep a car moving?
4. a. What is the net force on an object at its terminal velocity?
   b. Why do a stone and a feather have the same velocities in a vacuum?

★ 5. A skydiver weighing 600 N spreads her arms. The force of air resistance is 200 N. What is the acceleration of the skydiver?

MOTION IN TWO DIRECTIONS

GOALS

1. You will learn that projectile motion can be analyzed as constant horizontal velocity and downward accelerated vertical motion.
2. You will learn that, in order to produce circular motion, a force toward the center of the circle is needed.
3. You will learn that a body is weightless if it is in freefall.

We live in a three dimensional world. Most of the motion we see everyday is in two or three directions. Why do tether balls, cars on curves, and planets in their orbits move as they do? How do Newton's laws explain the motion in these cases?

4:3 Projectiles

Imagine you are standing in a moving bus. You drop your lunch bag on the floor. Will it land at your feet? If the bus had glass sides, what would a person standing outside see? Where would it land in relation to the road below? Remember that the bus is moving forward while the lunch falls. On a sheet of paper sketch the path of the lunch bag, first as seen by you and then as seen by the person standing outside.

Before you dropped it, the lunch bag was moving forward with the same velocity as the bus. It had only a **horizontal velocity,** velocity parallel to Earth's surface. When it fell, it gained a vertical velocity, velocity perpendicular to Earth. While falling, the only force acting on it was gravity. There was no horizontal force. Thus, there could be no change in horizontal velocity. While falling, the bag had velocities in two directions—a constant horizontal velocity and an accelerating vertical velocity due to gravity. During its fall, the bag continued forward along with you and the bus. The actual

Describe the motion of the falling lunch bag.

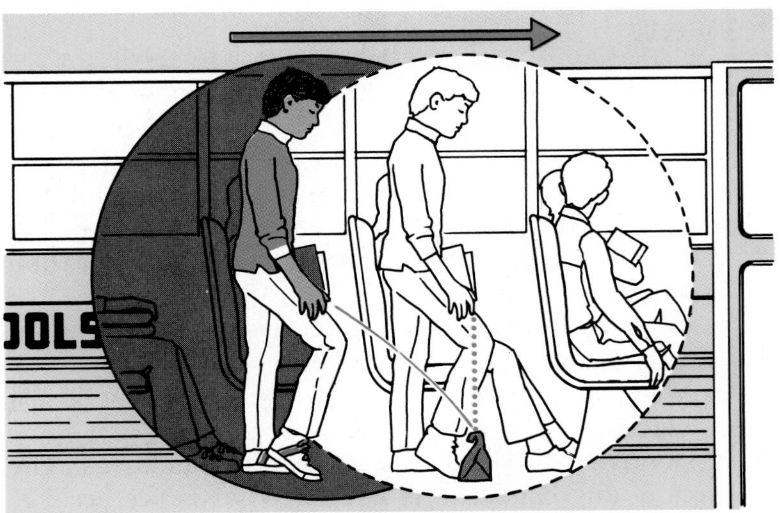

FIGURE 4–8. To the student on the bus, the lunch bag falls straight. To an observer outside, the path of the lunch bag is curved.

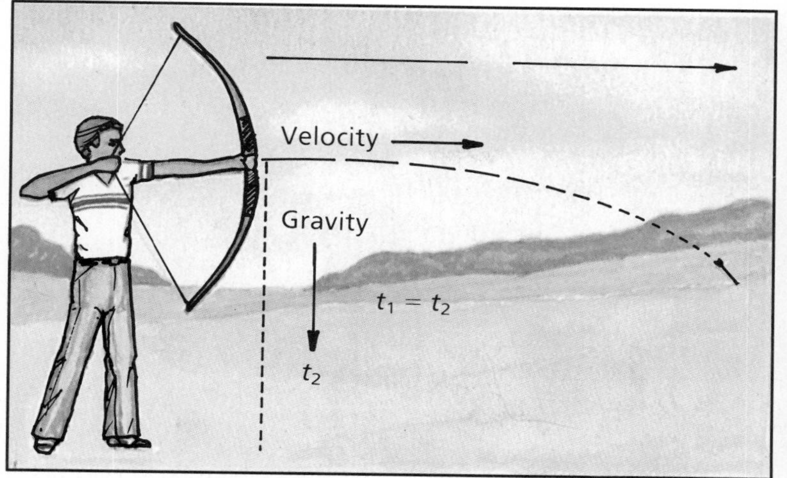

a

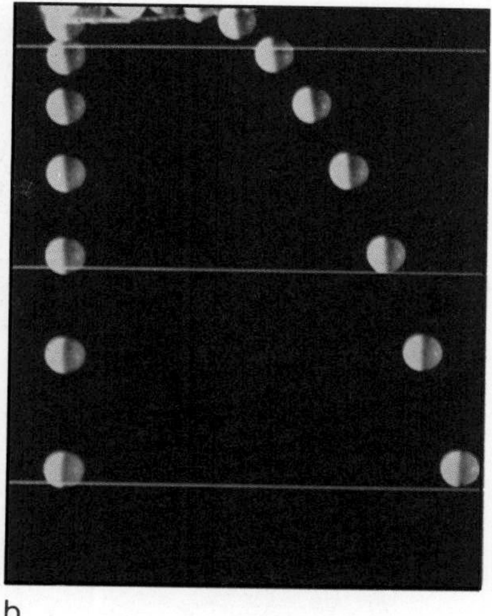

b

FIGURE 4–9. In (a), if the archer drops an arrow at the same time another is shot, both will hit the ground at the same time. In (b), the freely falling object and the projectile are falling at the same rate.

path of the bag as viewed by someone outside the bus is shown in Figure 4–8.

An arrow is shot horizontally, Figure 4–9a. How long does it take for the arrow to fall to the ground? Consider the viewpoint of a person moving along the ground at the speed of the arrow. That person would see the arrow falling straight down. However, as in the case of the lunch bag, the archer would disagree, saying the arrow followed a curved path. Both the archer and the moving viewer would agree on the time it took the arrow to hit the ground. The time to the ground depends only on the acceleration due to gravity and the vertical distance the arrow falls. The horizontal velocity of the arrow has no effect on the time it takes to fall. An experiment can be done to measure the time it takes a projected arrow and an arrow dropped from the same height to hit the ground. The experiment would show that both times are the same.

How are the horizontal velocity and the vertical velocity of thrown objects related?

When objects such as stones, balls, and arrows are thrown or shot, they have two kinds of motion—horizontal and vertical. The horizontal velocity is constant because once in flight, no more force is exerted in that direction. The **vertical velocity** is accelerating downward because of the force of gravity. The two motions are completely independent of each other.

Give three examples of objects with motion in two directions.

4:4 Motion in Circles

What causes a car to round a sharp curve? Remember that any object will continue in a straight-line path unless a net force acts on it. Thus, a force is needed to change the direction of the car. The acceleration of an

a

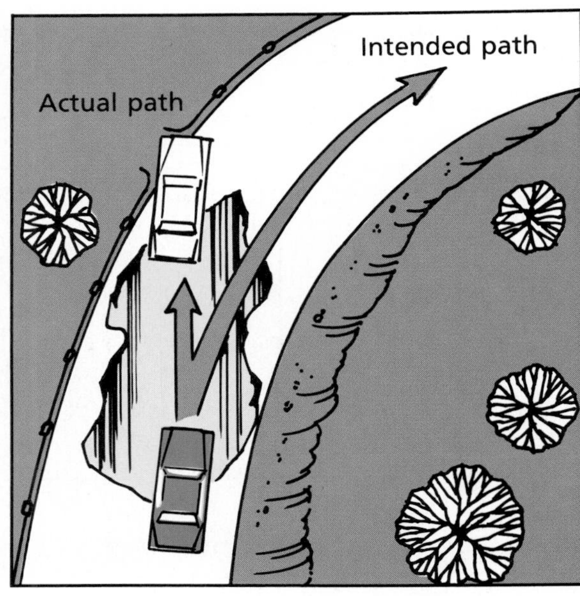

b

FIGURE 4–10. The banked track helps the racer around the curve (a). Friction between tires and road provide centripetal force to allow the car to turn (b).

What is centripetal force?

What keeps a satellite moving around Earth?

FIGURE 4–11. An Earth satellite falls 4.9 m toward Earth for each 8 km it travels horizontally.

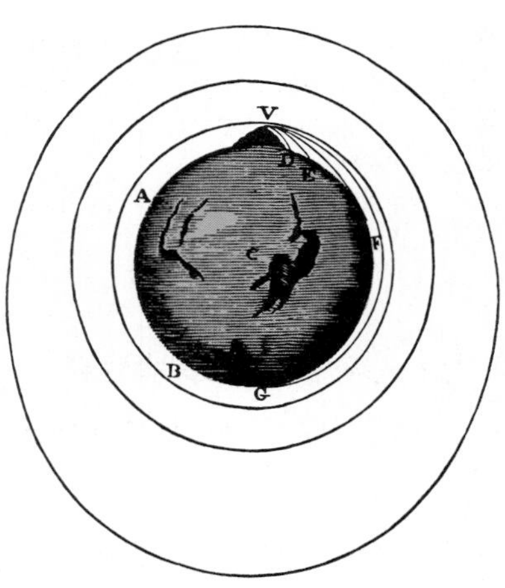

object moving in a circular path is toward the center of the circle. Therefore, the force that causes this acceleration is also toward the center of the circle. This force is called **centripetal force.** Centripetal means in the direction of the center. In the case of a car rounding a curve, the force of the road on the car tires is toward the center of a circle. Frictional force is limited, however. Tires can slip, especially if the road is wet. If the car goes too fast, the road may not exert enough force to accelerate the car toward the center of the circle. The car could go off the road. Highways are banked on curves to increase the available force toward the center.

A satellite in orbit about Earth is an example of circular motion. The force that keeps it moving in a circle is the force of Earth's gravity. It is a centripetal force. Without gravity, the satellite would continue along in a straight line, not in a circular path.

As the satellite circles Earth, the direction of its motion keeps changing. That is, the satellite always is accelerating. The direction of the acceleration is toward the center of Earth. In effect, the satellite keeps falling. There is no horizontal force on the satellite. Thus, its horizontal speed does not change. However, when the spacecraft has gained a certain horizontal velocity, it goes into orbit. In each second of time, it moves horizontally exactly as far as it falls toward Earth. As a result, it moves in a circle around Earth.

SKILL

Studying Science Assignments

Problem: How do you study your science assignment?

Materials

your science text book

paper and pencil

Background

Studying a science assignment is more than just reading words. You must process new knowledge and complex ideas. There are several strategies that will help you use your study time more efficiently.

Strategies

1. Always study with a paper and pencil handy.
2. Read every word of the text. Do not skip words or sentences.
3. Note all boldface headings, they will give you an idea of what you will be studying.
4. Be sure you know the meaning of every word. You may use context clues, or word analysis skills, or you may look for the definition in the glossary or dictionary. If you still don't know the meaning of the word, write it down. You can ask your teacher for a definition.
5. Make sure you understand each sentence before reading further. If you do not understand a new idea, go back and study the passage again until the meaning is clear. If you still have questions, write them down so you can ask them in class.
6. If the section you are studying refers to an idea that you have studied in earlier sections or chapters, go back and reread the material to refresh your memory.
7. Answer all of the questions in the margin notes.
8. Work out all of the EXAMPLE problems for yourself as you read your assignment. Be sure you understand each step in the solution.
9. Study all illustrations, graphs, and tables carefully. Be sure you understand what information they are trying to give you. Read all captions and titles carefully.
10. Answer all the Review Questions. They check your understanding of the concepts covered in the previous sections.
11. While studying, you may want to make some reading notes. Remember when taking notes, you cannot write down everything. You need to identify the main ideas. Use section titles and margin notes to help you focus on the important points.

Procedure

1. Study Sections 4:1 and 4:2, Accelerated Motion, using the Strategies listed above.
2. Use a checklist, and mark off each step as you do it.
3. Write one sentence that summarizes each section.
4. Make two word lists, one containing new science terms, and a second containing general words with which you are unfamiliar. Write definitions for each word.
5. Make a list of questions you would like to have answered in class.

Analysis and Conclusions

1. Why should you work all EXAMPLE problems?
2. Why is Step 9 important?
3. How is reading a science assignment different from reading a story?

a

b

FIGURE 4–12. A person on a trampoline experiences weightlessness while in the air (a). Astronauts in training experience a moment of weightlessness in a diving aircraft.

Why are objects in a spacecraft weightless?

4:5 Weightlessness and Freefall

You have heard of astronauts being weightless when in space. Yet the force of gravity exerted by Earth is almost as strong on a spacecraft in Earth orbit as it is on Earth's surface. What, then, is weightlessness? An object is **weightless** when it is in freefall. For example, if you jump on a trampoline, all the time your body is in the air the only major force acting on it is gravity. Your body is in freefall; it is weightless.

TECHNOLOGY: ADVANCES

Particle Colliders

Scientists have studied the forces that hold matter together for many years. One of the forces, the strong force, acts on the neutrons and protons that make up the nucleus at the center of every atom. It is much stronger than gravity, but only exists when the particles are touching each other.

Physicists study the strong force with huge particle accelerators. These machines speed up particles and race them around giant rings. Many accelerators have one group of particles moving in one direction in the ring and another group moving in the other direction. When the particles have reached the desired speed, the two groups are made to collide head-on. Physicists learn about the forces by studying the "debris" from the collisions.

A new ring is now being planned. It will be the world's largest scientific instrument. It will be 85 km in circumference, so large that a major city could fit inside it. To save electrical energy, the 10 000 electromagnets that will supply the accelerating force will use superconducting wire, wire that has no electrical resistance. Thus, the accelerator is called the *Superconducting Super Collider,* or SSC.

A spacecraft in orbit around Earth is weightless because it is in freefall. Earth's gravity accelerates it toward Earth. There is no other force on the spacecraft. Astronauts and objects inside the spacecraft are also weightless because they are in freefall. Water in a glass does not pour out when the glass is tipped. If you attached a spring scale to an object, the reading would be zero. The scale, the object, and the astronauts seem to have escaped the force of gravity. They are weightless because they are all falling at exactly the same rate.

FIGURE 4–13. The notebook appears to be floating because it is falling at the same rate as its surroundings.

Review

6. Why might a car slide off an icy road when the car rounds a curve?

7. What would happen to the moon if Earth's gravity suddenly stopped?

8. a. What condition must exist for an object to be weightless?
   b. How does weightlessness affect the mass of an object?

9. Would a force be necessary to change the velocity of a "weightless" can of soup in a spacecraft? Explain.

★ **10.** Clothes are partially dried in the spin cycle of an automatic washer. The sides of the tub have holes in them and the tub, containing the wet clothes, is turned rapidly. Explain how the clothes are dried.

MOMENTUM

If you have ever caught a fast ball you know that the impact of the ball can push you backwards, even as you stop its motion. This is an example of Newton's third law. When a ball team has a winning streak going, sportscasters say the team has "momentum." This term comes from physical science. Does it mean the same thing in physical science as it does in the sports world?

GOALS

1. You will learn that forces always come in pairs, and that members of the pair are equal in strength and opposite in direction.
2. You will learn that momentum, the product of mass and velocity, is an important property of moving matter.
3. You will learn that if no outside forces act on a system, the momentum of the system is conserved; it remains the same.

4:6 Newton's Third Law

Forces always come in pairs. Try standing on roller skates or ice skates and pushing against a wall. As you push on the wall, the wall exerts a force on you that accelerates you away. You exerted a force on the wall

FIGURE 4–14. As the skater pushes on the railing, the railing pushes back on the skater with an equal force.

and the wall exerted a force on you. The two forces had equal strength but opposite directions. They are called **action-reaction pairs.**

These observations are summarized in **Newton's third law of motion.** This law states *forces always come in pairs: when one object exerts a force on a second object, the second exerts an equal and opposite force on the first.* Informally, we can state "to every action there is an equal and opposite reaction."

Describe action-reaction forces.

What forces are involved in lifting a bucket of water? Look at Figure 4–15. Earth's gravitational force pulls down on the bucket. At the same time, the bucket's gravitational force pulls up equally on Earth. These forces form an action-reaction pair. They are equal and opposite. The bucket also exerts a downward force on your hand. This force is exactly equal and opposite to the upward force your hand exerts on the bucket. This is another action-reaction pair. Check the diagram. Be sure you see that in each action-reaction pair, the two forces act on different objects.

If all the forces are balanced, why does the bucket accelerate upward? Let's look at only the forces that are acting on the bucket, Figure 4–15. Now you can see a net force. The upward force you exert on the bucket is greater than the downward force Earth exerts on the bucket. There is a net upward force. Look carefully at the diagram. It is important to note that the forces causing the motion are both acting on the same object. Also, they are not equal in size. They are *not* action-reaction forces.

FIGURE 4–15. Each pair of action-reaction forces is equal (a). However, there is a net upward force on the bucket, causing it to accelerate upward (b).

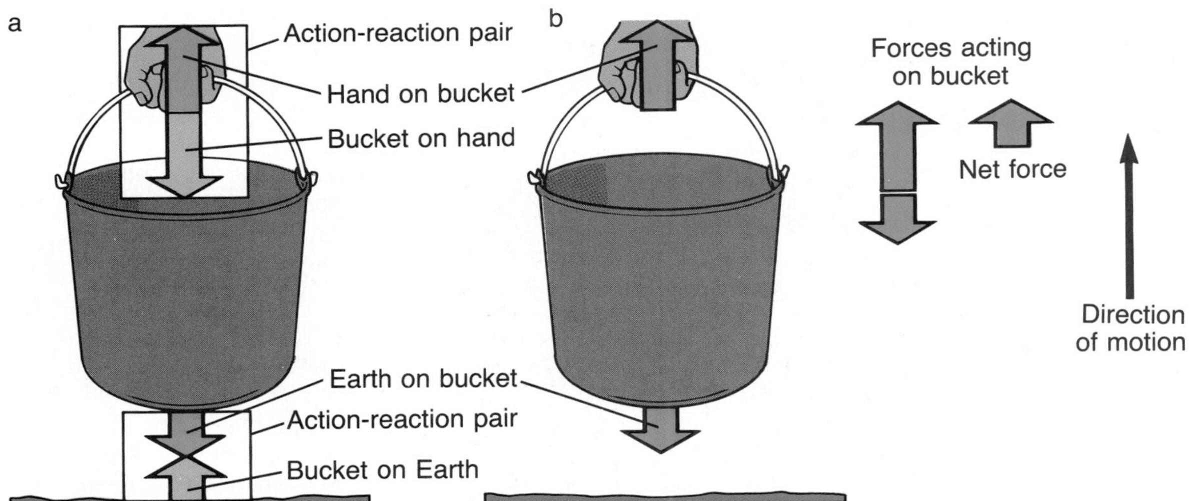

FIGURE 4–16. Between each team and the rope is a pair of action-reaction forces. If the magnitude of the red-team-rope force is greater than that of the blue-team-rope force, the rope will move toward the red team.

Case I

Figure 4–16 shows two teams having a tug of war. If we look at the rope, we can see two pairs of action-reaction forces. There is the rope-on-red-team and red-team-on-rope pair. The two forces are equal and opposite, and act on different objects. There is a similar pair of equal and opposite forces between the rope and the blue team.

Now look only at forces that act *on* the rope. There is the red-team-on-rope force and the blue-team-on-rope force. These two forces act on the same object and may or may not be equal. They follow Newton's first and second laws. If the red-team force equals the blue-team force, there is no net force on the rope. The rope does not move and the tug of war ends in a tie. Suppose the red-team force is larger than the blue-team force. There will be a net force on the rope toward the red team. If the force is large enough to accelerate the mass of the rope and the blue team, the red team will win the tug of war.

Case II

You stand in a boat on the water. If you walk toward the front of the boat, the boat will slide backward on the lake. The action-reaction pair is the backward force your feet exert on the boat and the forward force the boat exerts on your feet. The accelerations depend on the relative masses of you and the boat. If the boat is light, like a canoe or row boat, it will accelerate more than you do. If the boat is a large ocean liner, its acceleration will be too small to be noticed.

FIGURE 4–17. The person and the boat exert equal forces on each other. The boat accelerates more because its mass is less.

INVESTIGATION 4–2

Centripetal Force

Problem: How is centripetal force related to the velocity of an object moving in a circle?

Materials 

1.5 m of fishing line
15-cm piece of glass tubing (fire polished)
paper clips
two-hole rubber stopper
9 washers
timing device
tape
goggles

CAUTION: *Wear goggles during this activity.*

Procedure

1. Wrap the tubing with tape. Arrange the equipment as shown in Figure 4–18.
2. Now place 6 washers on the paper clip.
3. Stand in a clear area. Hold the tube with one hand. Whirl the stopper over your head in a horizontal circle.
4. Practice until you can whirl the stopper at a rate that keeps the clip hanging freely in a steady position. Have a classmate count the number of revolutions in 30 seconds. Record this value in a table.
5. Repeat Step 4 using 3 and 9 washers. Record the number of revolutions in 30 seconds.

FIGURE 4–18.

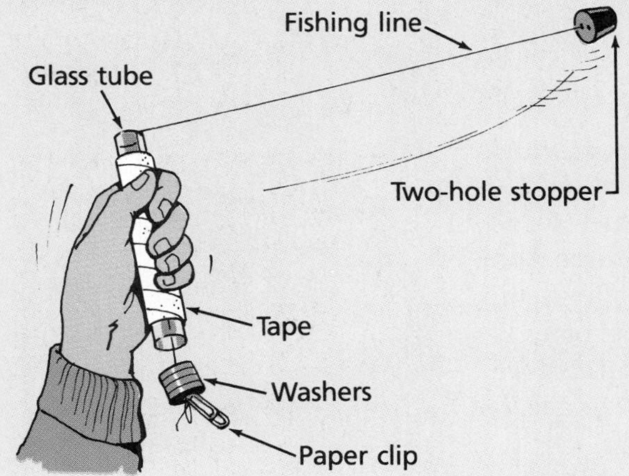

Data and Observations

Number of washers	Number of revolutions	Revolutions per second
3		
6		
9		

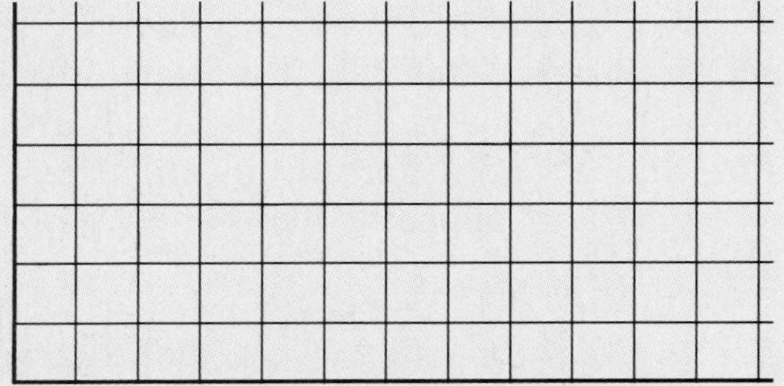

Analysis

1. Calculate and record the revolutions per second for 3, 6, and 9 washers.
2. Draw a graph plotting the revolutions per second versus number of washers.

Conclusions and Applications

3. How is the number of revolutions per second related to the mass of washers on the end of the string?
4. The number of washers on the string is proportional to centripetal force. The number of revolutions per second is a measure of the velocity of the stopper. How is the stopper velocity related to the centripetal force?

4:7 Momentum and its Conservation

Which do you think takes more force to stop, a baseball tossed during a friendly game of catch or the same ball pitched in a major league game? It would be the ball thrown by the major league pitcher, of course. You have learned that all matter has a property called inertia. Now you will learn that all matter in motion has another property called momentum. Mass is a measure of the amount of inertia of a body. The product of mass and velocity is the amount of **momentum** of an object. The two baseballs discussed above have the same mass, and thus, the same inertia. The pitched ball, however, has more momentum because of its greater velocity. The momentum of a body is calculated by multiplying its mass and velocity, $momentum = m \times v$. The units are kg • m/s.

Momentum can be used to help understand what happens when two objects collide. Consider one billiard ball hitting a second ball at rest on a pool table. At the start, the moving ball has momentum, the second does not. As a result of the collision, the moving ball loses momentum and the ball that was at rest gains momentum. The momentum lost by one ball exactly equals the momentum gained by the second ball. Thus, the total momentum of the two balls remains the same.

A quantity that is not changed is said to be "conserved." In a collision the total momentum of the colliding bodies is not changed. This is called the **law of conservation of momentum.** This law is another way of stating the third law of motion. Momentum is conserved provided there are no outside forces acting on a set of objects. For example, if two ice skaters bump into each other, the momentum of the pair will be the same before and after the collision. If, however, a third skater pushes both of them, the momentum of the pair will be changed.

BIOGRAPHY

Isaac Newton

1642–1727

Newton was born into an English farming family. He studied at Cambridge University but, after receiving his degree in 1665, fled back to the farm in Lincolnshire to escape the bubonic plague.

During the next year he made his greatest discoveries: the theory of gravitation, the principles of the calculus, and the spectrum of light. It was twenty years later that Newton recorded his theories in the famous *Principia.*

FIGURE 4–19. Momentum is transferred when the billiard balls collide. Some momentum is lost due to friction between the balls and the table.

4:8 Rockets

How can a rocket work in outer space where there is nothing to push it? Consider a rocket at rest in space. A rocket consists of its body and fuel. The rocket engine burns the fuel and expels the resulting gases toward the rear. The gas particles have small masses but are given very high velocities. That is, the engine gives the gases

F.Y.I. Momentum is like force in that it has both magnitude and direction.

a momentum toward the rear. The momentum of the entire rocket, body, and fuel, remains the same. Therefore, the body of the rocket must be given a forward momentum equal to the backward momentum of the burned fuel. A rocket works because of conservation of momentum. When the engine is shut off, the momentum of the rocket is still conserved. Any remaining fuel and oxygen now travels with the body. Because the rocket's momentum is constant, its velocity is also constant.

Review

11. a. A person lands on a trampoline and bounces upward again. Identify the action-reaction pair in this situation.
b. Identify the accelerating (net) force.

12. A bowling ball and a tennis ball have the same momentum. Which has the greater velocity?

13. Compare action-reaction forces with accelerating forces.

14. Describe the law of conservation of momentum. Illustrate with an example of gain and loss of momentum for two colliding bodies not mentioned in this section.

★ **15.** A model railroad car with a mass of 500 g, traveling at 0.80 m/s, bumps into a stationary car with a mass of 300 g. The cars hook together and move off down the track. How fast are they moving? Hint: Remember, the total momentum of the two cars before the collision must equal the total momentum after the collision.

PROBLEM SOLVING

Saved by the Book

Kevin volunteered to work in the high school library the last period every day. One of his jobs was to reshelve reference books used by the students during the day. He had just climbed up on a stool to put a large, heavy catalog back on the top shelf of a bookcase. As he was reaching up with the book, another student rushed past and accidentally bumped against him, causing him to lose his balance. Just as he was about to fall forward, he remembered how physical science could help him. What did he do and why?

Chapter 4 Review

SUMMARY

1. The acceleration of an object depends on the strength of the force and its mass. 4:1
2. On the surface of Earth a falling body accelerates at 9.8 m/s^2. 4:2
3. Air resistance causes falling bodies to reach a constant terminal velocity. 4:2
4. Objects that are thrown or shot have both horizontal and vertical velocities; the horizontal velocity of a thrown or shot object is constant; the vertical velocity is accelerated. 4:3
5. An object in a circular path has an acceleration toward the center of the circle. 4:4
6. An object that is in freefall is weightless. 4:5
7. Forces always act in pairs. The force of the first body on the second is equal and opposite to the force of the second on the first. 4:6
8. Every moving object has momentum that depends on both its mass and velocity. 4:7
9. The momentum of objects that have no net outside force on them is conserved. 4:7, 4:8

VOCABULARY

a. action-reaction pairs
b. air resistance
c. centripetal force
d. horizontal velocity
e. law of conservation of momentum
f. momentum
g. Newton's second law of motion
h. Newton's third law of motion
i. terminal velocity
j. vertical velocity
k. weightless

Matching

Match each description with the correct vocabulary word from the list above. Some words will not be used.

1. a body falling in air reaches this velocity
2. property of moving body that depends on mass and velocity
3. law stating forces come in action-reaction pairs
4. two forces that are equal in size but oppose each other
5. velocity of thrown ball that is constant
6. name for any force that produces motion in a circle
7. force that opposes gravity on falling bodies
8. law stating acceleration increases as the force on the body increases
9. motion of an arrow that is accelerating
10. law stating that the momentum of bodies with no outside forces on them is constant

Chapter 4 Review

MAIN IDEAS

A. Reviewing Concepts

Choose the word or phrase that correctly completes each of the following sentences.

1. The force needed to accelerate a car to a given velocity is *(larger than, smaller than, the same as)* the force needed to accelerate a bicycle to the same velocity.
2. In order to keep an object moving in a circular path, it must be acted on by *(momentum, friction, a centripetal force, inertia)*.
3. According to Newton's second law if the net force increases, the acceleration of the body *(remains the same, increases, decreases)*.
4. When an object falls in a vacuum its acceleration *(depends on its mass, increases steadily, decreases to zero, remains the same)*.
5. The force of a book lying on a table and the force of the table on the book are examples of *(a net force, balanced forces, centripetal forces, an action-reaction force pair)*.

Complete each of the following sentences with the correct word or phrase.

6. When an object reaches its terminal velocity, the air resistance force is equal to ____________________
7. The two velocities an arrow has in flight are horizontal and ______________________________.
8. The momentum of a massive object at rest is ____________________.
9. When two bodies interact, they exert a(n) ____________________ of forces between them.
10. When an object falls in a vacuum, its ____________________ does not change.

Determine whether each of the following sentences is true or false. If it is false, change the underlined word to make the sentence true.

11. An action-reaction force pair act on <u>the same object</u>.
12. A constant acceleration gives an object a <u>constant</u> velocity.
13. The <u>momentum</u> of a football changes when it is kicked.
14. As the speed of a moving object decreases, its <u>momentum</u> decreases.
15. <u>Inertia</u> causes a body to move in circular motion.

B. Understanding Concepts

Answer the following sentences using complete sentences when possible.

16. A body moves with constant velocity, can we assume that there are no forces acting on it? Explain.
17. Explain why two members of an action-reaction pair can never balance each other out and result in no net force.
18. Calculate the force required to accelerate a 0.14-kg hardball at 98 m/s^2.
19. We found that when a karate blow of a fist strikes a wooden block, the block can exert a force of 2450 N on the hand. What force is put on the wood to break it? Why?
20. An object dropped from a low-flying airplane takes 5 seconds to fall. How fast is it going when it strikes the ground?
21. A luxury car and a motorcycle are traveling at a speed of 70 km/h. If the same force is applied to both, which vehicle will stop first? Why?
22. If a raindrop fell from the height of a cloud in a vacuum, it would take 25 seconds to reach the ground. How fast

would it be traveling? Explain why, in this case, life without air resistance would be dangerous.

23. Why might a car that hits an oily part of the road while rounding a curve slide off the road?
24. Explain why the weight of an astronaut in orbit around Earth would read zero on a scale. Is her mass zero? Is there no gravity at that altitude?
25. An astronaut is sent from the spacecraft to fix a satellite. He has no rope connecting him to the spacecraft. He carries a pack of tools. His back-pack rocket fails. How could he return to the spacecraft?

C. Applying Concepts

Answer the following questions using complete sentences when possible.

26. Explain how air bags reduce the possibility of injury in an auto crash.
27. Describe how a fish moves forward by swishing its tail.
28. How can a rocket change the direction of its motion?
29. We claim momentum is conserved, yet most objects slow down. Explain.
30. Explain why catsup can be made to come out of the bottle by hitting the back of the bottle.

SKILL REVIEW

1. What should you do if the text refers to an idea you have studied earlier?
2. Why should you study your science lesson with a paper and pencil handy?
3. What are the first two important strategies when reading the text?
4. How can you often tell if you have set up a science problem correctly?
5. How are the terms inferring and observing related?

PROJECTS

1. Make a model of a lawn sprinkler. Punch 5 holes, one in the lower left corner of each side of a 2 L milk carton and one in the center of the top. Suspend the carton over a sink by a string through the top hole, and fill the carton with water. Explain what happens in terms of Newton's third law and momentum.
2. Prepare a report on the Superconducting Supercollider. Consider both its scientific and its economic importance.

READINGS

1. Champlin, Chuck. "HPV'S at the Races." *Bicycling*. March, 1984, pp. 74–80.
2. Fishman, Lew. "Physics of Golf." *Science Digest*. June, 1986, pp. 46–49, 78.
3. Kiester, Edward, Jr. "Aircraft of Tomorrow." *Science Digest*. May, 1985, pp. 38–45, 80–81.
4. Sabin, Francene. *Rockets and Satellites*. Mahwah, NJ: Troll Associates, 1985.

MECHANICAL ENERGY AND WORK
THERMAL ENERGY AND HEAT

Energy

Just before the American revolution, a young man, Benjamin Thompson, left the colonies for England because he sided with the British. While in England he wondered why some foods cooled quickly, but others, notably apple pie filled with nuts, remained hot enough to burn his mouth. At that time heat was thought to be an invisible fluid. Later in his life, he showed that hot bodies could not contain a fluid, but that they must contain particles that are in constant motion. His work led the way for our modern understanding of energy. He was also an inventor of many useful items that used scientific principles to make life more comfortable. He learned why clothing keeps you warm; he invented an improved fireplace, cooking stove, utensils, and the drip coffee maker.

MECHANICAL ENERGY AND WORK

GOALS

1. You will understand that energy appears in many forms that can be grouped into kinetic energy and various types of potential energy.
2. You will understand that work is the transfer of energy by mechanical means.
3. You will understand the meaning of the law of conservation of energy.

Your ideas about energy probably come from your everyday experiences. When you have a lot of energy you can run faster; you can jump higher. Objects as well as people can have energy. A stone falling off a cliff has enough energy to damage a roof. A car uses the energy in gasoline to move fast or to climb hills. Sunlight has the ability to warm you and to help plants grow. Sunlight carries energy to Earth in a form called radiant energy, or radiation. Later we will learn that light is one form of radiant energy.

Energy has been defined as the ability to do work, but this definition is not complete. From the examples given, you can see that an object has energy if it is able to produce a change in itself or in its surroundings. There

FIGURE 5–1. This magnificent humpback whale propels itself out of the water by changing the stored chemical energy in its muscles into gravitational potential energy. As the whale falls back into the water, the potential energy is changed into kinetic energy.

really is no better or more precise definition of energy. Physicists can describe how to calculate energy in its many forms, but they do not know exactly what energy is. In the following section, you will learn about a variety of forms of energy, how energy is changed from one form to another, and how to measure energy as it is changed.

What does energy do?

F.Y.I. "Energy is an eternal delight!"

William Blake

5:1 Energy of Motion

What is kinetic energy?

An object has energy either because of its motion or because of its condition or position. Energy that appears in the form of motion is called **kinetic energy.**

A moving car has energy of motion, or kinetic energy. The blades of a rotating fan and a bowling ball rolling down an alley have kinetic energy. The amount of kinetic energy a moving object has depends on the mass of the object and its velocity. A train has more kinetic energy than a car moving at the same speed. A car traveling at 90 km/h has more energy than the same car traveling at 50 km/h.

F.Y.I. One joule is about the amount of energy used to lift a medium apple one meter.

What is the unit of energy?

The unit of energy is the joule (JEWL) (J), named after James Prescott Joule, an English scientist.

5:2 Potential Energy

What is potential energy?

The energy that an object has as the result of its position or condition is called **potential energy.** If you lift a stone, it gains potential energy. If you then let go of the stone, it falls. It loses potential energy but gains kinetic energy. Consider an archer pulling back on the bowstring and bending a bow. The shape of the bow is

a

b

FIGURE 5–2. Potential energy is stored in the twisted rubber band (a). As the rubber band unwinds, its stored energy is transferred to the propeller, causing the airplane to fly (b).

its condition. As the bow is bent, it gains potential energy. When the string is released, the arrow is set into motion. The potential energy of the bow is transferred to the kinetic energy of the arrow. Kinetic energy and potential energy of lifting, bending, and stretching are grouped together and called **mechanical energy.**

What is mechanical energy?

The potential energy stored in food, gasoline, and storage batteries are examples of chemical potential energy. Other forms of potential energy, including electrical, magnetic, radiant, and nuclear, will be discussed in later chapters. Potential energy, like all other forms of energy, is measured in joules.

F.Y.I. The condition of an object might be a stretched elastic, a hot substance, or a charged car battery.

5:3 Work and Energy Transfer

What is work?

How is work calculated?

Energy is often changed from one form to another. When you drop the rock you lifted, the potential energy in the rock is transferred into kinetic energy of the falling rock. As the rock falls, gravity exerts a continuous net force on it. Therefore, its velocity and kinetic energy increase. As gravity does work on the rock, its potential energy is changed into kinetic energy. **Work** is the transfer of energy as the result of motion. You could think of potential energy as the amount of work an object could do because of its position or condition. The amount of energy a falling rock transfers depends on its weight and how far it falls. For example, a rock falling from a high cliff can do a great deal of damage.

In general, the energy transferred depends on the amount of force exerted and the distance over which that force is exerted. Therefore, the work done on or by an object, can be calculated as

$$Work = force \times distance$$
$$W = F \times d$$

FIGURE 5–3. Work is done on the box only when it moves in the direction of the applied force.

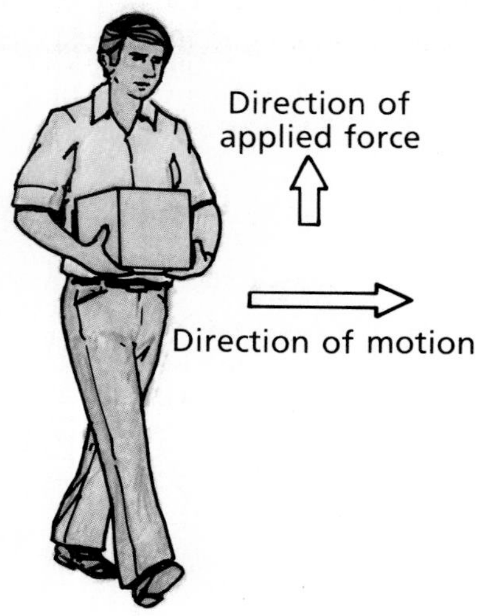

BIOGRAPHY

Walter E Massey
1920–

As director of the Argonne National Laboratory in Illinois, Walter Massey is responsible for research programs designed to find new ways of producing and conserving energy.

The laboratory's work is largely concerned with nuclear power, including an experimental nuclear breeder reactor.

Massey's research interest is theoretical solid state physics, which he teaches as Professor of Physics at the University of Chicago.

Work, like energy, is measured in joules. It is important to understand that the distance, in this equation, means the distance in the direction of the force. If the force is in the vertical direction, but movement in the horizontal direction, no work is done.

EXAMPLE Calculating Work

Find the work done by gravity when a 2.0 kg rock falls 1.5 m to the ground.

Given: mass (m) 2.0 kg
distance (d) 1.5 m
$g = 9.8\ \text{m/s}^2$

Unknown: work (W)

Basic Equations:
$W = F \times d$
$F = m \times g$

Solution: $W = (m \times g) \times d$
$= (2\ \text{kg})(9.8\ \text{m/s}^2)(1.5\ \text{m})$
$= 29.4\ \text{J} = 29\ \text{J}$

PRACTICE PROBLEMS

1. A force of 12 newtons is needed to push a suitcase across the floor a distance of 0.5 m. How much work is done?
2. A 1.0 kg mass is lifted 100 mm (0.10 m), as it moves 350 mm horizontally. How much work is done?

Work is done only when a force is exerted and motion in the direction of the force results. Notice that this scientific use of the word *work* is different from the way the word is used in everyday speech.

5:4 Energy Conservation

Let us take a closer look at energy changes. Consider a pendulum swinging back and forth. When the mass stops for an instant at the highest point in its swing, it has no kinetic energy. The energy is all potential. When the mass is at the lowest point on its swing, its velocity is greatest and its potential energy is smallest. The energy is all kinetic. The pendulum keeps swinging, reaching a point where the energy is again all potential. Energy has been changed from potential to kinetic and back to potential, but the total amount of energy has not changed.

The pendulum can continue swinging for a long time, with the mass swinging back to nearly the same height each time. The transfers between kinetic and potential keep repeating. No matter where in its swing, the sum of the kinetic and potential energy of the pendulum is

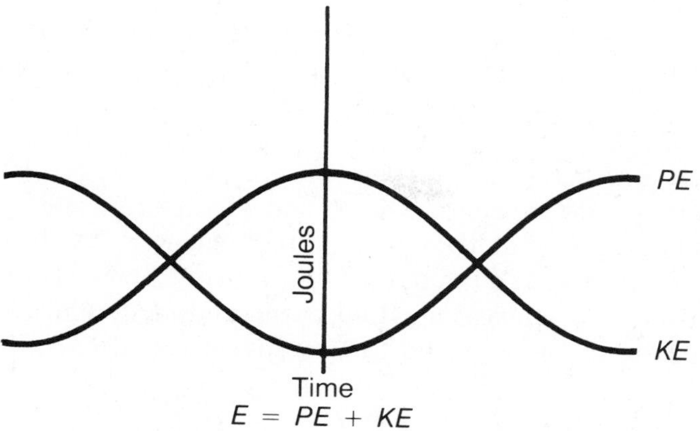

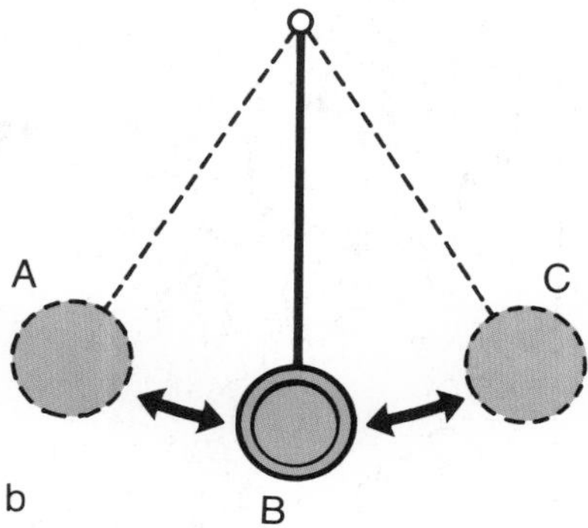

FIGURE 5–4. At points A and C, the pendulum has maximum potential energy and no kinetic energy. At point B, the kinetic energy is greatest and the potential energy the lowest. The graph in (a) shows the change in potential and kinetic energy over time.

the same. The sum of the pendulum's potential and kinetic energies is called its mechanical energy.

$$\textit{mechanical energy} = \textit{potential energy} + \textit{kinetic energy}$$
$$E = PE + KE$$

As the potential energy of the pendulum decreases, the kinetic energy increases, and visa versa. Thus the total energy in a pendulum is the same at all points in its swing, Figure 5-4. In other words, the mechanical energy is conserved.

In the middle of the nineteenth century a German physician, Julius Robert Mayer (1814–1878), studied energy conversions. He thought that energy never disappeared, but was simply changed from one form to another. The English scientist, James Prescott Joule (1818–1889), also made careful measurements of energy conversions. As a result of many investigations, all scientists now accept an important law of nature, the **law of conservation of energy.** According to this law, energy can change from one form to another. Energy, however, can never be created or destroyed. The total energy of the universe remains the same.

What is the law of conservation of energy?

Several times since the law of conservation of energy was accepted, scientists have thought they found a violation of the law. They thought energy was lost. Each time, however, they discovered a new form of energy. Energy was not being lost, it was being changed into this new form. To see how this works, think about your experience with another law, the law of conservation of matter. If you lose a school book, you do not think the book has disappeared. You just search more and more places until you finally find it.

FIGURE 5–5. The Foucault pendulum swings back and forth along the same path while Earth rotates beneath it.

If energy is conserved, why does the pendulum discussed earlier finally stop? You know that its swing gradually becomes smaller and its velocity becomes slower. After a long time, it stops swinging altogether. What has happened to the mechanical energy? If you measure the temperature of the string and the mass, you will find that they are a little warmer. Mechanical energy has been changed into a different form of energy. This form of energy is called thermal energy and can be detected by measuring the temperature of the object. You change mechanical into thermal energy every time you rub your hands together to warm them.

In some energy conversions, such as in the pendulum, most of the energy changes occur between kinetic and potential. During each swing, very little is converted to thermal energy. In other cases, such as rubbing your hands together, all the mechanical energy is changed to thermal energy. In every case, however, some thermal energy results. Thermal energy, on the other hand, never changes back into mechanical energy by itself. A warm mass on a string never becomes cooler and starts swinging by itself. Thermal energy, therefore, is less useful than mechanical energy because it cannot, by itself, change into mechanical energy. The change of mechanical into thermal energy is a loss of the usefulness of the energy. All natural energy changes result in less useful forms. Useful forms, such as nuclear or chemical (oil or natural gas), are eventually changed into the less useful thermal energy.

Why is mechanical energy more useful than thermal energy?

Review

1. a. Define potential and kinetic energy and give three examples of objects that have both.
   b. Explain how work is related to energy.
2. A concrete block is lifted 1.2 m by exerting a 96 N force. How much work is done on the block?
3. Suppose you stretch a 50-millimeter rubber band until it is 100 millimeters long. Does the potential or kinetic energy of the rubber band increase? Why?
4. How is a wound clock spring an example of potential energy? Into what form or forms of energy is the potential energy changed?
5. ★ You push a heavy box across the floor. List the energy changes that occur starting with food eaten until the box moved.

INVESTIGATION 5–1

Mechanical Energy and Work

Problem: How is a change in potential energy related to work done?

Materials

baseball and billiard ball
board for ramp
blocks or books to raise ramp
2 meter sticks
empty carton
balance or scale
ruler
masking tape
pencil
paper

Procedure

1. Remove 1 side of the carton as shown in Figure 5–6.
2. Find the masses of the 2 balls.
3. Place the 2 meter sticks on the board about 2 cm apart. Hold in place with masking tape. The sticks form a track to keep the balls rolling in a straight line.
4. Raise one end of the board 5 cm.
5. Place the carton at the other end so the ball can roll into it. Lay a piece of paper next to the carton, taping it to the table.
6. Hold the ball at the top of the ramp. Let it roll down and into the carton.
7. Mark the final location of the carton. Measure the distance it moved.
8. Repeat Steps 6 and 7 with the other ball.
9. Raise the top end of the ramp 5 cm more. Repeat Steps 6, 7, and 8.
10. Repeat Step 9.

Data and Observations

Height	Distance Ball 1	Distance Ball 2
5 cm		

Analysis and Conclusions

1. In what form was the energy of the ball at the top of the ramp?
2. In what form was the ball's energy at the bottom of the ramp?
3. What happened to the energy of the ball while in the carton?
4. Work done on the carton depends on the mass of the ball and carton and the distance it moved. For the two balls rolled from the same height, which ball did more work?
5. How does the work done on the carton depend on the initial potential energy of the ball?
6. How is potential energy related to work done?

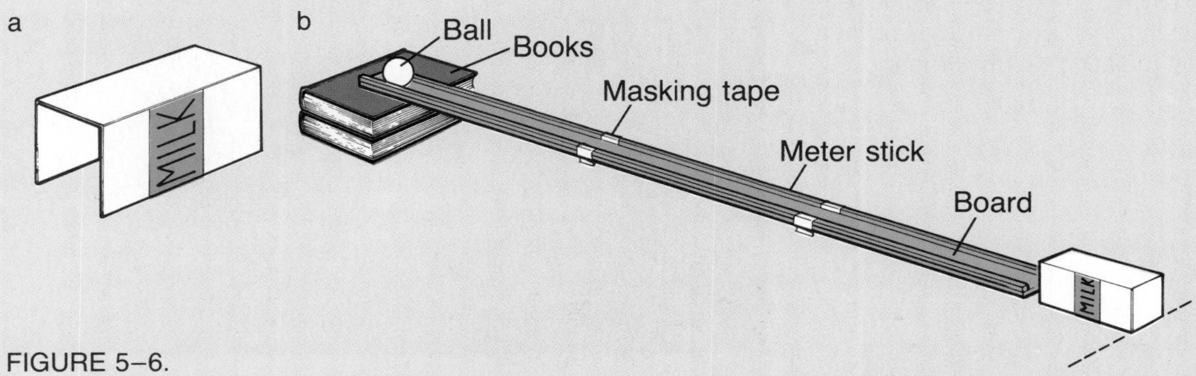

FIGURE 5–6.

CAREER

Biophysicist

A biophysicist combines a knowledge of physics, chemistry, engineering, and biology into a successful career. Biophysicists work primarily for drug companies, hospitals, universities, and in government labs for disease and pollution control.

For example, a biophysicist might study the retina in the eye of an animal. He could investigate how light is transmitted to the brain as a nervous impulse, allowing the animal to see.

This study might lead to the design of a photoelectric cell that can detect light and send messages to a computer. Most biophysicists have graduate degrees. They are leaders in developing new technology in medicine such as heart surgery techniques and electrosurgery.

For career information, write
The Biophysical Society
National Biomedical Research Foundation
Georgetown University Medical Center
3900 Reservoir Road
Washington, DC 20007

GOALS

1. You will understand the difference between thermal energy and the temperature of a body.
2. You will understand how heat and work are similar and different.
3. You will know how a calorimeter can measure thermal energy changes.

THERMAL ENERGY AND HEAT

How many different meanings do you know for the word *heat?* You could say you heated water to boiling on the stove. You might say that the refrigerator removes heat from food, or when you warm some soup, you add heat to it. Did you know that you talk about adding heat to things because of an old theory that was discarded over 100 years ago? That theory, the caloric theory, is also the origin of the word *calorie,* sometimes used to measure the energy content of foods. As with the term *work,* you will learn that the present scientific definition of the word *heat* is different from everyday meanings.

FIGURE 5–7. The people enjoying the campfire are warmed by radiating thermal energy.

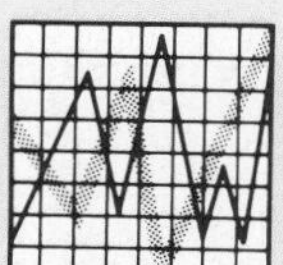

SKILL

Using a Calculator

Problem: How do you use a calculator correctly?

Materials

calculator

Background

Small, hand-held calculators can save you time, but they are only useful and accurate if you understand the mathematics involved in the problems you are solving.

There are many different kinds of calculators, performing a great many different functions. It is very important that you read the instruction manual very carefully before you attempt to use your calculator.

There are two basic types of hand-held calculators, algebraic (for example, Texas Instrument, Casio, Sharp), and reverse polish notation (for example, Hewlett-Packard). The simple calculators that will be useful in this class use algebraic logic.

Procedure

1. Try these examples on your calculator.

Problem	Keys	Answer
8 + 2	[8] [+] [2] [=]	10
9 − 6	[9] [−] [6] [=]	3
1.5 × 3	[1] [·] [5] [×] [3] [=]	4.5
66 ÷ 11	[6] [6] [÷] [1] [1] [=]	6

2. Calculators can do combination operations without your having to press the [=] key. However, you must be sure that you understand what you want the calculator to do. Consider the problem [4 × 3 ÷ 2]. It can be entered as [[4] [×] [3] [÷] [2]] without using the [=] key. The calculator will give the correct answer, 6.
3. Use your calculator to solve this problem.

   Enter: 30 × 20 + 20 ÷ 10 =

   You should get 62. Your calculator multiplied 30 and 20 to get 600, then added 20 to get 620, and divided by 10 to get 62.
4. Try the following:

$$\frac{16.5 \times 37.5}{18.2 \times 41.3}$$

This problem should be entered as

16.5 × 37.5 ÷ 18.2 ÷ 41.3 =

5. One very important factor to consider when using calculators is reporting the proper number of significant digits in your answer. In most cases, calculators will give answers in up to eight digits, whether the digits have meaning or not. Remember, when you are working problems using measurements, your answer cannot be any more precise than the least precise of your measurements. Suppose that a 9.7 N rock did 24.6 J of work when it fell from a high shelf. How high above the ground was the shelf? Dividing 24.6 J by 9.7 N on the calculator would give 2.5360824. However, your least precise measurement, 9.7 N, has only 2 significant digits. Therefore, your answer can only have 2. The correct answer is 2.5 m.

   Reporting an answer with too many digits is probably the most common mistake made by students using a calculator.

Questions

Work the following problems on your calculator.

1. (20.00°C − 5.00°C) × 0.100 kg × 4180 J/kg • C°
2. 25 km/s × 5.0 s + [(2.23 m/s^2 × 5.0 s × 5.0 s) ÷ 2]
3. $41 \text{ m/s} \times \dfrac{329 \text{ m}}{13 \text{ s} - 4 \text{ s}}$

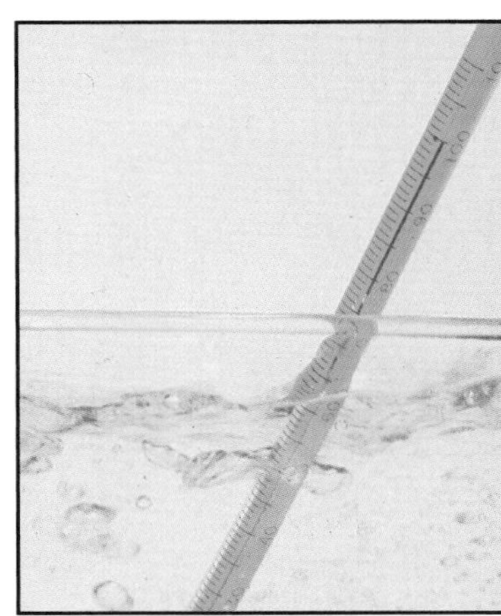

FIGURE 5–8. The thermometer shows 0°C in ice water (a). The mercury rises to the 100°C mark in boiling water (b).

a b

5:5 Temperature

What is temperature?

You could define temperature as the property of an object that is measured by a thermometer. It is better, however, to describe temperature in terms of the microscopic properties of matter. All matter is made up of tiny particles in constant motion. The motion of the particles means that they have kinetic energy. **Temperature** is a measure of the average kinetic energy of the particles. The particles in a body at a high temperature have a higher average kinetic energy than the particles in a body at a low temperature. When you put a fever thermometer in your mouth, the vibrating particles of your mouth and those of the thermometer bump into each other. In almost all the collisions, energy is transferred from faster moving particles to slower moving particles. When the average kinetic energy of the particles in the thermometer equals the average kinetic energy of the particles in your mouth, their temperatures are equal.

5:6 Thermal Energy

The energy of an object gives it the ability to change itself or its surroundings. Suppose you put a 10-gram cube of ice on a 1-kilogram block of ice, Figure 5–9. Nothing will happen. If you put 10 grams of hot water on the ice, however, some ice will melt. The hot water will have an effect on the ice. The hot water has more energy than the ice. The energy of the water does not depend on the motion or position of the water. The energy of the hot water depends on its temperature. The energy is thermal energy.

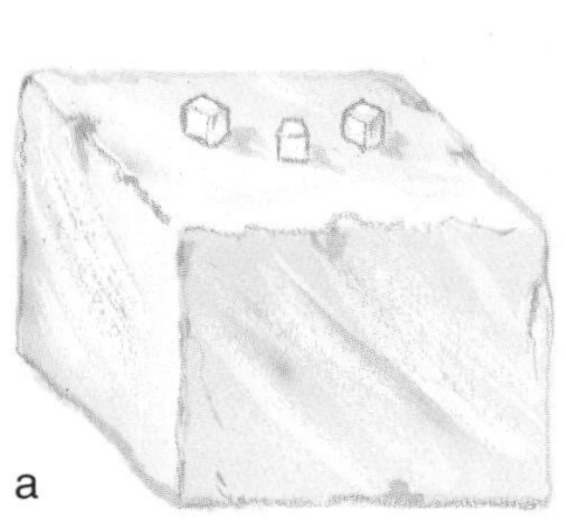

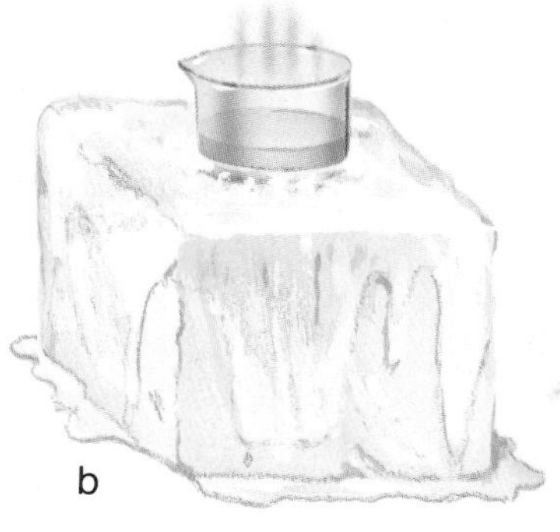

FIGURE 5–9. When an ice cube is placed on a block there is little change (a). The effect of increasing amounts of thermal energy being transferred is shown in (b) and (c).

Now suppose you put 20 grams of water at the same temperature on the ice. More ice will melt. A larger mass has more thermal energy than a smaller mass at the same temperature. Thermal energy also depends on the type of matter. The same mass of ice and water at the same temperature, 0°C, have different thermal energies. **Thermal energy** is the total energy of the particles that make up a body. Both the kinetic and the potential energy of each particle is included, but not the kinetic or potential energy of the body as a whole. A baseball at a temperature of 22°C has the same thermal energy whether it is on the ground or high in the air, at rest or moving fast.

What is thermal energy?

5:7 Heat and Work

Suppose your hands are cold. You put them against your warm cheeks. Your hands become warmer. That is, their temperature increases. At the same time your cheeks become colder, their temperature decreases. Energy flows from your warm cheeks to your cold hands. Energy that is transferred from an object at a high temperature to one at a lower temperature is called **heat.**

Define heat.

There is a second way to warm your hands. You could rub them together. Energy is changed from the kinetic energy of your moving hands into thermal energy. Energy that is transferred as the result of motion is work.

Heat and work are similar. Both are energy being transferred. Both are measured in joules. Objects can have kinetic, potential, or thermal energy. These energies are properties of objects. Objects cannot have either heat or work. Heat and work are not properties. Heat is energy transferred between objects at different temperatures. Work is energy transferred when objects exert forces on each other and are moved.

How are heat and work similar?

TECHNOLOGY: APPLICATIONS

The Slingshot Effect

Have you seen the detailed pictures of Jupiter, Saturn, and Uranus taken by the Voyager spacecraft? In 1989 the spacecraft reached Neptune, returning pictures of the most distant of the giant gas planets. For many years Voyager has only had enough fuel to steer, yet it is now moving faster than it was when it left Earth. You know that between planets, the only force on Voyager is the gravitational pull of the sun, and that force slows Voyager down. How can it be moving faster?

Space scientists have developed the use of the "slingshot" effect to give additional kinetic energy to space probes. For example, the kinetic energy of Voyager was almost nine times larger after it left Jupiter than when it arrived! Think of throwing a soccer ball at the front of a speeding truck. You will see the ball bounce off the truck with much more kinetic energy than it had when it left your hands. A spacecraft doesn't hit a planet. It swings behind the planet, coming close enough, from just the right direction, to make use of the planet's force of gravity to give it a push, just as the truck gave the ball a shove. Thus by using the laws of physics, space scientists can use gravitational energy to reduce the amount of fuel the rocket needs to carry.

5:8 Measuring Thermal Energy

Joule was the first person to make a careful measurement of the transfer of thermal energy into an object. During the years between 1845 and 1868, Joule did many experiments to measure the conversion of mechanical to thermal energy. In one, he fastened a large weight to a cord. The cord was wrapped around a rod that turned paddles in water. As the weight fell, its potential energy was transferred to kinetic energy of the paddles, and finally to thermal energy of the water. Joule measured the increase in temperature. He found that 4190 joules of energy are needed to raise the temperature of 1 kilogram of water 1 Celsius degree. The amount of energy needed to increase the temperature of 1 kilogram of any substance 1 Celsius degree is called the **specific heat** (C_p) of that material. Thus, the specific heat of water is 4190 J/kg • C° (joules per kilogram per Celsius degree).

What is specific heat?

Different materials have different specific heats. Iron has a specific heat of 450 J/kg • C°. It takes 450 joules of energy to raise the temperature of one kilogram of iron one Celsius degree. Notice that it takes about nine times as much energy to increase the temperature of water as it does iron. Table 5–1 shows the specific heat of several substances.

F.Y.I. Although the calorie is not an accepted SI unit, it is still widely used when discussing the nutritional value of food. 1 calorie = 4.18 J. The calories listed on food packages are actually kilocalories: 1 kcal = 4180 J.

Table 5–1

Specific Heat of Common Substances (J/kg • C°)	
water	4190
aluminum	920
carbon (graphite)	710
sand (SiO_2)	664
iron	450
copper	380
mercury	140
clay	130

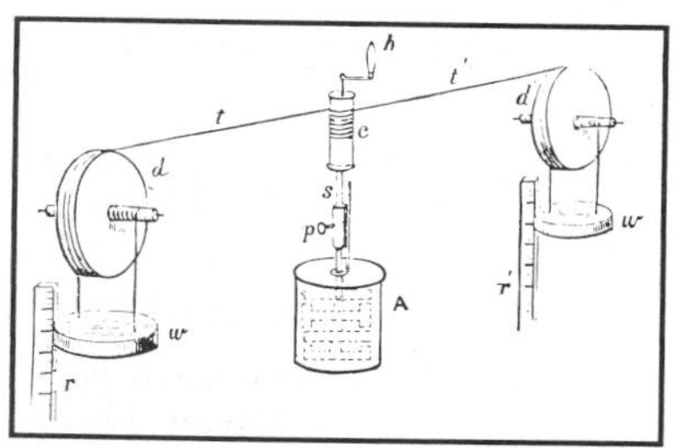

FIGURE 5–10. James Joule measured the temperature increase of the water when the potential energy of the weight was eventually converted into thermal energy.

Changes in thermal energy can be measured. Consider this example: A 0.10-kg block of metal is warmed to 100°C. The block is put into 0.20 kg of water at a temperature of 20°C. The water warms and the block cools until both are at the same temperature. The new temperature of the water is measured to be 23°C. From the change in water temperature, its mass, and specific heat, the increase in the thermal energy of the water can be calculated. The calculation of the change in thermal energy, Q, uses the equation

What are the units of specific heat?

$$\textit{Change in thermal energy} = \textit{Change in temperature} \times \textit{Mass} \times \textit{Specific heat}$$

$$Q = \Delta T \times m \times C_p$$

The symbol Δ(delta) means change, so ΔT means change in temperature.

$$\Delta T = T_{final} - T_{initial},$$

and thermal energy is gained by the object. When the temperature decreases,

$$\Delta T = T_{initial} - T_{final},$$

and thermal energy is lost by the object.

Thus, Q is always positive.

The increase in Q, the thermal energy of the water is $Q = (23°C - 20°C) \times 0.20\ kg \times 4190\ J/kg \cdot C° = 2500\ J$.

EXAMPLE Changes in Thermal Energy

An iron pipe with a mass of 510 g cools from 20.0°C to 10.0°C. How much thermal energy is lost by the pipe?

Given:

mass (m) = 0.51 kg

T_{final} = 10.0°C

$T_{initial}$ = 20.0°C

C_p = 450 J/kg • C°

Unknown: energy change Q

Basic Equations:

$Q = \Delta T \times m \times C_p$

$\Delta T = T_{initial} - T_{final}$

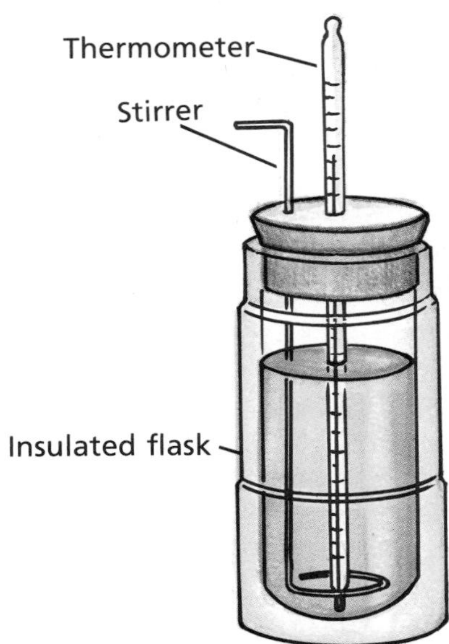

FIGURE 5–11. A simple calorimeter can be used to measure thermal energy transfer.

Solution: $Q = (T_i - T_f) \times m \times C_p$
$= (20.0°C - 10.0°C)(0.51 \text{ kg}) (450 \text{ J/kg} \cdot C°)$
$= 2295 \text{ J} = 2300 \text{ J lost}$

PRACTICE PROBLEMS

3. Calculate the energy gained by the water in the text example.
4. Calculate the energy lost when a 0.010-kg sample of aluminum foil cools from 75°C to 25°C. Use Table 5–1.

5:9 Using Calorimeters

The instrument used to measure changes in thermal energy is called a **calorimeter.** A calorimeter is designed so that energy can neither enter nor leave the instrument. A simple calorimeter consists of a Styrofoam cup fitted with a cover and a thermometer. A typical use of a calorimeter is to measure the specific heat of some material. Suppose you want to find the specific heat of the metal in the experiment described in Section 5:8, page 113. We calculated that water gained 2500 J. Because energy must be conserved, the energy lost by the metal must equal the energy gained by the water. Since we know the mass and temperature change of the metal from the experimental data, the specific heat can be calculated. Practice Problem 5 asks you to make the calculation.

PROBLEM SOLVING

Roll-back Toy

The diagram below shows the construction of a roll-back toy similar to those sold in stores for infants to play with. To build the toy you would need a 1-pound coffee can, both ends removed, with two plastic lids, a heavy rubber band, and a heavy fishing weight, about 2.5 cm long.

Describe what will happen if the toy is rolled along a table, and explain the physics that makes it work.

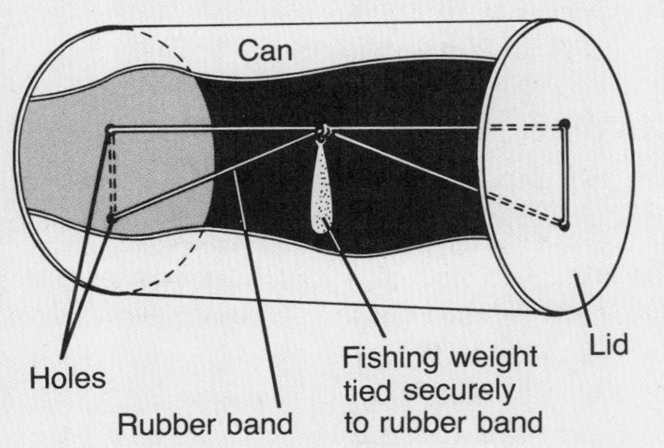

EXAMPLE Determining Specific Heat

A 250-g metal sample is heated to 59.0°C. It is put into 200 g of water at 10.0°C. The final temperature of the sample and water is 15°C. Find the thermal energy gained by the water, the energy lost by the sample, and the specific heat of the sample.

Given: Water
$m = 0.200$ kg
$T_i = 10.0°C$
$T_f = 15.0°C$

Unknown: Q_{gained}
Basic Equations:
$Q = \Delta T \times m \times C_p$
$\Delta T = T_f - T_i$

Sample: $m = 0.250$ kg
$T_f = 15.$
$T_i = 59.0°C$

Unknown: Q_{lost}, C_p
Basic Equations:
$Q = \Delta T \times m \times C_p$
$\Delta T = T_f - T_i$

Q_{lost} (by sample) $= Q_{gained}$ (by water)

Solution: For water

$Q_{gained} = (15.0°C - 10.0°C)(0.200 \text{ kg})(4190 \text{J/kg} \bullet C°)$
$= 4190$ J

Q_{lost} (by sample) $= Q_{gained}$ (by water) $= 4190$ J

$$C_p = \frac{Q_{gained}}{\Delta T \times m} = \frac{4190 \text{ J}}{(59.0°C - 15.0°C)(0.250 \text{ kg})}$$
$= 380$ J/kg • C°

PRACTICE PROBLEMS

5. Find the specific heat of the block of metal in the text example, p. 113.
6. 0.500 kg of water at 15.0°C is placed in a calorimeter. 0.0400 kg of zinc at 110.0°C is placed in the water. The final temperature of the water and zinc is 15.7°C. What is the specific heat of zinc?

Review

6. Carefully define the term *heat.*
7. Define, in words, *specific heat.*
8. Why does a cup of sand placed in the sunlight warm faster than a cup of water in the same place?
9. The aluminum foil of Practice Problem 4 lost 460 J. If the foil were cooled in 15 g of water, what was the temperature increase of the water?
10. ★ A ball of soft clay with a mass of 250 g fell from a fourth floor window 10 m to the ground. The ball was very soft and did not bounce at all. Assume that all the energy was converted into thermal energy. Calculate the change in temperature of the ball.

INVESTIGATION 5–2

Work and Thermal Energy

Problem: Can work produce a change in thermal energy?

Materials

4 polystyrene drinking cups
sand
masking tape
thermometer (graduated in 0.1C°)

Procedure

1. Fill a cup ⅓ full of dry sand that is at room temperature.
2. Place a thermometer in the sand and record the temperature. Remove the thermometer from the sand.
3. Invert the second cup over the first cup. Seal by wrapping a piece of tape around the seam between the two cups. Force the other 2 cups over the first cups to improve the insulation.
4. Turn the cups over so that the sand falls from one cup to the other.
5. Repeat Step 4 a total of 500 times. This should take about 5 minutes.
6. Punch a hole in the top of one of the cups. Insert the thermometer through the hole and into the sand. Record the temperature again.

Data and Observation

Beginning temperature of sand	
End temperature of sand	

Analysis

1. Calculate the change in temperature of the sand by subtracting the initial temperature from the final temperature.
2. What was the purpose of the foam cups?

Conclusions and Applications

3. Was the thermal energy of the sand increased in this experiment?
4. Where did the energy come from?
5. If you had turned the cups over 1000 times, how much change in temperature would you expect?
6. Can work produce a change in the thermal energy of an object?

FIGURE 5–12.

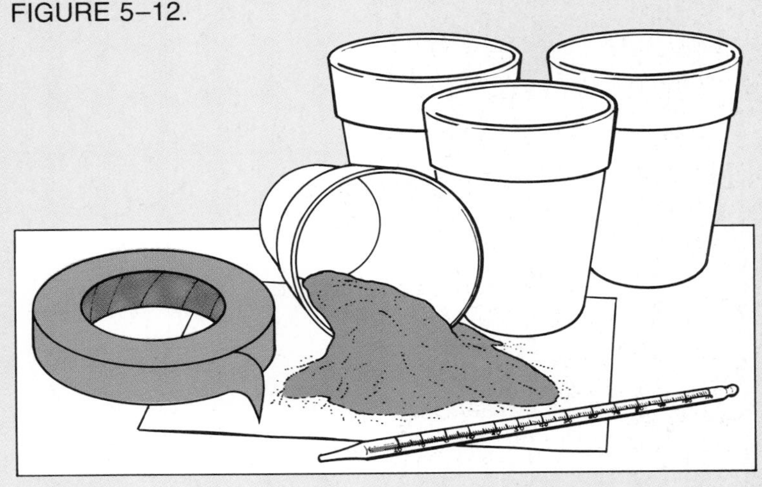

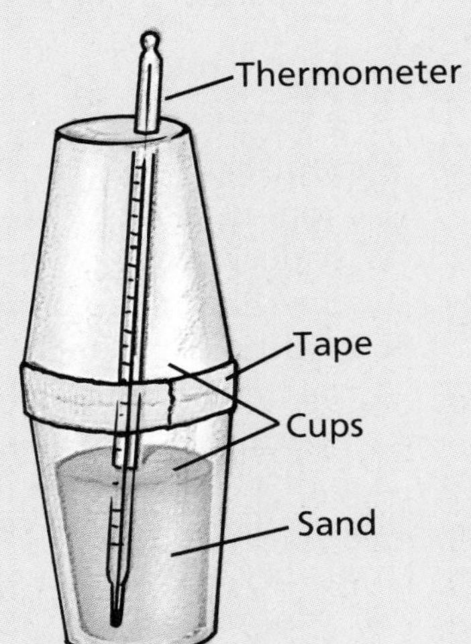

Chapter 5 Review

SUMMARY

1. An object in motion has kinetic energy. 5:1
2. An object that is bent or squeezed, or lifted against the force of gravity has potential energy. 5:2
3. Kinetic energy and potential energy of lifting and bending are grouped together and called mechanical energy. 5:2
4. Work is energy transferred as a result of motion. 5:3
5. Energy can change from one form to another, but can never be created or destroyed. 5:4
6. Temperature measures the average kinetic energy of the particles that make up an object. 5:5
7. Thermal energy is the total energy of the particles that make up a body. 5:6
8. Heat is the energy that flows from an object at a high temperature to one at a low temperature. 5:7
9. The specific heat of a material is the energy necessary to raise the temperature of 1 kg of the material 1°C. 5:8
10. A calorimeter measures thermal energy changes. 5:9

VOCABULARY

a. calorimeter
b. heat
c. kinetic energy
d. law of conservation of energy
e. mechanical energy
f. potential energy
g. specific heat
h. temperature
i. thermal energy
j. work

Matching

Match each description with the correct vocabulary word from the list above.

1. An auto moving at 90 km/h has this form of energy.
2. form of energy you have as you stand on a diving board
3. according to this law, the sum of the energy of a body in all its forms is constant
4. quantity that flows when bodies at different temperatures touch
5. quantity that measures the average kinetic energy of the particles of matter
6. quantity that tells you how much energy is needed to raise the temperature of one kilogram of a substance one Celsius degree
7. sum of the kinetic and potential energy of an object
8. tool used to measure changes in thermal energy of an object
9. transfer of energy by mechanical means
10. total energy of the particles of an object

MAIN IDEAS

A. Reviewing Concepts

Choose the word or phrase that correctly completes each of the following sentences.

1. Energy is measured in *(newtons, kelvins, joules, meters)*.
2. Changes in thermal energy can be measured with a *(thermometer, spring scale, two-pan balance, calorimeter)*.
3. An instrument used to measure temperature is a *(thermometer, spring scale, two-pan balance, calorimeter)*.
4. A temperature rise means that there is an increase in the *(mass, height, kinetic energy, weight)* of the particles making up the substance.
5. When a drill is used to make a hole in wood, the drill bit gets hot. This is an example of *(potential energy, heat transfer, work, equilibrium)*.

Complete each of the following sentences with the correct word or phrase.

6. A book on a table one meter above the floor has more ____________ than a book resting on the floor.
7. Specific heat is the change in ____________ for a given change in temperature.
8. Kinetic energy depends on mass and ____________.
9. When two bodies at different temperatures touch, energy in the form of ____________ flows from one to the other.
10. As a book falls from a table to the floor, its ________ energy changes to ________ energy.

Determine whether each of the following sentences is true or false. If the statement is false, change the underlined word to make the sentence correct.

11. A hot object contains more <u>heat</u> energy than a cold object.
12. Iron has a <u>smaller</u> specific heat than water.
13. When the temperature of water increases, its particles move more <u>slowly</u>.
14. <u>If</u> work is done, an object <u>must</u> be moved.
15. A soft lead ball falls to the ground and lies there without bouncing. All of its kinetic energy was <u>destroyed</u>.

B. Understanding Concepts

Answer the following questions using complete sentences when possible.

16. Describe energy.
17. How can the kinetic energy of a truck be increased without increasing its velocity?
18. How are heat and work similar?
19. A baseball of mass 0.145 kg is thrown 15 m high into the air. Find the work done on it as it rises.
20. Describe the transfer of energy from one form to another during the flight of a popped-up baseball, from just after it is hit until it has no velocity at the top of its flight.
21. A suitcase weighing 75 N is lifted from the floor, carried 15 m, and placed on a shelf 1.25 m high. Find the change in potential energy of the suitcase.
22. A copper block with a mass of 250 g is heated from 15.0°C to 95.0°C. How much energy is gained by the block?
23. A pile of books weighing 25 N is lifted from the floor, carried 5.5 m and placed on a shelf 1.5 m high. How much work is done on the books? Does your calculation depend on how high

the books were lifted before they were carried? Why?

24. A 0.50-kg bar of aluminum, heated to 98°C, is cooled in water to 41°C. How much energy is lost by the bar? How much energy is gained by the water?
25. If the aluminum bar in Problem 24 were placed in 0.740 kg of water, what was the change in temperature of the water? What was the initial temperature of the water?

C. Applying Concepts

Answer the following questions using complete sentences when possible.

26. When you put on the brakes on your bicycle, a rubber pad is rubbed against the steel wheel. What happens to the kinetic energy of the moving bike?
27. Suppose you have a 250-g cup of hot water at 90°C. To cool it you can either put in 20 g of water at 4°C or 20 g of aluminum at the same temperature. Which would cool the hot water more? Why?
28. Water in the cooling system of a car engine absorbs heat produced by the engine and carries it to the radiator where the hot water is cooled by transferring the thermal energy to air. Suppose you wanted to replace the water with another fluid. Would you want a fluid with a low or high specific heat? Why?
29. Choose the phrases that correctly describe the following event. A block falls from a ledge 10 m high. Just before it hits the ground, its kinetic energy is
    a. equal to its *PE* at that point.
    b. equal to zero.
    c. increasing.
    d. equal to its *PE* when on the ledge.
    e. all converted into thermal energy.
    f. the same as on the ledge.
30. Suppose the same amount of heat needed to raise the temperature of 0.050 kg of water 100C° is applied to 0.050 kg of copper. What is the temperature change of the copper?

PROJECTS

1. Investigate the life of Benjamin Thompson (Count Rumford) (1753–1814). Learn about his contributions to science and his inventions.
2. Prepare a report on how digital or liquid crystal thermometers work. Compare them to mercury or alcohol thermometers.

SKILL REVIEW

1. How would you enter $((41-5) \times 4)/(12 \times 5)$ into a calculator?
2. What is the easiest mistake to make when using a calculator?
3. What are two units for measuring volume?
4. Which variable goes on the horizontal axis of a graph?
5. When you study your science assignment, what should you do when you come to an **EXAMPLE?**

READINGS

1. Graham, Ada and Frank. *Big Stretch: The Complete Book of the Amazing Rubber Band*. New York: Knopf, 1985.
2. Smay, V.E. "Compact Storage 'Tank' for Solar Heat." *Popular Science*. June 1985, p. 118.
3. Weisburd, S. "Hydrothermal Discoveries from the Deep." *Science News*. December 20, 1986. p. 389.

KEEPING COMFORTABLE IN THE COLD
PUTTING HEAT TO WORK

Heat in our World

Humans have been able to live and thrive in most parts of Earth because they can make their own environments. Heating systems have been developed to keep homes warm on even the coldest winter day. Freezers and refrigerators allow us to eat healthful and good tasting food all year. However, all these appliances require energy. In recent years, we have found that this energy has become more and more expensive. In addition, the waste energy and chemicals produced by heating and cooling are beginning to affect Earth's water, air, and even its climate. We must learn to keep comfortable without polluting our planet.

KEEPING COMFORTABLE IN THE COLD

One way to keep warm is to stop the loss of thermal energy from our bodies. Another way is to transfer energy from electrical or chemical forms to warm our homes. In either case, it is important to understand how thermal energy is transferred and how other energy forms are converted into thermal energy.

GOALS

1. You will learn how thermal energy is transferred and how insulation can reduce heat flow from conduction, convection, and radiation.
2. You will understand how common heating systems work.

6:1 Thermal Energy Transfer

Thermal energy is transferred in three ways: conduction, convection, and radiation. In **conduction,** energy is transferred through matter from particle to particle. It occurs when two objects at different temperatures are in direct contact. There is transfer by conduction when a pan is placed on a hot stove, or when you put your hands into cold water, or when one end of a metal spoon is put into hot soup. Particles of matter at a higher temperature have more kinetic energy and vibrate further

Explain how conduction and convection transfer heat.

F.Y.I. All objects above 0 K produce some radiant energy. The higher the temperature, the more energy produced.

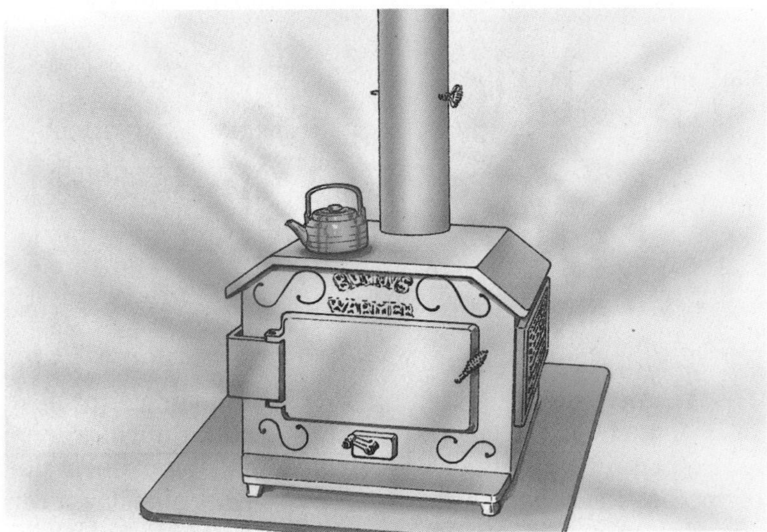

FIGURE 6–1. In the illustration, heat is being transferred by conduction, convection and radiation. Trace the heat flow.

than particles at a lower temperature. The rapidly vibrating particles collide with their less energetic neighbors, and energy moves through the material. Some materials conduct heat better than others. Metals such as iron, silver, and copper are good conductors; but stainless steel is not as good. Wood, plastic, and glass are poorer conductors. For this reason, a metal cooking pot may have a wooden handle. A gas is a very poor conductor, and no energy at all can be conducted across a vacuum.

How is heat transferred by radiation?

Convection is the transfer by the movement of matter. Convection is the most important method of transferring thermal energy in a fluid. Gases and liquids are called **fluids** because they flow. Whenever a fluid is heated, its density decreases; the same volume of the fluid has less weight. Think about a pot of water on a stove. Water at the bottom of the pot is warmed by conduction from the stove. When its temperature rises, its density decreases. Cooler, denser water sinks and pushes the hot water upward. As this water rises, it cools and sinks, pushing up more hot water. Fluid movements like this are called convection currents. Winds and ocean currents are convection currents that transfer heat on Earth. Clothing keeps you warm by making a thin air space around your body that is too thin to permit convection. Fur, wool, down, and feathers are especially warm because they contain many tiny air pockets.

FIGURE 6–2. Insulated clothing allows these young people to be comfortable at temperatures below freezing.

Radiation is a transfer of energy that does not require matter. You have felt the warmth of the sun on your face. The source of this energy is 150 million kilometers away, with mostly empty space between. No conduction or convection is possible. The sun's thermal energy is transferred to Earth as radiant energy. Black objects absorb radiant energy while shiny objects reflect it. Thus, a black roof is warmed by the sun more than a shiny roof.

TECHNOLOGY: ADVANCES

The Cool Stove

A new gas burner is being developed that may soon replace the traditional burners on kitchen stoves. The new burner transfers heat principally by radiation. It uses less fuel, cooks more uniformly, and is more efficient than older burners. Kitchens stay cooler, because the burner produces less wasted heat. More importantly, the amount of nitrogen oxides released into the air is much lower. Nitrogen oxides are toxic gases that are produced during the burning of fossil fuels. The new burner releases only about one-fifth as much of these unhealthy substances.

With a conventional burner, much of the oxygen needed to burn the cooking gas is taken from the air in the kitchen. This means that ignition takes place above the burner. Much of the heat produced simply warms the kitchen. In addition, the flame is concentrated in certain areas, instead of being evenly distributed across the burner. The bottom of the cooking pan may have "hot spots" that can cause food to burn.

In the new burner, a mixture of gas and air is forced through hundreds of tiny holes in a ceramic tile. The tile looks something like a honeycomb. The gas ignites on the surface of the tile. The tile is heated to about 800°C and glows bright red. The heat from the tile is transferred through a perforated glass plate to the cooking utensil. The glass plate protects the tile from spills. A series of holes in the plate directs hot exhaust gases to the pot or pan to aid in cooking. Nearly 95 percent of the heat produced by the tile is transferred to the cooking area where it is evenly distributed. Because of its new design features, the new burner should make cooking with gas cooler, easier, and more energy efficient.

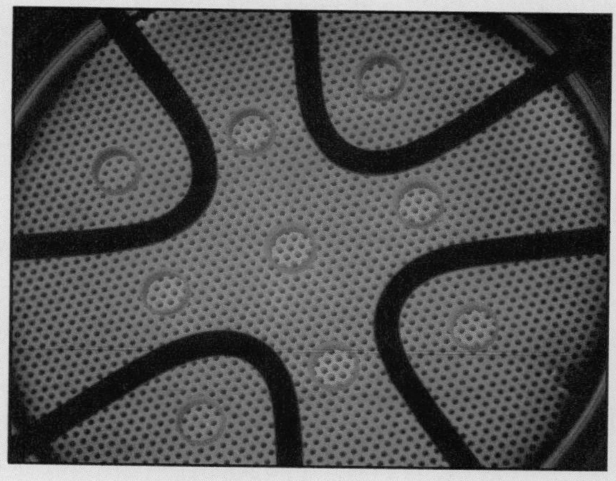

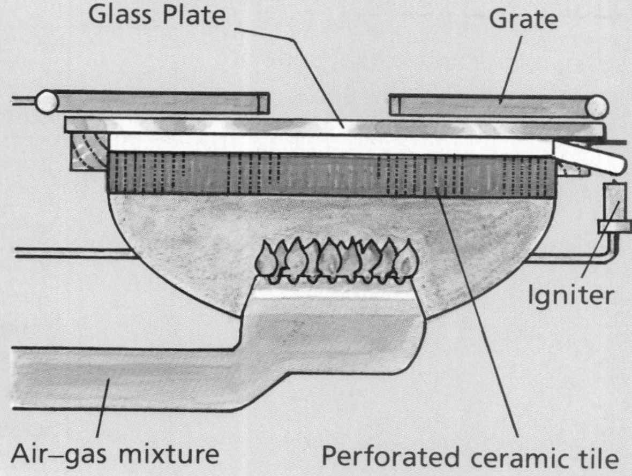

BIOGRAPHY

Mary Somerville
1780–1872

Mary Somerville became one of the most distinguished scientific writers of her century. The mathematics and science that she wrote about were almost entirely self-taught.

In her best-selling *Connexion of the Physical Sciences,* she discussed heat, light, matter, electricity, and astronomy. Her translation of La Place's *La Mechanique Celeste* was so highly thought of, that students at Cambridge University, all men, were required to read it.

Carefully try holding your hand a few centimeters from the surface of a bare light bulb. You will feel warmth. The warmth is a result of radiation from the bulb. If you put your hand the same distance above the bulb, you will feel the added warmth from convection currents of air heated by the bulb. You have to be careful not to touch the bulb, because the heat transferred by conduction may burn you.

6:2 Preventing Loss of Thermal Energy

Heat flows naturally from objects at a higher temperature to those that are colder. How could you keep cans of soda pop cold while on a picnic? You might use an insulated cooler. **Insulation** reduces the flow of heat by conduction, convection, and radiation. Coolers are often made from fiberglass or plastic foam. Not only are the materials poor conductors of heat themselves, but they are full of tiny air spaces. Air is also a poor conductor, and the air spaces are so small that convection currents cannot form.

Name at least three examples of insulation.

Buildings are insulated to keep them warm in winter and cool in summer. Fiberglass is often used as a building insulation. The fiberglass is an effective barrier against the flow of heat. In addition to fiberglass, extremely tiny pieces of treated paper, or loose-fill cellulose, are often used as insulation.

How is the effectiveness of insulation rated?

The effectiveness of a material as an insulator is measured by its R-value. "R" stands for resistance to heat flow. A piece of fiberglass 1-cm thick has an R-value of R-1.22. A well-insulated house should have insulation

Table 6–1

R-Values of Various Materials

Material	R-value
brick	0.08/cm
plasterboard (drywall)	0.35/cm
stucco	0.08/cm
wood siding	0.60/cm
air space	1.82–3.56/cm
fiberglass (bolts)	1.22/cm
loose cellulose	1.46/cm
aluminum siding	0.01/cm
loose foam	1.89/cm
loose vermiculite	1.09/cm

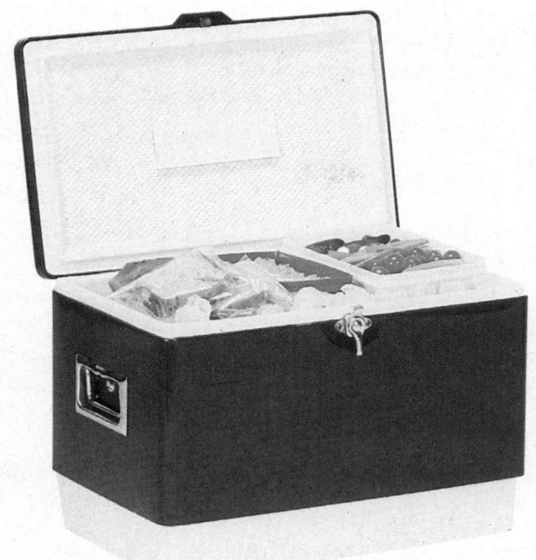

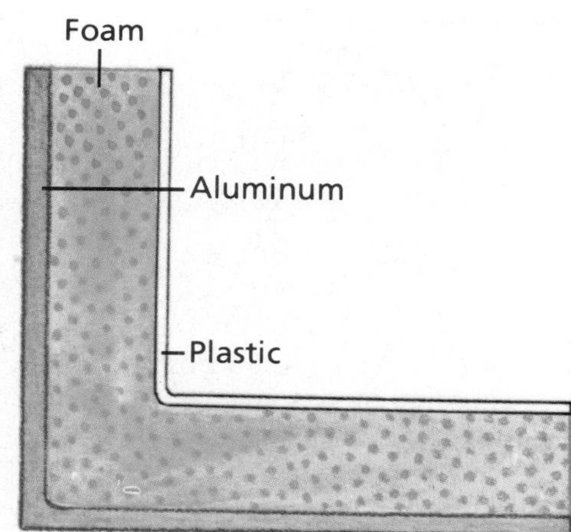

FIGURE 6–3. Air pockets are an important part of the insulating material used to slow the transfer of thermal energy in this picnic cooler.

with an R-value of at least R-19 in the walls and R-30 to R-44 in the ceiling. Ceiling insulation has to be better because convection currents inside the house carry the warmest air to the ceiling. Table 6–1 lists the R-value of some common materials.

Although glass is a relatively poor conductor, large windows can allow heat transfer to occur. Thermal windows are made of two panes of glass separated by a thin layer of air. The insulating properties of glass and air reduce loss by conduction through the window. The gap between the panes is made small enough to prevent convection currents from forming.

Aluminum foil prevents heat flow caused by radiation by reflecting heat back into a building. Builders often use fiberglass covered with aluminum foil to reduce heat

FIGURE 6–4. The energy efficiency of a house depends on the types and amounts of insulation it contains. Standard forms of insulation are shown in the house cross-section (a). Air spaces between the panes of glass in an energy efficient window prevent heat loss (b).

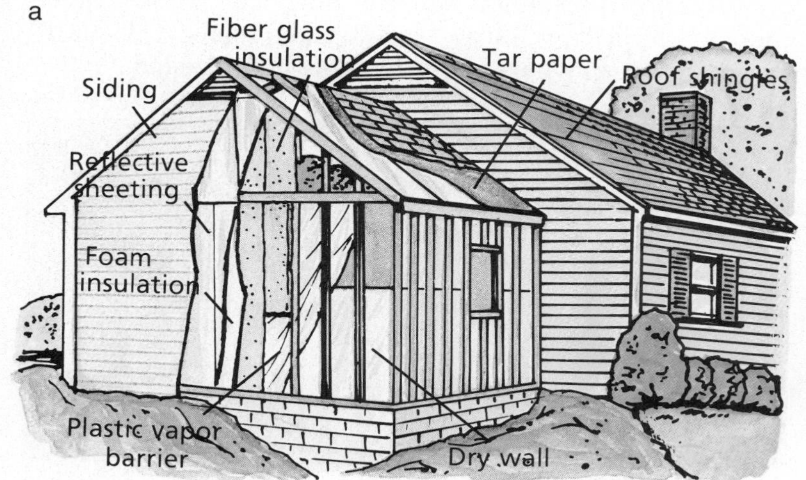

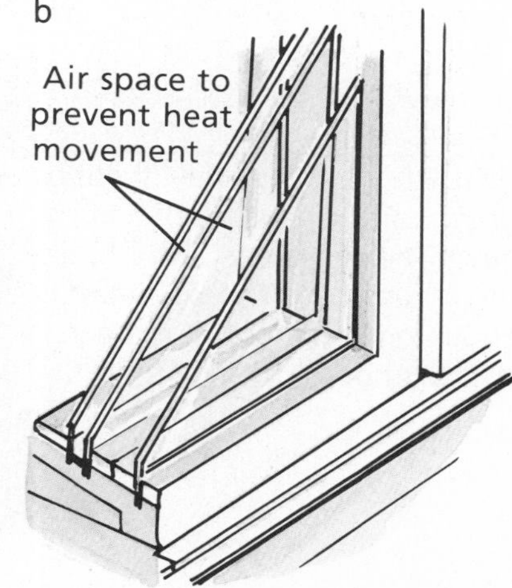

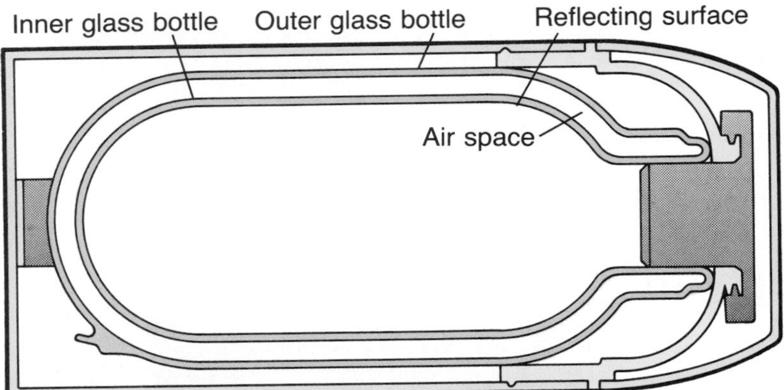

FIGURE 6–5. Insulated bottles, such as this, must prevent heat transfer by all three methods.

loss by radiation as well as conduction and convection. Special films can be put on windows to reflect thermal energy from the sun but allow light to pass through.

A vacuum bottle is often used to keep cold drinks cold or hot food warm. The bottle is actually two thin glass bottles, one inside the other. Air in the space in between is removed to prevent conduction and convection, and the inside surface of both bottles is coated with aluminum to prevent radiation.

Insulation alone will not keep a building from losing energy. Buildings also lose energy if air can enter or leave through gaps around windows and doors. Weather stripping closes these gaps and keeps the hot and cold air where they belong. Effective insulation must reduce heat loss by all mechanisms.

The effectiveness of insulation can be tested by thermography. **Thermography** is a technique that detects heat with a special photographic film. The hotter the object, the more energy it radiates. A thermogram is a photograph-like image of a building that shows areas that are emitting large amounts of energy. Usually these are areas where more insulation is needed.

FIGURE 6–6. Aerial thermograms show heat loss in buildings. The red areas show maximum heat loss. The white areas show temperatures that are not in the range of the scan.

INVESTIGATION 6–1

Absorbing Radiation

Problem: What color absorbs more radiation?

Materials

2 empty soup cans with labels removed, one painted black inside and out.
thermometer
light source: bright lamp or sunlight
50-mL graduated cylinder
hot and cold water
graph paper
clock or watch

FIGURE 6–7.

Procedure

1. Pour 50 mL of cold water into each can and place in sunlight or near a bright lamp.
2. Measure the temperature of the water in each can every 3 minutes for 15 minutes and record the data in the table.
3. Pour 50 mL of hot water in each can.
4. With cans out of sunlight or away from a lamp, repeat Step 2.

Data and Observations

Time	Temperatures(°C)	
	Painted Can	Unpainted Can

Analysis

1. Graph your data.
2. Which can had the larger decrease in temperature when out of the sunlight?
3. Which can had the greater increase in temperature when in the light?

Conclusions and Applications

4. Which can absorbed more radiant energy?
5. Which can radiated the thermal energy of the water to the room faster?
6. Why would solar heating panels be painted black?
7. The linings of vacuum bottles are silver. Why?
8. What color absorbs more radiation?

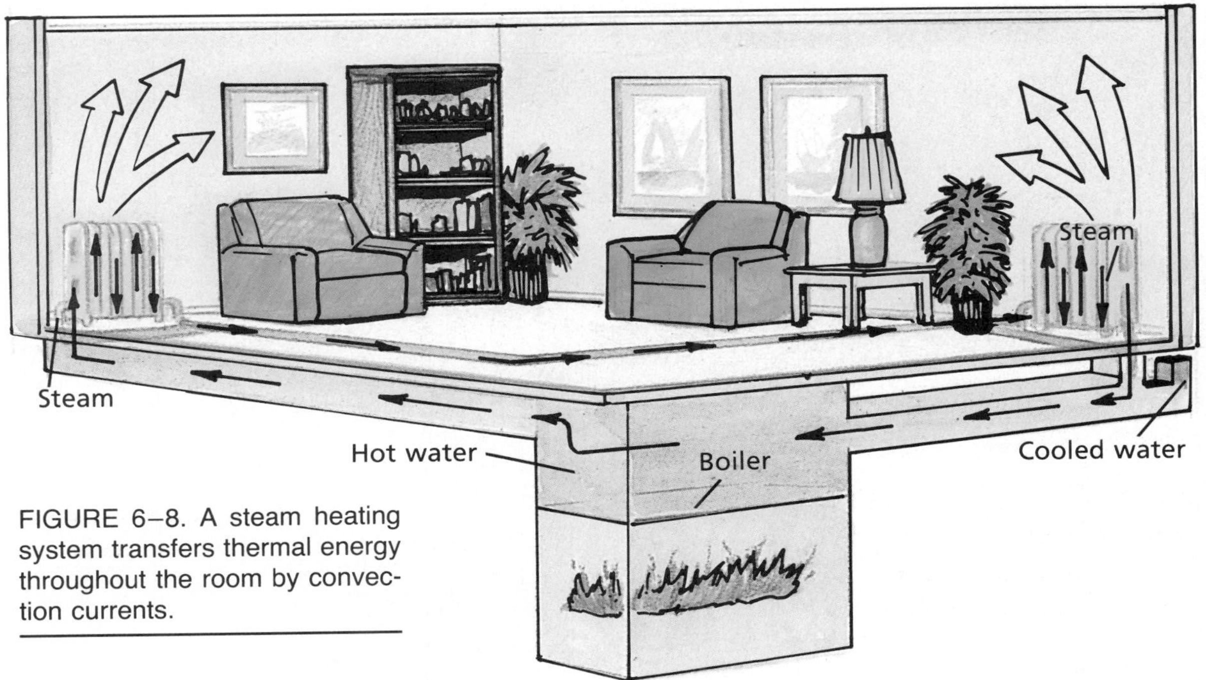

FIGURE 6–8. A steam heating system transfers thermal energy throughout the room by convection currents.

6:3 Heating Systems

How does a steam heating system work?

A number of different kinds of heating systems are used to heat buildings. One method is to put a hot object, such as a radiator, fireplace, or wood stove in a room. A **radiator,** like the one in Figure 6–9, is a device with a large surface area designed to warm the air. Air near the radiator is warmed by conduction. Colder, more dense, air sinks and pushes up the warm air near the heater. Thus, convection currents are formed that mix up and heat all the air in the room. The radiator also radiates energy to all parts of the room.

FIGURE 6–9. Radiators are designed to expose a large surface area to the air in the room.

Sometimes radiators are heated electrically. In other systems, a furnace burns a fuel such as oil or natural gas to heat water. A pump circulates the hot water to the radiators in the rooms. After the water has given up some of its thermal energy, it is returned to the furnace to be heated again.

In some systems the water is heated to the boiling point, forming steam. The steam is circulated from the furnace to the radiators. In the radiators the steam condenses to water, which runs back to the furnace to be boiled again. Steam radiators release more energy than hot water radiators. It takes about 50 times more hot water to produce the same energy as steam. However, the furnace and pipes have to be specially designed to

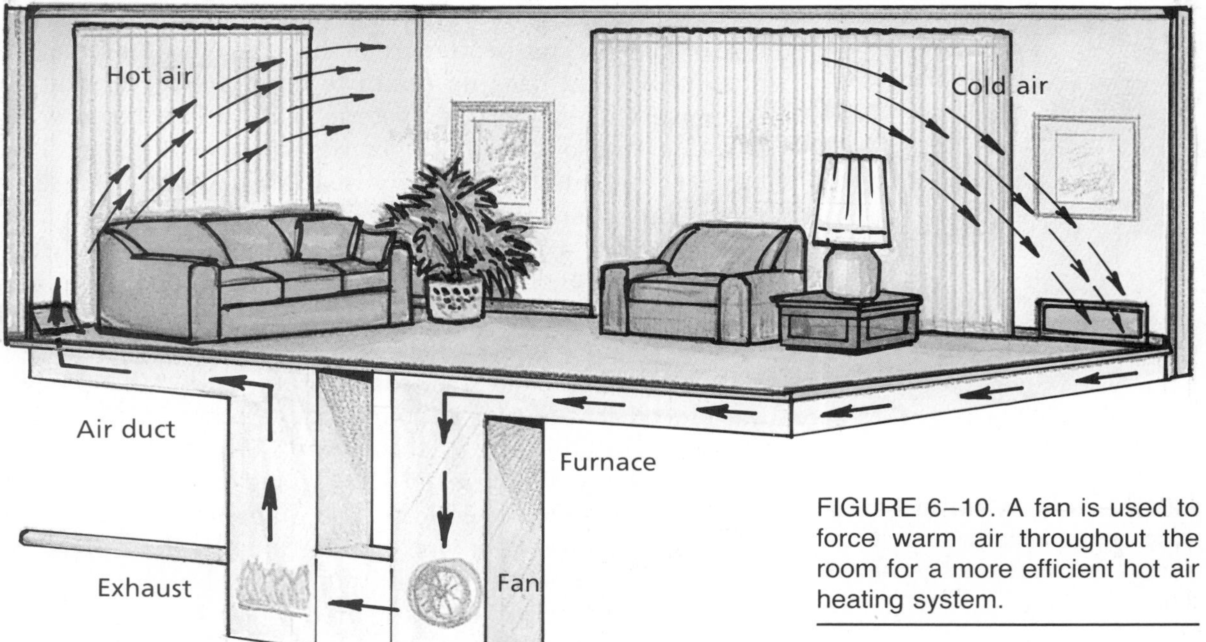

FIGURE 6–10. A fan is used to force warm air throughout the room for a more efficient hot air heating system.

work with steam. More insulation is needed to keep steam from condensing in the pipes before it gets to the radiator.

Some heating systems use furnaces to warm air. A blower moves the warmed air to other parts of the building. As the air is cooled, it returns to the furnace to be warmed again.

In some homes the entire ceiling is heated by electrical energy. Air near the ceiling is heated by conduction. Energy is also radiated to other objects in the room such as walls, floor, furniture, and people. Electrical heating gives uniform warmth, but is usually expensive.

FIGURE 6–11. Energy from the sun is used to heat this home. Most of the solar panels are on the south side.

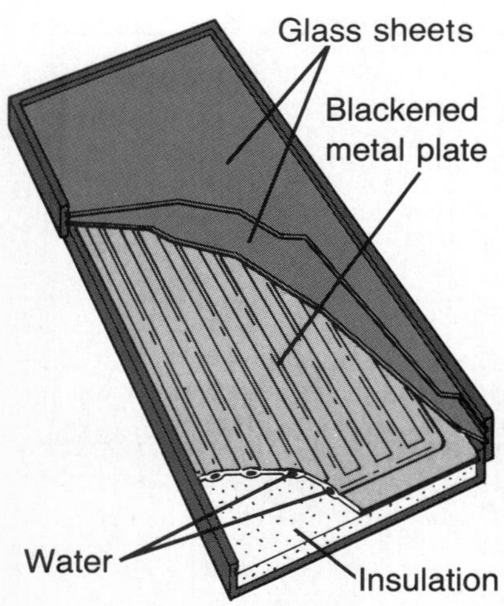

FIGURE 6–12. Solar energy is absorbed by the water in these tubes. The warmed water is then circulated through the house.

Describe an active solar heating system.

Solar heating systems use energy from the sun to heat houses. The systems can be passive or active. A passive system uses no pump to circulate air or water. A house with a passive system usually has large windows on the south side to get the most winter sun. The other three sides are heavily insulated. During the day, large containers filled with water or stones with a high specific heat are warmed by the solar energy. After dark, these containers radiate their stored energy to the house. Insulating panels are closed over the windows at night to reduce energy loss.

In an active solar heating system, collecting panels are placed on the roof or south side of a house. The panels are painted black to absorb the radiant energy from the sun. They are covered with glass or plastic to prevent loss from convection. The panels contain pipes filled with water. The water is warmed in the collectors and circulates through radiators in the building. Often a large water tank stores heated water for circulation after dark or on cloudy days.

Review

1. How does the energy from the sun reach us?
2. What is the difference between energy transfer by conduction and convection?
3. Make a list of some good conductors of heat.
4. People caught in cold weather with only light jackets are told to wrinkle up newspapers and place them inside their coats. Why?
5. ★ Food stores usually store frozen food in freezers that are open at the top. Why does the warm air in the store not melt the food?

PUTTING HEAT TO WORK

GOALS

1. You will learn how heat engines convert thermal energy to mechanical energy.
2. You will understand how refrigerators, air conditioners, and heat pumps move thermal energy from low to high temperatures.

Prehistoric humans learned how to convert mechanical energy to thermal energy. They learned to rub two sticks together to make fire. It was not until the 1700s that humans learned to do the reverse. Newcombe, Watt, and others invented steam engines that burned fuels and converted thermal energy to mechanical energy. These engines started the industrial revolution. We will study ways of converting heat to work as well as devices that can use work to move heat and make us more comfortable.

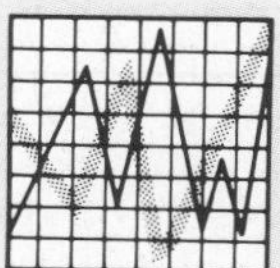

SKILL

Determining Cause and Effect

Problem: How do you determine cause and effect?

Materials

textbook
paper and pencil

Background

Have you ever wondered why something happened? Scientists often wonder "why?" They carefully observe an event, and then try to determine why it occurred. This relationship between an event and why it occurred, is called cause and effect. What happened is the *effect*. The reason it happened is the *cause*. One effect often may have more than one possible cause. It is often difficult to identify the specific cause, or causes, of a given event. For example, your grade on a test is an effect. The reasons you got that grade are the causes. These could include your study habits, attendance and attention in class, and your physical condition. Analyzing the causes of events can help change an effect if it was undesirable, or recreate it if it was good.

Was your score on the test high because you took notes in class? Was it because you studied for two nights before the test? Since you have gotten a good grade on the last two tests, and used the same new pen on both, perhaps it is the pen. Although this example may seem silly, it is often difficult to separate cause from coincidence.

Complete Tables A and B, filling in the appropriate cause or effect.

Table A

Cause	Effect
	1. Clothes keep you warm.
	2. Coolers are made of fiberglass and plastic.
	3. Everything in a room does not feel the same temperature.
	4. A large number of fish have died in a river that has flowed past a small city, an electrical power plant, and a manufacturing plant.

Table B

Cause	Effect
1. Aluminum foil prevents heat flow because it reflects thermal energy; fiberglass is a good insulator.	
2. Coolers are made of fiberglass and plastic.	
3. Internal combustion engines are only about 12% efficient.	
4. Steam radiators release a great deal more energy than hot water radiators.	

CAREER

Heating, Ventilation, and Air Conditioning Technician

The elementary school Greg Shockey attended was always either too hot or too cold. This is what he thinks initiated his interest in improving our environment. Today he is what is known as a HVAC, or heating, ventilation, and air conditioning mechanic. He installs, services, and designs machinery used to control the climate inside buildings.

Greg got his start as an apprentice at a hardware store while still in high school. At first he worked at the service counter in parts and inventory. Then he learned the art of drawing blueprints in his engineering design class at school. After graduating from high school, he continued studies in his field at a local technical college.

Once Greg felt he was well qualified as a HVAC technician, he began to make his own contracts to design units for new apartment buildings.

For career information, write

American Society of Heating,
Refrigeration, and Air
Conditioning Engineers
345 E. 47th Street
New York, NY 10017

6:4 Heat Engines

Heat engines convert thermal energy into mechanical energy. Gasoline and diesel engines are examples of heat engines. Each engine changes the thermal energy from a burning fuel into the mechanical energy of the moving parts of the machine. The machine transfers its energy by motion. Thus, a heat engine converts heat into work. Heat engines operate in a cycle. That is, the moving parts must periodically return to their original location.

FIGURE 6–13. Hot compressed gases explode in the cylinders of an internal combustion engine. The force of the expanding gases drives the piston down, turning the drive shaft.

Gasoline and diesel engines are called **internal combustion engines** because the **combustion,** or burning, of the fuel occurs inside the engine. Steam engines are external combustion engines because the fuel burns outside the engine to produce steam.

What are internal combustion engines?

Look at the internal combustion engine shown in Figure 6–13. Gasoline is broken into very fine droplets and mixed with air in the carburetor. In each cylinder is a piston that moves up and down. The piston first moves down, drawing the gasoline and air mixture into the cylinder through an intake valve. This is called the intake stroke. Next, the piston moves up, squeezing the mixture in the compression stroke. When the piston almost reaches the top of the cylinder, the spark plug ignites the fuel-air mixture with an electric spark. The mixture burns, producing very hot gases that force the piston down. This motion is the power stroke. As the piston moves up the cylinder again, it pushes the burned gases out through the exhaust valve in the exhaust stroke. Each piston makes four strokes in a cycle, Figure 6–14. An engine that operates this way is called a four-stroke engine.

What are the strokes of a 4-stroke engine?

Many automobiles use fuel-injected engines. There is no carburetor. Instead, very fine droplets of fuel are sprayed directly into the compressed air in the cylinders. The spark ignites the mixture as in a normal gasoline engine. A diesel engine also injects the fuel directly into the cylinders. However, in a diesel engine the

How is the fuel-air ignited in a diesel engine?

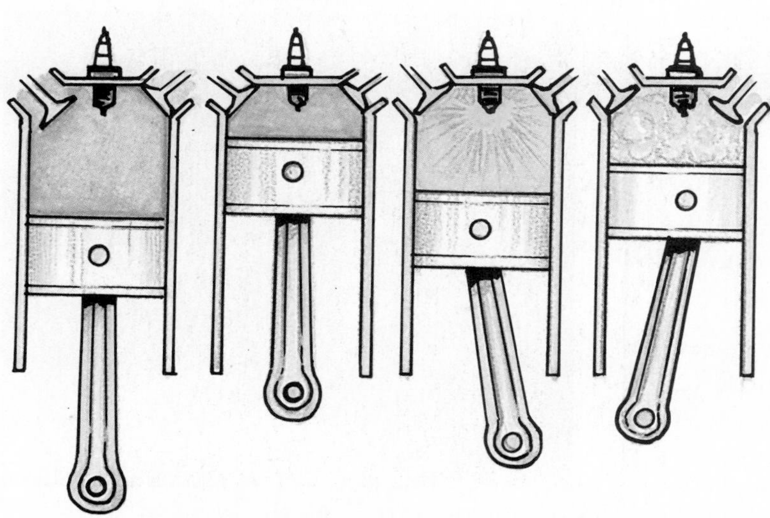

FIGURE 6–14. The steps in the combustion process for a four-stroke engine are shown. The energy from the combustion does work on the piston.

F.Y.I. The car engine has an efficiency of 12%.

fuel-air mixture is compressed more than in a gasoline engine. The mixture is made so hot (900°C) that it is ignited without a spark. Glow plugs are used to heat the air when the engine has not been operated for a while.

The mechanical energy produced by an automobile engine is transferred to the wheels of the car through a series of shafts and gears. The tires exert a force on the road. The road exerts an equal and opposite force on the tires, accelerating the car forward.

What happens to most of the potential energy from the fuel in internal-combustion engines?

Heat engines must obey the law of conservation of energy. They operate in a cycle, which means that they do not store energy. Thermal energy is put into the engine at the high temperature of burning fuel. It comes from the chemical potential energy of the fuel. The energy produced by the engine must equal the energy put in by the fuel. Both useful mechanical energy and extra thermal energy at a lower temperature are produced. The extra thermal energy is waste energy. An ideal engine would produce no waste energy, but such an engine is impossible. All heat engines produce some waste thermal energy.

Only about 12% of the chemical potential energy in the fuel burned by a gasoline engine is converted into the kinetic energy of the car. A diesel engine has an efficiency of about 25%. Most of the remainder of the energy becomes waste thermal energy. The cooling system transfers some of it to the radiator and then to the air. Most of the waste thermal energy flows out the exhaust system.

FIGURE 6–15. Early steam turbines (a) rotated because of steam issuing from curved tubes, in a manner similar to a rotating lawn sprinkler. In a modern turbine (b), thermal energy is converted into mechanical energy, and then electrical energy, as steam turns the turbine blades to produce electricity.

a

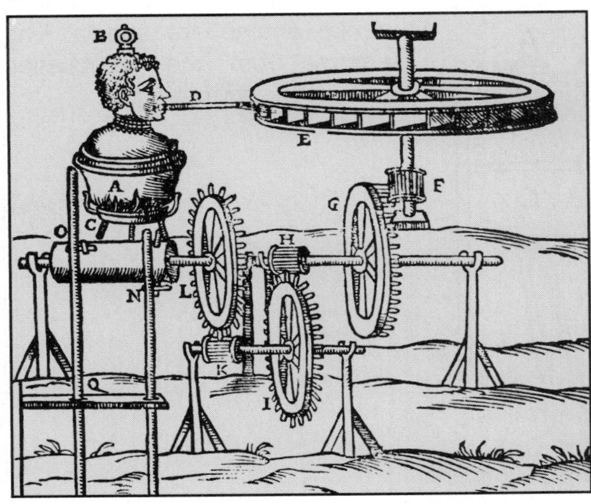

b

Steam engines are used when a large engine can remain in one place. In electrical power stations, steam produced by burning fuel turns large fans in machines called turbines. In a steam turbine, the steam is squeezed through a small opening, called a nozzle. It comes out at high speed, and is directed toward the blade of the turbine. It pushes against the blade, turning the turbine. Turbines are often huge engines, many meters in diameter. Steam engines also produce unwanted thermal energy that can be a source of thermal pollution.

6:5 Heat Movers

You have learned that heat naturally flows from hot to cold regions. Yet, if you put warm food inside a refrigerator, the thermal energy is removed, and the food cools. Where does the thermal energy go? If you feel the back of your refrigerator you will find that it is warm. The thermal energy removed from the food at low temperatures is put into the room at a higher temperature. How can a refrigerator move heat from low to high temperature regions? The answer to this question is that a refrigerator uses outside electrical energy to move the heat.

What is a heat mover?

What is a heat pump?

A refrigerator is an example of a **heat mover,** a machine that removes heat from an object at a low temperature and gives it to one at a high temperature. A heat mover requires outside energy, in some form, to do this. An air conditioner is another example of a heat mover. Thermal energy is removed from the air inside the house, cooling it to a comfortable temperature near 20°C. The energy is delivered to the outside at a higher temperature.

Some homes use heat pumps to heat in the winter and cool in the summer. A **heat pump** is a heat mover that can operate in two directions. In the summer it acts like an ordinary air conditioner. In the winter, however, it removes thermal energy from the outside air at a low temperature and delivers it to the inside at a higher temperature. Again outside electrical energy is needed to accomplish this. Heat movers, like heat engines, must obey the law of conservation of energy. In winter, the energy put into the heat pump, electrical energy and thermal energy at a low temperature, must equal the thermal energy produced at a high temperature.

FIGURE 6–16. Electrical appliances are sold with tags telling how much energy they require to operate.

PROBLEM SOLVING

Summer Breezes

Water has a higher specific heat than soil. This means that it takes a body of water longer to cool down or warm up than a body of land. Amos spent his summers along a seashore. He noticed that on hot summer days there was usually a cooling breeze from the ocean. Almost every night, however, the wind shifted and blew from the land out to sea. Amos wrote to the weather person on the local TV station, to find out if there was a scientific reason for this. Pretend you are the meteorologist and write an explanation for Amos.

6:6 Thermal Pollution

Furnaces, stoves, and electric lamps produce thermal energy. All heat engines and heat movers also produce thermal energy. Much of the energy we use—radiation, electrical, chemical, and mechanical energy—ends up as thermal energy. Someone has said that thermal energy is the graveyard of all kinds of energy at low temperatures. This means that all processes produce waste thermal energy. This extra energy is eventually radiated into space.

What is thermal pollution?

What are some solutions to thermal pollution?

Waste thermal energy can cause a problem if it raises the temperature of the environment. It is then called **thermal pollution.** Excess thermal energy in the air around cities makes them warmer and wetter than surrounding areas. Power plants and industries use water to remove the thermal energy from their buildings and manufacturing processes. The warmed water is then dumped into a nearby river, lake, or ocean. Sometimes the water is returned 10°C or more warmer than when it was taken in. More than 200 trillion liters of warm water are discharged into the environment each year. The warmer water may increase plant growth. It may also kill fish. For example, brook trout can live only 12 hours at 25°C and just 30 minutes at 28°C.

FIGURE 6–17. Gases are more soluble in cooler liquids. Active fish seek colder water, where there is more oxygen in solution.

One solution is to spread the thermal energy out by increasing the water flow, while reducing the increase in temperature. Another solution is the use of cooling towers. Hot water from a power plant is cooled with air driven by large fans inside the tower. In some cooling towers the water is further cooled by evaporation

FIGURE 6–18. A cooling tower is used to prevent thermal pollution of the environment. The hot water is cooled inside the tower and as it splashes down the outside of the tower.

as it is sprayed into the moving air inside the tower. It is returned to the environment with its temperature only slightly raised. Thermal pollution is reduced, but the cooling tower produces large amounts of warm, humid air.

A second solution is to use the thermal energy rather than to waste it. Some power plants pump the hot water to nearby buildings and greenhouses where it is used for heating. Another use is to remove salt from seawater. The salt water is warmed and evaporated. The water vapor has no salt in it. The vapor is cooled and condensed to form pure water.

Review

6. What starts the fuel burning in a gasoline engine? In a diesel engine?

7. Why can we call a diesel engine an internal combustion engine?

8. What two energy transformations occur in an internal combustion engine?

9. How does clothing keep us warm?

★ **10.** If you leave the door of the refrigerator open in a closed room, does the room get warmer or colder?

INVESTIGATION 6–2

Conduction and Convection

Problem: How is heat transferred by conduction and convection?

Materials

metal rod or knitting needle
candle, matches
laboratory burner
food coloring
clock
ring stand
water
beaker
glass rod
ring and screen
dropper
cork

Procedure

Part A

1. Gently push one end of a metal rod or knitting needle into the cork. Use the cork as a handle, Figure 6–19 a.
2. Light the candle.
3. Melt some wax from the candle onto the rod at three points, 2 cm apart. Do this by tipping the candle so the wax drips on the metal rod. Let the wax cool.
4. Hold the tip of the free end of the metal rod in the candle flame. Record the time when each drop of wax melts.
5. Repeat Steps 1–4, using the glass rod instead of the metal rod. Be sure to place the wax at the same points on the glass rod as you did on the metal one.

Part B

6. Fill the beaker about 2/3 full of water.

FIGURE 6–19.

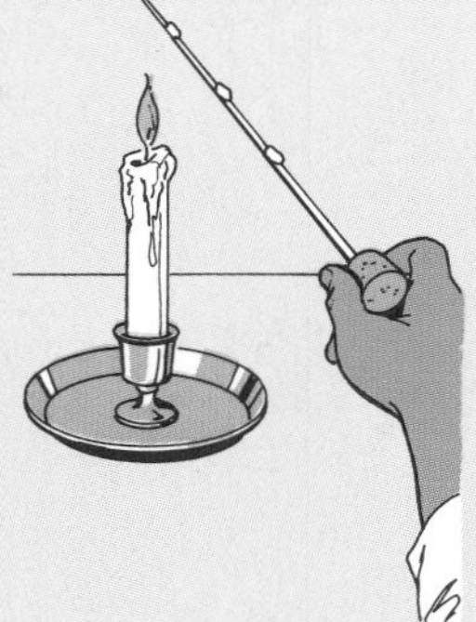

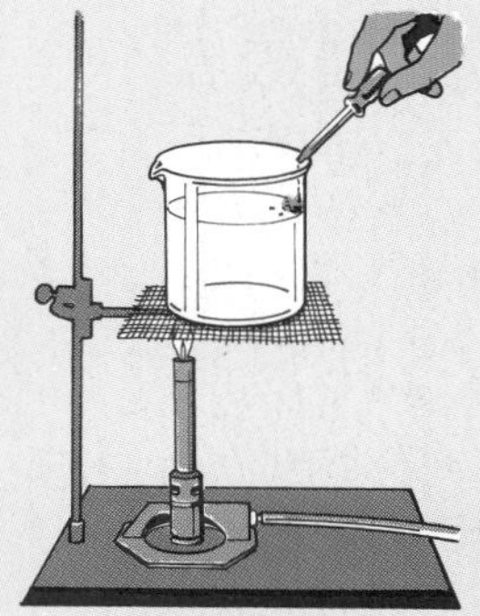

7. Place the beaker on the wire screen on the ring stand.
8. Add a drop of food coloring to the water at the side of the beaker as shown in Figure 6–19 b. Do not stir and be very careful not to disturb the water in the beaker.
9. Gently warm the water by holding the burner against the side of the beaker opposite the food coloring. Watch and record your observations.

Data and Observations

Part A

Metal rod starting time ______________
time 1st drop melts ______________
time 2nd drop melts ______________
time 3rd drop melts ______________
Glass rod starting time ______________
time 1st drop melts ______________
time 2nd drop melts ______________
time 3rd drop melts ______________

Part B

Observations from Step 9. ______________

Analysis and Conclusions

1. Describe what happens to the wax on the metal rod.
2. Compare and contrast the effects on the metal and glass rods.
3. Explain your observations of the time required to melt the 3 drops of wax on the metal rod in terms of conduction of heat.
4. Compare the conduction of the metal and glass rods.
5. What causes the behavior of the food coloring when the water is warmed?
6. How is heat being transferred in the beaker?
7. Compare the way heat is transferred by conduction and convection.

Chapter 6 Review

SUMMARY

1. Thermal energy can be transferred by radiation, conduction, and convection. 6:1
2. Liquids and gases are called fluids because they flow. 6:1
3. Insulation reduces heat flow by reducing radiation, conduction, and convection. 6:2
4. Fiberglass, plastic foam, and air are poor heat conductors. 6:2
5. Heating systems make use of the three methods of transferring thermal energy. 6:3
6. Solar heating systems absorb radiation from the sun and transfer this energy throughout the building. 6:3
7. Heat engines convert thermal energy into mechanical energy. 6:4
8. Heat movers, such as refrigerators, freezers, air conditioners, and heat pumps, remove heat at low temperatures and deliver it at high temperatures, with the aid of added energy. 6:5
9. Thermal pollution results when too much waste heat is put into the environment. 6:6

VOCABULARY

a. combustion
b. conduction
c. convection
d. fluids
e. heat engine
f. heat mover
g. heat pump
h. insulation
i. internal combustion engine
j. radiation
k. radiator
l. solar heating system
m. thermal pollution
n. thermography

Matching

Match each description with the correct vocabulary word from the list above. Some words will not be used.

1. a device that heats your home by removing energy from the cold outside air
2. a method of making a picture of heat leaking from a building
3. a method of transferring of thermal energy that does not require matter
4. the general name of a device to change thermal energy to mechanical energy
5. an engine that burns fuel inside the engine
6. material that reduces heat flow
7. transfer of thermal energy in solids
8. the general name of a device that takes in energy and heat at low temperatures and produces thermal energy at high temperature
9. method of energy transfer using moving fluids
10. a method of heating that uses the energy from the sun

Chapter 6 Review

MAIN IDEAS

A. Reviewing Concepts

Choose the word or phrase that correctly completes each of the following sentences.

1. Thermal energy travels through a metal spoon in hot cocoa mostly by *(radiation, conduction, convection, insulation).*
2. When a pot of water is put on a hot stove, the water at the top gets warm mostly by *(radiation, conduction, convection, insulation).*
3. When a cold can of soda pop is insulated, the heat flow into the can on a hot day is *(increased, decreased, not changed).*
4. A heat pump is a device that *(converts mechanical to thermal energy, converts thermal to mechanical energy, transfers thermal energy from low to high temperatures, conducts heat from hot to cold regions).*
5. A diesel engine ignites the fuel-air mixture using *(spark plugs, glow plugs, hot fuel, glow lighters).*

Complete each of the following sentences with the correct word or phrase.

6. When waste heat is used to take ____________ out of seawater, thermal pollution is ____________.
7. ____________ is the movement of thermal energy through an object from particle to particle.
8. Energy from the sun travels the distance from the sun to Earth by means of ____________.
9. Fiberglass can be used as ____________.
10. Hot vapors move a ____________ wheel in a steam engine.

Determine whether each of the following sentences is true or false. If it is false, change the underlined word to make the sentence true.

11. <u>Convection</u> is the transfer of energy from one particle to the next.
12. Insulation <u>allows</u> heat to flow easily.
13. Heat engines convert thermal to <u>mechanical</u> energy.
14. Energy travels from the sun to Earth by <u>radiation.</u>
15. Air is a <u>good</u> conductor of thermal energy.

B. Understanding Concepts

Answer the following questions using complete sentences when possible.

16. Explain why a metal handrail feels colder in winter than a wooden one.
17. Why would wearing several layers of light clothing keep you warmer than one heavy coat?
18. Why are houses in the tropics seldom painted black or made with black roofs?
19. How does fiberglass reduce heat flow?
20. Why does dirty snow melt faster than clean snow?
21. The R-value of a piece of insulation is found by multiplying the R-value per centimeter by the thickness in centimeters. What is the R-value of 15 cm of fiberglass?
22. If you open windows at both the top and bottom, you will increase air flow through the room. Why?
23. How can a refrigerator take heat in at low temperatures and put it out at a higher temperature?
24. Why is a down parka useless if it gets soaked with water?
25. If you hold a tissue over an electric stove, the tissue will wave up and down. Why?

C. Applying Concepts

Answer the following questions using complete sentences when possible.

26. Why are the basements of houses often cooler than the rest of the house, even on the warmest days?
27. Explain how a gasoline engine produces the kinetic energy that moves the car forward.
28. Why does Earth cool at night more quickly when the sky is clear than when it is cloudy?
29. Why does a fluffy bathroom rug feel warmer to your feet than the tile floor, even though they are at the same temperature?
30. Why do people who live in the desert wear several layers of clothes, even when the temperature reaches 45°C?

SKILL REVIEW

1. How are cause and effect related?
2. The early Greeks observed that the sun rose in the east everyday and set in the west (effect). What are two possible causes they might have suggested?
3. Is a hypothesis more likely to be a cause or an effect?
4. Why is it necessary to determine the range of values in a set of data to be graphed?
5. How might observations and inferences be related to cause and effect?

PROJECTS

1. Write a report on the types of solar heating systems that are used in your area.
2. Write a report on the steps the electric utility in your region is taking to reduce thermal pollution.

READINGS

1. "Home Heating." *Popular Science*. October, 1985, pp. 104–113.
2. Kozlov, Alex. "Hopping Heat Waves." *Science Digest*. June, 1986, p. 28.
3. Langley, Billy C. *Comfort Heating*. Englewood Cliffs, NJ: Reston, 1985.
4. Santrey, Lawrence. *Heat*. Mahwah, NJ: Troll Associates, 1985.

SIMPLE MACHINES
USING MACHINES

Machines

Our lives are affected in many ways by machines. They may help us to move heavy objects or travel rapidly from place to place. You might think that machines are a modern invention. Automobiles and airplanes have been in use less than one hundred years. However, 4000 years ago the Egyptians used simple machines to help them build pyramids.

SIMPLE MACHINES

GOALS

1. You will understand how to calculate the mechanical advantage of a machine.
2. You will recognize that a machine can increase force, but not work done.
3. You will learn the six simple machines and be able to find the mechanical advantage of each of them.

Machines, powered by engines or humans, do make our jobs easier. Modern machines may seem very complex. However, if you examined them, you would find that they are all combinations of a few simple machines. Gears, pulleys, and lever arms are all examples of devices called simple machines.

7:1 What is a Simple Machine?

A machine can make a job easier by changing the size or direction of the force you must exert. Suppose you want to pull a nail out of a piece of wood. You might use a claw hammer. A claw hammer is a lever, an example of a simple machine. A **simple machine** is a machine consisting of only one part. There are six types of simple machines. They are shown in Figure 7–1. A bicycle is a compound machine. A bicycle is made of more than one simple machine. Compound machines are discussed in Section 7:7.

What is a simple machine?

Some machines make a job easier because they increase the amount of force you can exert. For example, the force exerted on the nail by the hammer claw is greater than the force you apply to the handle with your hand. The force exerted by the machine is the **resistance force.** The **effort force** is the force you apply to the machine.

F.Y.I. "Mind is the great lever of all things . . ."
Daniel Webster

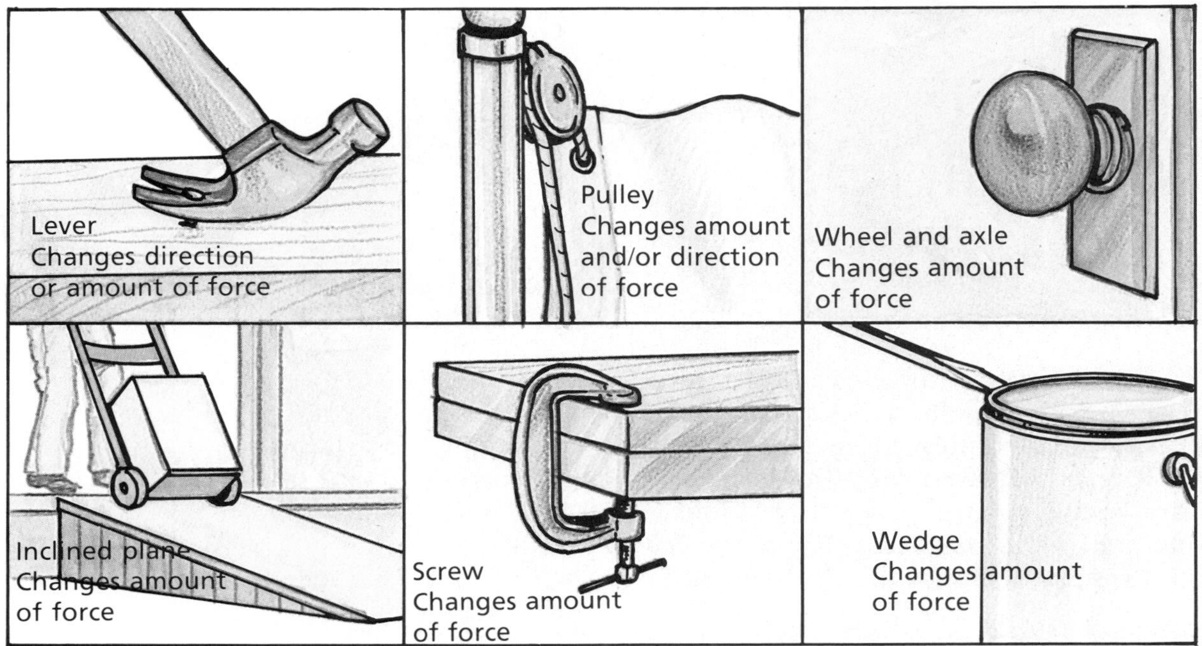

FIGURE 7–1. Simple machines change the direction or amount of force needed to do work.

List the six simple machines.

A machine exerts a resistance force over a distance. Therefore the machine does work. The work put out by the machine is never more than the work put into it. A machine cannot increase the amount of work done.

7:2 Mechanical Advantage

How is mechanical advantage calculated?

The number of times a machine multiplies an effort force is called the **mechanical advantage** (*MA*) of the machine. In many cases, like the hammer example before, machines have a mechanical advantage greater than one. The equation to calculate the mechanical advantage is

$$MA = \frac{\textit{resistance force}}{\textit{effort force}} = \frac{F_r}{F_e}.$$

EXAMPLE Calculating the Effort Force

A claw hammer has a mechanical advantage (*MA*) equal to 15. It is used to pull a nail that exerts a resistance force of 3000 N. What effort force is needed to pull the nail?

Given: mechanical advantage

$MA = 15$

resistance force

$F_r = 3000$ N

Unknown:
effort force (F_e)

Basic Equation:
$MA = F_r/F_e$

Solution: $MA = \dfrac{F_r}{F_e}$ so $F_e = \dfrac{F_r}{MA}$

$F_e = (3000\text{ N})/15 = 200\text{ N}$

PRACTICE PROBLEM

1. An iron bar is used to lift a slab of sidewalk. The mechanical advantage of the bar is 16.0. If the slab weighs 6400 N, what effort force is needed to lift the slab?

It takes energy for you to pull a nail out of a board. The energy comes from the stored chemical energy in your body. A simple machine aids in the conversion of energy from one form to another. The machine can increase the force you apply, but it cannot increase the energy. Energy is conserved, so the machine can at most transfer as much energy to the nail as you put into pulling the hammer handle.

The energy is transferred in and out of the machine by mechanical means. That is, work is done on the hammer, and the hammer does work on the nail. Work is the product of a force times the distance moved in the direction of the force, or $W = F \times d$. The work done by the machine, *work*$_{out}$, is the product of the resistance force, F_r, times the distance the object moves, d_r,

$$W_{out} = F_r \times d_r.$$

CAREER

Metallurgical Engineer

Jerry Green always enjoyed using leftover pieces of metal to make toys for his younger brothers. After attending the state fair and seeing a blacksmith forging iron, he became interested in learning more about working with metal. In high school he took all the industrial technology courses he could, especially the metals and design classes.

In college, Jerry learned about the physical properties of metals. What interested him most, however, was the mechanical process of casting, forging, and shaping metal and metal alloys.

Today, Jerry is a metallurgical engineer working for a farm machinery company. He designs new machinery and tools to make the farmer's job easier, and decides what types of metals would make those tools strong and long lasting. His current project is a combine that requires the smallest amount of physical effort from the farmer and has easily replaced parts.

For career information, write
The Metallurgical Society of AIME
420 Commonwealth Drive
Warrendale, PA 15086

a

b

FIGURE 7–2. Some simple machines, like the hammer in (a), increase the force applied to the resistance. The pulleys on the flagpole (b) make the task easier by changing the direction of the force. Neither machine increases the output work.

The work you do on the machine, *work*$_{in}$, is the product of the effort force, F_e, times the distance you move, d_e,

$$W_{in} = F_e \times d_e.$$

Energy is conserved. The machine cannot create energy. The best a machine can do is to convert all the energy put into it to useful energy out. That is, $W_{out} = W_{in}$. Such a device is called an ideal machine. For an ideal machine

$$\textit{Work done by machine} = \textit{Work put into machine}$$

$$W_{out} = W_{in}$$

$$F_r \times d_r = F_e \times d_e.$$

Therefore, if the effort force is less than the resistance force, the effort distance must be greater than the resistance distance. That is, you move the hammer farther than the hammer moves the nail.

Some machines only change the direction of the effort force. They have a *MA* equal to one. The effort and resistance distances are equal. A flagpole is an example. The ropes are arranged so that you pull down to make the flag go up.

Other machines are used to increase the distance an object is moved or its speed. These machines have a *MA* less than one. Rowing a boat is an example. The blade of the oar moves farther and faster than the handle. The effort distance moved by the oar handle is less than the resistance distance moved by the blade. Therefore, the effort force must be greater than the resistance force, and the *MA* is less than one.

INVESTIGATION 7–1

Pulleys

Problem: What is the mechanical advantage of a pulley system?

Materials

2-newton weight
meter stick
2 spring scales
3 pulleys
string or cord
extension clamp
ring stand

Procedure

1. Cut a piece of string 1.5 meters long. Run the string through a movable pulley.
2. Attach each end of the string to a different spring scale as in Figure 7–3a.
3. Attach the 2-newton weight to the pulley.
4. Raise the weight 20 centimeters. Record the force readings on the spring scale in a table. Record the distances the spring scales are moved.
5. Now set up the pulley as in Figure 7–3b. Attach the weight and lift it 20 centimeters again. Use the spring scale to record the force for this pulley system. Record the distance the spring scale moves.
6. Repeat Step 5 for Figure 7–3c and 7–3d. Record the force and distance.

Data and Observations

Pulley system	Force	Distance
7–3a	1.0 N, 1.0 N	0.2 m

Analysis

1. How does the number of supporting strings affect the force needed to lift the weight?
2. How much work is done to lift the weight with the pulley systems in 7–3a, b, c, and d?

Conclusions

3. How did the number of supporting strands affect the effort force?
4. What is the mechanical advantage of a pulley system?

FIGURE 7–3.

a b c d

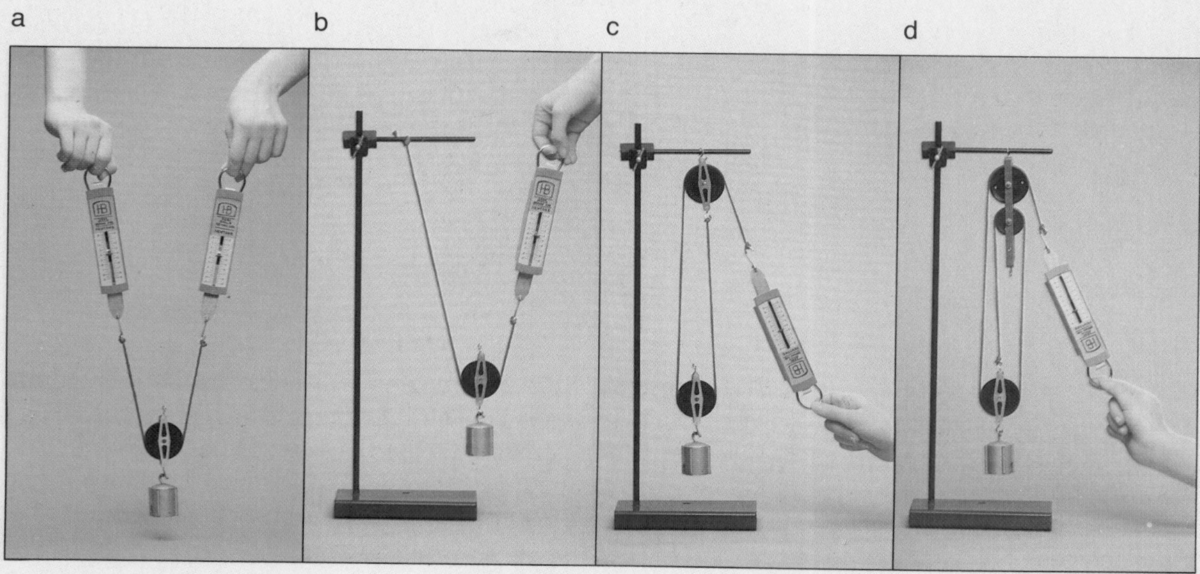

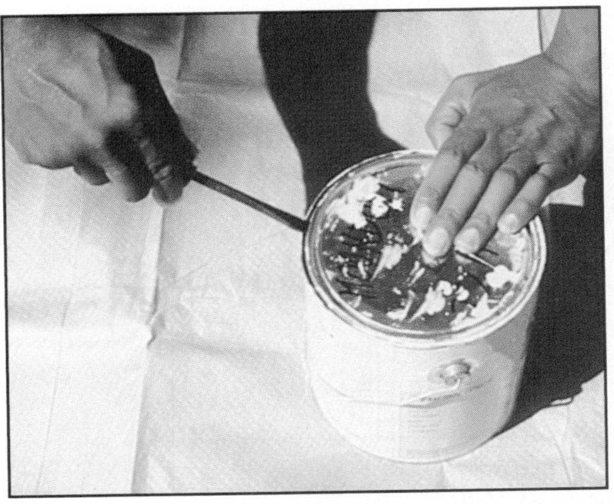

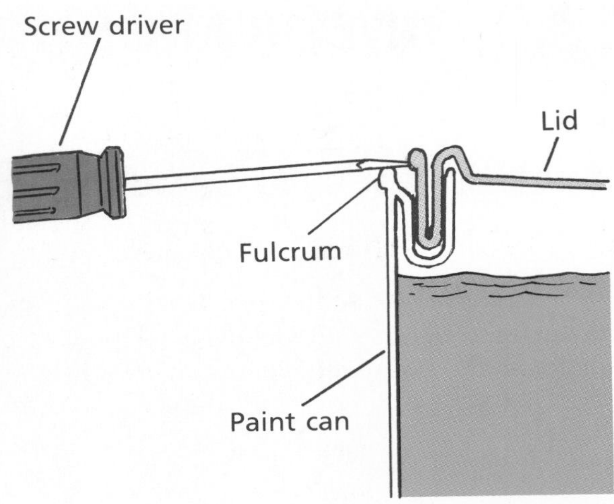

FIGURE 7–4. A screwdriver is used as a lever to pry the lid off of a paint can. The resistance force moves a smaller distance than the effort force: the *MA* is greater than one.

7:3 The Lever

What are the three parts of a lever?

A lever is one of the six simple machines. A **lever** is a bar that is free to pivot about a fixed point. The oar described before is a lever. The point at which a lever pivots is called the **fulcrum.** An effort force is applied to a lever on the **effort arm.** The **resistance arm** exerts the resistance force. In Figure 7–4, a screwdriver is used as a lever to open a can of paint. The fulcrum of the lever is the edge of the can. The screwdriver pivots on the edge of the can to pry up the lid. The effort force is applied to the handle of the screwdriver. The resistance force is the force the blade exerts on the can lid. This force is opposed by the frictional force between the lid and the can.

F.Y.I. The "Jaws of Life," used by fire departments and rescue squads to rescue people trapped in cars, are a form of lever.

The length of the effort arm (l_e) is the distance from the fulcrum to the place where the effort force is applied. The length of the resistance arm (l_r) is the distance from the fulcrum to the place where the resistance force acts. The distance the effort force is moved is proportional to the length of the effort arm. The same is true for the resistance force. For an ideal lever,

$$work_{in} = work_{out}$$
$$F_e \times d_e = F_r \times d_r$$
$$\text{and } F_e \times l_e = F_r \times l_r.$$

If the effort force is smaller than the resistance force, the effort arm must be longer than the resistance arm.

F.Y.I. Because the mechanical advantage of third class levers is less than one, they are used on many muscle developing machines.

Levers are often divided into three classes. The classes differ in the position of the fulcrum, effort force, and resistance force. Figure 7–5 shows an example of each class.

The mechanical advantage of an ideal lever can be calculated by using the lengths of the effort arm and the resistance arm.

How is the *MA* of a lever calculated?

$$MA = \frac{\text{effort arm length}}{\text{resistance arm length}} = \frac{l_e}{l_r}$$

EXAMPLE **Mechanical Advantage of a Lever**

A screwdriver is used to pry the lid off a paint can. The resistance arm is 0.50 cm long. The effort arm is 20 cm long. What is the mechanical advantage of the screwdriver?

Given: length of resistance arm

$l_r = 0.50$ cm

length of effort arm

$l_e = 20$ cm

Unknown: mechanical advantage *MA*

Basic Equation: $MA = l_e/l_r$

Solution: $MA = \frac{l_e}{l_r} = \frac{20 \text{ cm}}{0.50 \text{ cm}} = 40$

Describe the three classes of levers.

PRACTICE PROBLEMS

2. An oar used to row a boat has the handle 50 cm from the fulcrum and the blade 125 cm from the fulcrum. Find the mechanical advantage of the oar.
3. A claw hammer is used to pull out a nail. The resistance arm is 2.6 cm and the effort arm is 32 cm. Find the mechanical advantage of the hammer.

FIGURE 7–5. The three types of levers differ in the position of the fulcrum, effort force, and resistance force.

First class

R

F

E

Second class

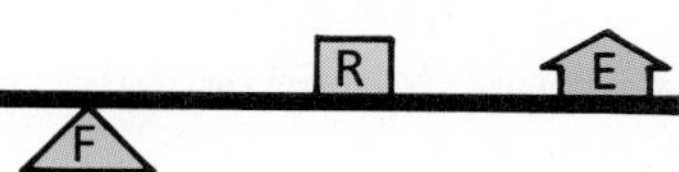

Third class

TECHNOLOGY: APPLICATIONS

The Flushing Machine

A toilet is a machine consisting of two main parts, a tank and a bowl. A discharge pipe removes water from the toilet and a water supply pipe returns water to the toilet.

When you push down the handle to flush a toilet several things happen. First, the handle lifts the flapper over the discharge pipe, opening the pipe. The opening allows rushing water to flow downward to the bowl and then exit through the drainpipe.

As the water level goes down, a float in the tank lowers, opening an inlet valve from the water supply pipe. Thus, clean water enters the tank and bowl. As the water level rises, so does the float. When the water reaches a certain level, the float causes the inlet valve to close. The water stops flowing until the next flush.

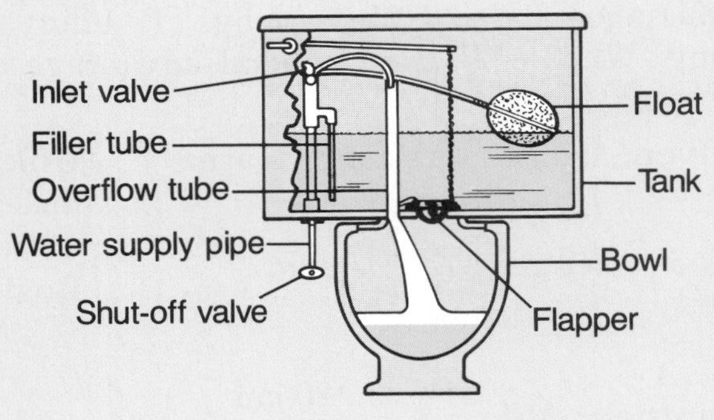

7:4 Pulleys

How is a pulley used to do work?

A pulley is another simple machine. It is easier to understand when you see that it acts like a lever. The pulley arrangement shown in Figure 7–6a is an example of a fixed pulley. It simply changes the direction of the effort force. The flagpole we talked about on page 146 is an example. A pulley at the top of the flagpole allows you to raise the flag while standing on the ground. The effort and resistance arms, the two ropes, are equal. Therefore the $MA = 1$.

A pulley can also be used to reduce the effort force needed. Figure 7–6b shows a movable pulley. For a movable pulley, the effort arm is equal to both of the ropes that support the resistance. Therefore, the effort arm is twice as long as the resistance arm. The $MA = 2$. Just as in the case of a lever, the distance the effort force must move is twice as far as the distance the resistance force moves. The rope must be pulled up twice as far as the weight rises.

Often a combination of fixed and movable pulleys is used. An arrangement of several pulleys, called a **block and tackle,** allows a person to lift heavy machinery. The mechanical advantage of an ideal block and tackle is equal to the number of ropes supporting the resistance weight.

FIGURE 7–6. Pulleys may be used to change the direction of a force or may reduce the effort force necessary to move an object. A pulley is really a form of lever.

a b

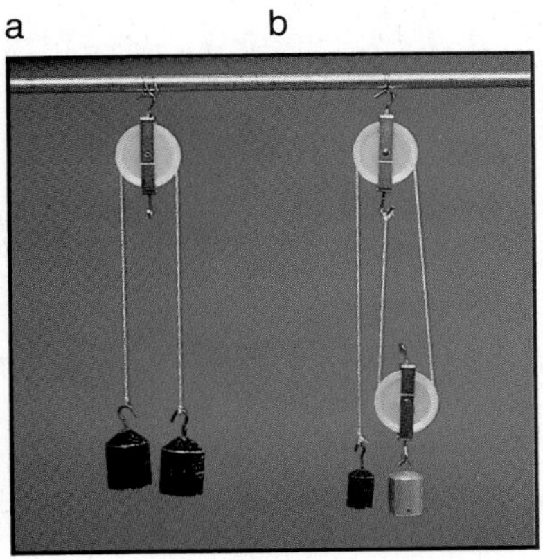

7:5 The Wheel and Axle

Bicycles, eggbeaters, and doorknobs all contain wheels and axles. A **wheel and axle** is a simple machine that consists of a large wheel fixed to a smaller wheel or shaft called the axle. The two rotate together. The radius of the wheel is larger than the radius of the axle.

Describe two examples of a wheel and axle.

A crank used to lift a bucket of water from a well is a wheel and axle. The effort force is applied by your hand on the crank handle. The resistance force is exerted on the rope around the axle.

F.Y.I. The radius is the distance from the center of the circle to the outside edge.

It is important that there is no slipping between the wheel and axle. To prevent slippage, the wheel or axle can have teeth cut into it. It is then called a gear. Two gears can touch each other, or a chain can be used to transfer the force from one gear to the next.

The wheel and axle can be considered a special type of lever. The effort arm is the radius of the wheel, and the resistance arm is the radius of the axle. The fulcrum is the center of the axle. The mechanical advantage of the wheel and the axle is equal to the radius of the wheel divided by the radius of the axle.

How is the *MA* of a wheel and axle calculated?

$$MA = \frac{\textit{radius of wheel}}{\textit{radius of axle}} = \frac{r_w}{r_a}$$

EXAMPLE **Mechanical Advantage of a Wheel and Axle**

What is the mechanical advantage of the wheel and axle in Figure 7–7b? The wheel has a radius of 40 cm. The axle has a radius of 5 cm.

a

b

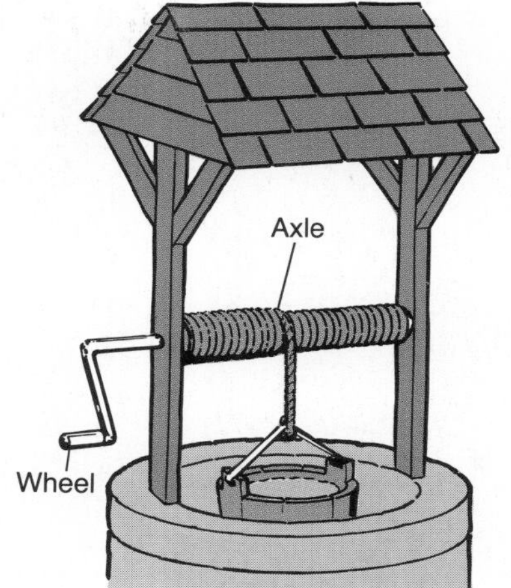

FIGURE 7–7. A number of gears, really combinations of wheels and axles, make up the works of this watch (a). To make drawing water from the well easier, the path of the handle, the wheel, has a large radius, and the axle has a small radius (b).

FIGURE 7–8. Moving up the inclined plane that forms this ramp requires less force, but not less work.

Given: radius of wheel
$r_w = 40$ cm
radius of axle
$r_a = 5$ cm

Unknown: mechanical advantage, *MA*

Basic equation:
$$MA = \frac{r_w}{r_a}$$

Solution: $MA = \frac{r_w}{r_a} = \frac{40 \text{ cm}}{5 \text{ cm}} = 8$

PRACTICE PROBLEM

4. A doorknob has a 45 mm radius. The radius of the axle is 5 mm. Find the *MA* of this machine.

7:6 Inclined Plane, Screw, and Wedge

What is an inclined plane?

Suppose a heavy refrigerator is delivered to a house. It would be very difficult to lift it up the steps. However, if a plank is placed with one end on the ground and the other on the top step, the refrigerator can be pushed up the plank with much less force. The plank is a simple machine called an inclined plane. An **inclined plane** is a slanted surface used to raise objects.

How is the *MA* of an inclined plane calculated?

The work done in raising the refrigerator is the same in both cases. When lifting it up the steps the force is large and the distance small. Pushing it up the plane requires less force, but it must be moved a larger distance. The mechanical advantage of an inclined plane is the ratio of the length of the plane to the height. That is, for an ideal inclined plane,

$$MA = \frac{length}{height} = \frac{l}{d}.$$

Under actual conditions, you must consider friction. It takes more force to push an object up the ramp because the force of friction must be overcome. Often wheels or rollers are used to reduce friction on inclined planes.

EXAMPLE Mechanical Advantage of an Inclined Plane

A refrigerator must be raised up steps that are 0.6 m high. You use a 3 m long plank. Find the mechanical advantage of the inclined plane.

Given: height $(d) = 0.6$ m
length $(l) = 3$ m

Unknown: *MA*

Basic Equation: $MA = \frac{l}{d}$

Solution: $MA = \frac{l}{d} = \frac{3 \text{ m}}{0.6 \text{ m}} = 5$

INVESTIGATION 7–2

The Inclined Plane

Problem: How does an inclined plane make a job easier?

Materials

roller skate
spring scale
smooth board at least 0.50 meters long
string
books
metric ruler

Procedure

1. Set up a stack of books as in Figure 7–9.
2. Measure the height of the stack in centimeters. Record this number in a table like the one shown.
3. Set up the inclined plane on the books. Measure the distance from the base of the plane to the stack of books as shown in Figure 7–9.
4. Tie a string to the skate. Use the spring scale to lift the skate the same height as the stack of books. Record in the table the force needed to lift the skate.
5. Use the scale to drag the skate slowly at constant speed up the inclined plane. Read the scale while the skate is moving uniformly and record the force.

Data and Observations

height of books	
length of plane	
force needed to lift the skate	
force needed to drag the skate	

Analysis

1. Does it take more or less force to move the skate using the inclined plane?
2. How much work is done in lifting the skate without the inclined plane?
3. How much work is done using the inclined plane?

Conclusions

4. Does it take more or less work to move the skate using the inclined plane?
5. How could the amount of input work be reduced?
6. What is the ideal mechanical advantage?
7. How does an inclined plane make a job easier?

FIGURE 7–9.

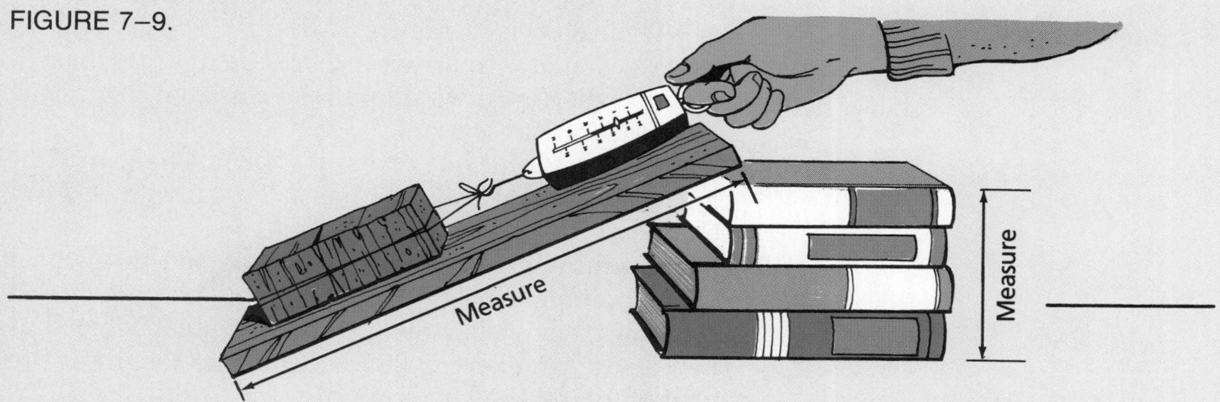

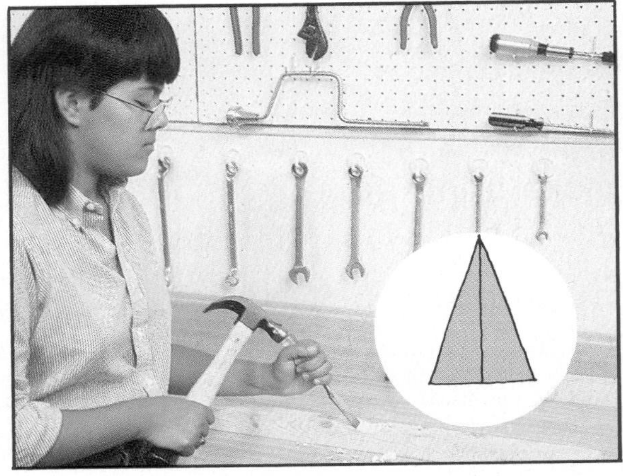

a

b

FIGURE 7–10. A wedge (a) is made of two inclined planes. A screw (b) is an inclined plane around a cylinder.

PRACTICE PROBLEM

5. A highway up a mountain rises 3000 m over a distance of 60 km (60 000 m). What is the mechanical advantage of the highway?

A **wedge** is an inclined plane with either one or two sloping sides. A knife blade is a wedge.

Wedges are found in many tools. A nail point is a wedge, as is the cutting edge of an ax or hatchet. Wood planes, chisels, saws, and many other cutting tools contain wedges.

A **screw** is an inclined plane wound around a cylinder. The thread is the spiral ridge that runs down a screw. Figure 7–10 shows several uses of screws.

Review

1. Explain how simple machines can make a job easier and still follow the law of conservation of energy.
2. List the effort force, fulcrum, and resistance force for each lever shown in Figure 7–5.
3. Suppose you use a scissors to cut heavy cardboard. Explain where you would put the cardboard in terms of the *MA* of the scissors.
4. The radius of a bicycle wheel is 34 cm. The gear that can be considered the axle has a 2.0 cm radius. Find the *MA*.

★ 5. Design an inclined plane to help a person in a wheel chair up steps that are 75 cm high. The person and chair together weigh 800 N. The greatest force that the person can exert is 200 N. Find the length of the inclined plane that is required.

USING MACHINES

GOALS

1. You will be able to identify the simple machines that make up a compound machine.
2. You will be able to calculate the efficiency of a machine.
3. You will be able to calculate the power required by a machine.

The bicycle is a complex machine. It is easy to see that it is made up of combinations of simple machines. Many complex machines are hard to understand until you see that they are made up of the simple machines you have studied.

7:7 Combining Simple Machines

Many machines you use consist of several simple machines. For example, a shovel combines a blade that is a wedge to cut into the soil with a lever to help lift it. A bicycle contains many wheels and axles. The brakes on a bicycle consist of several levers connected together. A **compound machine** is made by combining two or more simple machines.

How is a compound machine different from a simple machine?

Look at the bicycle shown in Figure 7–11. Between the pedals and the rear tire are two connected wheels and axles. You apply the effort force to the pedal. The resistance force is the force the tire exerts against the road. The pedal is a wheel, and the pedal sprocket, or gear, is its axle. A chain connects this sprocket to a sprocket in the rear wheel. The chain makes the wheel sprocket move the same distance as does the pedal sprocket. In the rear wheel another axle, the wheel sprocket, turns the much larger wheel. The overall mechanical advantage of the machine is the ratio of the force exerted by the tire to the force on the pedal.

FIGURE 7–11. By choosing different combinations of gears between the pedals and the wheels, the bike can be set to output greater force or greater speed.

F.Y.I. Narrow, hard bicycle tires make the ride bumpier, but they make the bicycle more efficient by reducing the energy needed to bend the rubber and to overcome friction.

In many bicycles you can change the sizes of one or both sprockets to vary the mechanical advantage. You would want a large mechanical advantage to multiply your effort when you climb a hill. On level ground you might want a mechanical advantage of one or less to give you greater speed. As a result of the conservation of energy, the distance you must move the pedals changes when the mechanical advantage is varied. With a high MA you have to move the pedals farther to get the same forward motion as when you have a lower MA.

7:8 Efficiency

Why is the work output of a machine less than the work input?

When you push a lever and make it move, you are putting work into a machine. When you pull a rope through a pulley, you are putting work into the machine. Work must be put into a machine if you want it to do any work for you. A machine can produce a larger force than you applied, but it can never do more work than you put into it. This is the law of conservation of energy.

All real machines contain moving parts that produce friction. Some of the input work acts against friction. It is changed into thermal energy as a result of the friction. Therefore, the useful work produced by real machines is less than the work put into them.

How is the efficiency of a machine calculated?

If, for example, you push a box up an inclined plane, some of the force you apply balances the force of friction. The remainder moves the box up the plane. Some of the input work is changed into thermal energy that warms the box and inclined plane. There is always some friction in your bicycle wheel. Thus, some of the energy you put into moving the pedal is changed into thermal energy that heats the wheel.

FIGURE 7–12. Oil is used to reduce the input work lost to friction and to increase the efficiency of a machine.

The ratio of work output to work input is called the **efficiency** of the machine. High efficiency means that much of the input work is changed to useful work by the machine. Low efficiency means much of the input work is changed into waste thermal energy. The machine does not do much useful work. Efficiency is calculated by dividing the work output by the work input. It is often expressed as a percent. The equation is

$$efficiency = \frac{W_{out}}{W_{in}} \times 100\% = \frac{F_r \times d_r}{F_e \times d_e} \times 100\%.$$

All machines have efficiencies less than 100%.

How can the efficiency of a machine be increased? Efficiency is increased by reducing friction. Sanding or waxing smooths a surface and reduces friction. Oil and grease are used in many machines to reduce friction. Bearings in bicycle wheels replace sliding with rolling friction and improve efficiency.

EXAMPLE Calculating Efficiency

A box weighing 210 N is pushed up an inclined plane that is 2.0 m long. A force of 140 newtons is required. If the box is lifted 1.0 m, calculate the efficiency of the inclined plane.

Given: $F_e = 140 \text{ N}$

$d_e = 2.0 \text{ m}$

$F_r = 210 \text{ N}$

$d_r = 1.0 \text{ m}$

Unknown: efficiency

Basic Equation:

$$efficiency = \frac{F_r \times d_r}{F_e \times d_e} \times 100\%$$

Solution:

$$efficiency = \frac{F_r \times d_r}{F_e \times d_e} \times 100\%$$

$$= \frac{210 \text{ N} \times 1.0 \text{ m}}{140 \text{ N} \times 2.0 \text{ m}} \times 100\% = 75\%$$

PRACTICE PROBLEM

6. You pull up a 75 N bucket using a fixed pulley. The rope does not stretch, so the effort and resistances are the same. However, you must exert a 80 N force because of friction. Find the efficiency.

BIOGRAPHY

Lillian Moller Gilbreth
(1878–1972)

As an industrial engineer and psychologist, Lillian Gilbreth developed many innovative ways to do jobs more efficiently. She showed workers how to gain more satisfaction from their jobs by using fewer steps, less time, and increasing quality. She also invented an electric mixer and other kitchen tools.

How can the efficiency of a machine be increased?

7:9 Power

Suppose two workers are pushing identical boxes up an inclined plane. One pushes a box up the plane in 20 seconds, the other in 40 seconds. Both do the same amount of work. They change the energy of the box by the same amount. The difference is in the time required to do the work. The two workers differ in the rate at which they do the work.

What is the unit used to express power?

How is power calculated?

The rate of doing work is called power. In science **power** is the amount of work done per unit of time. The worker who moved the box in 20 seconds used more power than the worker who took 40 seconds. Power is work done divided by the time required to do the work.

$$power = \frac{work}{time}; P = \frac{W}{t}$$

a

b

FIGURE 7–13. The motorized lawnmower (a), and the hand mower (b) do the same amount of work. Since the motorized mower takes less time, it produces more power.

The unit for power is the watt (W). One **watt** is one joule of work per second. This unit is named in honor of James Watt, the inventor of the steam engine. The watt is a very small unit of power, so power is often expressed in kilowatts. One **kilowatt** (kW) equals 1000 watts.

F.Y.I. 748 watts = 1 horsepower

EXAMPLE **Calculating Power**

A set of pulleys is used to lift a boat weighing 1980 N. The boat is lifted 2.0 m in 55 seconds. How much power is required?

Given: $F = 1980\text{ N}$, $d = 2.0\text{ m}$, $t = 55\text{ s}$

Unknown: Power (P)

Basic Equations: $P = \frac{W}{t}$; $W = F \times d$

Solution:

$$P = \frac{W}{t} = \frac{F \times d}{t}$$

$$= \frac{1980\text{ N} \times 2.0\text{ m}}{55\text{ s}}$$

$$= 72\text{ W}$$

PRACTICE PROBLEMS

7. An elevator weighing 26 000 N is lifted 41 m in 82 s. Find the power in kilowatts that the elevator motor must generate to do this job.

PROBLEM SOLVING

Complex Machine Project

Design a complex machine to perform some common activity, using at least four simple machines. Avoid using wedges or screws because of the amount of friction involved.

You should make a careful drawing of the machine, identifying each of the simple machines.

Calculate the mechanical advantage of each of the simple machines and the overall mechanical advantage of the complex machine.

8. A 880-N student is almost late for science class. He hurries up a flight of steps 3.0 m high. If he develops 1200 W of power, how much time does it take him?

9. A worker pushes a box up an inclined plane. He develops 75 W of power when he pushes the box over a distance of 3.0 m in 2.0 seconds. What force did he exert?

Review

6. Name the simple machines in each of these tools.

a. shovel
c. c-clamp
b. axe
d. can opener

7. A force of 32 N is needed to push a bicycle up a ramp. The bicycle weighs 96 N, the ramp is 2.4 m long and 0.60 m high. Find the efficiency of the ramp.

8. If the wheel bearings in your bicycle become filled with dirt, how will the efficiency of the bicycle be affected? Why?

9. What is the power of a small appliance motor that can do 4500 J of work in 25 seconds?

★ **10.** A 15-speed bicycle has three sprockets of different radii on the pedal axle. Consider the pedal to be the wheel and a sprocket to be the axle. Which sprocket would you choose when bicycling on a very rough, hilly path? Why?

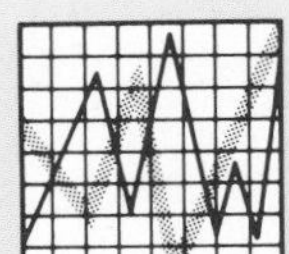

SKILL

Determining Constants and Variables

Problem: How do you choose the constants and variables for an investigation?

Background

A constant is a quantity that does not change throughout an investigation. A variable is a quantity that can have different values at different times. In an investigation there are two kinds of variables: independent variables, which the investigator changes, and dependent variables, which change because of changes in the independent variable. For example, suppose you are arranging a picnic and want to provide two soft drinks for every guest. In this situation, the number of soft drinks per guest is a constant. The number of guests is the independent variable, controlled by you; and the number of bottles of soft drink is the dependent variable, controlled by the number of guests. All investigations have independent and dependent variables, as well as constant factors.

Materials

ruler
pencil
coins

Procedure

1. Lay a ruler on a pencil, the fulcrum of the lever, so the ruler is balanced. Record the position of the pencil.
2. Place a coin on the 10-cm mark of the ruler.

FIGURE 7–14.

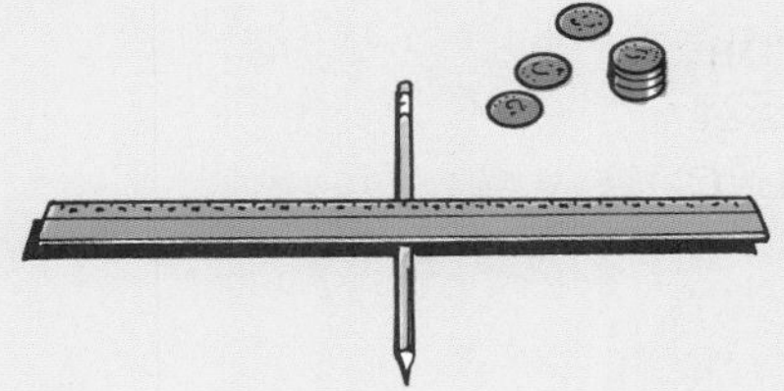

3. Place another coin on the opposite end of the ruler.
4. Move the second coin until the ruler is balanced again. Record the position of both coins.
5. Move the first coin to the 15-cm mark.
6. Move the coin on the opposite side until the ruler balances. Record the position of both coins.
7. Move the first coin to the 5-cm mark.
8. Repeat Step 6.

Data and Observations

Length of ruler ____________.
Position of pencil ____________.

Position of Coin 1	10 cm	15 cm	5 cm
Position of Coin 2			

Analysis and Conclusions

1. What effect did changing the position of the first coin have on the position of the second coin?
2. Could you predict the position of the second coin if you moved the first coin to the 20-cm mark?
3. If you moved both the fulcrum and the first coin, could you still predict the position of the second coin?
4. What are the constants in this activity?
5. What are the independent and dependent variables?

Applications

6. Design a similar activity with a different set of constants and different dependent and independent variables.

Chapter 7 Review

SUMMARY

1. Machines can change the amount, direction, or distance through which a force moves. 7:1
2. The six simple machines are the lever, pulley, wheel and axle, inclined plane, wedge, and screw. 7:1
3. The mechanical advantage of a machine is the number of times an applied force is multiplied by the machine. 7:2
4. A machine cannot increase energy. 7:2
5. A lever consists of an effort arm, fulcrum, and resistance arm. 7:3
6. The *MA* of a pulley is equal to the number of supporting strands. 7:4
7. The *MA* of a wheel and axle is equal to the ratio $\frac{r_w}{r_a}$. 7:5
8. A screw is an inclined plane wound around a cylinder. 7:6
9. A compound machine is made up of two or more simple machines. 7:7
10. Increasing the efficiency of a machine decreases the energy used to run it without changing the work the machine does. 7:8
11. Power is the amount of work done in a unit of time. 7:9

VOCABULARY

a. block and tackle
b. compound machine
c. efficiency
d. effort arm
e. effort force
f. fulcrum
g. inclined plane
h. kilowatt
i. lever
j. mechanical advantage
k. power
l. resistance arm
m. resistance force
n. screw
o. simple machine
p. watt
q. wedge
r. wheel and axle

Matching

Match each description with the correct vocabulary word from the list above. Some words will not be used.

1. rate at which work is done
2. ratio of resistance force to effort force
3. ratio of output work to input work of machine
4. the pivot point of a lever
5. a machine consisting of a bar pivoted about one point
6. the force you apply to a simple machine
7. the longer arm in a lever with *MA* greater than one
8. the unit to measure power
9. a bicycle is an example of this type of machine
10. a device consisting of several pulleys

Chapter 7 Review

MAIN IDEAS

A. Reviewing Concepts

Choose the word or phrase that correctly completes each of the following sentences.

1. The following is an example of a simple machine (*gasoline engine, bicycle, sewing machine, lever*).
2. The work output for a given input for a highly-efficient machine is (*high, low, constant, zero*).
3. Machines can change the (*magnitude and direction, magnitude and amount, direction and energy, magnitude and output*) of a force.
4. A doorknob is an example of a (*pulley, lever, wheel and axle*).
5. The point around which a lever rotates is the (*resistance arm, effort arm, fulcrum, mechanical advantage*).

Complete each of the following sentences with the correct word or phrase.

6. The effort arm of a lever is 4 m long and the resistance arm is 1 m long. The mechanical advantage of the lever is ____________.
7. Reducing friction increases the ____________ of a machine.
8. The mechanical advantage of a pulley system is equal to the number of ________________.
9. Friction changes the useful work of a machine to ____________.
10. A screw and wedge are forms of a(n) ____________.

Determine whether each of the following sentences is true or false. If the statement is false, change the underlined word(s) to make the sentence correct.

11. A <u>compound</u> machine is composed of more than one simple machine.
12. The watt is a unit of <u>energy</u>.
13. The mechanical advantage of a machine is <u>always</u> greater than one.
14. If you do 1000 J of work in less time than your friend does the same amount of work, then your power output was <u>less</u> than his.
15. One kilowatt is equal to <u>1000</u> watts.

B. Understanding Concepts

Answer the following questions, using complete sentences when possible.

16. In what ways are a lever, wheel and axle, and pulley alike?
17. A machine was 80% efficient. A repair person lubricated it and found that it was now 85% efficient. If the input work did not change, did the output work increase, decrease, or not change as a result of the lubrication?
18. After riding your bicycle, you feel the front axle and find that it has become warm. Why is it warm, and what should you do?
19. A wheel and axle are used to lift a bucket. When the bucket is halfway up, the rope has filled the entire axle. The rope now winds on top of the other turns of rope. Would you expect the force you exert to increase, decrease or remain the same? Why?
20. A claw hammer has a mechanical advantage (*MA*) equal to 12. It is used to pull a nail that exerts a force of 3000 N. What effort force is needed to pull the nail?
21. A movable pulley is used to lift an unknown weight. When you pull on the rope, holding the weight steady, you exert a force of 50 N. How heavy is the weight?
22. You need a ramp to bring a cart filled with books up three steps into your school. The janitor finds one ramp 3 m

long and a second 2 m long. Which should you use? Why?

23. The family car runs out of gas. You have to push it up the driveway into a service station. The ramp is 4 m long and rises 0.10 m. The car weighs 9000 N. You push with a force of 300 N. How efficient is the ramp.
24. When you pushed the car in Question 23 up the ramp, you exerted a force of 300 N over a distance of 4 m. It took you 9 seconds. What power did you produce?
25. Your television set uses electrical energy at a rate of 180 W. How many joules of energy are used if the set is on 4 hours?

C. Applying Concepts

Answer the following questions using complete sentences when possible.

26. An inventor claims to have built a machine that can produce 120 J of work with an input of 110 J. Would you believe the inventor's claim? Why or why not?
27. Tin snips, designed for cutting metal, have long handles and short blades. Shears built for cutting paper have short handles and long blades. Why?
28. A crowbar has a resistance arm 5 cm long and an effort arm 75 cm long. What effort force would be needed to lift a rock that weighs 3000 N?
29. A 500-watt gasoline engine and a 250-watt electric motor both do 15 joules of work. Which machine can do the work faster? Why?
30. A sledge hammer is used to break up concrete. Concrete is broken up by giving the head a large amount of kinetic energy. Explain why the hammer has a long handle and a heavy, metal head.

SKILL REVIEW

1. How many variables should there be in an investigation?
2. When you did the skill in this chapter, what kind of factor was the position of the fulcrum?
3. Is it possible for a factor to be a variable in one investigation and a constant in another? Explain, using the skill in this chapter as an example.
4. If you divided 9.7 g by 3.2 cm^3 on a calculator, what answer should you report?
5. In an investigation, would your observations of the dependent variable probably be causes or effects?

PROJECTS

1. Make a mobile to hang in class. Each arm can be considered a lever. Weigh the objects hanging from the ends of each arm. Measure the lengths of the arms. The ratio of the weights, F_r/F_e, should equal the ratio of the lengths, l_e/l_r.
2. Visit a machine shop. Report the types of simple machines you see. Measure the lengths of the arms of any levers you find and calculate the *MA*.

READINGS

1. Bains, Rae. *Simple Machines.* Mahwah, N.J.: Troll Associates, 1985.
2. Gardner, Martin. "Perpetual Motion: The Quest for Machines That Power Themselves." *Science Digest.* October, 1985, pp. 68–72.
3. Major, J. Kenneth. *Animal-Powered Machines.* Cincinnati: Seven Hills Books, 1985.

SCIENCE AND SOCIETY

COGENERATION

Heat engines are very important in today's society, but they convert less than half the energy produced from burning fuel into mechanical or electrical energy. Only 12% of the energy stored in gasoline ends up as kinetic energy of an automobile, and only 40% of the energy stored in coal generates electricity in a coal-burning power plant. The rest of the thermal energy is given off as waste.

One way to use this thermal energy more efficiently is through cogeneration. What is cogeneration? As the prefix *co* suggests, cogeneration is two things happening at once. Usually it involves the burning of fuels to produce steam in a turbine. The steam is then used to produce electricity and to warm buildings.

Background

In order for part of the steam to be used to warm buildings, it must be withdrawn from the steam turbine at a higher temperature and pressure than if only electricity is being produced. This early withdrawal results in a loss of efficiency in the electrical generating system. However, this loss is overcome by the gain in net usable thermal energy from the steam used for heating. The overall efficiency of the cogeneration system is greater than the sum of the two energy systems working separately.

The following example will help to illustrate the added efficiency of a cogeneration system. An electrical power plant operates at approximately 40% efficiency. A steam boiler operates at approximately 80% efficiency. A cogeneration system is about 70% efficient. Let us compare the amount of input energy required to produce the same amount of usable output energy in all three systems. Suppose, in an industrial cogeneration system, 100 kilojoules (kJ) of energy from burning fuels produced 25 kJ of electricity and 45 kJ of usable thermal energy in the steam. There is a loss of 30 kJ as waste heat. A coal-burning power plant would need 62.5 kJ of input energy to produce 25 kJ of electricity. A steam boiler would need 56.25 kJ of input energy to produce 45 kJ of usable thermal energy. Separate generation requires 18.75 kJ more input energy to get the same output as the cogeneration system. The energy savings is almost 16%.

FIGURE 1. The photograph shows a family-sized cogeneration plant, no larger than a telephone booth.

Case Studies

1. Many users have benefited from cogenerated power. The Scott Paper Co. and 69 others have signed contracts to sell 370 megawatts of cogenerated electricity to Central Maine Power. Increased cogeneration in Maine eventually could be responsible for 20% of the electricity there. Cogeneration now accounts for 6% of the electricity throughout the United States.

2. Many industrial users who install a cogeneration system find they produce more electricity than they use themselves. A 1978 federal law told local power companies that they had to buy power from independent producers if it was channeled back into the power grid.

3. In 1985 cogeneration produced about 3% of California's power. One power company complained that the higher prices it had to pay for the cogenerated power were unfair. It said it had paid $261 million dollars more in 1981 for alternatively generated power than it would have spent to produce the power on its own.

FIGURE 2. Cogeneration wastes 28% less energy than separate generation of steam and electricity.

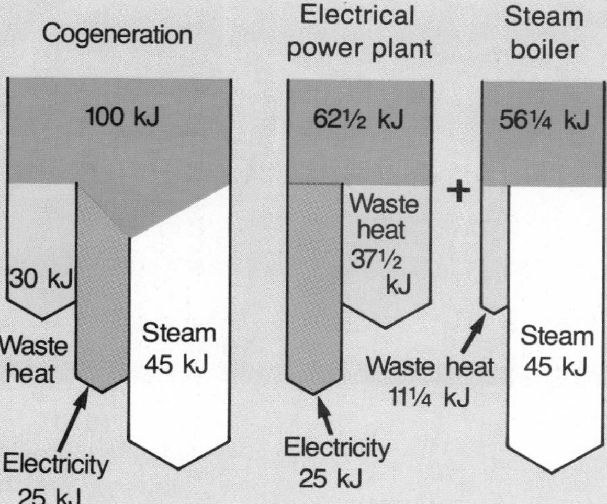

4. A $175,000 cogeneration system provides 50% of the electricity and 80% of the thermal energy used by the Holiday Inn at LaGuardia Airport in New York City. Saving $90,000 per year, the system has paid for itself in only two years.

5. Cogeneration systems also are available for individual homes. For about $10,000, families can buy systems that generate up to 10.5 kilowatts of electrical power and enough heat for 3000 gallons of hot water each day.

Developing a Viewpoint

1. Suppose you are the president of a utility company that was told by the federal government that you had to buy power generated by private companies. The price set for this power is higher than the cost at which you can produce it yourself. Prepare a defense for the regulatory commission to get the rates that you have to pay for the power reduced.

2. Brainstorm with the class to make a list of possible uses for cogeneration systems. Think of places where these independent systems would be useful.

Suggested Readings

Clifford, Mark. "Charged Up Down East." *Forbes, 136*. July 29, 1985, pp. 82 and 85.

Freundlich, J. "Baby Cogenerators." *Popular Science*. October, 1986, p. 51.

Jones, Stephen. "A Short Circuit for Cogeneration." *Business Week*. August 25, 1986, p. 90D.

Myers, Richard J. "A Dimmer Future for Cogeneration." *Fortune*. October 14, 1985, p. 29.

Ross, Joan and Marc Ross. "Some Energy Problems and Solutions." *Physics Teacher*. August, 1978, p. 272.

UNIT 3

Matter—what it is, how it is put together, how its forms change—has intrigued people since the beginning of time. Discoveries of scientists all over the world have led to our present understanding of matter. Some of their discoveries have been recognized and honored on stamps.

1610
Galileo discovers moons of Jupiter.

1620
Mayflower lands at Plymouth.

1670
Newton states the laws of motion.

THE NATURE OF MATTER

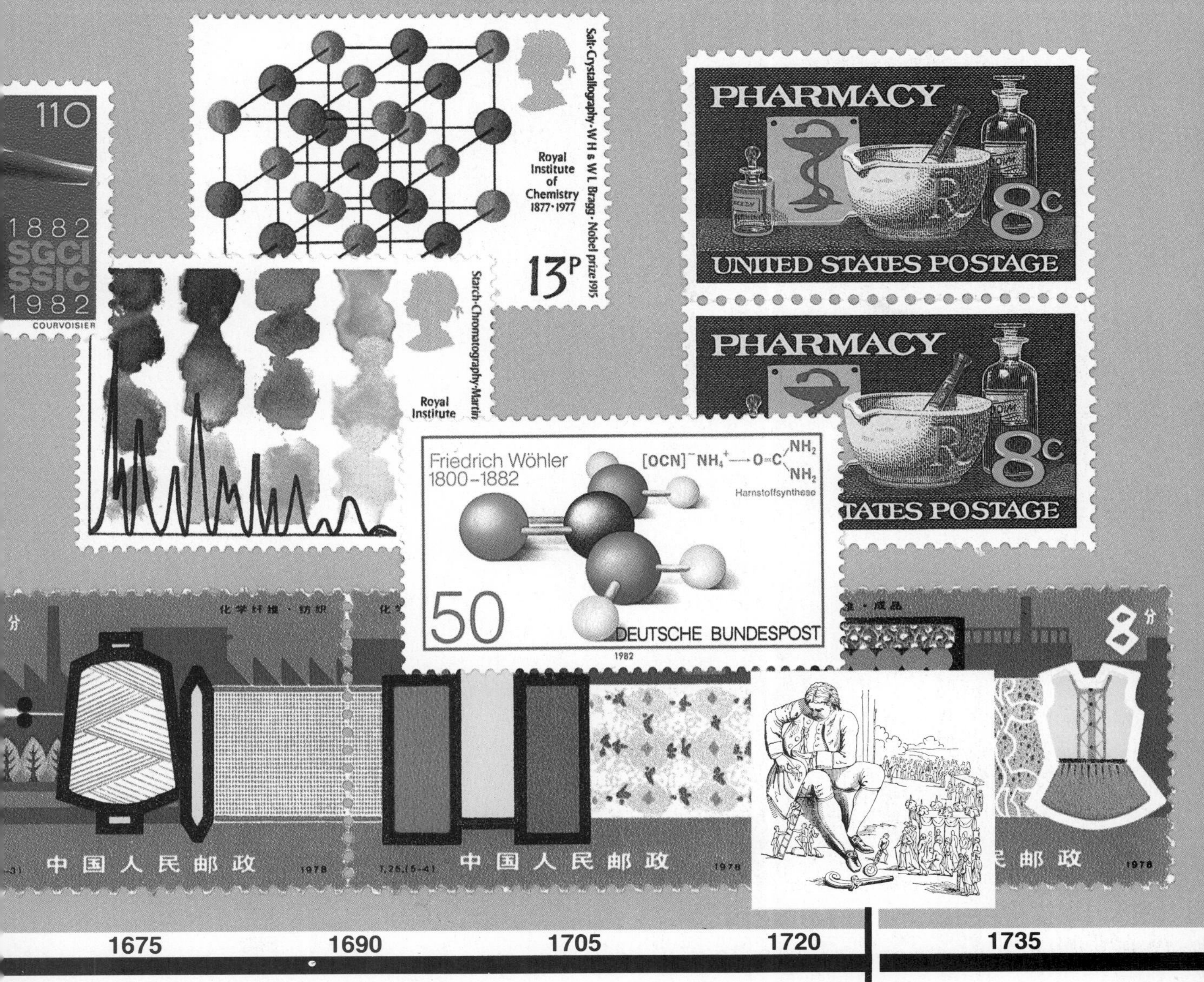

1683
William Penn signs peace treaty with North American Indians.

1726
Jonathan Swift writes *Gulliver's Travels.*

1738
Bernoulli publishes his principle.

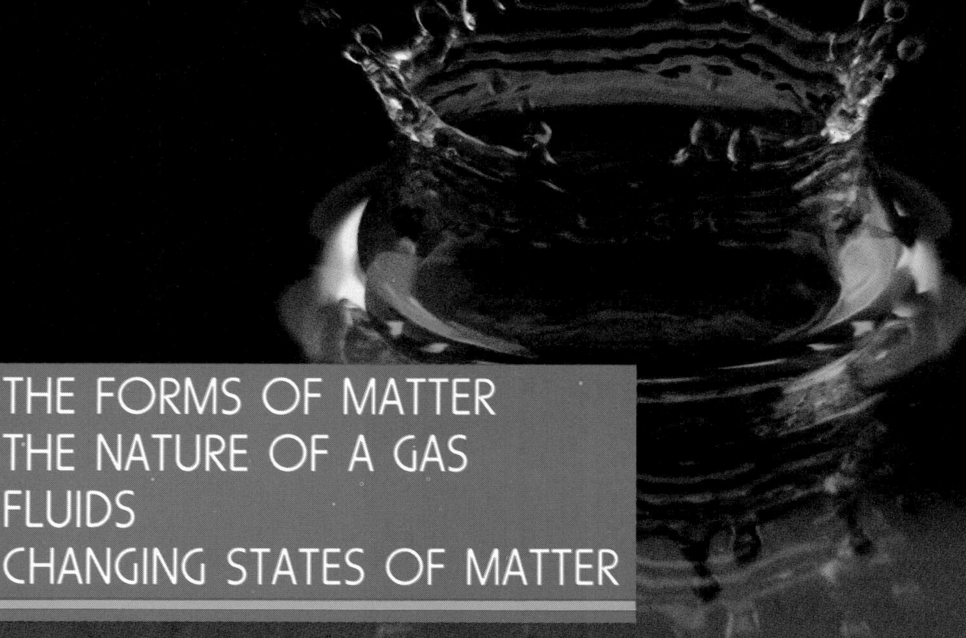

THE FORMS OF MATTER
THE NATURE OF A GAS
FLUIDS
CHANGING STATES OF MATTER

Solids, Liquids, and Gases

Look around. Everything around you is matter. You are matter. What is matter? Matter has mass and takes up space. Mass has the property of inertia. Matter resists changes in motion. It takes a force to accelerate matter. Mass also takes up space; two pieces of matter cannot occupy the same space at the same time.

You already know these properties of matter. But do you know how ice melts or why an airplane flies? Both depend on other characteristics of matter that we will talk about in this chapter.

THE FORMS OF MATTER

You are familiar with the three different forms or states of water: solid ice, liquid water, and gaseous steam. No doubt you have also heard that all forms of water are made up of the same material, "H_2O." How can one material take so many forms? How do scientists explain the different properties of solid ice, liquid water, and gaseous steam?

GOALS

1. You will learn the properties of the four states of matter.
2. You will learn how the kinetic theory explains the properties of solids, liquids, and gases.

8:1 The States of Matter

Ice and water are obviously different. One is rigid, the other is not. Yet, if you let a piece of ice sit on your desk, it quickly becomes water. Ice and water are two different forms, or states, of matter. There are three ordinary states of matter: solid, liquid, and gas. There is also a fourth state of matter, the plasma state. It exists only at extremely high temperatures, such as those found on the sun. **Plasma** consists of high energy, electrically charged particles. You create a plasma inside a fluorescent lamp, whenever you turn it on.

Name the four states of matter.

F.Y.I. Most of the matter in the universe is in the form of plasma.

a

b

c

FIGURE 8–1. A solid keeps its shape over time and has a definite volume (a). A liquid flows, takes the shape of its container, and has a definite volume (b). A gas fills the space in which it is placed (c).

Give some properties of solids.

Give some properties of liquids.

Give some properties of gases.

Solids have definite volume and shape. A stone is in the solid state. **Liquids** also have a definite volume, but no definite shape. Liquids take on the shape of their container. Suppose a liter of water in a bottle is poured into a pitcher. The water will take the shape of the pitcher, but will still measure a liter. A **gas** does not have a definite shape or volume. It fills whatever space it is placed in. If you fill a balloon with air, you can change the shape of the balloon by squeezing it. If you press the balloon down at one place, it will pop out somewhere else. If you press the whole balloon at one time, you can squeeze it into a smaller volume. Plasmas also act like gases—they do not have a definite shape or volume.

The state of matter depends on its temperature. At cold enough temperatures, almost all materials become solids. As they warm they can form liquids. At still higher temperatures they can become gases. At very high temperatures they may become plasmas. The change of state changes some of the properties of materials, but does not change others.

F.Y.I. Have you ever played with Silly Putty? No matter what shape you give the material, within a few minutes it will flow and take the shape of its container. The viscosity of this liquid is not constant but changes with time.

8:2 The Kinetic Theory of Matter

State the kinetic theory.

How can the properties of the states of matter be explained? In the middle of the nineteenth century scientists developed a theory to explain the properties of solids, liquids, and gases. According to the **kinetic theory** of matter, all matter is made of tiny particles. The particles are in constant motion. The higher the temperature, the faster the motion. The motion and spacing of these particles determines the state of the matter.

Describe a solid in terms of particle spacing and motion.

The particles of a solid are packed very close together. Forces between the particles hold them in a fixed

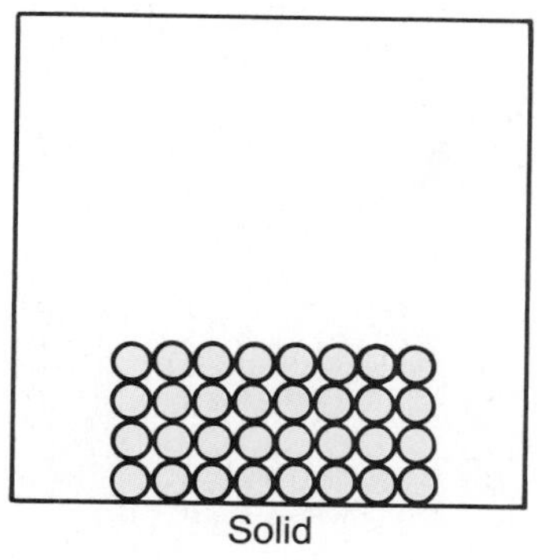

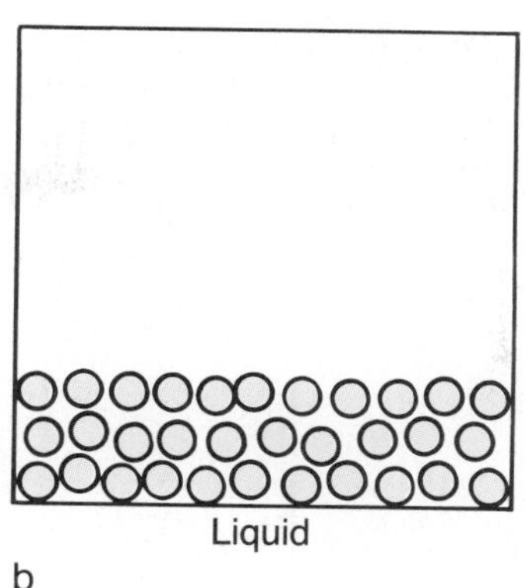

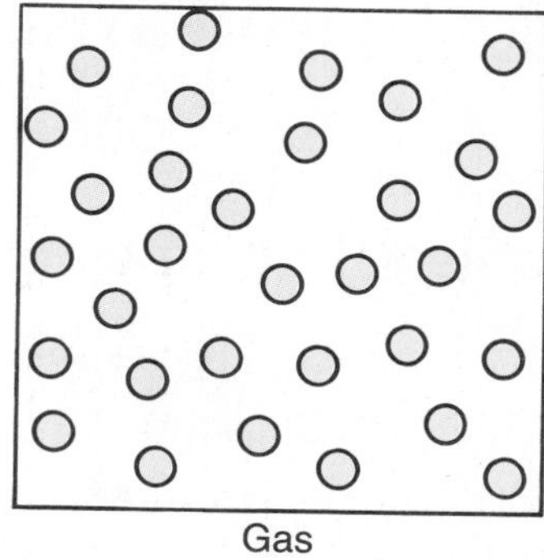

FIGURE 8–2. The particles of a solid are packed closely and held in a definite pattern (a). The particles of a liquid are very close but move freely and have no definite pattern (b). The particles of a gas move freely and are far from one another (c).

arrangement. In solids, particles move back and forth, but do not change positions. Most solids form crystals. In **crystals,** the particles are arranged in repeating patterns. Salt, sugar, and diamonds are examples of crystals. A beautiful form of a crystal is a snowflake or frost. When you break a crystal, a flat surface is left.

Other materials appear to be solids, but the arrangement of the particles is less regular. They do not form repeating patterns. Sometimes these materials are called amorphous solids. Other times they are considered to be very thick liquids. Glass, butter, and candle wax are examples. Broken glass has curved surfaces, not flat surfaces.

Describe a liquid in terms of particle spacing and motion.

The particles of a liquid are also very close to one another. Thus, liquids have about the same volume as solids. However, particles in a liquid have enough energy so that the forces between them cannot hold them in fixed positions. The particles are free enough to slip past each other. Some liquids, such as water, flow easily. Others, such as syrup, pour more slowly. Tar hardly pours at all. The property of a liquid that describes how it pours is called its **viscosity.** Tar is a liquid with a very high viscosity.

Describe a gas in terms of particle spacing and motion.

The particles in a gas have so much energy that the forces between them can be ignored. As a result the particles move in straight lines, flying all over the container. A gas is mostly empty space. You can demonstrate this by opening a container of perfume in one corner of a room. In a few minutes, you will be able to detect the smell of it all over the room. If air were not mostly empty space, the particles of perfume could not have so easily moved through it. The particles of a gas change direction only when they strike the walls of their containers or other particles.

FIGURE 8–3. Some materials, such as glass, paraffin, and hard candy, appear solid but are really very viscous liquids.

INVESTIGATION 8–1

All About Air

Problem: How does air behave?

Materials 

empty "pop-top" soda can
water in large dish or beaker
hot plate
heat-proof glove or tongs
plastic bag
several books
sheets of paper
string
2 apples
goggles

Procedure

A. Air Pressure

1. Pour water to a depth of about 1 cm in an empty soda can.
2. Place can on hot plate, heating until water boils for several minutes.
3. Wearing a glove or using tongs, remove can from hot plate. Turn it over and immediately put top of can just under the surface of the water in the dish. Record all of your observations.

B. Pascal's Principle

4. Gather up the open end of the plastic bag and practice inflating the bag.
5. Lay the bag on a table with the open end over the edge. Place a stack of books on top of the bag.
6. Blow into the bag. Record all of your observations.

C. Bernoulli's Principle

7. Place two books 10 cm apart on a table. Place a piece of paper over the gap and blow into the gap. Record all of your observations.
8. Hang two apples from strings. They should be about 5 cm apart. Blow between them. Record all of your observations.

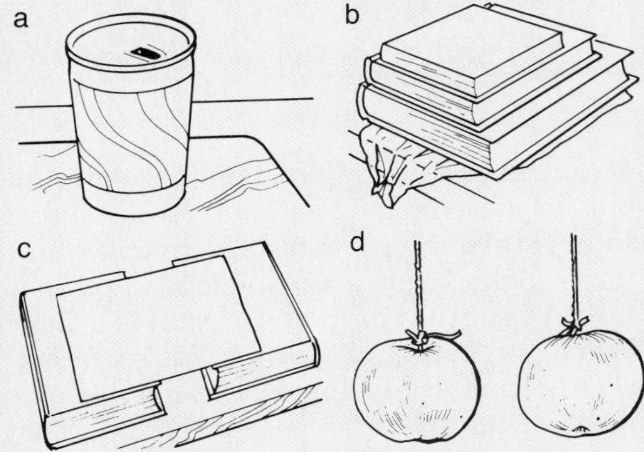

FIGURE 8–4.

Data and Observations

1. Describe what happened in the can experiment. Include as many observations as you can, but do not try to *explain* what happened.
2. Describe what happened, when you blew into the bag. Include in your observations how hard you had to blow.
3. Describe what happened both when you blew in the gap between the books and in the gap between the apples.

Analysis and Conclusions

1. When you boiled water in the can, the water turned to steam. The water cooled the can, but could not be pulled in through the narrow mouth of the can quickly. Use these two facts to explain why the can behaved as it did.
2. The force that lifted the books was about 20 N. Find the area of the books. Compute the pressure lifting the books. Compare that to atmospheric pressure (about 100 kPa).
3. Explain why the paper and the apples moved in the direction they did.

8:3 Thermal Expansion

Have you ever been in a crowd of people? If people stand very still they can pack tightly together. If they get excited and move around, they take up more room and the crowd expands. The same thing happens to almost all matter.

When you add heat or do work on matter, its thermal energy increases. The kinetic and potential energy of its particles increase. As a result of the increase in kinetic energy, the particles move faster and collide with other particles more violently. Thus, the particles move farther apart, and the volume of the material increases. The increase in volume of matter as the temperature goes up is called **thermal expansion.**

FIGURE 8–5. When the weather is cold, the gap between the bridge and the roadbed is wide. On warm days, the metal of the bridge expands and the gap is narrow.

Bridges are built with a space between the bridge and the roadbed, as shown in Figure 8–5. This space allows for the thermal expansion of the bridge at high temperatures. In winter the space is wide. On hot summer days, however, the space is narrow.

Why do most substances expand when they are warmed?

Materials expand at different rates. A strip of metal can be made of brass and iron bonded together, Figure 8–6. This piece, called a bimetallic strip, will bend when heated. The strip bends toward the iron because brass expands faster than iron. Bimetallic strips are used in house thermostats to control furnaces and air conditioners.

Liquids expand and contract in the same way solids do. For example, consider a gasoline can filled to the top

FIGURE 8–6. The iron side of a bimetallic strip is shown in (a). The strip bends toward the iron when heated (b).

a

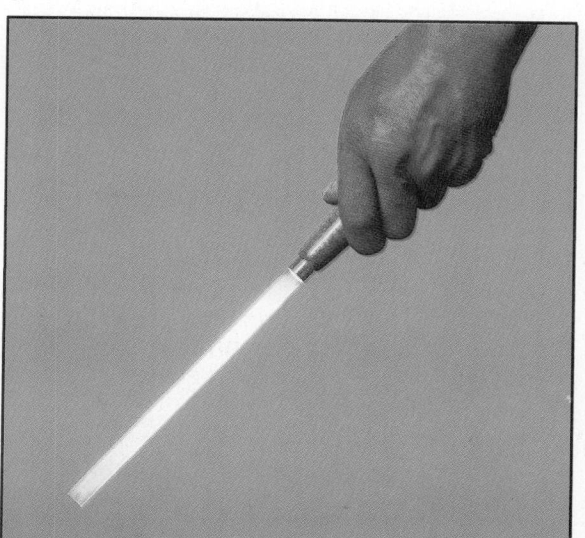

b

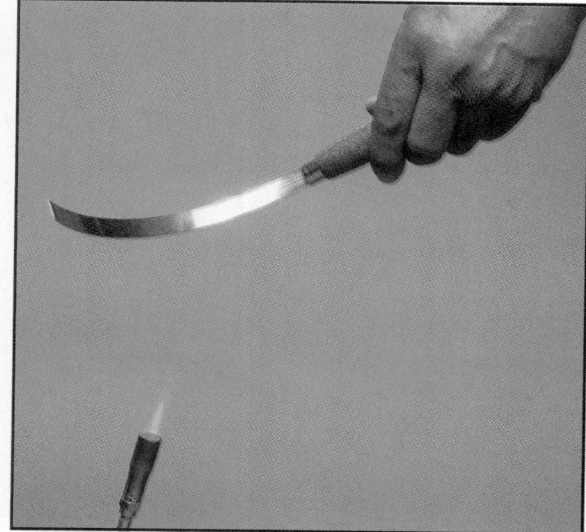

during the heat of the day. During the night, the temperature drops. In early morning, the gasoline no longer fills the can to the top.

Gases expand and contract, but much more than do either solids or liquids. The fact that cold air expands and becomes less dense when heated is one of the main causes of weather on Earth.

Review

1. a. List the three ordinary states of matter.
   b. Give three examples of matter in the three ordinary states.
   c. Describe the fourth state of matter.
2. a. Give three examples of crystals that you can easily see.
   b. Name three solid-like materials that do not form crystals.
3. State the kinetic theory.

CAREER

Hydraulic Engineer

Matthew Scott liked working with formulas, measurements, statistics, and graphs. He found his physical science classes in high school to be especially fun when he learned about power sources, did soil testing, or experimented with fluid dynamics.

Matthew remembers his favorite project was the designing of a dam that crossed the creek in the land lab at his school. He had to study the creek to determine how drainage and water supplies would be affected. He had to analyze the stress on the dam from storms as well as from normal water pressure.

Today Matthew works as a civil hydraulic engineer in Texas. His main duty is to plan and design the construction of new bridges.

For career information, write
American Society of Civil Engineers
345 E. 47th Street
New York, NY 10017

4. a. If you melt paraffin wax, the melted wax takes up only a little more space than did the solid wax. How would you use the kinetic theory to explain this observation?
   b. Explain why an object expands as the temperature increases.

★ 5. People have found that very old glass windows have sagged. They are thicker at the bottom than at the top. How do you explain this?

THE NATURE OF A GAS

Air, as well as most other gases, is hardly noticeable. Unpolluted air cannot be seen, tasted, or smelled. Unless there is a wind, you hardly feel it. It is only when you squeeze air into a balloon or tire, that you realize the air has a springiness. You recognize that air pushes back. In this section, you will learn how that springiness depends on other properties of a gas.

GOALS

1. You will understand that a gas exerts a pressure and what pressure is.
2. You will learn the effect on the pressure of a gas due to a change in its volume.
3. You will learn the effect on the volume of a gas due to a change in its temperature.

8:4 Pressure

If you squeeze a balloon filled with gas, the gas will exert an outward force. The amount of force depends on the size of the surface of the balloon. Gases exert forces on everything. For example, air exerts a force on the top of your desk. The larger the desk, the more the force. The total force depends on the size of the surface. The amount of force per unit area is called **pressure.** The pressure on your desk is the same everywhere on its surface. Pressure does not depend on the size of the surface it presses on. The pressure is the total force divided by the area of the surface. That is,

How is pressure calculated?

$$P = F/A.$$

Air pressure at sea level is 101 300 newtons per square meter. The SI unit for pressure is one newton per square meter. It is called a **pascal** (Pa).

What is the SI unit for pressure?

Why does a gas exert pressure? According to the kinetic theory, the particles of a gas are in constant motion. As they move about, they strike the surfaces of their container. Every time they hit the surface and bounce off again, they exert a tiny force. The combined effect of a very large number of particles constantly bouncing off the surface causes the pressure of the gas.

What causes pressure?

FIGURE 8–7. The particles in a gas exert pressure by colliding with the walls of the container.

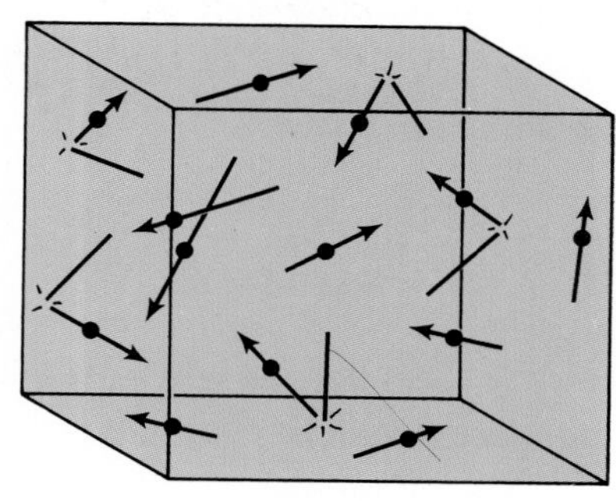

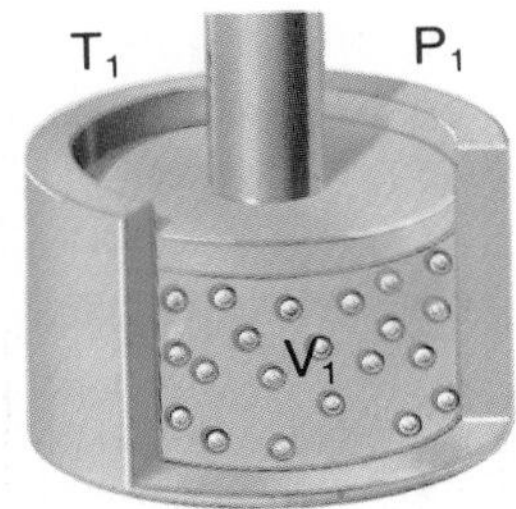

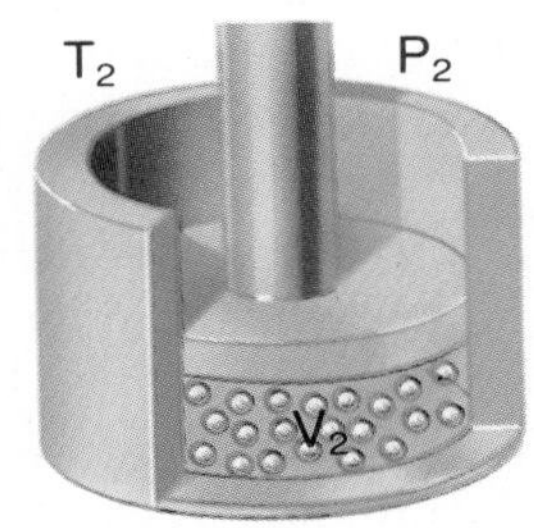

FIGURE 8–8. As the volume of a fixed amount of gas is decreased, the particles hit the sides of the container more often, and the pressure increases.

8:5 Boyle's Law

What are the factors that affect the pressure of a gas? Consider the air in a bicycle tire. If you measure the air pressure in your tire and find it too low, you might stop at a service station. At the station you pump more air into the tire. The pressure increases. Thus the more gas there is in a container, the higher the pressure. According to the kinetic theory, the more particles there are in the container, the more collisions there are with the surface and, the greater the pressure.

State Boyle's law.

Another relationship was discovered by Robert Boyle, an English scientist, in 1662. **Boyle's law** states that *if a sample of gas is kept at constant temperature, decreasing the volume will increase the pressure the gas exerts.* If you increase the volume, the pressure will decrease.

According to the kinetic theory, if you do not change the amount of gas or its temperature, the number of particles and their speeds remain the same. If you decrease the size of the container, the particles will strike the walls more often. Thus the pressure will rise. If you make the container larger, the particles will spend more time traveling from one side to the other. They will hit the walls less often, and the pressure will be smaller.

8:6 Charles' Law

State Charles' law.

About 100 years after Boyle's discovery, two French scientists, Jacques-Alexandre Charles and Joseph Gay-Lussac, discovered a relationship between the volume of a gas and its temperature. According to **Charles' law,** *if a sample of gas is kept at constant pressure, the volume increases if the temperature increases.* Charles' measurements suggested that the volume of a gas would become zero at a temperature of –273°C. The temperature –273°C is called absolute zero. It is also zero on the Kelvin scale. It is important to remember that Boyle's and

F.Y.I. Review the Kelvin temperature scale, Section 2:8.

a

b

FIGURE 8–9. The volume of air in the balloon expands as it is moved from an ice-water bath (a) to a hot-water bath (b).

Charles' laws apply only to gases. Scientists have found that all gases become liquids or solids before they are cooled to this temperature. Nevertheless, they have been able to cool objects to within one one-hundred thousandths of a kelvin (0.00001 K). They are trying to reach still lower temperatures.

The kinetic theory explains Charles' law. The temperature of a gas increases when energy is added to the gas. The kinetic energy of the particles is increased. The particles move faster and strike the walls of the container more often. If the walls are flexible, the gas pushes them out. Thus the volume increases.

List the four factors needed to describe a gas.

As you have seen, four factors are needed to describe a gas, the amount of mass, the volume, the pressure, and the temperature. The changes in these factors are related by Boyle's and Charles' laws and are explained by the kinetic theory.

Review

6. Why do we call the relationships found by Boyle and Charles "laws" but speak of the kinetic theory?

7. a. What happens to a gas if the pressure is decreased and the temperature remains the same?
   b. What happens to the pressure in a tire if the temperature increases?

8. a. In theory, what would happen to a gas at absolute zero?
   b. Why would this not actually happen?

SKILL

Asking the Right Question

Problem: How do you ask the right questions about observations?

Background

Scientists are continually concerned with explaining what they observe in the physical world. What processes do they use to help them arrive at explanations? Often they start by critically observing a phenomenon. Then they review their observations and formulate a group of probing questions. These questions need to be answered before any explanation will be acceptable. Often the questions asked will make further observations and experiments necessary.

Using this technique is not limited to scientists. You can use it to understand the world around you. Follow the steps listed below.

1. Use all your senses to observe a phenomenon.
2. Carefully review your observations to decide just what details you want explained.
3. Check reference sources to see if some of the questions you ask may already have been answered.
4. Decide whether some of your questions will require additional observations. If so, arrange to get the additional information.
5. Try to explain the phenomenon based on the answers to your questions.

Materials

thermometer
250-mL beaker
paper and pencil
water
2 ice cubes

Procedure

1. Fill the beaker two-thirds full of water.
2. Start recording all of your observations.
3. Measure the temperature of the water. Add the ice cubes.
4. Continue to record the temperature of the water every 30 seconds for five minutes.
5. *Be sure to make continuous observations during this time. Be as detailed as possible.*
6. Review your observations and formulate the questions you feel need answering. Make a note of how you think an answer to each question might best be found.
7. Submit your list to your teacher and participate in a class discussion of some of the most informative questions.

FIGURE 8–10.

9. Use the kinetic theory to explain how the temperature and the pressure of a given amount of gas are related.

★ 10. Calculate the pressure your shoe exerts on the ground when you are standing on both feet. Do the same for standing on one foot.

FLUIDS

Both liquids and gases flow. For this reason both are called fluids. You have experienced many of the fluid properties of water. You know that some objects sink while others float. You may have watched water move in streams and noticed how much faster the water moves when the stream is narrow. You have probably heard of hydraulic brakes or lifts. These properties of fluids will be studied in these sections.

GOALS

1. You will learn the forces acting on objects placed in fluids.
2. You will learn how the flow of a fluid changes the pressure it exerts.
3. You will learn how pressure is transmitted throughout a fluid.

8:7 Archimedes' Principle

Have you ever lifted a rock from the bottom of a river? It may have seemed very light until it reached the surface, when it suddenly felt heavier. Some materials, like wood and cork, come to the surface by themselves. That is, they float. Earth exerts a downward force of gravity on all objects. The upward force of a fluid on an object in it is called the **buoyant force.** If the buoyant force is less than the force of gravity, the object sinks. If the buoyant force is greater than the weight, the object floats. The net force on an object is the weight downward minus the buoyant force upward. That is why the rock you were lifting seemed lighter under water than it did in the air.

What is buoyant force?

State Archimedes' principle.

How big is the buoyant force? The Greek mathematician Archimedes (287–212 B.C.) discovered that *the buoyant force on an object submerged in a fluid is equal to the weight of the fluid displaced by that object.* This is known as **Archimedes' principle.** What does it mean? What is the fluid displaced? If you drop a marble into a glass of water, the level of the water in the glass will rise. Some of the water had to move out of the way to make room for the marble. The volume of this water is the "fluid displaced" by the marble. It is exactly the same as the volume of the marble. The weight of this water is the weight of the fluid displaced.

FIGURE 8–11. The weight of the water displaced by the submerged part of the block is equal to the weight of the whole block.

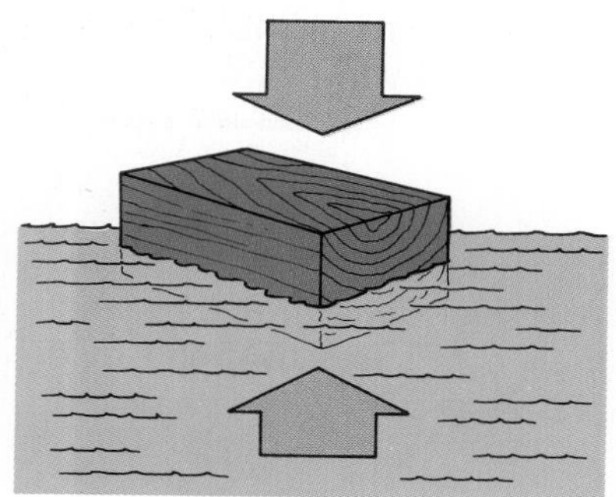

BIOGRAPHY

Mary G. Ross
1908–

Mary Ross used the gas laws for many years as an engineer for Lockheed. There she worked on rocket propulsion and the deceleration of high-velocity bodies entering Earth's atmosphere. She was involved in studies of the Agena booster rocket which was used in all the Apollo flights. In addition, she did studies on the underwater-launched Polaris missile. More recently she determined launch characteristics for Mars and Venus fly-by missions.

She is proud of her Cherokee heritage and her ancestor, John Ross, who was chief of the Cherokee for nearly 40 years.

Have you ever noticed how wood floats in water? Part of the wood is under water, part is above the surface. If you push wood under water, you feel an upward force on your hand. If you let the wood go, it rises to the surface and floats. This means that when it is completely submerged, the upward force of the water is larger than the downward force of gravity.

Steel is much denser than water. Many ships are made of steel. How, then, do steel ships float? A ship is not solid steel, but only a thin layer of steel. Most of the ship is filled with air. Therefore, the combined density of the ship and the air inside it is much less than that of water. When a ship is loaded with cargo, it sinks deeper into the water. When the cargo is removed, the ship floats higher again.

Denser fluids, such as salt water, exert a larger buoyant force than less dense fluids, such as fresh water. You may have swum in the ocean and noticed that you float more easily in seawater than in fresh water. Mercury is a liquid much denser than water. Aluminum, steel, and most other metals float in mercury.

8:8 Pascal's Principle

Have you ever dived deep into a swimming pool or lake? If so, you were probably aware of the pressure that the fluid was exerting on your ears. You also may have noticed that the pressure was the same whether your head was held straight up or tilted to the side. These observations are examples of behavior described by a

FIGURE 8–12. Submarines can vary their density, and therefore their buoyancy, by filling different areas with water or air.

French doctor, Blaise Pascal (1623–1662). **Pascal's principle** states that *pressure applied to a fluid is transmitted unchanged throughout the fluid.* This means that if you apply a certain amount of pressure to the air in a balloon, that same pressure is exerted anywhere on the interior of the balloon. The force on every square centimeter of the balloon is the same. In the first example, the water pressure would be the same on all sides of the diver's body. Only the depth of the diver would affect the pressure.

FIGURE 8–13. Divers feel equal pressure on all sides of their bodies. This is an example of Pascal's principle.

Pascal's principle can be used to construct machines that multiply forces. Hydraulic lifts are an example. These machines are used in factories and warehouses to lift heavy loads. Let us see how a hydraulic lift multiplies force. Look at Figure 8–14. A fluid, such as oil, is placed in two connected cylinders. The cross section of cylinder A has an area of five square centimeters. The cross section of cylinder B has an area of fifty square centimeters, 10 times the area of A. Each cylinder has a piston that can move up and down.

State Pascal's principle.

How is Pascal's principle useful in a warehouse?

Suppose that 100 N of force are applied to piston A. Pressure equals force divided by area, so a 100-N force will exert a pressure on piston A equal to

$$P_A = \frac{F_A}{A_A} = \frac{100 \text{ N}}{5 \text{ cm}^2} = 20 \text{ N/cm}^2.$$

According to Pascal's principle, pressure exerted anyplace on a fluid will be felt equally everywhere else in the fluid. Therefore, the pressure on piston B must be the same as the pressure on piston A. The pressure on piston B must be 20 N/cm^2. This means that the fluid is exerting a force of 20 N on every square centimeter of piston B. Since the area of piston B is 50 cm^2, the total force is 50 cm^2 × 20 N/cm^2 = 1000 N. The force has been multiplied by ten. What is the mechanical advantage of the machine?

F.Y.I. Lift is also created by angling the front of the wing upward so it is pushed up by air molecules striking the under surface.

FIGURE 8–14. A hydraulic lift works because of Pascal's principle. Force is increased but work is not.

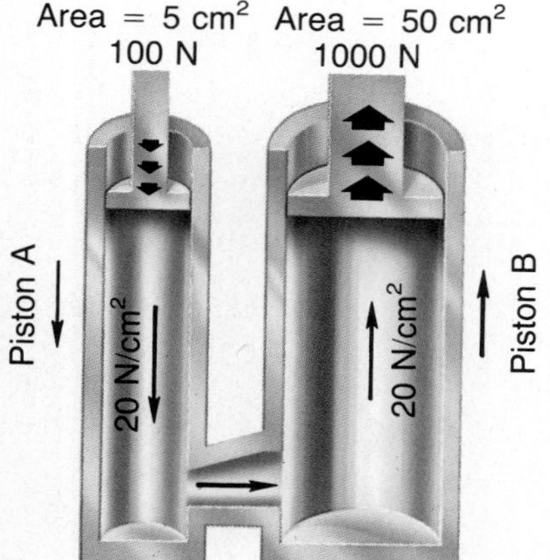

8:9 Bernoulli's Principle

Archimedes' and Pascal's principles deal with fluids that are not moving. Fluids in motion, fluids that are flowing, have many interesting properties. A fluid moves when there is a difference in pressure between two regions. For example, when you press upward on your diaphragm, the pressure inside your lungs is greater than outside, and air flows out of your lungs. When you pull downward on the diaphragm, the pressure inside is reduced and air flows inward.

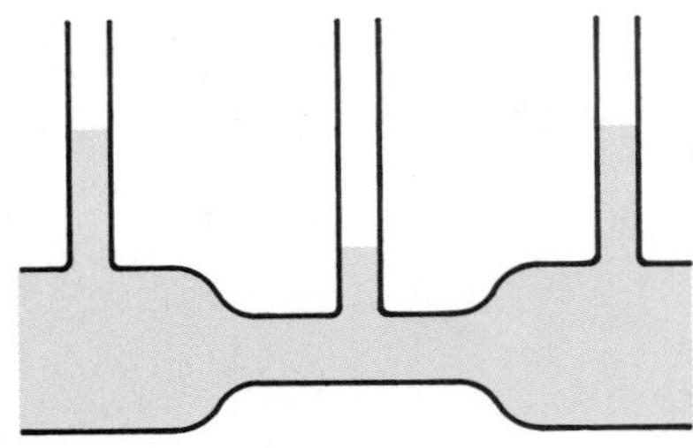

FIGURE 8–15. The velocity of the fluid through the narrow part of the tube is greater, so the pressure it exerts is less.

State Bernoulli's principle.

List three examples of Bernoulli's principle in action.

Hold a sheet of paper horizontally just under your lower lip. What will happen if you blow hard across the top of the paper? Try it. The paper moves up. Is that surprising? It is an example of a principle discovered by the Italian, Daniel Bernoulli (1770–1782). **Bernoulli's principle** states that *the pressure in a fluid is high where its velocity is low; the pressure is low where the velocity is high.* The velocity of the air above the paper is greater than the velocity of the air below it. Therefore, the pressure above the paper is lower than the pressure below it. There is a net upward force, and the paper rises.

Bernoulli's principle explains many common occurrences. For example, it explains why a pitched baseball curves. When a pitcher throws a curve ball, he gives the ball a sideways spin. That is, he makes the ball spin around a vertical axis as it moves through the air. The

TECHNOLOGY: APPLICATIONS

Physics of the Knuckleball

Bernoulli's principle can explain why a pitched baseball curves. The spin of the ball makes the air rush by faster on the side of the ball spinning forward, reducing the pressure on that side, and producing a net force on the ball toward that direction. Photographs show that the ball curves smoothly, in agreement with the explanation.

A knuckleball behaves very differently, making sudden, unpredictable motions. One reason for its behavior is in the way the pitcher grips and throws the ball. He holds the ball with his fingertips and releases it with as little spin as possible. As the ball moves through the air, the amount of friction depends on the smoothness of the ball. The rough stitches on the ball cause much more friction than the smooth surfaces. The stitches first cause a larger frictional drag on one side. Then, when the ball rotates a little, the drag is larger on the other side. As a result, the direction of the pitch suddenly changes. Tests in wind tunnels and computer studies support these ideas. Further studies on the effect of air temperature, wind, and humidity are in progress.

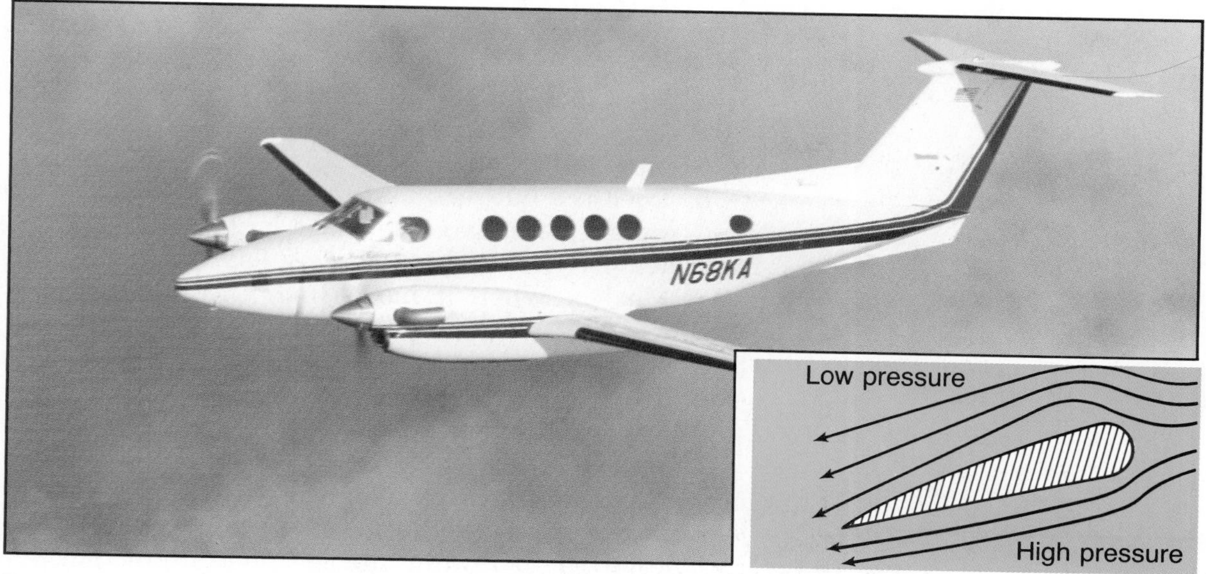

FIGURE 8–16. Airplanes are designed with many airfoils (a). Besides the wings, the fuselage, engine housings, tail assembly, and propellers are airfoils. Airfoils are designed so that the air travels faster over the top and creates an area of low pressure (b).

air moves faster past the side of the ball spinning forward, Figure 8–17. As a result, the air pressure on that side of the ball is reduced. Thus there is a net force on the ball toward that side, resulting in a curved path.

Airplane wings are designed so that the air must travel farther over the top of the wing than over the bottom, Figure 8–16. As long as the flow is smooth, air takes the same time to move over the top and bottom sides. Thus, the velocity over the top must be larger than over the bottom of the wing. This means that the pressure above the wing is reduced, and there is a net upward force on the wing. This force creates part of the lift that allows airplanes to fly.

You may have noticed how the water in a stream runs faster in places where the stream bed is narrower. This is another example of Bernoulli's principle, called the Venturi effect. If a moving fluid is forced to travel in a narrower path, its velocity increases. As the velocity of the fluid increases, the pressure exerted by the fluid decreases, Figure 8–15. Automobile carburetors and perfume atomizers work because of the Venturi effect. In recent years, this effect has given architects nightmares. Strong winds blowing through a city may be forced into narrow streets, lined with tall buildings. An area of low pressure is created along the restricted path of the wind. In some cases, the pressure difference has been great enough to cause window panes to pop out of buildings.

FIGURE 8–17. The figure shows the top view of a spinning baseball. The air moves faster past the side spinning forward, creating an area of low pressure. The ball moves in that direction.

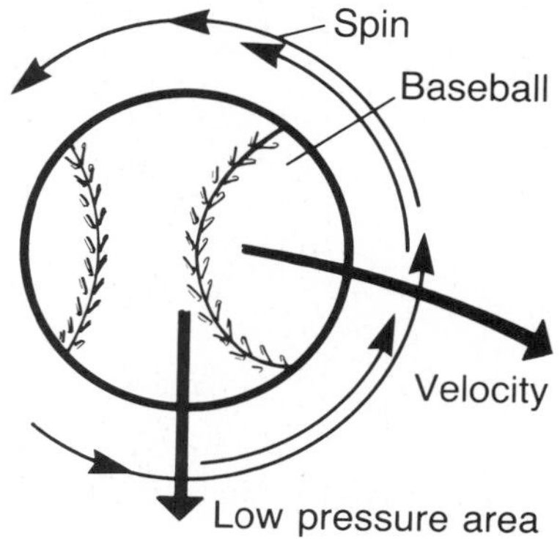

Review

11. a. Does the weight of the water displaced by an object depend on the mass of the object, on its volume, or on both?
    b. Does the buoyant force on a body depend on its weight, on its volume, or on both?
12. A heavily loaded ship is barely floating in the Gulf of Mexico. When it moves into the Mississippi it sinks. Why?
13. If a large boat docks beside a concrete pier, it is pulled toward the pier. Why?
14. Alcohol has a density of only 0.79 g/cm^3. Would an ice cube (density 0.92 g/cm^3) float in alcohol? Why?

★ 15. In Chapter 7 you learned a machine can never put out more work than has been put into it. This is also true for the hydraulic lift described in Section 8:8. Suppose piston A moved down 0.1 m when 10 N of force were exerted on it. Calculate how far piston B moved up.

CHANGING STATES OF MATTER

GOALS

1. You will learn names of state changes and the temperatures at which the changes occur.
2. You will understand the energy flows that are required to cause changes of state.

Now that you understand the properties of solids, liquids, and gases, it is time to learn how one form can be converted into another.

8:10 Changes of State

Define melting.

Define condensation.

Any change in the state of matter is a physical change. Melting is the change from solid to liquid state. It occurs at a temperature called the **melting point.** A liquid changes back into a solid by freezing at the same temperature, the **freezing point.** A liquid boils and changes into a gas at a temperature called the **boiling point.** When a liquid boils, it vaporizes. The gas cools and changes back into a liquid at the same temperature at which it boils. **Condensation** is the name of this process. If you put a cold cover over a pot of boiling water, the steam condenses on the cover. Fog, clouds, and rain are the result of condensation of water vapor in the air when the temperature is lowered.

a

b

FIGURE 8–18. When ice melts at 0°C (a), it changes to liquid at 0°C (b).

A liquid can change into a gas without boiling. This change can occur at any temperature, although it is much slower than at the boiling point. The process is called **evaporation.** Perhaps you have seen a puddle of water evaporate on a warm day.

How are boiling and evaporation related?

What is sublimation?

Solids can also change directly into gases. The change from a solid to a gas or gas to a solid without becoming a liquid is called **sublimation.** Frost is sublimation of water vapor in the air into ice crystals. Ice and snow can sublime. When frozen foods dry out, it is because the frozen water in them has sublimed. Solid carbon dioxide (dry ice) and iodine are two examples of substances that have no liquid state at ordinary air pressure.

8:11 Heats of Fusion and Vaporization

Let us examine the processes of melting and boiling in more detail. Suppose you start with a beaker containing ice at –20°C. Thermal energy is added at a constant rate. The temperature is measured every 30 seconds and recorded on a graph such as that in Figure 8–19. Between points A and B the temperature rises. The energy added increases the kinetic energy of the particles in the ice. After 2 minutes, however, the temperature stops rising. Between points B and C the temperature is a constant 0°C. Look at the beaker. You see that the ice is melting. The energy being added is now being used to overcome the forces holding the ice particles rigidly together. The energy needed to change from the solid state to the liquid state is called the **heat of fusion.** The heat of fusion of water is 334 kJ/kg.

Define heat of fusion.

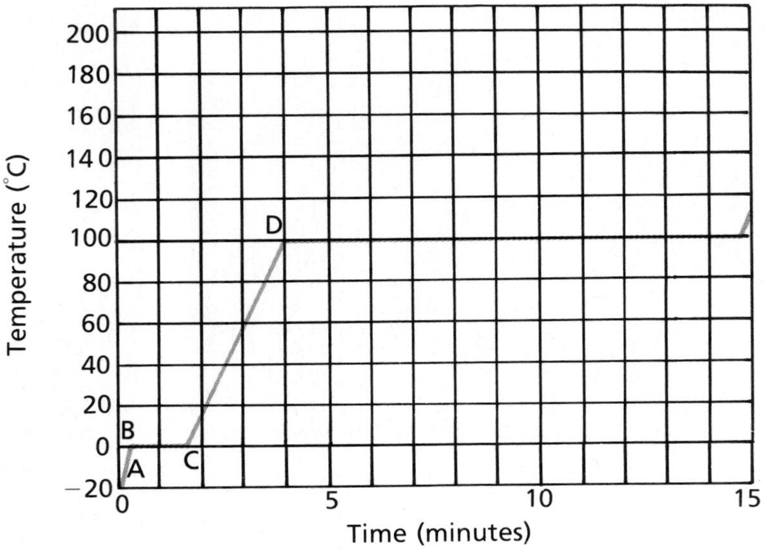

FIGURE 8–19. A time/temperature graph shows periods of constant temperature during the changes of state for water.

Once all the ice has melted, the temperature begins to rise again. The energy added between points C and D is turned into kinetic energy of the particles of the liquid. When the temperature reaches the boiling point, 100°C, it stops rising again. The water is now changing to water vapor, or steam. You will notice that the temperature remains constant for a longer time. More energy is needed to change from a liquid to a gas than to change from a solid to a liquid. The energy needed to change from a liquid to a gas is called the **heat of vaporization.** The heat of vaporization of water is 2260 kJ/kg. After all the liquid is changed to a gas, the temperature begins to rise again.

Define heat of vaporization.

According to the kinetic theory, when a substance is warmed and its temperature increases, the energy added goes into the kinetic energy of the particles. When a substance changes state, it also gains energy. During a change of state, however, the temperature remains constant. Energy added during a change of state is used to overcome the forces of attraction between the particles. That is, the added energy increases the potential energy of the matter, not the kinetic energy.

Explain change of state in terms of the kinetic theory.

The evaporation of water also requires energy. The energy comes from the thermal energy of the water itself. As a result, the temperature of the remaining water drops. Evaporation is used by animals and humans to cool themselves. The skin perspires, and the water on the skin evaporates. The energy comes from the thermal

F.Y.I. Evaporation is a cooling process because the particles with the greatest kinetic energy are the ones that evaporate. This means that the average kinetic energy, thus the temperature, of the remaining liquid molecules is lower.

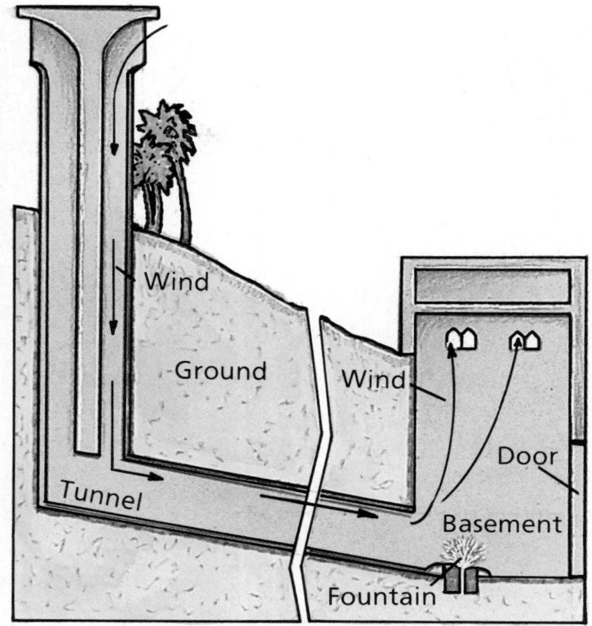

FIGURE 8–20. Passive cooling systems have been used in desert countries for many years. The evaporation of water into the unsaturated air is fueled by the thermal energy in the air. As the evaporation increases, the temperature decreases. The result is natural air conditioning.

energy of the skin. As a result the skin is cooled. Chilling water by evaporation is also used in air conditioning systems in dry climates, Figure 8–20.

Condensation and freezing are the opposites of boiling and melting. Boiling and melting absorb heat; condensation and freezing produce it. When a material cools, the particles move more slowly. The forces of attraction among the particles cause them to liquefy or solidify. The potential energy of the particles is reduced. This energy is released as thermal energy. For example, an electric freezer removes the heat of fusion, 334 kilojoules, for each kilogram of ice it freezes.

8:12 Refrigerators and Heat Pumps

Refrigerators, freezers, air conditioners, and heat pumps make use of the heat of vaporization for moving heat. Many systems use Freon, CCl_2F_2, in their cooling systems. Freon vaporizes at a much lower temperature than water. One kilogram of Freon absorbs 167 kilojoules of energy when it evaporates. In a heat mover, liquid freon starts under high pressure, Figure 8–21. As the Freon flows through the coiled pipes in the evaporator, the pressure is reduced. At this lower pressure, the Freon evaporates and absorbs thermal energy from its surroundings. The surroundings are cooled as a result. The Freon gas flows to a compressor that squeezes the gas back to the liquid state. As the gas condenses, the energy it gained during evaporation is transferred out of the compressor. The liquid Freon is then pumped back to the evaporator.

In a refrigerator or freezer the evaporator is inside the unit. It removes heat from the stored food. The compressor is outside the unit, transferring the heat into the room. In an air conditioner, a fan blows air over the evaporator, cooling the air and circulating it around the room. The compressor is outside the house, where a second fan blows the hot air into the surroundings.

Trace the steps in a heat mover.

Why might Freon be an environmental problem?

Freon sometimes leaks out of appliances. It is not poisonous, but many scientists now believe that Freon can rise high in the atmosphere and destroy the layer of ozone that protects us from the dangerous rays of the sun. Replacements for Freon in heat movers may have to be developed in the next few years.

FIGURE 8–21. The evaporation of Freon cools the surroundings in a refrigeration system. The compressor liquefies the Freon to begin the cycle again.

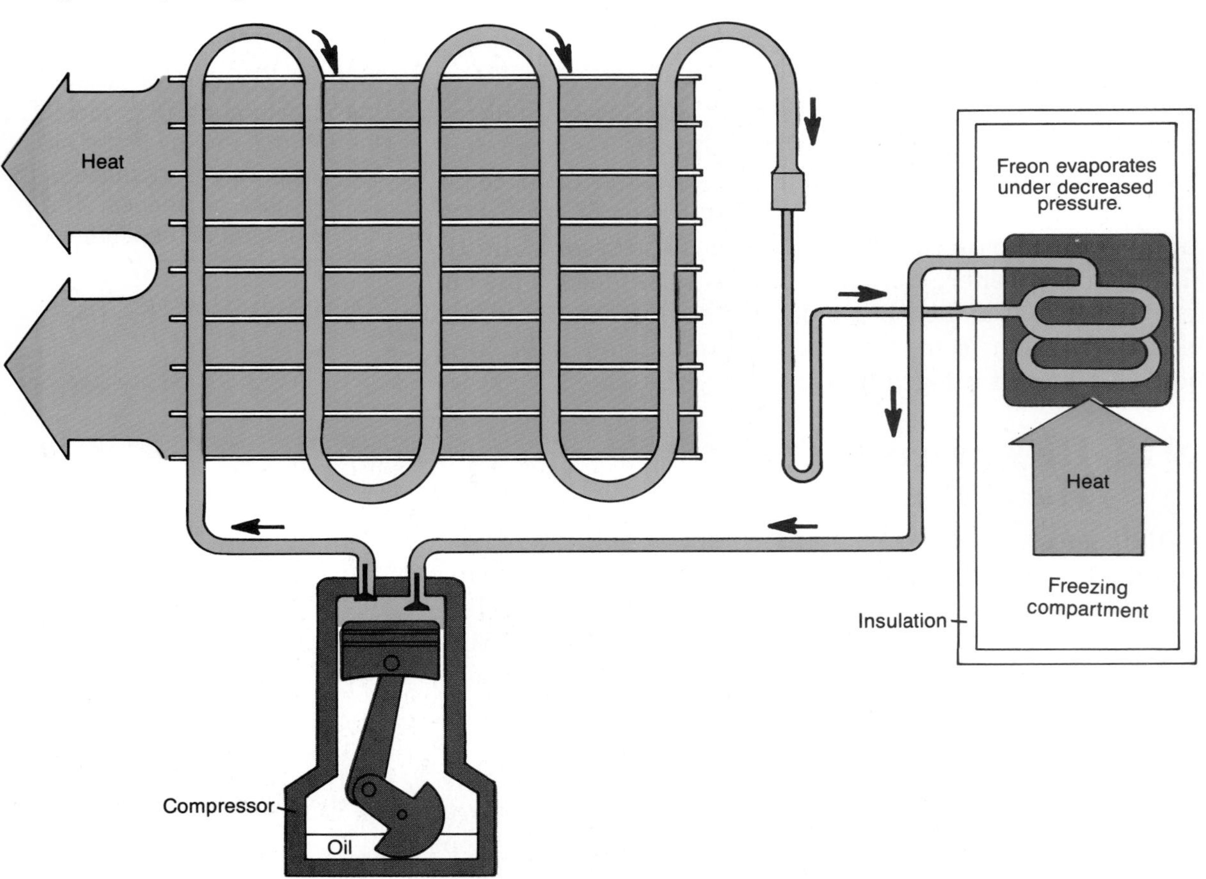

Review

16. If you were looking up the properties of a substance in a handbook, how would you tell whether it was a solid, liquid, or gas at room temperature?

17. Why does the temperature of an ice cube stay at 0°C when it is melting, even though energy is flowing into it?

18. Does steam gain or lose energy when it condenses to form water?

19. You get out of a swimming pool. Why might you become chilled?

★ **20.** If you bring a pail of water at 0°C into a room at −10°C it will freeze. Does it warm or cool the air around it as it freezes? Explain your answer.

PROBLEM SOLVING

Too Close for Comfort

Merrilynn and her mother were on their way to visit friends in the next state. They were driving along an interstate highway in their compact car. Since the speed limit was higher for passenger cars than for large trucks, Merrilynn's mother decided to pass a low, wide, moving van. As the car passed close to the van, Merilynn's mother suddenly looked surprised and gripped the steering wheel more tightly. In a startled voice she said, "Did you feel that? It seemed as if our car was pulled toward that truck." Merrilynn thought for a few minutes. Then she smiled and explained to her mother what had happened. What explanation did she give?

INVESTIGATION 8–2

Change of State

Problem: How is energy absorbed when matter changes state?

Materials

600-mL beaker
ice cubes, water
thermometer
hot plate
clock
graph paper
goggles, apron

Procedure

1. Put 100 mL of water into a 600-mL beaker. Add 4 or 5 ice cubes to the water.
2. After waiting several minutes, measure and record the temperature of the ice-water mixture.
3. Place the beaker of ice and water on the hot plate and heat slowly.
4. Read the temperature of the mixture every minute and record the data in the table.
5. Continue heating and measuring the temperature. Note the time when the ice melts.
6. Heat the water until it begins to boil. Note the time when boiling started.

FIGURE 8–22.

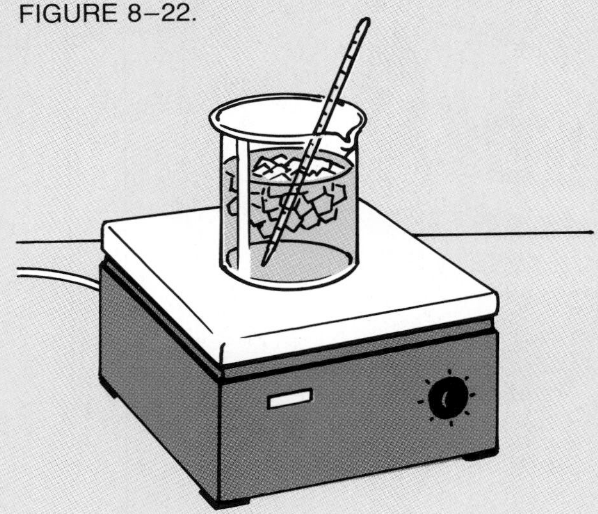

7. Continue to measure and record the temperature until the water has boiled for five minutes.

Data and Observations

Temperature of water	Time	Temperature of water	Time

Analysis

1. Graph your data.
2. Describe how temperature varies with time.
3. What do the horizontal portions of your graph represent?
4. What was the maximum temperature reached when there was still ice in the beaker?
5. What was the maximum temperature reached by the water?

Conclusions

6. How would the experiment have been changed if a hotter hot plate had been used?
7. How is energy absorbed when matter changes state?

Chapter 8 Review

SUMMARY

1. The states of matter are solid, liquid, gaseous, and plasma. 8:1
2. The kinetic theory of matter states that all matter is made of tiny particles in constant motion. 8:2
3. Most matter expands when heated. 8:3
4. Pressure is the force per unit area. 8:4
5. Boyle's law states that for a fixed amount of gas at constant temperature, decreasing the volume increases the pressure. 8:5
6. Charles' law states that for a fixed amount of gas at constant pressure, volume increases as temperature increases. 8:6
7. Archimedes' principle states that the buoyant force on an object is equal to the weight of the fluid displaced. 8:7
8. Pascal's principle states that pressure applied to a fluid is transmitted unchanged throughout the fluid. 8:8
9. Bernoulli's principle states that the pressure in a fluid decreases as its velocity increases. 8:9
10. Changes of state are physical changes. 8:10
11. During a change of state, only the potential energy changes. 8:11
12. The heats of fusion and vaporization are used to move heat. 8:12

VOCABULARY

a. Archimedes' principle
b. Bernoulli's principle
c. boiling point
d. Boyle's law
e. buoyant force
f. Charles' law
g. condensation
h. crystal
i. evaporation
j. freezing point
k. gas
l. heat of fusion
m. heat of vaporization
n. kinetic theory of matter
o. liquid
p. melting point
q. pascal
r. Pascal's principle
s. plasma
t. pressure
u. solid
v. sublimation
w. thermal expansion
x. viscosity

Matching

Match each description with the correct vocabulary word from the list above. Some words will not be used.

1. matter that has a fixed volume and is rigid
2. the temperature at which a material freezes
3. the unit of pressure, force per unit area
4. upward force of a fluid on an object
5. the energy released when steam condenses to water
6. the state of matter with neither fixed volume nor shape
7. a liquid changes to gas below the boiling point
8. material in which the particles are regularly arranged
9. phase change directly between solid and gas
10. The volume of a gas is reduced when the pressure is increased.

Chapter 8 Review

MAIN IDEAS

A. Reviewing Concepts

Choose the word or phrase that correctly completes each of the following sentences.

1. At room temperature air is usually a *(solid, liquid, gas, plasma).*
2. The state in which the particles are not electrically charged and are very far apart is *(solid, liquid, gas, plasma).*
3. When a substance changes from a solid to a liquid *(condensation, boiling, freezing, melting)* occurs.
4. When gas cools to form a liquid, the process is *(condensation, boiling, freezing, melting).*
5. A balloon filled with air is squeezed to a smaller volume. The air pressure inside is *(increased, held constant, decreased, made zero).*

Complete each of the following sentences with the correct word or phrase.

6. The ____________ theory states that tiny particles make up matter and are in constant motion.
7. A solid ____________, changing directly to a gas.
8. The melting point and ____________ point of a substance are characteristic properties.
9. When a person stands first on two feet, then on only one foot, the ____________ on the ground doubles.
10. Gasoline is drawn into the carburetor of a car because of ____________.

Determine whether each of the following sentences is true or false. If it is false, change the underlined word to make the sentence true.

11. Pressure is transmitted through a fluid <u>unchanged</u>.
12. A gas is composed of particles that <u>may be</u> in motion.
13. When the temperature of a gas is increased, the pressure <u>decreases</u>.
14. If the force on an area increases, the pressure <u>increases</u>.
15. Bernoulli's principle applies to fluids <u>at rest</u>.

B. Understanding Concepts

Answer the following questions using complete sentences when possible.

16. When you wade at a rocky beach, the rocks hurt your feet less when you are in deeper water. Why?
17. Why does an object expand as the temperature increases?
18. Why do we not call Archimedes' principle, Pascal's principle, and Bernoulli's principle "theories"?
19. Two cylinders filled with water are connected by a pipe, Figure 8–14. If 10 N of force is exerted on piston A, does the force on piston B increase, decrease, or remain the same?
20. In Question 19, does the pressure on piston B increase, decrease, or remain the same?
21. What happens when you breathe on a mirror? Explain.
22. Water flows much more easily than does honey. How do the viscosities of water and honey compare?
23. Steam burns are more serious than burns from hot air. Why?
24. Suppose you hang two pieces of paper about 2 cm apart, then you blow downward between the two pieces. What will happen and why? Try it!
25. Alcohol has a lower density than water. Would you expect wood to float in alcohol with more or less material above the liquid surface than in water?

C. Applying Concepts

Answer the following questions using complete sentences when possible.

26. Alcohol evaporates more quickly than water. From this fact, what can you tell about the forces between the alcohol particles?

27. Closed bottles placed in a fire sometimes explode. Why?

28. If you press down on paper with a sharp knife, it will cut through the paper. If you use the same force on a dull knife, the paper will not be cut. Does this mean that paper is cut as a result of force or pressure? Why?

29. The Freon in a refrigerator evaporates and condenses as it passes through the pipes in the appliance. Should it be evaporated or condensed inside the refrigerator? Why?

30. The specific heat of water is 4180 J/kg • C°. Suppose you have two liters (2 kg) of hot water at 80°C that you want to cool to 0°C. How much ice at 0°C would have to be melted to cool the water?

SKILL REVIEW

1. Why is it necessary to think about what questions you should ask in an experiment?
2. Where might you look for answers to the questions you formed from your observations?
3. How is coincidence related to cause and effect?
4. Why is it necessary to think creatively when you are looking for a solution for a problem?
5. How can asking the right questions help determine cause and effect relationships?

PROJECTS

1. Push a sharp knife against an ice cube. You should see some melted water. That is, pressure raises the melting temperature of ice. Report on how this fact explains how ice skates work.
2. Helium has the lowest boiling point of any material, only 4.2 kelvins above absolute zero. Write a report about the uses of liquid helium in science and in industry.
3. Do some research on the latest results of studies on the effect of releasing Freon into the atmosphere. Find out what efforts are now being made to reduce the problem?
4. Obtain a book on growing crystals. Grow crystals and explore the conditions needed to obtain large, perfect, crystals. Try splitting some crystals to see the flat faces that result.

READINGS

1. Arnold, Guy. *Gas*. New York: Franklin Watts, 1985.
2. Maxwell, James C. *Maxwell on Molecules and Gases*. Cambridge, MA: MIT Press, 1986.
3. Powell, E. "Energy's New Champs?" *Popular Science*. October, 1984, p. 103.
4. Sprackling, Michael. *Liquids and Solids*. New York: Methuem, 1985.

COMPOSITION OF MATTER
PROPERTIES OF MATTER

Classification of Matter

A new medicine may cause harmful side effects. To prevent ill effects, a researcher may replace one substance in the medicine with another. This can be done because different substances may have similar properties. One way scientists classify matter is according to its properties. In Chapter 8, matter was classified according to state. In this chapter, you will learn to classify matter by properties and composition.

COMPOSITION OF MATTER

GOALS

1. You will learn the difference between elements and compounds.
2. You will learn to distinguish heterogeneous and homogeneous mixtures.
3. You will understand the differences among solutions, suspensions, and colloids.

One method of classifying matter is to find out if it is a substance or a mixture of substances. Substances and mixtures, in turn, can be further compared by their makeup. Each term in this section has a specific meaning related to the classification of matter.

9:1 Substances

What makes up an element?

You have learned that all matter is made of tiny particles called atoms. If a sample of matter is composed of one kind of atom, that sample is an **element.** Examples of elements are sulfur, oxygen, gold, silver, zinc, iron, and carbon. Scientists have found 90 of these elements in nature. Another 20 or so have been produced in the laboratory. A table of the elements is found on pages 228–229.

Some matter, such as water, is composed of more than one kind of atom. These atoms are joined together in a certain ratio. Water contains atoms of the elements hydrogen and oxygen. In every sample of pure water, there are two hydrogen atoms for every one oxygen atom. They are in a ratio of 2 to 1. Ammonia is made of the elements nitrogen and hydrogen in the ratio of 1 to 3. Every sample of ammonia will contain three atoms of

CAREER

Science Textbook Editor

Madelaine Kane is a science textbook editor. Previously, Madelaine taught chemistry and physics in high school.

As an editor, Madelaine helps to plan textbook revisions. First she researches how teacher and student needs may have changed. Then she works with authors, reviewers, and consultants to get text material that is accurate, current, and interesting. She also coordinates designers, artists, photo editors, and production staff to put the text in an attractive and usable form. She even goes to press to see that the book is printed properly.

Science textbook editors must keep pace with changes in science, technology, and education. For Madelaine, this career is a perfect way to combine her experience in teaching with her science and communication skills.

For career information, write
Association of American Publishers
220 East 23rd Street
New York, NY 10010

hydrogen for every one atom of nitrogen. If a sample of matter is made of atoms of two or more elements joined together, always in the same ratio, then that matter is a **compound.** Water and ammonia are compounds.

What does a scientist mean by the word *substance?*

Elements and compounds are classified as **substances.** When scientists refer to substances, they mean elements or compounds. Every substance always has a definite composition. If it is made of only one kind of atom, it is an element. If a substance is made of two or more kinds of atoms joined together, always in the same ratio, the substance is a compound.

a

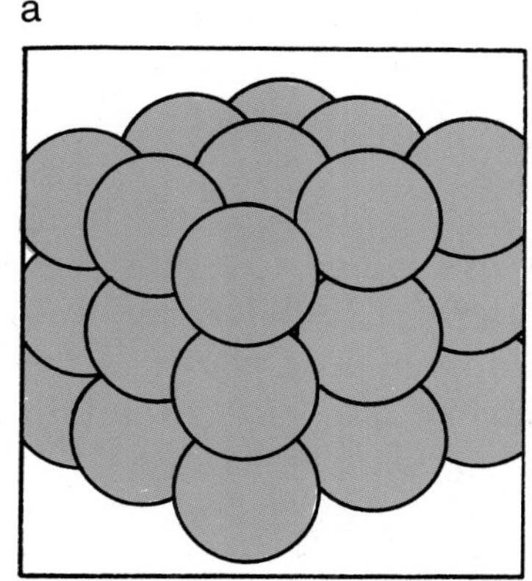

b

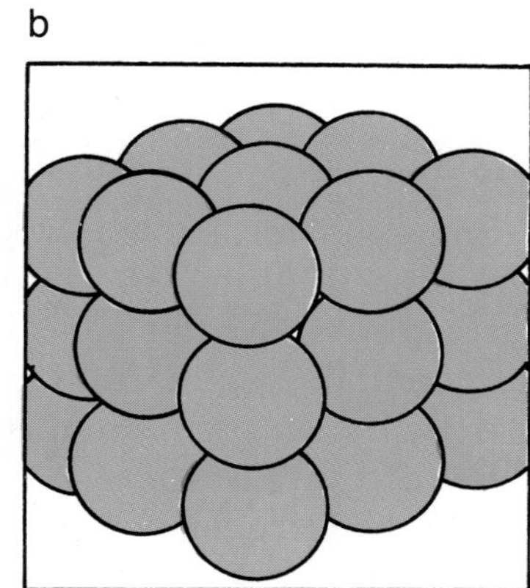

FIGURE 9–1. An element is composed of one kind of atom (a). A compound (b) is composed of two or more kinds of atoms in a definite ratio.

9:2 Mixtures

FIGURE 9–2. Many rocks are heterogeneous mixtures of several minerals.

Not all samples of matter are substances. Most of the common matter around you is made of two or more substances forming a mixture rather than a compound. Matter is classified as a mixture if each part of the matter has its own properties. The parts of a mixture need have no certain ratio to each other.

Many fabrics are mixtures. The label on a shirt may list the fabric as 60% cotton and 40% polyester. Another label may read 80% cotton and 20% polyester. Cotton is a substance called cellulose. Cotton is absorbent. It is easily dyed and does not attract lint. Polyester is a different substance. It resists wrinkles, shrinkage, and mildew. The properties of the shirt fabric are a combination of cotton and polyester properties. If you looked at the shirt fabric with a microscope, you could pick out polyester fibers and cotton fibers.

Define heterogeneous mixture.

If the substances in a mixture are not spread out evenly, it is a **heterogeneous mixture.** A bottle of liquid salad dressing is a mixture of different ingredients. If you look closely at the mixture, you may see that some of the liquids have separated. Many of the solid spices will have settled to the bottom of the bottle. The salad dressing is a heterogeneous mixture. The parts of the mixture are not spread evenly throughout.

But what about the vinegar used in the dressing? Vinegar is mostly a mixture of two compounds, acetic acid and water. If you examine the labels of the bottles of

FIGURE 9–3. Every sample of matter is an element, a compound, or a mixture.

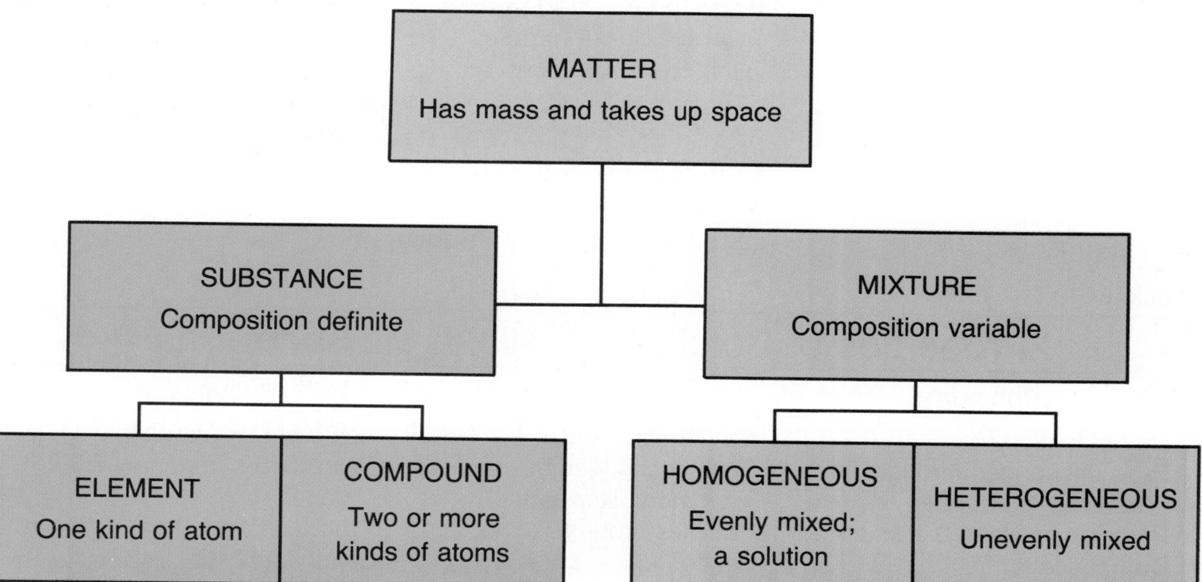

FIGURE 9–4. When shaken, the white flakes in this paperweight form a suspension. If left standing, the flakes will settle.

vinegar on a store shelf, you will see that the ratio of water and acetic acid can vary. However, if you look at vinegar under a microscope, you cannot see particles of acetic acid and water. The vinegar seems to be the same throughout. A sealed bottle of vinegar will not separate into acetic acid and water. This is true no matter how long it stands.

Vinegar is a homogeneous mixture. In a **homogeneous mixture,** the substances are spread evenly throughout. A homogeneous mixture is called a **solution.** Other solutions include seawater, soft drinks, and even glass. Tea is a homogeneous mixture. Tea with ice is a heterogeneous mixture. The ice is not evenly distributed. When will the iced tea be a solution again?

9:3 Solutions, Suspensions, and Colloids

Solutions are homogeneous mixtures. They are made of tiny particles of one substance spread throughout the particles of another substance. The size of a particle in a solution is about one-millionth of a millimeter in diameter. Particles never separate from solution.

What is a suspension?

A **suspension** is a heterogeneous mixture in which the particles are large enough to be seen by a microscope or the unaided eye. They are affected by gravity. In time, they settle out of the mixture. By shaking, the particles can be temporarily suspended again. The "snowfall" inside some paper weights is an example of a suspension. Stirring up the bottom of a river or a lake produces a suspension. In time, the sand or soil settles back to the bottom.

What is a colloid?

If the size of particles in a mixture is between those of a solution and a suspension, the mixture is a **colloid.** Colloidal particles appear evenly distributed even when viewed with a light microscope. Some examples are listed in Table 9–2 on page 200.

Table 9–1

Properties of Solutions, Colloids, Suspensions

Solutions	Colloids	Suspensions
Do not settle out	Do not settle out	Settle out on standing
Pass unchanged through ordinary filter paper	Pass unchanged through ordinary filter paper	Separated by ordinary filter paper
Particles between 0.1 and 1 nm	Particles around 1–1000 nm	Particles larger than 1000 nm
Do not scatter light	Scatter light	Scatter light

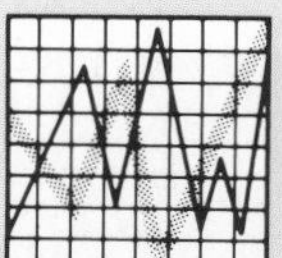

SKILL

Separating a Mixture

Problem: How can materials in a mixture be separated?

Materials

prepared mixture
sheet of paper
sheet of clear acetate
magnet
screen
400-mL beaker
filter paper
funnel
porcelain triangle
ring stand
iron ring
distilled water
hot plate
250-mL beaker
goggles
apron

CAUTION: *Handle boiling water and the hot beaker with care.*

Procedure

1. Place a small amount of the prepared mixture on a clean sheet of paper. Observe the mixture. Record your observations.
2. Spread the prepared mixture across half of the paper. Place the acetate sheet over the mixture.
3. Pass a magnet across the top of the sheet of acetate. Try to draw one of the materials onto the clean half of the paper. Record your observations.
4. Place a screen on top of the 400-mL beaker. Slide the remaining mixture onto the screen. Gently sift the mixture over the beaker. Record your observations.
5. Add about 50 mL of water to the beaker and swirl the beaker gently.
6. Set up a filtering apparatus as shown in Appendix B–4. Place the 250-mL beaker under the funnel. Pour the contents of the 400-mL beaker into the funnel. Rinse this beaker and the solid it contains with about 10 mL of water. Pour this rinse into the funnel.
7. Observe the contents of each of the two beakers and the filter paper. Record your observations.
8. Place the 250-mL beaker and its contents on a hot plate set on medium heat. Allow most of the liquid to evaporate. If spattering occurs, turn down the heat. When only a small amount of liquid remains, turn off the hot plate. Allow the remaining liquid to evaporate.
9. After the beaker is cool, examine its contents. Record your observations.

Data and Observations

Procedure	Observations
Step 1	
Step 3	

Analysis

1. How many materials were you able to separate from the mixture?
2. What properties did you use to separate out the materials?
3. Did any material undergo a change of state?

Conclusions and Applications

4. How can the materials in a mixture be separated?
5. Ripe tomatoes float but unripe tomatoes sink in water. Tomato harvesters use this fact to separate mixtures of ripe and unripe tomatoes. What property of the tomatoes do harvesters use to separate the mixture of tomatoes?

a

b

FIGURE 9–5. The gelatin dessert and the whipped topping (a) are both colloids. Colloids and some suspensions show the Tyndall effect (b). Here tiny particles of dust and water make the searchlight become visible.

What is the Tyndall effect?

Colloids have two interesting properties. The **Tyndall effect** refers to the ability of colloids to scatter light. If light is passed through a colloid, the beam becomes visible. A searchlight in the night air or the light beam from the projector in a movie theater shows the Tyndall effect. Dust, smoke, and water droplets in the air scatter the light. Suspensions may also scatter light. The particles in solutions are too small to scatter light. Because colloids scatter light, they often appear cloudy or even opaque.

What is Brownian motion?

Colloids also show Brownian motion. If you looked at a colloid with a microscope, you would see the colloidal particles in constant, zigzag motion. They are being hit continually by the smaller, invisible, molecules in the mixture. The random motion of particles in a colloid is called **Brownian motion.** It is easy to observe with grains of dust or pollen on the surface of water using a light microscope.

Table 9–2

Some Colloids

Type	States	Examples
Foam	Gas in liquid	Whipped cream, suds
	Gas in solid	Marshmallow
Aerosol	Liquid in gas	Fog, clouds
Emulsion	Liquid in liquid	Milk, mayonnaise, salad dressings
	Liquid in solid	Cheese, butter
Smoke	Solid in gas	Dust and other particles in smog
Sol	Solid in liquid	Jellies, latex paint
	Solid in solid	Pearls, opals

F.Y.I. An emulsion is a colloid made of droplets of liquid in another liquid. A material called an emulsifying agent is needed to keep the colloid from separating. Milk is an emulsion of fat droplets in water. Casein, a protein, is the emulsifying agent.

INVESTIGATION 9–1

Mixtures

Problem: How can you distinguish solutions, colloids, and suspensions?

Materials

4 small beakers
balance
graduated cylinder
stirring rod
funnel
4 pieces filter paper
4 large test tubes
test tube rack
flashlight
powdered milk
starch
powdered gelatin
table sugar
goggles
apron

Procedure

1. Place 1-g samples of powdered milk, sugar, gelatin, and starch in separate beakers. Label the beakers.
2. Add 15 mL of distilled water to each beaker. Mix thoroughly.
3. Set up a filtering apparatus as in Appendix B:4. Use a large test tube instead of a beaker to catch the filtrate.
4. Pour the powdered milk into the funnel. Collect the filtrate in a test tube and label the tube near the top. Save for Step 6. Record your observations of the filter paper and filtrate. Replace the used filter paper.
5. Repeat Step 4 for each of the other three liquids. Record your observations.
6. Place the 4 test tubes from Steps 4 and 5 in a line.
7. Darken the room and shine a flashlight beam through the contents of the test tubes. Record your results.

FIGURE 9–6.

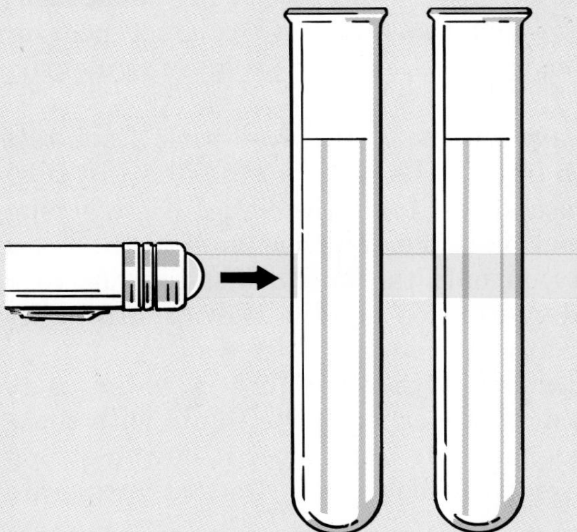

Data and Observations

Material	Filter	Flashlight
powdered milk		
sugar		
gelatin		
starch		

Analysis

1. Which materials passed unchanged through the filter paper?
2. Was a beam of light visible through any of the four materials? If so, which?

Conclusions and Applications

3. Using Table 9–1 and your data, state which materials are solutions, colloids, or suspensions.
4. How can you distinguish solutions, colloids, and suspensions?

Review

1. What is the difference between a bottle of water and another bottle containing hydrogen and oxygen?
2. Identify each of the following materials as a substance, a solution, or a heterogeneous mixture.
   a. copper c. air e. oxygen
   b. salt water d. soil f. orange juice
3. How does a mixture differ from a substance?
4. Is a solution a mixture or a compound? Explain your answer.
5. ★ You are given three beakers of liquids. One contains a solution, one a colloid, and one a suspension. How could you distinguish among these?

PROPERTIES OF MATTER

GOALS

1. You will learn that matter has chemical and physical properties.
2. You will learn about physical and chemical change.
3. You will learn that chemical changes produce new substances.

How do you tell glass and plastic apart? The answer is simple, by their properties. Properties are the characteristics of a substance. We use properties to identify and describe objects. No two substances have the same set of properties.

9:4 Physical Properties

What is a physical property?

List several physical properties.

A **physical property** is a characteristic of matter that can be observed without changing the makeup of a substance. Boiling points and freezing points are examples of physical properties. We can observe the freezing point of water without changing the water into a different substance. Other physical properties are color, odor, hardness, density, and the ability to conduct heat or electricity. Physical properties often are used to identify materials.

Suppose you have four test tubes in a rack. Each test tube is filled with liquid. The liquid in the first test tube is blue. In the second test tube, the liquid has a strong odor. A small steel ball floats on the liquid in the third test tube. When you hold the fourth test tube in your hands, the liquid evaporates rapidly. How could you determine whether any of the liquids are water?

One way to decide whether a liquid is water, is to compare the physical properties of the liquid with those of water. Is water normally blue? Does it have a strong odor? Will a steel ball float in it? Does it evaporate

FIGURE 9–7. A mixture of sand and iron filings can be separated with a magnet. The iron filings are magnetic. The sand is not.

quickly? None of these properties is a property of water. Thus, none of the test tubes contains pure water.

Physical properties can be used to separate mixtures. A mixture of iron and sand can be separated by a magnet. Iron is magnetic. Sand is not. A mixture of water and alcohol can be separated by heating. This procedure works because alcohol has a lower boiling point than water.

Give two examples of physical properties that can be used to separate mixtures.

You observe the physical properties of matter every day without realizing it. You consider the physical properties of materials you select to wear. Many different materials are used to make shoes. What kind of material properties would you look for in a shoe to wear for playing basketball? For ballet dancing? For hiking? For climbing?

FIGURE 9–8. Shoe manufacturers select materials of different properties to make shoes for various purposes.

TECHNOLOGY: APPLICATIONS

The Fight Against Rust

Rain, snow, acid rain, and sodium and calcium chloride can attack unprotected metal on an automobile, corroding its body. One of the new methods in the fight against rust is the use of electrogalvanized sheet metal. In the electrogalvanizing process, strips of steel are electrically charged. The strips are then dipped into a zinc solution. Because the zinc has an opposite charge, it is attracted to the steel and spreads evenly across the metal. The smooth surface is then painted. The zinc coating protects the steel because corrosive materials react first with the zinc.

Electrogalvanized steel is now used mostly in the underbody structure and the interior unseen panels of a car. More car manufacturers may begin redesigning their automobiles so that the metal may also be used in exterior panels.

Another technique used to increase rust protection is rustproofing. This process involves treating the car's underside and panels such as the trunk, doors, and hood with sealants. These sealants penetrate all the seams, cracks, and holes of the automobile to keep out the moisture that may cause rust.

9:5 Physical Changes

When a pane of glass breaks, the shape of the glass changes. However, the pieces contain the same materials and have the same properties as the original pane of glass. When wood is used to make a shelf or a chair, it is still wood. Only its size and shape have changed. When ice melts, the substance water remains the same. When matter changes in size, shape, color, or state, it undergoes a physical change. A **physical change** is a process that does not change the chemical composition of a substance.

What is a physical change?

Both heterogeneous mixtures and solutions can be separated by physical change. For example, salt water is a mixture of salt and water. If the mixture is heated, the water can be boiled away. The salt remains. Thus, salt water is separated by a physical change, the evaporation of water. A wire screen can be used to separate a mixture of pebbles and sand. This is a separation by mechanical means and is a physical change.

9:6 Chemical Properties

Suppose you have three test tubes and each contains a colorless liquid. How could you decide if any of the three liquids are water? Earlier we used physical prop-

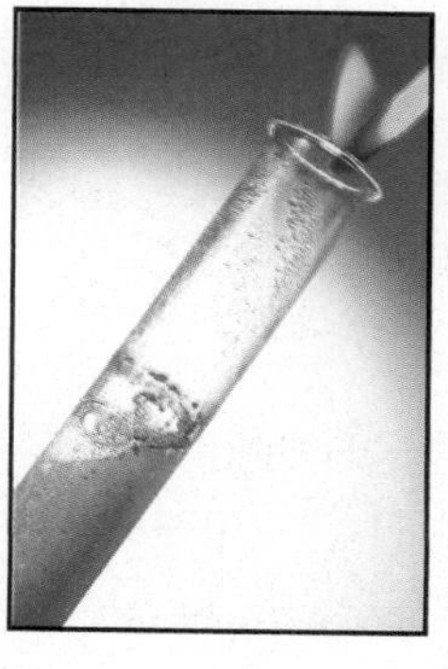
a

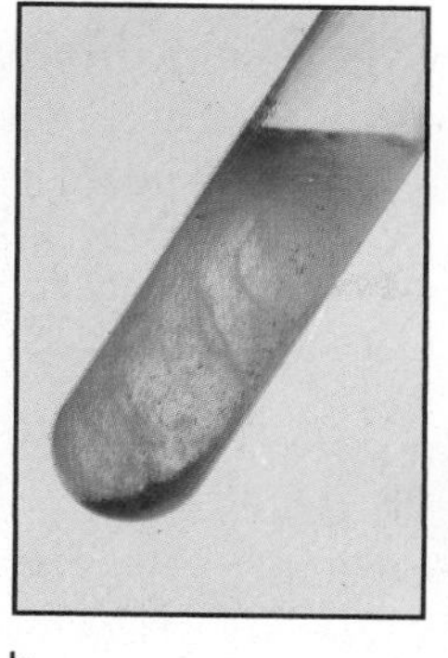
b

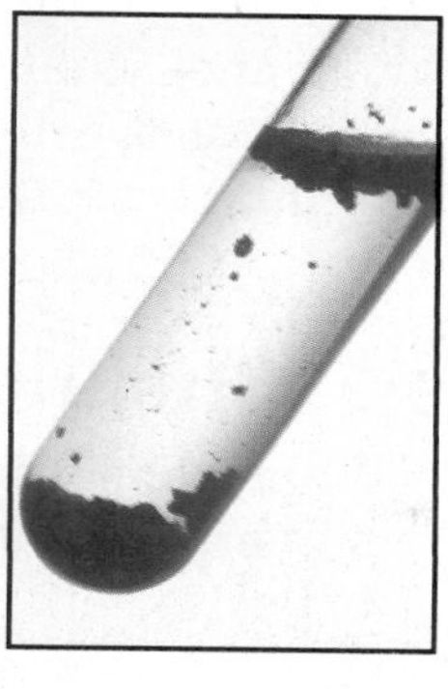
c

FIGURE 9–9. Chemical changes are used to determine if any of these test tubes contain water.

erties to find out if any of four liquids were water. Another way is to observe how each reacts with other substances. Then, compare these observations with the way water reacts with the same substances. When iron filings are sprinkled into the first test tube, bubbles form and a gas escapes, Figure 9–9a. This gas burns with a blue flame when tested with a flaming wood splint. When small pieces of iron are sprinkled into the second test tube, another gas is given off, Figure 9–9b. This gas has a sharp, unpleasant odor. The liquid in the third test tube forms a black solid when iron is added, Figure 9–9c. What does water do when iron is added to it? Try it. Observe any change that takes place. Are any of these three liquids pure water? How do you know?

The properties described for these liquids are chemical properties. A **chemical property** is a characteristic that determines how a substance reacts to form other substances. For example, charcoal can combine with oxygen. It burns to form carbon dioxide. Some metals may combine with oxygen and corrode. Rusting is an example of a chemical property, corrosion. **Corrosion** occurs when metals are destroyed as they combine chemically with other substances. If a substance does not corrode, that is also a chemical property. Some medicines are

What is a chemical property?

FIGURE 9–10. Air, moisture, and salts can cause iron to corrode (a). Gold is valuable both because it is scarce and because it does not corrode (b).

a

b

compounds that break down into simpler compounds when exposed to light. Because of this chemical property, many medicines are stored in dark bottles.

BIOGRAPHY

Agnes Pockels
1862–1935

Agnes Pockels investigated the properties of liquid surfaces. She invented her own apparatus for this research. Her basic design is still used in equipment to measure and compare surface tension.

9:7 Chemical Changes

What happens when a piece of wood is burned? Thermal energy, light, and smoke are given off. A small pile of ashes is left. More than just the appearance of the wood has changed. The substances in the wood have changed. Wood is made of compounds of the elements carbon, hydrogen, and oxygen. When wood burns, these compounds unite with oxygen in the air. The compounds in the wood are changed into other substances, including carbon dioxide and water. If not enough oxygen is present, carbon monoxide may form. The compounds in wood have been transformed into new compounds by chemical change.

In a **chemical change,** a substance is changed to a new substance. Because it is a new substance, it has different properties. Chemical changes may release thermal energy, light, or electricity. Some chemical changes need energy. All changes, chemical and physical, involve an energy change of some kind.

Compounds are formed from elements by chemical change. Aluminum is a shiny metallic element. Oxygen is a colorless, gaseous element in the air. When these two elements combine by a chemical change, a new substance is formed. It has different properties. The compound is aluminum oxide. It is a white coating on the aluminum.

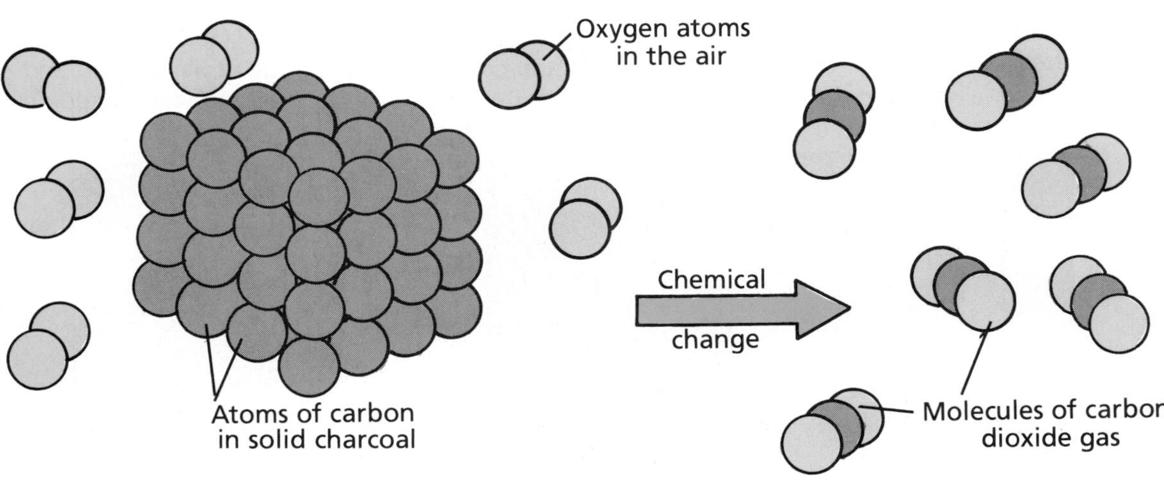

FIGURE 9–11. When charcoal burns, atoms of carbon combine with oxygen from the air. This change forms a new substance, carbon dioxide.

INVESTIGATION 9–2

Chemical Properties

Problem: How do zinc and copper differ in their reaction to hydrochloric acid?

Materials: 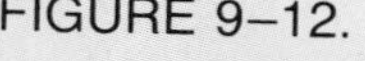

dilute hydrochloric acid
2 test tubes
test tube rack
mossy zinc
copper pellets
wooden splint
matches
goggles
apron

CAUTION: *Handle hydrochloric acid with care. Wear safety goggles and an apron.*

FIGURE 9–12.

Procedure

1. Place 3 mL of dilute hydrochloric acid in a test tube.
2. Stand the test tube in a test tube rack or beaker.
3. Add a piece of mossy zinc to the acid.
4. Light a wooden splint and bring the flame carefully to the mouth of the test tube as in Figure 9–12.
5. Repeat Steps 1–4 using a pellet of copper in another test tube.
6. Dispose of all chemicals as your teacher directs.
7. Record your observations.

Analysis

1. What evidence is there of a chemical change between the mossy zinc and the hydrochloric acid?
2. What happens to the burning splint when it is placed over each test tube?
3. How do you know a chemical change took place when the burning splint was placed over the zinc reaction?

Conclusions and Applications

4. How do zinc and copper differ in their reaction to hydrochloric acid?
5. List two other ways in which zinc and copper differ in properties.
6. What chemical property of hydrogen makes it useful in rockets?

Data and Observations

Element	Reaction with Hydrochloric Acid	Reaction to Burning Splint
mossy zinc		
copper		

F.Y.I. Pure water does not conduct electricity. Therefore, in the electrolysis of water to produce hydrogen and oxygen, a small amount of sulfuric acid is added to the water so it will conduct a current.

FIGURE 9–13. When an electric current is passed through water, a chemical change occurs.

The breakdown of compounds is also an example of chemical change. For example, an electric current can be passed through water, Figure 9–13. Water, a compound, will break into the two elements, hydrogen and oxygen, Figure 9–14. The properties of hydrogen and oxygen are different from the properties of water.

What is electrolysis?

Any chemical change produced by electric current is **electrolysis.** The process of electrolysis often is used to obtain elements from their compounds. It is especially useful in separating some metals from the compounds in which they naturally occur.

Chemical changes are going on around us all the time. Our bodies digest and use food. The starches we eat, for example, are changed to sugars. Plants grow by using carbon dioxide in the air and water to make a sugar. It is a chemical change when milk sours or when batteries light a flashlight.

FIGURE 9–14. During the electrolysis of water, water molecules break apart. Molecules of hydrogen and oxygen form.

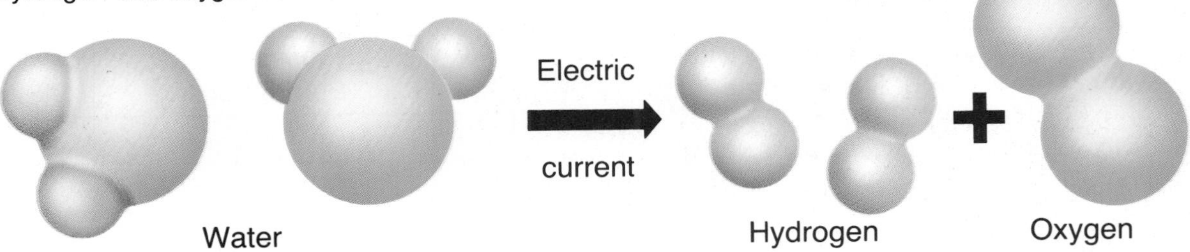

When chemical changes occur, there are always physical changes as well. However, physical changes, such as ice melting or grass being cut, do not require chemical change. When a candle is lit, a pool of melted wax forms. The wax continues to melt as some of it burns. Through chemical change, the wax changes into carbon dioxide gas and water vapor. The candle becomes smaller. Its mass is less after burning. This is a physical change caused by the chemical change.

Review

6. What physical properties could you use to tell the difference between each of the following kinds of matter?
   a. coal and snow
   b. vinegar and water
   c. lead and copper
   d. strawberry and vanilla ice cream
   e. salt and sugar
   f. a baseball and a football

7. Name and describe the physical change taking place in each of the following situations.
   a. A pan of soup bubbles and steams on the stove.
   b. Liquid candle wax drips and becomes hard.
   c. Car windows begin to "fog" on the inside.
   d. A pile of snow seems to shrink on a cold, dry day.
   e. Clothes dry in a clothesdryer.

8. What physical property do all of the following have in common: glass, water, carbon dioxide, plastic wrap, and air?

9. Which of the following changes are chemical changes?
   a. forming a bar of copper into wire
   b. frying an egg
   c. breaking a glass
   d. bleaching your hair
   e. transferring "lead" to paper when writing
   f. cutting up vegetables
   g. shooting off fireworks
   h. squeezing an orange for juice
   i. dew disappearing from the grass

★ **10.** The following paragraph is a description of the properties of silver. Determine whether each of the underlined properties is chemical or physical. Use a dictionary to find the definitions of words you do not know.

Silver*

White metal, more malleable and ductile than any other metal except gold. Density of silver is 10.49 g/cm^3 at 15°C. Silver is an excellent conductor of heat and electricity. Melting point 960.5°C; boiling point about 2000°C. Silver is not attacked by water or atmospheric oxygen. It is inert to most acids; reacts readily with dilute nitric acid.

*MERCK INDEX, Tenth Edition (Merck & Co., Inc., 1983) p. 1221

PROBLEM SOLVING

Can you classify matter?

The fifteen diagrams below contain different types and numbers of atoms and molecules. Label each diagram as one or more of the following: solid, liquid, or gas; element(s) only, compound(s) only, element(s) and compound(s); homogeneous mixture or heterogeneous mixture.

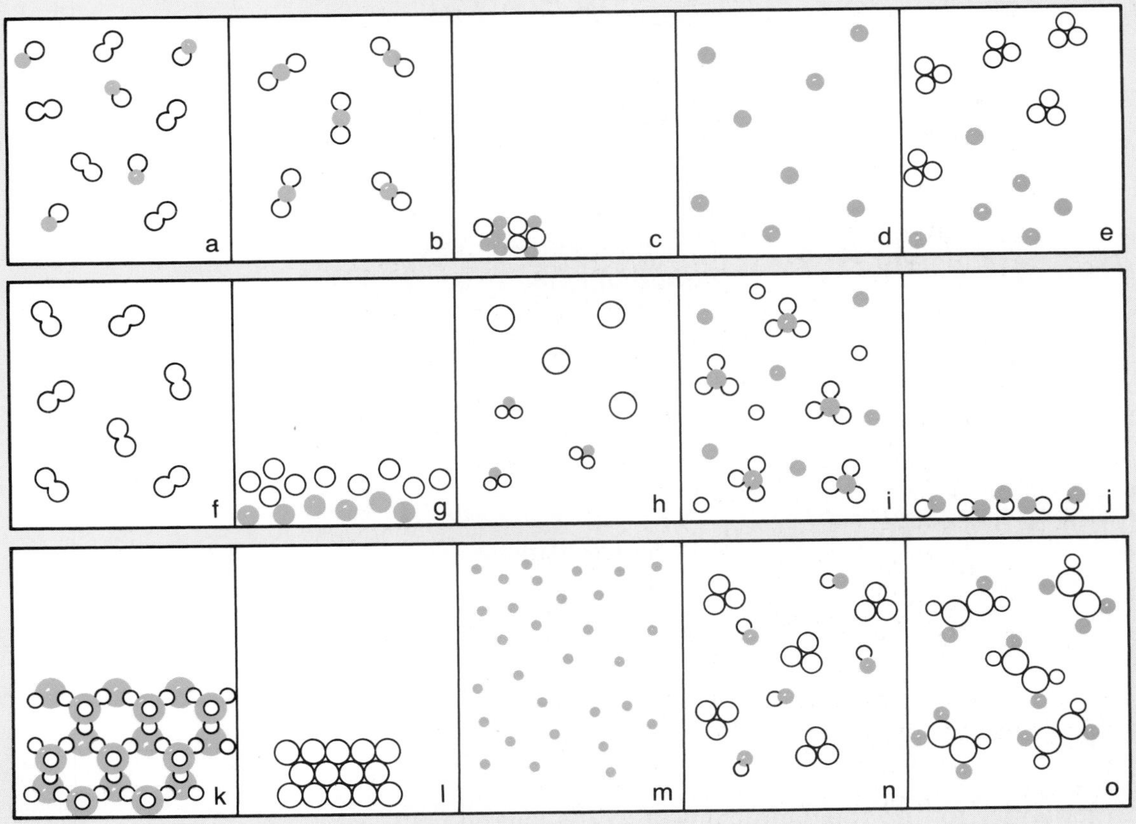

Chapter 9 Review

SUMMARY

1. Substances are either elements or compounds. 9:1
2. Mixtures may be heterogeneous or homogeneous. 9:2
3. Solutions are homogeneous mixtures. 9:2
4. Suspensions are heterogeneous mixtures in which the particles settle out. 9:3
5. A colloid is a mixture in which the particle size is between that of solutions and suspensions. 9:3
6. Colloids scatter light and show Brownian motion. 9:3
7. A physical property is a characteristic that can be observed without changing the makeup of a substance. 9:4
8. A physical change may alter the size, shape, or state of matter but not its chemical composition. 9:5
9. A chemical property is a characteristic that determines how a substance reacts to form other substances. 9:6
10. Corrosion occurs when metals are destroyed by chemical reaction with substances around them. 9:6
11. In chemical changes, new substances are produced. 9:7
12. Electrolysis is a chemical change produced by electric current. 9:7

VOCABULARY

a. Brownian motion
b. chemical change
c. chemical property
d. colloid
e. compound
f. corrosion
g. electrolysis
h. element
i. heterogeneous mixture
j. homogeneous mixture
k. physical change
l. physical property
m. solution
n. substance
o. suspension
p. Tyndall effect

Matching

Match each description with the correct vocabulary word from the list above. Some words will not be used.

1. a change in shape or state
2. the rusting of iron
3. two or more elements joined in a definite ratio
4. particles spread evenly throughout
5. particles visible to unaided eye
6. smoke, fog, or whipped cream
7. uses electric current to produce a chemical change
8. density or boiling point
9. contains one kind of atom
10. element or compound

Chapter 9 Review

MAIN IDEAS

A. Reviewing Concepts

Complete each of the following sentences with the correct word or phrase.

1. Making ice cubes is a(n) ___________ change.
2. Density is a(n) ___________ property.
3. Concrete is an example of a(n) ___________ mixture.
4. A beam of light is visible when shined through a(n) ___________.
5. A(n) ___________ is composed of only one kind of atom.
6. Particles settle out of a(n) ___________.
7. A solution is also known as a(n) ___________ mixture.
8. ___________ changes produce new substances.
9. Boiling point and freezing point are ___________ properties of matter.
10. The breakdown of matter by electricity is a(n) ___________ change.
11. A(n) ___________ is composed of two or more kinds of atoms, always in the same ratio.
12. That stainless steel resists rust is a(n) ___________ property.

Choose the word or phrase that correctly completes each of the following sentences.

13. A gelatin dessert is a *(solution, suspension, colloid)*.
14. *(Boiling, Melting, Burning)* is an example of a chemical change.
15. *(Vinegar, Carbon, Water)* is not a substance.

B. Understanding Concepts

Answer the following questions using complete sentences when possible.

16. List two chemical and two physical properties of water.
17. What properties would help you describe an apple? What kind of properties are these?
18. Compare and contrast solutions, suspensions, and colloids.
19. Compare the composition of elements, compounds, and mixtures.
20. How are heterogeneous mixtures different from homogeneous mixtures?
21. What is the relationship between chemical properties and chemical changes?
22. A beaker contains a salt water solution. What happens if a spoonful of soil is added and stirred in? What is formed?
23. Why are physical changes preferable to chemical changes to separate two or more substances?
24. What physical properties of a coat would you think about, if the temperature were 0° Celsius?
25. Compare and contrast a tire and a doughnut.

C. Applying Concepts

Answer the following questions using complete sentences when possible.

26. What properties would a manufacturer look for in a material for auto seat covers?
27. Describe electrolysis and give an example.
28. By mistake, sugar was mixed with dry rice. Describe a method you could use to separate them.
29. How could you find out whether a liquid is pure water or salt water without tasting it?
30. You are given a beaker filled with a liquid. How could you determine whether it is a solution, a suspension, or a colloid?

SKILL REVIEW

1. What is the most important step in solving a word problem?
2. Maria is studying her science assignment. She comes to a passage that refers to material that was covered earlier in the year. What should she do to help improve her studying?
3. A metalsmith was working on a variety of metal pieces one day. Some of the pieces were iron and some were gold. By the end of the day, metal filings from the various pieces were scattered on the workbench and floor. The metalsmith swept up the filings and placed the mixture in a pan. He wanted to keep the gold filings so that he could melt them down and reuse the gold. How could he separate the two metals?
4. During the gold rush of the mid-1800s, many people flocked to California to seek their fortunes. Much of the gold was obtained by a process called "panning." To pan for gold, one needed only a shallow tin pan with small holes in the bottom. The pan was used to separate stream or river water, silt, rocks, and gold. Explain how this simple tool could be used to separate the parts of this mixture.
5. David was baking cookies for a school bake sale. He accidentally mixed chocolate pieces and shredded coconut together. He needed the chocolate pieces for one recipe and the coconut for another. John walked into the kitchen and suggested that David pour cold water on the mixture. David did not understand how the cold water could help. Explain why John's suggestion can be used to separate the chocolate pieces and coconut.

PROJECTS

1. Visit a materials testing laboratory. Learn what a Brinell test is. Find out how it is used in the laboratory.
2. Obtain a chemistry handbook. What kinds of properties are listed as physical properties for each substance? How could this information be used?

READINGS

1. Cobb, Vicki. *Chemically Active!* New York: Lippincott, 1985.
2. Fialkov, Yu. *Extraordinary Properties of Ordinary Solutions*. Chicago: Imported Pubns, 1985.
3. Smay, V. E. "Thinking Window Can Switch Off the Sun." *Popular Science*. March, 1984, pp. 102–104.

STRUCTURE OF THE ATOM THE PERIODIC TABLE

Chapter 10

Atomic Structure and the Periodic Table

Imagine that you have a tiny gold nugget. You cut it in half. Then you cut each half in half. If you could continue cutting the piece in half, what would be the smallest piece of gold you could have? Over 2400 years ago, some Greek thinkers considered this question. They decided that the smallest "piece" of gold or any other element you could have is the atom. Since then, we have discovered only 109 totally different kinds of atoms. As far as we know, these 109 types of atoms make up all matter.

STRUCTURE OF THE ATOM

The understanding of atomic structure has developed over hundreds of years. Throughout the history of science, various models of the atom have been developed. As more information was learned, old models were discarded in favor of new ones. Our study of the structure of the atom begins with a look at the elements.

GOALS

1. You will learn that symbols are used to represent elements.
2. You will learn how models are used to explain the structure of the atom.
3. You will learn about protons, neutrons, mass number, atomic number, and isotopes.

10:1 Elements

Elements are substances made up of only one kind of atom. Elements cannot be broken down by a chemical change. Carbon, tin, and aluminum are common elements. The air we breathe is a mixture of mostly the elements nitrogen and oxygen. The element hydrogen is also a gas at ordinary temperatures. It is the lightest and most abundant element in the universe. We usually see the element mercury in its liquid state. What are some uses of mercury? The element copper is a shiny solid at room temperature. It is often made into electrical wires.

There is a shorthand way to write the names of elements. Table 10–1 gives the names of some of the common elements and the symbols used to represent them.

Table 10–1

Names and Symbols for Some Common Elements					
Element	**Symbol**	**Element**	**Symbol**	**Element**	**Symbol**
aluminum	Al	hydrogen	H	nitrogen	N
carbon	C	iron	Fe	oxygen	O
chlorine	Cl	magnesium	Mg	silver	Ag
copper	Cu	mercury	Hg	sodium	Na

Note that the symbols for some elements are one letter. This letter is always a capital letter. If the symbol has two letters, the first letter is always an uppercase letter. The second is always a lowercase letter. Follow this rule carefully to avoid confusing such symbols as Co and CO. Co is the element cobalt and CO is the compound carbon monoxide.

Often, the symbol for an element is quite different from the element's English name. The symbol for iron, Fe, is taken from the Latin word for iron, *ferrum*. The symbol for sodium, Na, comes from the Latin word, *natrium*. In recent years, several new elements have been produced by scientists. The newest of these elements have been assigned three-letter symbols. For example, Unp stands for element 105. Its name is unnilpentium.

What is an atom?

10:2 Models of the Atom

The smallest piece of gold that exists is an atom of gold. An **atom** is the smallest particle of any element that has the properties of that element. All elements are composed of atoms. The pictures of atoms in this book are models. When you read about the parts of the atom, the mental picture you have of the atom is also a model. Scientists have used various models to describe the atom, Figure 10–2.

FIGURE 10–1. In past centuries, scientists used other kinds of symbols for the elements. Some of these "elements" are now known to be compounds.

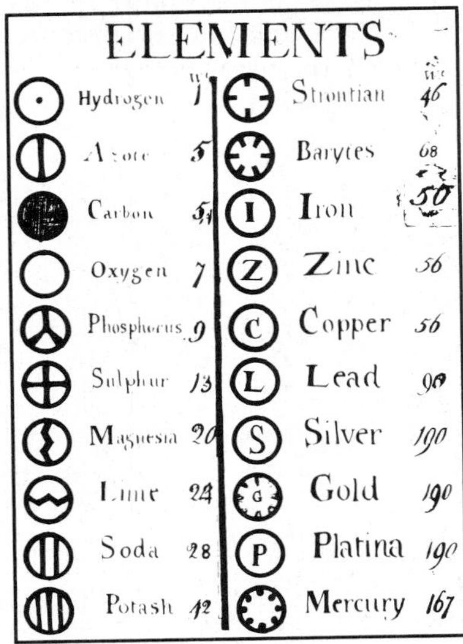

In the early 1800s, John Dalton proposed that atoms were solid spheres. He said that each element was composed of the same kind of atoms. These atoms were different from those of any other element. Later, scientists found that matter has positive and negative electric charges. J.J. Thomson suggested that an atom was a ball of positive electric charge. In this positive charge were the negative particles, much like chocolate chips in a cookie.

Further experiments led Ernest Rutherford and Niels Bohr to a different view. They proposed that the atom had a dense center. The center was positively charged. Negative particles orbited this center, or nucleus. Their

Dalton 1803

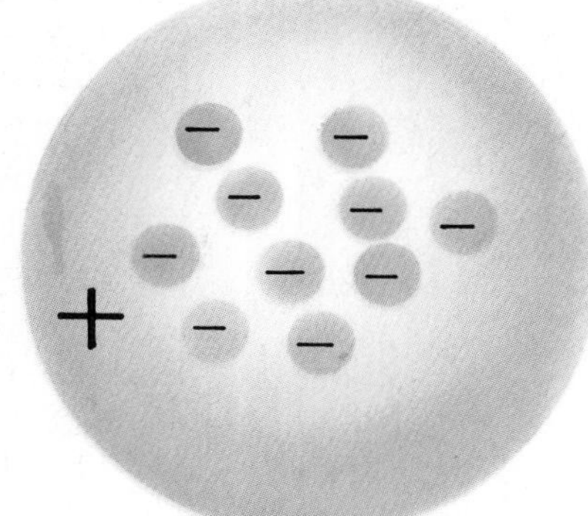

Thomson 1897

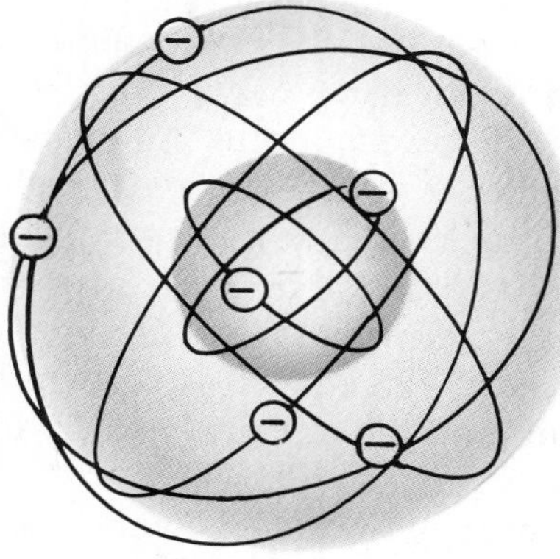

Bohr 1913

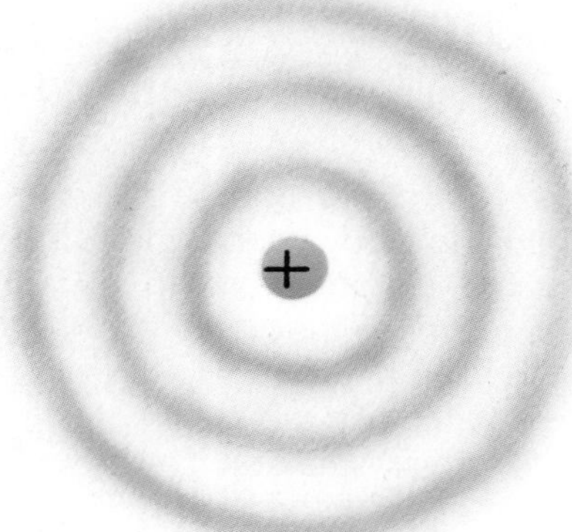

Electron Cloud
Model 1926

FIGURE 10–2. As scientists learned more, the model of the atom changed. The electron cloud model is now used to describe the atom.

model was a solar system, or planetary, model. In place of the sun was a small ball of positive charge. Around this moved negative particles in much the same way that planets orbit the sun.

The present model of the atom proposes that an atom consists of a tiny positive core surrounded by a cloud of negative electric charge. The central core is called the **nucleus** of the atom. The nucleus is a dense center of positive electric charge. Almost all of the mass of an atom is in the nucleus. The atom's nucleus is very small compared to the size of the negative cloud. Imagine that a nucleus were the size of a golf ball. The negative cloud would then have a diameter of about one kilometer.

What part of an atom has most of the atom's mass?

10:3 Parts of the Atom

Experiments with electricity in the late 1800s led to the discovery of electrons. An **electron** is a particle that moves around the nucleus forming a cloud of negative charge. About fifteen years later, scientists discovered a

What is an electron?

BIOGRAPHY

Homer Neal
1942–

Homer Neal uses particle accelerators to study protons, electrons, and other small pieces of matter as they interact at very high energies. His research takes him all over the world, from accelerators in Illinois and California to one at CERN, an international laboratory in Geneva, Switzerland.

positive particle and called it a proton. A **proton** is a particle that gives the nucleus its positive charge. The positive charge of a proton is equal in size, but opposite, to the negative charge of an electron.

A third part of the atom, the neutron, was not discovered until 1932. A **neutron** is a particle with no charge. That is why it was difficult to find. Neutrons are also in the nucleus of the atom. A proton and a neutron are about equal in mass. However, both have masses more than 1800 times that of an electron.

What identifies an element?

All atoms of an element have the same number of protons. For example, every hydrogen atom has one proton in its nucleus. Every carbon atom has six protons. The number of protons in the nucleus of an atom determines what the element is. The number of protons in an atom is called the **atomic number.**

Atoms are neutral. That is, atoms have no overall electric charge. The cloud of negative charge exactly balances the positive nucleus. The number of electrons equals the number of protons. For each proton in the nucleus, there is one electron moving in the cloud of negative charge. As you will see later, the number of neutrons in an atom of an element may vary from atom to atom.

The electron is a basic particle. However, protons and neutrons are made of other particles. These smaller particles are called quarks. At least 6 different kinds of quarks are believed to exist. Scientists believe that protons and neutrons are each made of two different kinds of quarks.

10:4 Electron Cloud

Electrons move very quickly about the nucleus but not in circular orbits. According to our present model, the region around the nucleus occupied by electrons is

FIGURE 10–3. A galaxy is similar to a model of an atom's electron cloud.

an **electron cloud.** This model of an electron cloud is much like a galaxy in space, Figure 10–3. The galaxy is brighter and more dense at the center. Its outer edges are not clearly defined. They fade out into space.

The region occupied by electrons is much the same as our picture of a galaxy. Scientists have calculated the most likely, or probable, locations of an electron within the electron cloud. The density of the cloud decreases farther from the nucleus, because electrons are less likely to be found there. They are more likely to be found close to the nucleus. The electrons making up the cloud should be thought of as being everywhere in the cloud at once. This is much like the whirling blades of a fan. The blades seem to fill the space around the hub of the fan. However, we know the blades are not everywhere at the same instant.

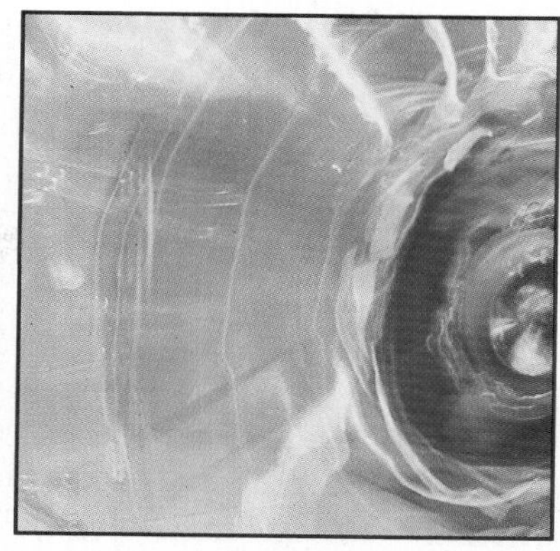

FIGURE 10–4. Like the electrons of an atom, the blades of a moving fan seem to be everywhere at once.

Where in an atom are electrons most likely to be found?

Not all electrons in an electron cloud have the same energy. In our model of the atom, electrons occupy certain energy levels. Every atom has several possible energy levels in its electron cloud. The farther an electron is from the nucleus, the more energy the electron has. Electrons with the lowest amount of energy are in the first energy level. This energy level is closest to the nucleus, Figure 10–5. Only two electrons can be in this first energy level. The atom's second energy level can have up to 8 electrons. The third energy level can have up to 18 electrons. Energy levels farther from the nucleus can have 32 or more electrons.

TECHNOLOGY: ADVANCES

Viewing Atoms

Solids are made of regular patterns of tiny atoms. Not even powerful electron microscopes can see the pattern directly. However, a new instrument, the scanning tunneling microscope (STM), produces pictures of the arrangements of atoms on solid surfaces. With it, scientists can even see bonds between atoms.

The STM views a surface much like a blind person reads braille. A blind person rubs his or her fingers over a page to find patterns in raised dots. An STM uses a very sharp "finger" that is brought near, but not touching, the surface. Electrons flow across the gap between the surface and the point. The more electrons, the closer the surface. In this way the STM maps out the "hills and valleys" of a surface.

The use of the STM has already led to new understanding of chemical reactions like those that occur in the catalytic converter of a car. Scientists have also used it to see the shape of a virus and a DNA molecule while in water. The STM may be useful in learning more about the role of these particles in disease.

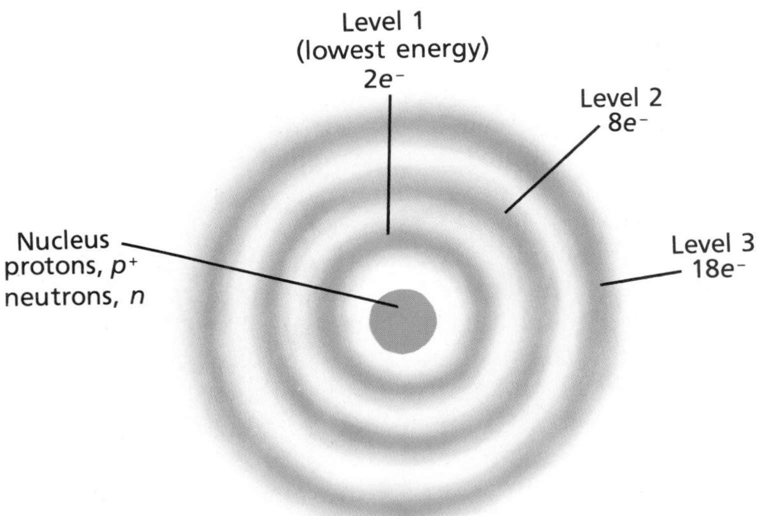

FIGURE 10–5. Each energy level can hold a specific number of electrons. Symbols may be used to show electrons (e^-), protons (p^+), and neutrons (n).

F.Y.I. Most of the atom is empty space through which electrons move. If the atom were scaled up in size so that its nucleus were the size of a small marble, the diameter of the atom would be about the width of the Houston Astrodome.

Electrons are arranged in pairs in energy levels. As an example, magnesium has an atomic number of 12. Thus, a magnesium atom contains 12 protons and 12 electrons. The first energy level has 2 electrons (one pair). The second energy level has 8 electrons (four pairs). The two remaining electrons are in the third energy level.

Atoms of most elements have electrons in more than three energy levels. Uranium has 92 electrons in seven energy levels. Many of the properties of elements can be explained by the number and arrangement of electrons in the energy levels of their atoms.

10:5 Atomic Mass

On what does the mass of an atom depend?

The mass of an atom depends on the number of protons and neutrons in its nucleus. Compared to the nucleus of an atom, the electrons have very little mass. The mass of a single proton or neutron itself is extremely small. A proton, for example, has a mass of 0.000 000 000 000 000 000 000 001 673 g. Because of this, scientists have agreed upon a standard atomic mass unit to measure the mass of atoms. The standard atomic mass unit (u) is defined as 1/12 the mass of a carbon-12 atom. A carbon-12 atom has 6 protons and 6 neutrons. Thus, protons and neutrons have a mass of about 1 u each.

The **mass number** of an atom is simply the sum of the number of protons and the number of neutrons. Therefore, if you know the number of protons and neu-

Table 10–2

Mass Numbers of Some Atoms			
Element	**Protons**	**Neutrons**	**Atomic mass**
carbon (C)	6	6	12 u
oxygen (O)	8	8	16 u
sodium (Na)	11	12	23 u
potassium (K)	19	20	39 u
iron (Fe)	26	30	56 u

Be
Beryllium
4 protons
+5 neutrons
Mass number = 9
atomic mass = 9 u

FIGURE 10–6. The atomic mass for beryllium is the sum of the number of neutrons and protons in the nucleus of the beryllium atom.

trons in an atom, you can find the mass number. For example, an atom of beryllium has 4 protons and 5 neutrons. Its mass number is 9. Mass number can be used to find an approximate atomic mass of an atom. The atomic mass of beryllium is approximately 9 u.

If you know the mass number and the atomic number, you can find the number of neutrons. The number of neutrons is found by subtracting the atomic number from the mass number.

number of neutrons = mass number − atomic number

10:6 Isotopes

All atoms of an element have the same number of protons. However, some of these atoms may have more or fewer neutrons than others. Atoms of the same element with different numbers of neutrons are called **isotopes** (I suh tohps). For example, hydrogen has three isotopes. A hydrogen atom may contain zero, one, or two neutrons. Every atom of carbon has six protons, but some

What are isotopes?

Table 10–3

Naturally Occurring Isotopes of Tin (Sn)			
Electrons	**Protons**	**Neutrons**	**Mass number**
50	50	62	112
50	50	64	114
50	50	65	115
50	50	66	116
50	50	67	117
50	50	68	118
50	50	69	119
50	50	70	120
50	50	72	122
50	50	74	124

FIGURE 10–7. The three isotopes of hydrogen differ in the number of neutrons each has in its nucleus.

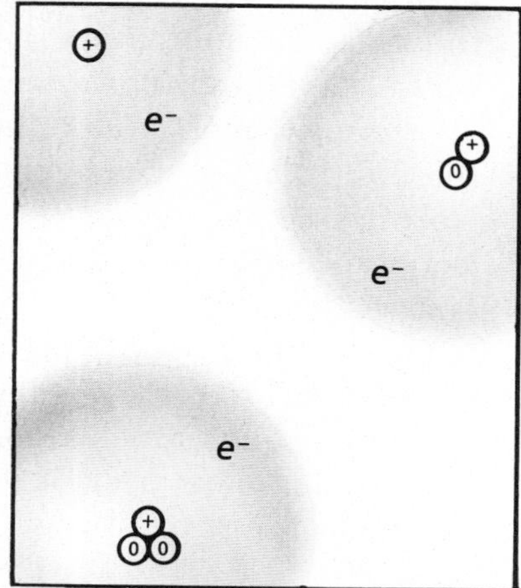

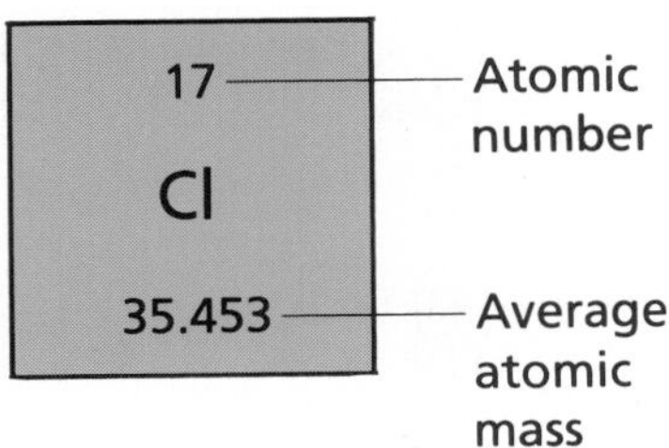

FIGURE 10–8. The periodic table shows the atomic number and the average atomic mass for each element with the element symbol.

carbon atoms have six neutrons and some have eight neutrons. These two types of carbon atoms are isotopes. Ten isotopes of tin are found in nature. Some elements have only one natural isotope. Isotopes of elements not found naturally can be produced in the laboratory.

There are two ways to show the difference between isotopes of an element. In one way, the name of the element is followed by the mass number. For example, oxygen-16 stands for an atom of oxygen that has a mass number of 16. Carbon-12 is the isotope of carbon that has a mass number of 12. The numeral is the mass number of the isotope being discussed. The second way is to write the symbol of the element with the mass number and atomic number. For example $^{39}_{18}Ar$ is argon-39. The carbon-12 isotope has the following symbol.

$$\text{Mass number} \longrightarrow \; ^{12}_{6}C \longleftarrow \text{Element symbol}$$
$$\text{Atomic number} \longrightarrow \uparrow 6$$

Most elements in nature are found to be mixtures of isotopes. For example, a sample of chlorine gas is a mixture of two isotopes, chlorine-35 and chlorine-37. There are about three chlorine-35 atoms for each chlorine-37 atom. Therefore, the average mass of a chlorine atom in the sample is nearer to 35 than to 37.

CAREER

Electron Microscopist

Understanding the nature of the electron was only the beginning for Nerma Clark as she studied to be an electron microscopist. Just as a light microscope uses light particles to display an image, the electron microscope uses electrons. These subatomic particles are bounced off the specimen and reflected back to the observer by electromagnetic plates. Nerma learned to read the pictures projected on a screen, much like a radiologist reads an X ray.

As an electron microscopist, Nerma enjoys working with small structures and she spends much time in research. Most of her time is spent in labs preparing and observing slides. Some microscopists look for signs of disease while Nerma studies cell structures. The computer industry uses microscopists to check for flaws in computer chips.

For career information, write

Electron Microscopy and Photography
Eastman Kodak Company
Rochester, NY 10017

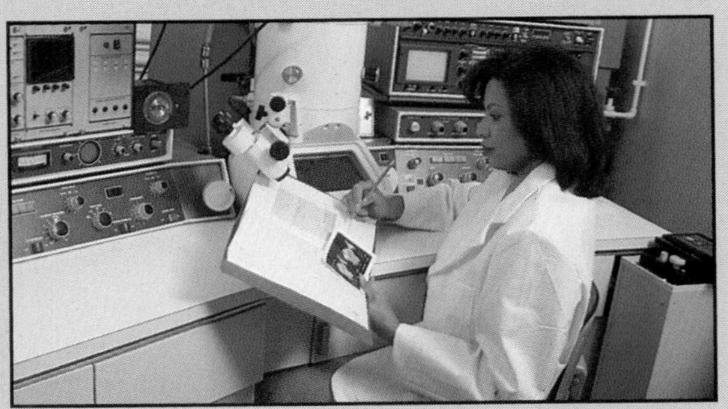

SKILL

Predicting

Problem: How can you predict an element's group and period?

Materials

paper and pencil

Background

Mendeleev and other early scientists grouped elements according to properties. They found that these properties repeated in a regular or periodic manner. Scientists used this fact to predict properties of undiscovered elements.

Let's see if you can predict a property of the elements. The property we will examine is electron arrangement. First you need to review what you know about electron arrangement. Refer to Table 10–5 and Section 10:4. How does the number of electrons in an atom change from left to right across a period in the periodic table? From Table 10–5, we see that the number of electrons increases by one for each element in a period. How does the number of electrons compare with the number of protons in an atom? If you said they are the same, you are correct.

Procedure

1. Copy the table below in your notebook.

Element	Electrons			
	Total	Level 1 ___	Level 2 ___	Level 3 ___
argon carbon helium lithium silicon sodium				

2. Write the maximum number of electrons in each energy level on the blanks in the table heading.
3. Write the total number of electrons for atoms of each element in the first column.
4. For each element, assign the correct number of electrons to each energy level.

Analysis

1. Prepare another table using the headings shown below. Complete the table by using the information from the six elements studied.
   Element
   Energy level of outer electrons
   Period element is located in
   Number of outer electrons
   Group element is in
2. How is the period an element is in related to the number of energy levels over which its atom's electrons are spread?

Conclusions and Applications

3. How can you predict an element's group and period?
4. Element Q has 2 electrons in the sixth energy level. These are its highest energy electrons. Predict the period and group in which Element Q can be found.
5. Element X has 7 electrons in the second energy level. Predict the period and group in which Element X can be found.
6. Potassium has 19 electrons. In what energy level will its outer electron(s) be located? In what period and group is potassium located?
7. Element G is located in Group 3 and Period 2. Over how many energy levels are its electrons spread? How many are in its outer level?

INVESTIGATION 10–1

Atomic Models

Problem: How do pencil models of atoms differ from real atoms?

Materials

periodic table
compass
paper and pencil

Procedure

1. Use the periodic table to find the number of protons, neutrons, and electrons in a lithium atom. Use a mass number of 7. List the number of each particle in a data table.
2. On a piece of paper, draw a circle about 2 cm in diameter.
3. Write the number of protons in the circle next to a p^+ symbol.
4. Write the number of neutrons in the circle next to an n symbol.
5. Now draw another circle around the circle you have already drawn. On this circle, write the number of electrons in the first energy level next to an e^- symbol.
6. Draw another circle and write the number of electrons in the second energy level.
7. Repeat until all the electrons are placed.

FIGURE 10–9.

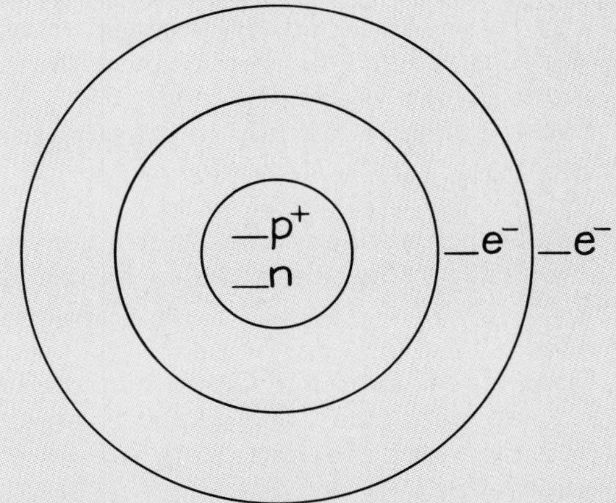

8. Using the steps given above, draw diagrams for atoms of boron (mass number = 11), oxygen (mass number = 16), and neon (mass number = 20). Before drawing the diagrams, list the numbers of protons, neutrons, and electrons in each of these types of atoms in a data table.

Data and Observations

Atom	Protons	Neutrons	Electrons
Lithium			
Boron			
Oxygen			
Neon			

Analysis

1. What part of your diagram represents the nucleus of an atom?
2. What particles are found in the nucleus of an atom?
3. What part of your diagram represents the electron cloud?

Conclusions and Applications

4. How would electrons be distributed in a sulfur atom?
5. The electrons in calcium atoms are spread over four energy levels. Draw a diagram for calcium similar to Figure 10–9 and show the arrangement of its electrons.
6. How do pencil models of atoms differ from real atoms?

Review

1. Oxygen has an atomic number of 8; carbon, 6; magnesium, 12; chlorine, 17; and argon, 18. How many electrons are in an atom of each?
2. How many electrons are in each energy level for an atom of each element listed in Question 1?
3. Draw energy level diagrams for carbon and chlorine.
4. Copy the following table on a sheet of paper. Complete the table by filling in the empty boxes.

Element	Atomic Number	Number of Protons	Number of Neutrons	Atomic Mass Number
Calcium (Ca)		20	20	
Nickel (Ni)		28		59
Gold (Au)	79		118	
	6			14

★ 5. Assume that an element found in nature has two isotopes: 40% is an isotope with atomic mass 35, and 60% is an isotope with atomic mass 37. What would be the average atomic mass of the element?

THE PERIODIC TABLE

The periodic table is one of the most useful tools for a scientist. It came about through the efforts of a great number of scientists over a period of years. Dimitri Mendeleev is given much of the credit for the modern table. However, he stood on the shoulders of others who had tried before him. Science always builds on the efforts of others.

GOALS

1. You will learn about the structure of the periodic table.
2. You will learn that relative chemical activity of elements can be determined from the periodic table.

10:7 Structure of the Periodic Table

Dimitri Mendeleev (men duh LAY uf) (1834–1907), a Russian chemist, classified the elements known at his time. He wrote information about each element on a card. By arranging the elements in order of increasing mass, Mendeleev found that they showed a pattern of properties that repeated. By arranging the cards to begin a new row each time the pattern repeated, he saw that the elements formed a table, Figure 10–10.

			Ti=50	Zr=90	?=180
			V=51	Nb=94	Ta=182
			Cr=52	Mo=96	W=186
			Mn=55	Rh=104,4(103)	*Pt=197,4
			Fe=56	Ru=104,4(101)	*Ir=198(193)
			Ni,Co=59*	Pd=106,6	*Os=199(191)
H=1			Cu=63,4	Ag=108	*Hg=200
	Be=9,4	Mg=24	Zn=65,2	Cd=112	
	B=11	Al=27,4	? 68	*Ur=116(238)	*Au=197?
	C=12	Si=28	? 70	Sn=118	
	N=14	P=31	As=75	Sb=122	Bi=210
	O=16	S=32	Se=79,4	Te=128?	
	F=19	Cl=35,5	Br=80	I=127	
Li=7	Na=23	K=39	Rb=85,4	Cs=133	*Tl=204
		Ca=40	Sr=87,6	Ba=137	*Pb=207
		?=45	*Ce=92(138)		
		*Er=56 (166)	*La=94 (137)		
		*Yt=60 (88)	*Di 95 (140)		
		*In=75,6 (113)	*Th 118 (231)		

FIGURE 10–10. Mendeleev's early periodic tables had question marks to represent elements that had not yet been discovered.

Mendeleev's chart is known as the periodic table. The **periodic table** is a table of elements classified by their properties. Periodic means that something "repeats at regular intervals."

How was Mendeleev able to predict the properties of undiscovered elements?

However, there were some blank spots in this table. Mendeleev believed these blank spots would be filled with elements yet to be discovered. From the patterns in the table, he was able to predict the properties of these unknown elements. For example, Mendeleev predicted the existence of the element germanium. He called this element "ekasilicon." He believed its proper-

FIGURE 10–11. Mendeleev predicted the properties of germanium and other elements that had not been discovered.

"EKASILICON" (GERMANIUM)

Properties	Predicted	Actual
Atomic mass	72	72.6
Density	5.5 g/cm^3	5.35 g/cm^3
Color	dark grey	grey-white
Effect of water	none	none
Effect of acid	slight	HCl-no effect
Effect of base	slight	KOH-no effect

ties would be like the properties of silicon. As Figure 10–11 shows, Mendeleev's predicted properties were fairly açcurate.

There was a problem with Mendeleev's table. When he arranged the elements by their properties, the atomic masses did not all fit. When he put them in order of increasing mass, the properties did not all match. Later, when a way of measuring atomic number was found, the elements were arranged by atomic number rather than mass. The properties matched.

F.Y.I. Henry Moseley (1887–1915) discovered a way to determine the atomic numbers of elements using X rays. His work led to the present arrangement of elements in the periodic table. Moseley's brilliant scientific career was cut short at the age of 27. He was killed during World War I while fighting as a foot soldier in Gallipoli.

The periodic table on pages 228–229 shows how the elements are classified today. Each box contains one element. The name and symbol for the element are in the center of the box. Below the name is the atomic mass of the element. The atomic masses given for elements in the periodic table are average atomic masses. An **average atomic mass** is an average of the masses of all the isotopes that occur in nature for that element. When doing calculations with atomic masses of elements in this textbook, you should round the average atomic mass on the periodic table to the units place. Use the rounded value to carry out your calculations.

What is an average atomic mass?

10:8 Groups of Elements

In the periodic table, elements are arranged in vertical rows, or columns. These columns are called **groups** or families. Groups on the table are labeled 1 through 18. Each group contains elements with similar properties. For example, 17 contains fluorine, chlorine, bromine, iodine, and astatine. This group of elements is known as the **halogen** (HAL uh jen) **family.** Each element in this group has seven electrons in its outer energy level. The highest energy electrons of an atom are in the outer energy level. This level is farthest from the nucleus. Chemical reactions usually involve outer level electrons. Because all halogens have the same number of electrons in the outer energy level, they have similar chemical reactions.

How many groups of elements are in the periodic table?

The elements of Group 18 are called the **noble gas family.** All but one of the elements in Group 18 have eight electrons in their outer energy level. Helium has two electrons in its outer energy level. These electron arrangements are very stable. As a result, the noble gases occur in nature as single atoms. No compounds of the noble gases are found in nature. At one time, Group 18 elements were called inert gases. It was thought that they did not form any compounds.

FIGURE 10–12. The halogen family makes up Group 17 on the periodic table. Group 18 is the noble gas family.

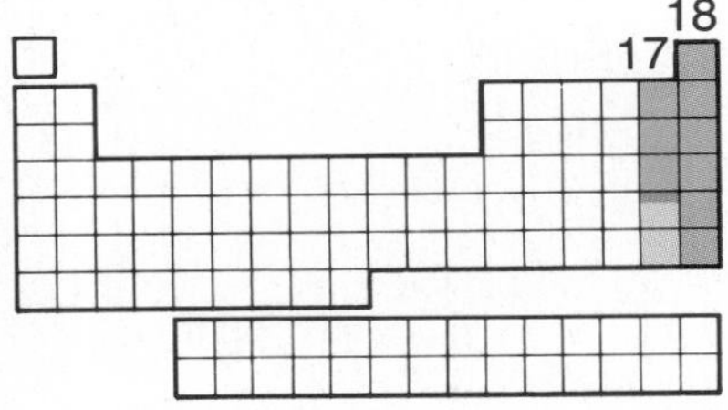

Table 10–4

The Periodic Table
Based on Carbon 12 = 12.0000

	1
1	1 **H** Hydrogen 1.00794

Atomic number
Symbol
Element name
Atomic mass

Metallic Properties

Transition Elements

Period	1	2	3	4	5	6	7	8	9
2	3 **Li** Lithium 6.941	4 **Be** Beryllium 9.01218							
3	11 **Na** Sodium 22.98977	12 **Mg** Magnesium 24.305							
4	19 **K** Potassium 39.0983	20 **Ca** Calcium 40.078	21 **Sc** Scandium 44.95591	22 **Ti** Titanium 47.88	23 **V** Vanadium 50.9415	24 **Cr** Chromium 51.9961	25 **Mn** Manganese 54.9380	26 **Fe** Iron 55.847	27 **Co** Cobalt 58.9332
5	37 **Rb** Rubidium 85.4678	38 **Sr** Strontium 87.62	39 **Y** Yttrium 88.9059	40 **Zr** Zirconium 91.224	41 **Nb** Niobium 92.9064	42 **Mo** Molybdenum 95.94	43 **Tc** Technetium 97.9072*	44 **Ru** Ruthenium 101.07	45 **Rh** Rhodium 102.9055
6	55 **Cs** Cesium 132.9054	56 **Ba** Barium 137.33	71 **Lu** Lutetium 174.967	72 **Hf** Hafnium 178.49	73 **Ta** Tantalum 180.9479	74 **W** Tungsten 183.85	75 **Re** Rhenium 186.207	76 **Os** Osmium 190.2	77 **Ir** Iridium 192.22
7	87 **Fr** Francium 223.0197*	88 **Ra** Radium 226.0254	103 **Lr** Lawrencium 260.1054*	104 **Unq** Unnilquadium 261*	105 **Unp** Unnilpentium 262*	106 **Unh** Unnilhexium 263*	107 **Uns** Unnilseptium 262*	108 **Uno** Unniloctium 265*	109 **Une** Unnilennium 266*

Metallic Properties

Lanthanoid Series	57 **La** Lanthanum 138.9055	58 **Ce** Cerium 140.12	59 **Pr** Praseodymium 140.9077	60 **Nd** Neodymium 144.24	61 **Pm** Promethium 144.9128*	62 **Sm** Samarium 150.36
Actinoid Series	89 **Ac** Actinium 227.0278*	90 **Th** Thorium 232.0381	91 **Pa** Protactinium 231.0359*	92 **U** Uranium 238.0289	93 **Np** Neptunium 237.0482	94 **Pu** Plutonium 244.0642*

10	11	12	13	14	15	16	17	18 Noble Gases
								2 **He** Helium 4.002602
			5 **B** Boron 10.811	6 **C** Carbon 12.011	7 **N** Nitrogen 14.0067	8 **O** Oxygen 15.9994	9 **F** Fluorine 18.998403	10 **Ne** Neon 20.179
			13 **Al** Aluminum 26.98154	14 **Si** Silicon 28.0855	15 **P** Phosphorus 30.97376	16 **S** Sulfur 32.06	17 **Cl** Chlorine 35.453	18 **Ar** Argon 39.948
28 **Ni** Nickel 58.69	29 **Cu** Copper 63.546	30 **Zn** Zinc 65.39	31 **Ga** Gallium 69.723	32 **Ge** Germanium 72.59	33 **As** Arsenic 74.9216	34 **Se** Selenium 78.96	35 **Br** Bromine 79.904	36 **Kr** Krypton 83.80
46 **Pd** Palladium 106.42	47 **Ag** Silver 107.8682	48 **Cd** Cadmium 112.41	49 **In** Indium 114.82	50 **Sn** Tin 118.710	51 **Sb** Antimony 121.75	52 **Te** Tellurium 127.60	53 **I** Iodine 126.9045	54 **Xe** Xenon 131.29
78 **Pt** Platinum 195.08	79 **Au** Gold 196.9665	80 **Hg** Mercury 200.59	81 **Tl** Thallium 204.383	82 **Pb** Lead 207.2	83 **Bi** Bismuth 208.9804	84 **Po** Polonium 208.9824*	85 **At** Astatine 209.98712*	86 **Rn** Radon 222.017*

Nonmetallic Properties

- Metallic Properties
- Nonmetallic Properties
- Metalloids
- Synthetic Elements

63 **Eu** Europium 151.96	64 **Gd** Gadolinium 157.25	65 **Tb** Terbium 158.9254	66 **Dy** Dysprosium 162.50	67 **Ho** Holmium 164.9304	68 **Er** Erbium 167.26	69 **Tm** Thulium 168.9342	70 **Yb** Ytterbium 173.04
95 **Am** Americium 243.0614*	96 **Cm** Curium 247.0703*	97 **Bk** Berkelium 247.0703*	98 **Cf** Californium 251.0796*	99 **Es** Einsteinium 252.0828*	100 **Fm** Fermium 257.0951*	101 **Md** Mendelevium 258.986*	102 **No** Nobelium 259.1009*

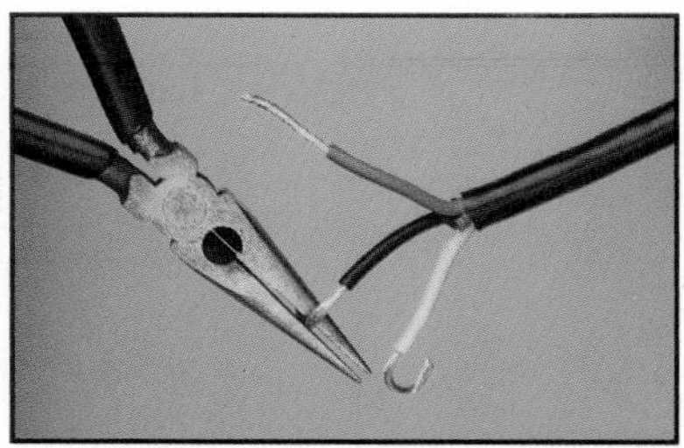

a

b

FIGURE 10–13. Copper (a) has metallic properties: it is shiny, malleable, and can be made into wire. Sulfur (b) is nonmetallic: it is a brittle, yellow solid at room temperature.

10:9 Periods of Elements

The horizontal rows of the periodic table are called **periods.** Period 2 begins with lithium and ends with neon. Each element across a period is in a different group. Each group has different properties. The elements on the left side of the table are metals. Atoms of most **metals** have three or fewer electrons in the outer energy level. Elements such as copper, iron, and zinc are metals. Metals are similar to each other in several properties. They are shiny. Generally, they conduct heat and electricity well. Metals tend to lose electrons when they react.

Elements on the right side of the periodic table are nonmetals. **Nonmetals** usually have five or more electrons in their outer energy level. Carbon, hydrogen, and helium are exceptions. Nonmetals also have characteristic properties. Most are poor conductors of heat and electricity. Most are gases at room temperature. Some are brittle solids. Nonmetals tend to gain electrons when they react with metals.

What elements lie along the stair-step line that divides the periodic table?

Note the stair-step line that divides the periodic table on pages 228–229. Elements to the left of this line have more metallic properties. Elements to the right of this line are more nonmetallic. The elements located along this line are called metalloids (MET ul oyds). **Metalloids** have some properties of both metals and nonmetals. The element boron is considered a metalloid. The other metalloids are silicon, germanium, arsenic, antimony, tellurium, polonium, and astatine.

Table 10–5

Reading the Periodic Table Left to Right

	Lithium Li	Beryllium Be	Boron B	Carbon C	Nitrogen N	Oxygen O	Fluorine F	Neon Ne
Atomic number	3	4	5	6	7	8	9	10
Atomic mass number	7	9	11	12	14	16	19	20
Group	1	2	13	14	15	16	17	18
Outer electrons	1	2	3	4	5	6	7	8
How atom combines with other atoms	gives up electrons	gives up electrons	shares electrons	shares electrons	shares electrons	usually shares electrons	gains an electron	very stable, seldom combines
Type of element	metal	metal	metalloid	nonmetal	nonmetal	nonmetal	nonmetal	nonmetal

Periods 4 through 7 contain rows of transition elements. The **transition elements** make up Groups 3 through 12. Atoms of transition elements have one or two electrons in their outer energy level. Many familiar metals, such as iron, copper, and nickel, are transition elements.

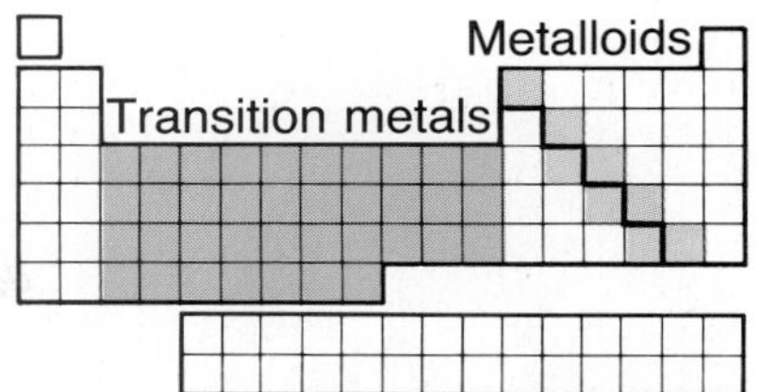

FIGURE 10–14. The eight metalloid elements occur in Groups 13–17. Transition metals make up Groups 3–12.

10:10 Chemical Activity

How reactive an element is can be determined from its position in the periodic table. The **chemical activity** of an element is how easily the element reacts with other elements. For example, oxygen is one of the most active elements. It reacts with most elements to form compounds. In contrast, the noble gases have low chemical activity. They react with few elements.

What is the chemical activity of an element?

The activity of an element depends on how easily it gains or loses electrons. For example, cesium and lithium are in Group 1. Atoms of both elements have one electron in the outer energy level. In lithium, this one electron is in the second energy level. However, cesium's outer-level electron is in the sixth energy level. It is much farther away from the positive nucleus than the outer-level electron of lithium. In addition, the outer-level electron of cesium is shielded from the positive

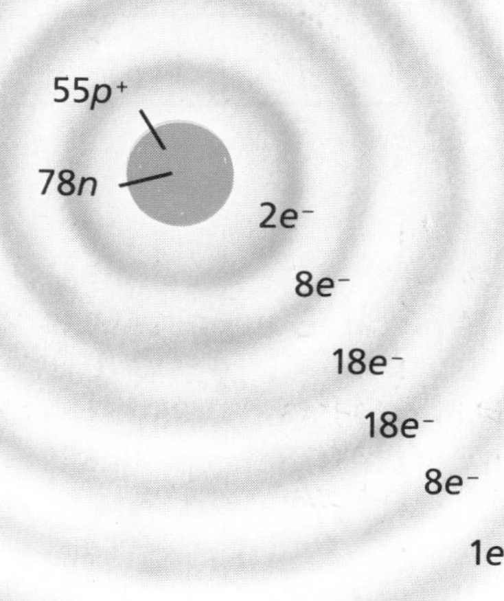

FIGURE 10–15. The outer-level electron of a cesium atom is loosely held because of its distance from the nucleus. Also, it is shielded by five other energy levels of electrons.

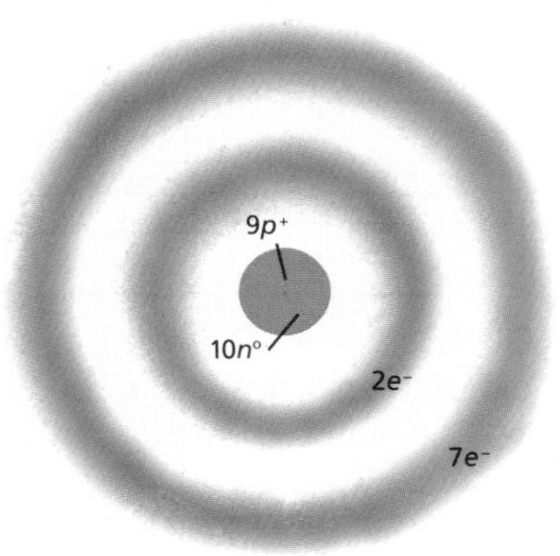

FIGURE 10–16. The outer energy level of fluorine is close to the nucleus. Thus, fluorine atoms strongly attract electrons of other atoms and they are very reactive.

nucleus by five other levels of electrons. As a result, the attraction between the outer electron of a cesium atom and the positive nucleus is weak. The attraction between the outer electron and the nucleus of a lithium atom is much stronger. Thus, the outer electron of cesium is more loosely held than that of lithium. It is easier for cesium to lose its electron. Thus, cesium is more chemically active than lithium.

The same holds true for the other metals. The most active metals of a group are at the bottom of the group. The most active metals are, on the whole, at the bottom left of the periodic table.

Where are the most active nonmetallic elements located in the periodic table?

The activity of nonmetals can also be determined from the periodic table. Fluorine and iodine are both in Group 17. Group 17 elements usually gain an electron when combining with other atoms. The electrons in the outer energy level of fluorine are much closer to the nucleus than the outer-level electrons of iodine. Also, in fluorine there are fewer shielding electrons between the outer level and the nucleus. Thus, fluorine is more active than iodine because fluorine has a much greater attraction for the electrons of other atoms. Fluorine is above iodine in the table. The most active nonmetals are at the top right of the periodic table, excluding Group 18.

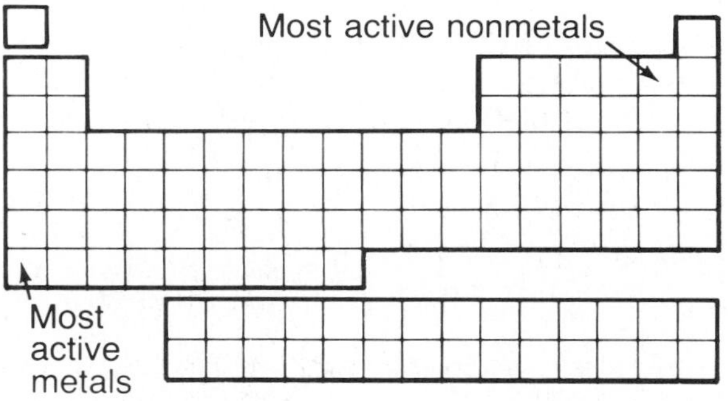

FIGURE 10–17. The most active metals are in the lower left corner of the periodic table. The most active nonmetals are in the upper right corner (excluding the noble gases).

Review

Use the periodic table on pages 228–229 to answer questions 6–10.

6. Write the symbol or name for each of the following elements, as appropriate.

a. gold	e. Mn	i. Fe
b. Hg	f. Zn	j. lead
c. uranium	g. fluorine	k. Co
d. sodium	h. unnilquadium	l. nitrogen

7. List the atomic number and average atomic mass of each of these elements.
   a. Li b. N c. Al d. Ti e. Os
8. Indicate which element in each set is not in the correct group or period.
   a. hydrogen, calcium, sodium, cesium
   b. calcium, barium, magnesium, vanadium
   c. sulfur, phosphorus, nitrogen, arsenic
   d. uranium, neon, xenon, helium
   e. Cl, Al, Tl, Na, Ar
9. Use the periodic table to decide which element in each of the following pairs is more active.
   a. potassium-sodium
   b. oxygen-sulfur
   c. chlorine-iodine
   d. magnesium-calcium

★ 10. Mendeleev's table as he derived it did not work for three pairs of elements. He assumed their atomic masses were incorrect. Which pairs are reversed in Mendeleev's original table?

PROBLEM SOLVING

Can you correctly place elements into a periodic table?

Copy the abbreviated periodic table. Use the clues to place symbols for the fictitious elements into the table. Once a letter or letter combination has been used, it cannot be used again. If you solve the problem correctly, a question can be read from left to right.

Clues

1. Elements Y, Ic, Re, S, and Ly are noble gases. Y is the lightest, Ic is the heaviest. The number of electrons increases from Re to S to Ly.
2. Element Wh has only one electron.
3. Elements Pe, Ex, El, and A have more than one electron each. They are shown in order of decreasing chemical activity.
4. Elements Me, T, and D are a nonmetallic family. T is most reactive. Me is smaller in size than D.
5. En, E, and O form a group. E has an atomic number of 12. En is in the third period.
6. Elements Tr, Ri, and Em are metals. Each has two electrons in its outer energy level. Em has the fewest total electrons. Tr is less reactive than Ri.

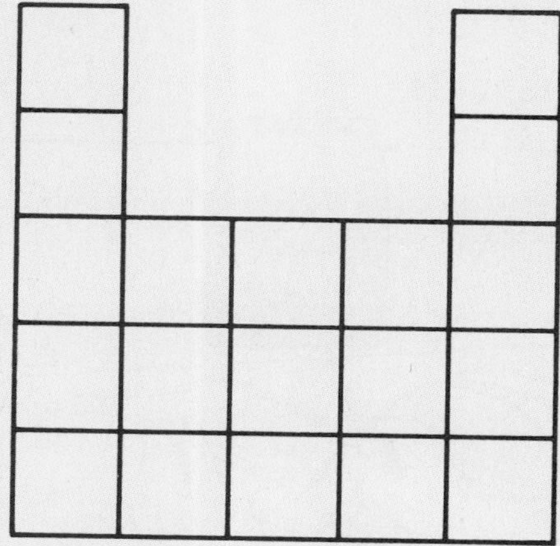

INVESTIGATION 10–2

Metals and Nonmetals

Problem: What are some properties of metals and nonmetals?

Materials

samples of elements
dilute hydrochloric acid
small hammer
chisel or nail
conductivity apparatus
beaker
5 test tubes
dropper
goggles
apron

CAUTION: *Handle acid with care. If spillage occurs, rinse area with plenty of water.*

Procedure

1. Obtain a small sample of each element. Observe the physical properties that are apparent. Record your observations.
2. With the small hammer, try to drive the chisel or nail into each sample. This procedure tests the malleability of your sample. Record your observations for each sample.
3. Using the conductivity apparatus, Figure 10–18, touch the two rods to each sample of Al, Cu, C, Pb, S, and Zn. Record your observations.
4. Place a small sample of each element in separate labeled test tubes. Add a few drops of acid to each test tube. Record your observations.

FIGURE 10–18.

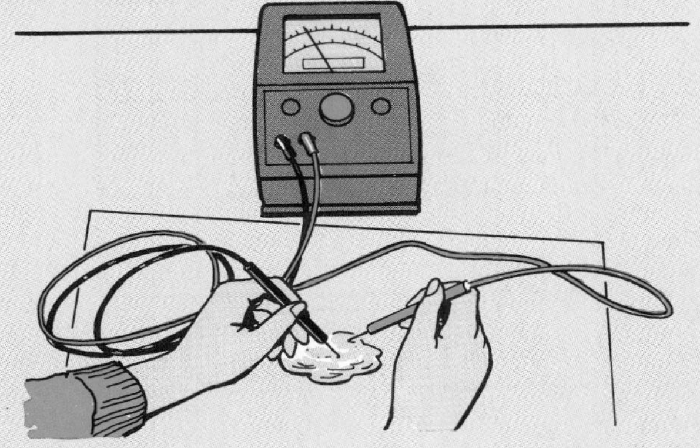

Data and Observations

Element	Physical properties observed
Al	
Cu	
C	
S	

Element	Conductivity	Hammer	Acid
Al			
Zn			
Cu			
C			
S			
Pb			

Analysis

1. Rank the elements tested according to their conductivity. List the best conductor first.
2. Rank the elements according to their malleability and then by reactivity.

Conclusions and Applications

3. Based on information from the periodic table, classify your elements as metals or nonmetals.
4. How do the properties of the elements you observed compare to their positions in the periodic table?
5. What are some properties of metals and nonmetals?

Chapter 10 Review

SUMMARY

1. Elements contain one kind of atom, cannot be broken down by chemical change, and are represented by symbols. 10:1
2. The present model of an atom is that of a dense, positive, central nucleus surrounded by a cloud of negative charge. 10:2
3. The three major particles of an atom are electrons, protons, and neutrons. 10:3
4. Electrons that make up the cloud of negative charge occupy different energy levels. 10:4
5. The mass number of an atom is the sum of the protons and the neutrons in the nucleus. 10:5
6. Isotopes are atoms of an element with different numbers of neutrons. 10:6
7. When arranged in a periodic table according to atomic number, element properties repeat. 10:7
8. Elements in the same group (column) have similar properties. 10:8
9. Elements are metals, nonmetals, or metalloids. 10:9
10. Metals at the bottom of a group are most reactive; nonmetals at the top of a group are most active. 10:10

VOCABULARY

a. atom
b. atomic number
c. average atomic mass
d. chemical activity
e. electron
f. electron cloud
g. groups
h. halogen family
i. isotopes
j. mass number
k. metalloids
l. metals
m. neutron
n. noble gas family
o. nonmetals
p. nucleus
q. periodic table
r. periods
s. proton
t. transition elements

Matching

Match each description with the correct vocabulary word from the list above. Some words will not be used.

1. the columns on a periodic table
2. atoms of an element that have different numbers of neutrons
3. another name for the group in which argon is found
4. one of the two particles that make up the atomic mass number of an element
5. the number of protons in an atom
6. region around nucleus occupied by electrons
7. elements generally on the left of the table
8. another name for elements of the fluorine family
9. horizontal rows of periodic table
10. elements on the top right of the periodic table

Chapter 10 Review

MAIN IDEAS

A. Reviewing Concepts

Complete each of the following sentences with the correct word or phrase.

1. Electrons are particles with a(n) ____________ electric charge.
2. All atoms of the same element contain the same number of ____________.
3. Isotopes are atoms of an element that contain different numbers of ____________.
4. A column on the periodic table is also called a(n) ____________.
5. The most active metals are found at the ____________ of the periodic table.
6. The first energy level contains no more than ____ electrons.
7. The elements in the periodic table are arranged according to ____________.
8. Iron-56 has ____ protons, ____ neutrons, and ____ electrons.
9. Lithium is found in Group ____.
10. Most of the mass of an atom is in the ____________.
11. The sum of neutrons and protons in an atom is the ____________ number.
12. The charge of the nucleus of an atom is ____________.

Choose the word or phrase that correctly completes each of the following sentences.

13. The mass of an electron is *(greater than, less than, equal to)* the mass of a proton.
14. The transition elements are *(metals, nonmetals, metalloids)*.
15. Nitrogen-15 atoms have *(7, 8, 15)* protons.

B. Understanding Concepts

Answer the following questions using complete sentences when possible.

16. A boron atom has 5 protons and 6 neutrons. What is its mass number?
17. From the periodic table, list three differences between magnesium and chlorine.
18. What is the maximum number of electrons in each of the first three energy levels?
19. Name two noble gases and tell why they are not very active.
20. How do protons, electrons, and neutrons differ in charge, mass, and location within an atom?
21. State three differences between metals and nonmetals.
22. An atom of an element with mass number 42 and atomic number 20 has how many electrons?
23. If an element has 60% of its atoms with mass number 30 and 40% with mass number 32, will its average atomic mass be more or less than 31?
24. What change occurs in atomic number and average atomic mass
    a. from left to right across a period in the periodic table?
    b. as you read down a column of elements in the periodic table?
25. For the element $^{15}_{7}N$, find the number of protons, neutrons, and electrons and draw a model of the atom.

C. Applying Concepts

Answer the following questions using complete sentences when possible.

26. Explain why fluorine is more active than iodine.
27. How does the chemical activity of an element relate to its location in the periodic table?

28. What can you tell about the atoms $^{35}_{17}Cl$ and $^{133}_{55}Cs$?
29. A certain element has an average atomic mass of 137.33. What can you tell about this element from looking at the periodic table?
30. For the following pairs of elements, tell which is more active.
    a. fluorine, iodine
    b. lithium, rubidium
    c. strontium, magnesium
    d. oxygen, selenium

3. Element G has eight electrons in its outer energy level. Do you think element G will be very reactive? Explain your answer.
4. Element Z has two outer electrons. Do you think element Z will show the properties of a metal or a nonmetal?
5. Element A has one outer electron in the third energy level. Name two elements that should have properties similar to element A.

SKILL REVIEW

1. Use your calculator to find the density of a solid with a mass of 14.8 g and a volume of 6.5 cm^3.
2. One year Susan planted the front half of her vegetable garden early in the morning and the back half of the garden late in the day. She was glad to have the shade of a large oak tree during her afternoon planting. The front half of the garden was quite sunny. Susan watered and weeded her garden all summer. When it came time to harvest her vegetables, Susan found that the plants in the back of the garden had a much lower yield than those in the front of the garden. Susan thought about the way she cared for her garden. She decided that the cause of the low yield was that the back half of the garden had been planted later in the day. What do you think the cause of the lower yield was?

PROJECTS

1. Report on the dispute between the United States and the USSR that has led to the temporary use of three-letter symbols for elements beyond 103.
2. Lothar Meyer invented a periodic table at the same time as Dimitri Mendeleev. Write a report about Meyer's life and work.
3. Find the derivation of all of the names of the elements. Also find some early symbols other than letters.

READINGS

1. Bains, Rae. *Molecules and Atoms.* Mahwah, NJ: Troll Associates, 1985.
2. Berger, Melvin. *Atoms, Molecules and Quarks.* New York: Putnam, 1986.
3. Thomson, D. E. "On the Trail of Element 110." *Science News.* May 17, 1986, p. 319.

HOW ATOMS COMBINE
KINDS OF BONDS
WRITING FORMULAS

Chapter 11

Chemical Bonds

Except for a few metals, elements are not generally used by themselves. Compounds made of two or more elements are, however, found everywhere in the home, school, and stores. In a compound, the atoms of the elements are attached to each other. They are bonded. How the elements are bonded to each other determines to a great extent the properties of the compound. For example, hydrogen and oxygen are two common elements that form two well-known but different compounds. When one atom of oxygen is bonded to two atoms of hydrogen in a certain way, water is formed. If two atoms of hydrogen are bonded in a different way to two atoms of oxygen, hydrogen peroxide, a bleach and disinfectant, is formed.

In this chapter, you will learn what causes atoms to form bonds. You will learn the different kinds of chemical bonds and how those affect the properties of compounds.

HOW ATOMS COMBINE

Compounds are formed during chemical changes. The way that the changes take place depends on the chemical activity of the elements. This is related to the number of electrons in the outer energy levels of the atoms. Elements bond in compounds in order to achieve the most stable structure. These sections will explain what those stable structures are.

GOALS

1. You will learn that chemical formulas are used to represent compounds.
2. You will learn how atoms combine to form compounds.

11:1 Compounds

A compound is a substance formed when two or more elements combine chemically. "Combine chemically" means the elements join together in a way that makes it impossible to separate them by physical changes. A

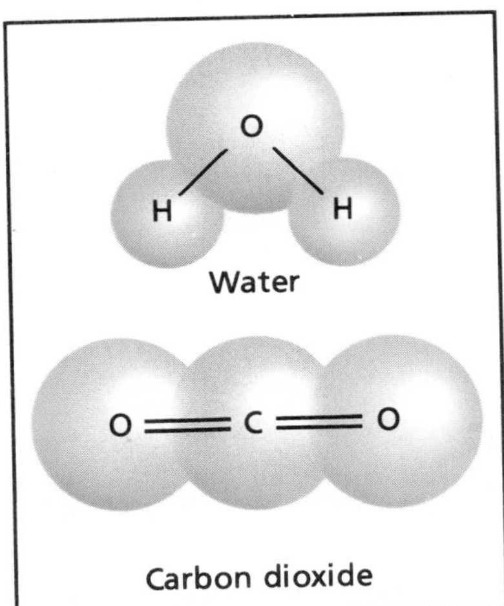

FIGURE 11–1. These models for carbon dioxide and water molecules show the ratios and arrangements of atoms.

compound has an identity all its own. The properties of a compound may be much different from the elements that form it.

Water is a compound formed from hydrogen and oxygen. Hydrogen will burn. Oxygen will not burn but must be present for ordinary burning to take place. Both elements are gases at room temperature. Water is a liquid that can put out fires. Sodium chloride is a compound made from sodium and chlorine. Sodium is a shiny metal that reacts violently with water. Chlorine is a yellowish-green poisonous gas. Sodium chloride is a white crystalline substance we use to season our food.

Elements in a compound always combine in the same ratio. The ratio between carbon (C) and oxygen (O) in carbon monoxide is 1 to 1. There is always one atom of carbon to one atom of oxygen in this compound. The ratio between carbon and oxygen in carbon dioxide is 1 to 2. There is always one atom of carbon to two atoms of oxygen. Every sample of water contains two atoms of hydrogen to one atom of oxygen, a 2 to 1 ratio.

What is a chemical formula?

A **chemical formula** is a group of symbols that represent a compound. A formula shows the elements in a compound. It also shows the ratio between the numbers of atoms of each element. Symbols are used to represent the elements present. The formula for carbon monoxide is CO. The formula CO shows a ratio of one atom of carbon to one atom of oxygen.

What is a subscript?

The formula for carbon dioxide is CO_2. The small number 2 in the formula is called a subscript. A **subscript** is a number that shows how many atoms of each element combine to form a compound. The subscript 2 in CO_2 means two atoms of oxygen. The absence of a subscript next to C means one atom of carbon. The numeral 1 is never used as a subscript. The formula CO_2

Table 11–1

Some Compounds and Their Formulas

Common name	Chemical name	Chemical formula
cane sugar	sucrose	$C_{12}H_{22}O_{11}$
baking soda	sodium hydrogen carbonate	$NaHCO_3$
hydrogen peroxide	hydrogen peroxide	H_2O_2
sand	silicon dioxide	SiO_2
rubbing alcohol	2-propanol	C_3H_7OH
chalk	calcium carbonate	$CaCO_3$
stannous fluoride	tin(II) fluoride	SnF_2

F.Y.I. Greek prefixes are often used in naming compounds. The first ten are as follows:

1	*mono-*	6	*hexa-*
2	*di-*	7	*hepta-*
3	*tri-*	8	*octa-*
4	*tetra-*	9	*nona-*
5	*penta-*	10	*deca-*

means that 1 atom of carbon bonds with 2 atoms of oxygen to form carbon dioxide. It also means that twice as many oxygen atoms as carbon atoms are used in making any sample of carbon dioxide.

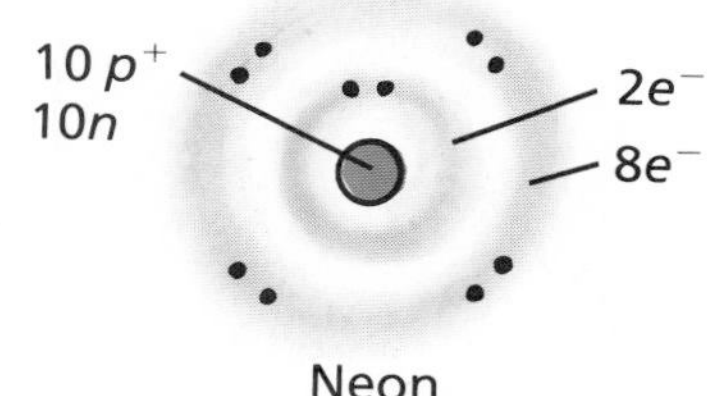

11:2 Which Elements Combine?

The noble gases, Group 18 on the periodic table, are very stable. They occur as single atoms and do not form many compounds. The compounds that do form will break down easily. Except for helium, the elements of this group have eight electrons in their outer energy level. Helium has only two electrons, but these electrons fill the first energy level. Atoms with full outer energy levels, or outer energy levels holding eight electrons, are chemically stable.

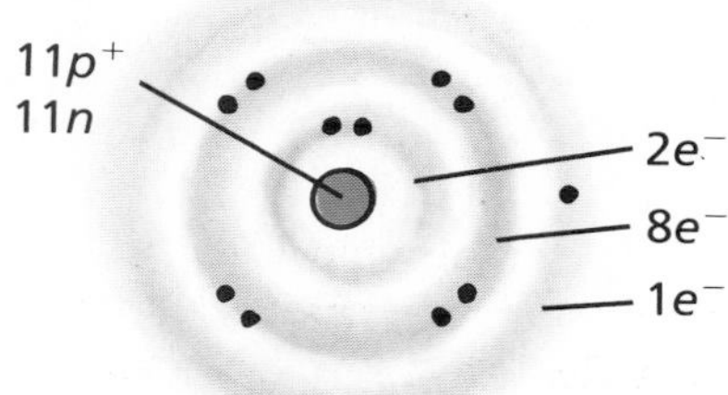

The elements of Group 1 are reactive. They do not have eight electrons in their outer energy level. All of the Group 1 metals have one electron in their outer energy level. These elements are found in nature in compounds. They combine chemically with other elements quite easily.

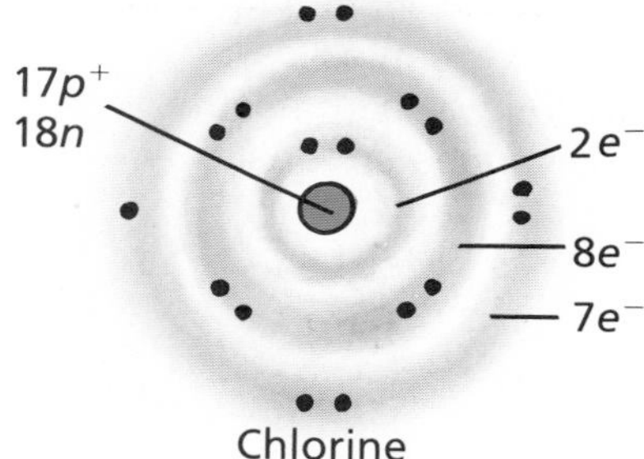

FIGURE 11–2. Compare the numbers of electrons in the outer energy levels of neon, sodium, and chlorine.

The halogens, Group 17, are also highly reactive. These elements are always found combined in nature. For example, the main source of the element chlorine is the salt, sodium chloride. All of the Group 17 elements have seven electrons in their outer energy level.

Why do atoms form bonds?

Atoms tend to combine in ways that allow their outer energy levels to have a stable number of electrons. This is the number of electrons found in the outer energy levels of the chemically stable noble gases. Generally, this number is eight electrons. Atoms share, gain, or lose electrons in order to have this number in their outer energy level. When atoms combine chemically, a bond is formed that holds the atoms together. This bond may come from the loss and gain of electrons, as with sodium chloride. A bond may also result when electrons are shared between atoms, as in the chlorine molecule, Cl_2. In some compounds, more than one bond may be formed. A water molecule contains two bonds, one between each hydrogen atom and the oxygen atom.

Review

1. Laughing gas is a compound containing a ratio of two atoms of nitrogen to one atom of oxygen. What is the formula for laughing gas?

2. Name the elements in each of the following compounds. What is the ratio of elements present in each of the compounds?
   a. H_2O_2 c. $NaC_2H_3O_2$ e. H_2SO_4
   b. KCl d. NaOH f. HF
3. What is the number of oxygen atoms in each compound in Question 2?
4. Give the definition of a compound.

★ 5. How many electrons are in the outer energy levels of the elements in the following groups?
   a. Group 14 c. Group 2
   b. Group 1 d. Group 16

KINDS OF BONDS

GOALS

1. You will learn how ionic and covalent bonds are formed.
2. You will learn three kinds of bonding in solids.
3. You will learn about hydrated crystals.

In the preceding section, you learned that atoms form bonds to complete a stable energy level. Generally, this gives each of the bonded atoms eight electrons in its outer energy level. As we will see in these sections, bonds form as the result of gaining, losing, or sharing electrons by atoms.

11:3 Electron Loss and Gain

How can a sodium atom become stable?

Some compounds are formed as the result of a transfer of electrons. Sodium chloride is one of these. A sodium atom has one electron in its outer energy level. A chlorine atom has seven electrons in its outer energy level. Chlorine needs only one electron to give it eight electrons in its outer energy level. Sodium needs seven electrons. However, if sodium loses its outermost electron, it can become stable. Then the next lower energy level contains eight electrons. If sodium's outermost electron were transferred to chlorine, both atoms would have a stable outer energy level. Figure 11–4 is a model for the transfer of an electron between sodium and chlorine. The outer electron of the sodium atom is loosely held by the sodium nucleus. Thus, the electron can be removed easily by an atom that holds its outer electrons tightly. Chlorine is such an atom. Its outer electrons are tightly held by its nucleus, and it has a strong attraction for loosely held electrons of other atoms.

FIGURE 11–3. Salt mines deep below Earth's surface are a source of sodium and chlorine.

After the transfer, the sodium atom has 11 protons and 10 electrons. The sodium atom now has a positive charge. The chlorine atom now has a negative charge, because it has 18 electrons and only 17 protons. Sodium

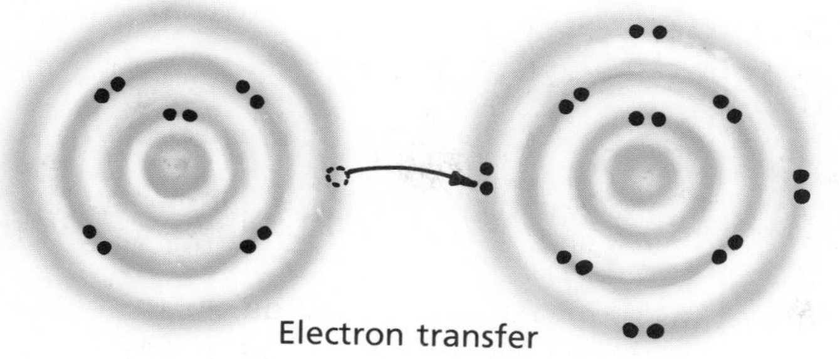

FIGURE 11–4. In this model of electron transfer, a sodium atom loses an electron to chlorine.

and chlorine now have opposite electrostatic charges. Opposite charges attract each other. The charged atoms bond to form a new compound. When an atom gains or loses one or more electrons, the charged particle that results is called an **ion.** Bonding that occurs between ions is called **ionic bonding.** Since the ratio of sodium ions to chloride ions is 1:1, the formula for the compound formed is NaCl.

What is ionic bonding?

Calcium also combines with chlorine to form an ionic compound. Two electrons are lost from each calcium atom. Since a chlorine atom needs only one electron to complete its outer energy level, two chlorine atoms are needed to accept the electrons. In this way, all three atoms (one calcium and two chlorine) have stable outer energy levels. Calcium has a 2+ charge because it now has two more protons than electrons. Each chlorine has a 1− charge. What is the formula for the compound formed?

PROBLEM SOLVING

Can you prove that borax softens water?

Hard water contains dissolved salts of iron, magnesium, and calcium. These salts can damage plumbing as they deposit on the inside of water pipes. The deposits, called scale, also form inside hot water heaters and boilers. The scale inhibits heat conduction and causes energy loss. Soaps do not work well in hard water. When soap mixes with hard water, a soap scum forms. This scum has no cleaning ability, hence more soap is needed to clean with hard water. The scum may also cling to clothing washed in hard water. In soft water, soap lathers well and easily breaks up grease.

Sodium tetraborate decahydrate, borax, ($Na_2B_4O_7 \cdot 10H_2O$) is said to be a water softener. How could you devise a simple test of this property? Use the information given to help you design your test. Include a test in hard water and one in soft water (distilled water) as controls in your experimental design.

INVESTIGATION 11–1

Ionic and Covalent Bonds

Problem: How do models aid in writing formulas for ionic and covalent compounds?

Materials

compass

paper and pencil

Procedure

Part A

1. Use your compass and pencil to draw an electron diagram model of a lithium atom. See Investigation 10–1, page 224 and Figure 11–4.
2. Draw an electron diagram of a chlorine atom next to the lithium atom.
3. Draw an arrow to show that the outer electron of the lithium atom moves to the outer energy level of chlorine.
4. Repeat Steps 1–3 using calcium and bromine atoms.

Part B

5. Draw an electron diagram model of a hydrogen atom.
6. Draw a fluorine atom next to it in such a way that the outer energy level overlaps with the hydrogen energy level. Align the one electron in hydrogen with the electron in the unfilled energy level of fluorine.
7. Indicate which electrons are being shared by drawing a small box around them.
8. Draw an electron diagram model to show how a carbon atom can form four covalent bonds with four hydrogen atoms.

Analysis

1. How many electrons transferred between the lithium and chlorine atoms when they bonded? Between the calcium and bromine atoms?
2. How many electrons were shared between the hydrogen and fluorine atoms? Between the carbon and each hydrogen atom?

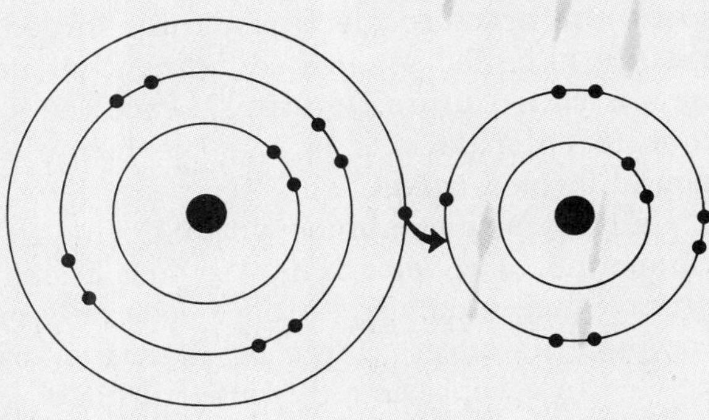

FIGURE 11–5.

Data and Observations

Combining elements	Type of bond	Chemical formula
Li and Cl		
Ca and Br		
H and F		
C and H		

Conclusions and Applications

3. What kind of bond is formed in each of these four compounds?
4. Predict what the formula would be for a compound formed between potassium and sulfur. Draw a diagram of the bonding of these atoms.
5. How do models aid in writing formulas for ionic and covalent compounds?

11:4 Electron Sharing

Chlorine gas particles are made up of pairs of chlorine atoms, Cl_2. Each chlorine atom has seven electrons in its outer energy level. If a chlorine atom could get one more electron, for a total of eight, its outer energy level would be stable. Figure 11–6 is a model of how two chlorine atoms combine when sharing electrons. Each atom shares one electron. Thus, each chlorine atom has eight electrons in its outer energy level. Atoms that combine by sharing electrons form a **covalent bond.**

Electron sharing

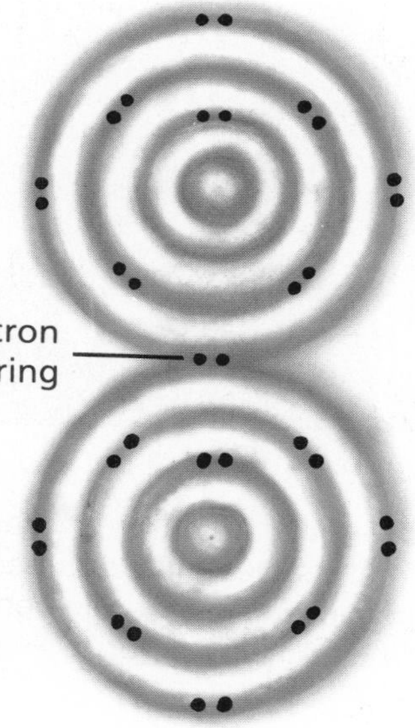

FIGURE 11–6. This bonding model for Cl_2 shows a shared pair of electrons.

When two or more atoms bond covalently, they form a neutral particle called a **molecule.** A molecule is different from the particles formed by ionic bonding. In covalent bonding, a molecule, an actual new particle, is formed. The compound formed through ionic bonding is simply an ordered group of ions.

Many elements exist in nature as molecules. For example, oxygen in the air we breathe is a diatomic molecule. It is formed from two oxygen atoms. The formula for oxygen gas is O_2. Nitrogen (N_2), hydrogen (H_2), and the halogens are also found as diatomic molecules. Many compounds also form molecules. Water (H_2O) exists as molecules. Hydrogen chloride (HCl) and hydrogen peroxide (H_2O_2) do also.

What is a molecule?

11:5 Bonding in Solids

The structures and properties of crystals show the effects of different kinds of bonding. A **crystal** is a solid in which the particles are arranged in a repeating pattern. All true solids are crystalline. Salt, sugar, and ice are common examples of crystals.

What is a crystal?

There are four main types of bonds between the particles in crystals. They are bonds formed by weak forces, ionic bonds, covalent bonds, and metallic bonds. The metallic bond will be discussed in Chapter 12. The types of particles in a crystal and the bonding between them determine the crystal's properties.

Many crystals are held together by weak attractive forces. This is true of molecular compounds. These weak forces result from the attraction of the positively charged nucleus of one atom or molecule for the electron cloud of another atom or molecule. The molecules remain at some distance from each other because of the repulsion of their electron clouds. The distance between atoms within a molecule is less than the distance between molecules in a crystal of the substance.

FIGURE 11–7. The regular, repeating pattern of particles forming a crystal gives it its regular geometric shape.

a

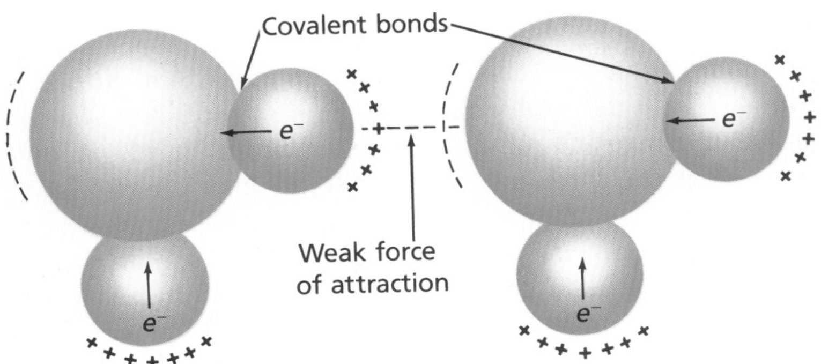

b

FIGURE 11–8. Ice crystals (a) form as weak forces attract the negative to the positive ends of water molecules (b).

How is ice held together?

F.Y.I. Snowflakes have regular, symmetrical shapes because of the very organized way that molecules of water pack together in crystals of ice.

When water molecules are brought together, the positive end of one molecule will attract the negative end of another water molecule. This attraction occurs throughout the crystal. It results in the crystal structure of ice. Ice is held together by weak attractive forces. These forces are less than the attractive forces in an ionic crystal such as salt. Crystals held together by weak attractive forces have low melting points. They also do not conduct electricity.

When the particles in a crystal are ions, they are held together by ionic bonds. For example, sodium chloride crystals are made of sodium ions and chloride ions. Each sodium ion is surrounded by six chloride ions. Each chloride ion is surrounded by six sodium ions. Since the ions are of opposite charge, the force of attraction is very strong. Thus, ionic crystals have high melting points. They are brittle solids. When an ionic crystal dissolves in water, its ions become mobile. This solution of

Table 11–2

Crystal Properties and Bonding

Example	Bonding	Particles	Properties
sulfur	weak forces	molecules	soft, nonconductors, low melting point
copper sulfate	ionic	ions	brittle, conduct when melted, high melting point
quartz	covalent	nonmetallic atoms	hard, nonconductors, high melting point

a

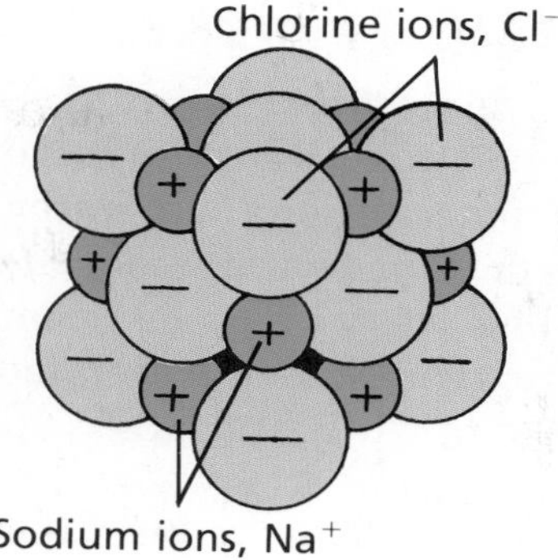

b

FIGURE 11–9. Sodium and chloride ions combine to form the ionic crystal sodium chloride (a). Crystals of sodium chloride (table salt) are cubic (b).

charged particles conducts electric current. Ionic crystals also conduct electricity in their melted forms. A section of a crystal of sodium chloride is shown in Figure 11–9. The formula for sodium chloride, NaCl, gives the ratio of sodium ions to chloride ions in a crystal of sodium chloride. What is the ratio of ions in a crystal of $MgBr_2$?

What is a network crystal?

A crystal formed by covalent bonds between atoms becomes one large molecule. A crystal such as this is called a **macromolecule** or network crystal. A network crystal is generally nonmetallic. Diamond is a good example of this type of bonding. Each carbon atom in a diamond crystal is bonded covalently to four other carbon atoms. Other compounds, such as silicon carbide, SiC, also crystallize with covalent bonds between atoms.

The properties of diamond are typical of crystals that are covalently bonded throughout. These crystals are extremely hard. They have high melting points and do not conduct electricity.

FIGURE 11–10. Silicon and carbon atoms bond covalently to form silicon carbide, SiC, a network crystal.

FIGURE 11–11. The anhydrous form of cobalt chloride is blue. The hydrated form is pink. Objects treated with this chemical are sometimes used to indicate changes in humidity.

Define anhydrous.

11:6 Hydrated Crystals

Some crystals contain water molecules as part of their structure. When copper(II) sulfate, $CuSO_4$, crystallizes from solution, four water molecules attach to each Cu^{2+} ion. One water molecule attaches to each sulfate ion. The crystal has the formula $CuSO_4 \cdot 5H_2O$. The formula represents five water molecules in the crystal for each set of Cu^{2+} and SO_4^{2-} ions. A crystal containing a definite number of water molecules is called a **hydrate.** The name of this hydrate is copper(II) sulfate pentahydrate. Many ionic substances form hydrated crystals. Sodium dichromate dihydrate is another example. Its formula is $Na_2Cr_2O_7 \cdot 2H_2O$.

Hydrated crystals give off water molecules when warmed. When the water is driven off, a dry crystalline powder remains. This dry powder is the anhydrous form of the compound. **Anhydrous** means without water.

Concrete is a practical example of the use of hydrated crystals. Concrete is made from gravel and sand mixed with water and portland cement, an anhydrous calcium aluminum silicate. The silicate in portland cement contains calcium, aluminum, silicon, and oxygen in crystal form. When mixed with water, the silicate material absorbs water into its crystal structure, forming solid hydrated compounds. The compounds formed in this way contain bonds that cement the pieces of gravel together. Contrary to what some people believe, concrete is not made by allowing the water in the concrete mixture to dry out. If concrete is heated and dried, it becomes brittle and crumbles. Concrete should be kept wet while it "cures." This allows as much of the cement to become hydrated as possible.

Review

6. What type of crystalline bonding produces crystals with the weakest bonds?
7. What is the structure of a macromolecule?
8. List two properties of ionic crystals.
9. Why do you think the water in a hydrate can be driven off so easily? What kind of bonding do you think the water has with the ions in the hydrated crystal?
★ 10. Carbon and silicon are in the same family on the periodic table. They would be expected to form sim-

ilar compounds. However, CO_2 is a soft, low-melting solid (dry ice), while SiO_2 is a hard, high-melting solid (sand). What types of bonding in these crystals could account for the different properties?

WRITING FORMULAS

Just as symbols enable scientists to discuss elements easily, formulas are shorthand ways of writing names of compounds. In these sections, you will learn some rules for writing formulas for compounds and for naming compounds when the formulas are given.

GOALS

1. You will learn how oxidation numbers are used in writing formulas.
2. You will learn to name binary chemical compounds.
3. You will learn to write formulas and name compounds containing polyatomic ions.

11:7 Oxidation Numbers

Oxidation number is the name given to the combining ability of an atom. This number tells how many electrons an atom gains, loses, or shares in forming a compound. For example, Group 1 elements lose one electron when they bond. These elements have an oxidation number of 1+. Group 17 elements may gain or share one electron. They have an oxidation number of 1–. With some exceptions, oxidation number is a periodic property of elements, Table 11–3.

What is oxidation number?

In sodium chloride, NaCl, sodium (Group 1) has lost one electron so it has an oxidation number of 1+. Chlorine (Group 17) has gained one electron so it has an oxidation number of 1–. In potassium bromide, KBr, potassium (Group 1) also has an oxidation number of 1+. Bromine (Group 17) has an oxidation number of 1–.

It is fairly easy to assign oxidation numbers to elements that form ionic compounds. Group 1 is 1+ and 2 is 2+. These elements lose electrons and carry a positive charge for each electron they lose. In the same manner, Group 17 elements gain an electron and take on a charge of 1–.

Oxidation numbers in covalent bonding are often determined from experimental data. There are a few set rules. Hydrogen, with few exceptions, has an oxidation number of 1+. Oxygen, with rare exceptions, is 2–. Each hydrogen atom in water, H_2O, shares one electron with the oxygen atom. The oxidation number for each hydrogen is 1+. The oxidation number for oxygen is 2–. What is the oxidation number for sulfur in H_2S?

Table 11–3

Metals	
Group	**Oxidation Number**
1	1+
2	2+
3–12 (Transition)	tend to have more than one
13	3+
14	2+ or 4+
Nonmetals	
15	3–
16	2–
17	1–

TECHNOLOGY: APPLICATIONS

A Common Hydrate

Children use it to make molds and leaf prints. Doctors use it to set broken bones. Artists use it in sculptures. This substance is the mineral gypsum.

Gypsum is a hydrate of calcium sulfate. From its formula, $CaSO_4 \cdot 2H_2O$, you can see that gypsum contains water. When heated, it loses most of its water and changes to a substance known as plaster of paris. When water is added to powdered plaster of paris to form a paste, it hardens within minutes. As the plaster hardens, it expands, and its crystals interlock to form a solid. The solidification is the result of a chemical reaction in which the calcium sulfate absorbs water and again becomes a hydrate.

Its many uses make gypsum the basis of a multi-million dollar industry. Ground gypsum is used as a fertilizer. Plaster of paris is used to make molds of many kinds, from artistic to dental. Anhydrous gypsum is used in plasterboard, Keene's cement, and other building materials. It is even used as a filler in candy and paint.

What is the sum of oxidation numbers in a compound?

The sum of the oxidation numbers for the atoms in a compound is zero. Therefore, when Na^+ and Cl^- combine, one sodium ion bonds with one chloride ion. Thus, the formula is NaCl.

$$(1+) + (1-) = 0$$

One atom of hydrogen (1+) will bond with one atom of chlorine (1–) to form HCl. Magnesium has an oxidation number of 2+. One atom of magnesium combines with two chlorine atoms. Each chlorine atom has an oxidation number of 1–. Thus, the formula is $MgCl_2$.

$$(2+) + 2(1-) = 0$$

Some elements have more than one oxidation number. Iron can have oxidation numbers of 2+ and 3+. It may form two different compounds with bromine, $FeBr_2$ and $FeBr_3$. If an element has more than one oxidation num-

a

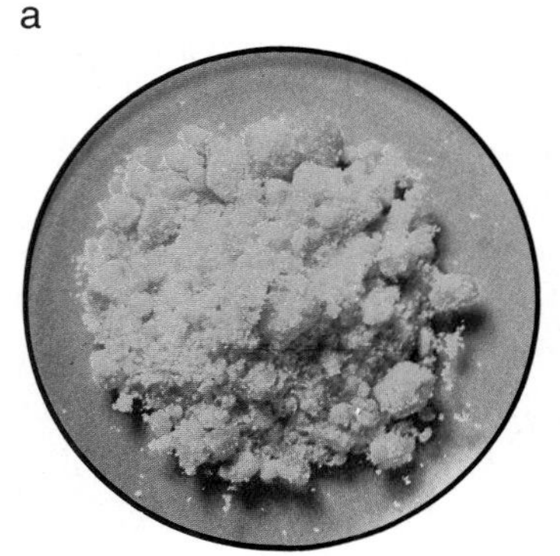

b

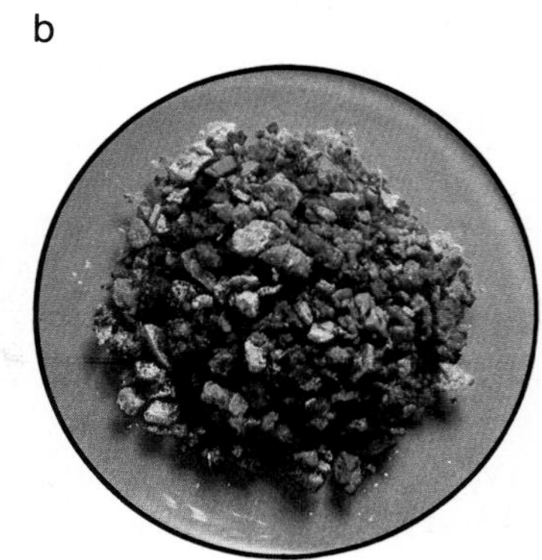

FIGURE 11–12. The compound $FeBr_3$ (a) is different in appearance and properties from $FeBr_3$ (b).

ber, the number intended is written in parentheses after the element's name. Roman numerals are used to indicate the oxidation number. For example, iron(II) means 2+; iron(III) means 3+. If bromine has an oxidation number of 1–, which compound, $FeBr_2$ or $FeBr_3$, contains Iron(III)?

In writing formulas for compounds, the symbol of the metal or element with the positive oxidation number is written first. There are few exceptions to this rule. For example, aluminum chloride, $AlCl_3$, is a compound formed between aluminum and chlorine. Aluminum is written first because it is a metal. Chlorine is a nonmetal. When writing formulas, you can check the periodic table on pages 228–229 to determine which elements are metals. A good rule of thumb is that elements on the left side of the table are written to the left in the formula. The oxidation numbers of some common elements are listed in Table 11–4.

BIOGRAPHY

Emma Carr
1880–1972

Emma Carr was professor of chemistry at Mount Holyoke College. She is remembered for her research into the nature of the carbon-carbon double bond. She investigated carbon bonds using spectroscopy, the analysis of the way these bonds absorb certain wavelengths of light.

What element is written first in a formula?

Table 11–4

Oxidation Numbers of Some Elements

1+	2+	3+
copper(I), Cu^+ hydrogen, H^+ lithium, Li^+ potassium, K^+ silver, Ag^+ sodium, Na^+	barium, Ba^{2+} calcium, Ca^{2+} copper(II), Cu^{2+} iron(II), Fe^{2+} magnesium, Mg^{2+} zinc, Zn^{2+}	aluminum, Al^{3+} chromium, Cr^{3+} iron(III), Fe^{3+}
1–	**2–**	**3–**
bromine, Br^- chlorine, Cl^- fluorine, F^- iodine, I^-	oxygen, O^{2-} sulfur, S^{2-}	nitrogen, N^{3-} phosphorus, P^{3-}

EXAMPLES Writing Formulas

1. What is the formula for a compound of silver and sulfur?

Solution:

a. Use Table 11–4 to find the oxidation numbers of silver and sulfur.

silver, 1+ sulfur, 2–

b. Two atoms of silver are needed to combine with one atom of sulfur. Silver is a metal and is written first.

$$Ag_2S$$
$$2(1+) + (2-) = 0$$

F.Y.I. It was not until the end of the eighteenth century that scientists began using letters for elements and compounds. Until this time, they used a complex system of symbols.

INVESTIGATION 11–2

Hydrated Crystals

Problem: What happens when hydrated crystals are heated?

Materials    

copper(II) sulfate
test tube
laboratory burner
water
dropper
watch glass
beaker
hot plate
goggles
apron

CAUTION: *Copper(II) sulfate is poisonous; avoid skin and eye contact. Do not inhale. Rinse spills with plenty of water.*

Procedure

1. Place a few crystals of copper(II) sulfate in a test tube.
2. Heat strongly over a burner flame until a change occurs. **CAUTION:** *Always point the mouth of a test tube away from other students.*
3. Record what happens to the crystals and what happens at the mouth of the test tube.

FIGURE 11–13.

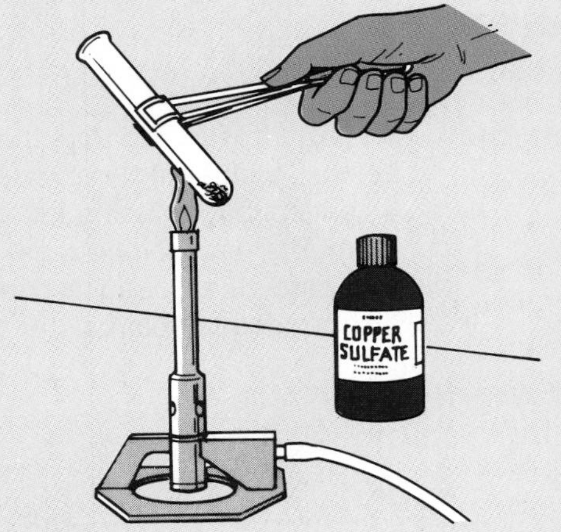

4. Now add a few drops of water to the powder in the test tube.
5. Record what happens.
6. Pour the liquid into a watch glass. Place the watch glass on a beaker that is about one third full of water. Heat gently on a hot plate to evaporate the liquid.
7. Record what happens.

Data and Observations

Treatment	Observations
heat strongly	
add water	
heat to evaporate	

Analysis

1. What happened to the copper(II) sulfate crystals when they were heated?
2. What formed at the mouth of the test tube?

Applications and Conclusions

3. What do you think caused the color of the copper(II) sulfate crystals to change?
4. What happens when hydrated crystals are heated?
5. What was the final product in the watch glass?
6. A compound of cobalt is sometimes used to show changes in humidity. The compound changes from blue to pink, and vice versa. Explain how this works.

2. What is the formula for the compound composed of aluminum and oxygen?

Solution:

a. The oxidation numbers for aluminum and oxygen are

aluminum, 3+ oxygen, 2–

b. Two Al^{3+} will combine with three O^{2-}.

$$2 \times (3+) + 3 \times (2-) = 0$$

Al^{3+} is a metal and is written first.

$$Al_2O_3$$

Remember, subscripts give the ratio of atoms of the elements in the compound.

11:8 Naming Binary Compounds

What is a binary compound?

A **binary** (BI nayr ee) **compound** is composed of two elements. Binary compounds are named beginning with the element with the positive oxidation number. The name of the second element is changed to end in *–ide*. For example, $MgCl_2$ is magnesium chloride. HCl is hydrogen chloride. $FeCl_2$ is iron(II) chloride. How do you know it is iron(II)? CuF is copper(I) fluoride. How do you know it is copper(I)?

EXAMPLES Naming Binary Compounds

1. What is the name for FeS?

Solution: Using Table 11–4, we see that Fe exists as iron(II) or iron(III). The oxidation number of sulfur is 2–. The formula indicates only one atom of each element. Therefore, the oxidation number of iron must be 2+. The name of the compound is iron(II) sulfide.

2. What is the name for Cu_2O?

Solution: Using Table 11–4, we see that Cu exists as copper(I) or copper(II). Because oxygen has an oxidation number of 2–, each copper atom must be 1+. Therefore this is copper(I) and the compound is copper(I) oxide.

What is a polyatomic ion?

FIGURE 11–14. Many common acids contain polyatomic ions.

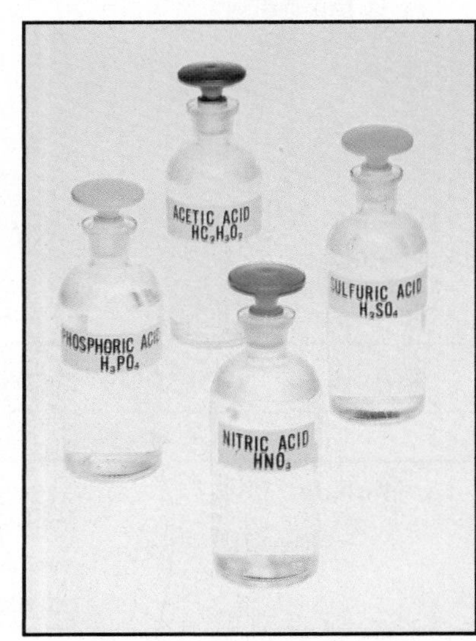

11:9 Polyatomic Ions

A **polyatomic ion** is a group of covalently bonded atoms that act together as one charged atom. The atoms are generally not rearranged in chemical reactions but remain as one group. Compounds containing polyatomic ions are named in much the same way as binary compounds. The positive part of the compound is given first.

For example, the compound formed by sodium and the sulfate ion has the formula Na_2SO_4. It is called sodium sulfate. The compound formed from the ammonium ion and sulfur is $(NH_4)_2S$. Its name is ammonium sulfide. The subscript 2 is written outside the parenthesis to show two ammonium ions. Table 11–5 lists some polyatomic ions and their charges.

EXAMPLE Writing Formulas with Polyatomic Ions

Write the formula for calcium hydroxide.

Solution:

1. Use Tables 11–4 and 11–5 to find the oxidation numbers (charges) of calcium and the hydroxide ion.

$$Ca^{2+} \qquad OH^-$$

2. Two hydroxide ions are needed for one calcium ion. Calcium has the positive oxidation number and is written first. Use parentheses and a subscript to show two hydroxide ions.

$$Ca(OH)_2$$
$$(2+) + 2(-1) = 0$$

EXAMPLE Determining Oxidation Number

Find the oxidation number of sulfur in the sulfate ion.

Solution:

1. Use Table 11–5 to find the oxidation number of the sulfate ion.

$$SO_4^{2-}$$

The sum of the oxidation numbers of the 4 oxygen atoms and the sulfur must be 2–.

What is the oxidation number of the sulfate ion?

2. Oxygen has an oxidation number of 2–. There are 4 oxygen atoms in the sulfate ion.

$$\underline{\quad ? \quad} + 4(2-) = 2-$$
$$\underline{\quad 6 \quad} + 8- = 2-$$

The oxidation number of sulfur in the sulfate ion is 6+.

Table 11–5

Some Polyatomic Ions and Their Charges			
1+	1–	2–	3–
ammonium, NH_4^+	acetate, $C_2H_3O_2^-$ chlorate, ClO_3^- hydroxide, OH^- nitrate, NO_3^-	carbonate, CO_3^{2-} sulfate, SO_4^{2-}	phosphate, PO_4^{3-}

Review

11. Using Table 11–4, write formulas for compounds formed from the following.

a. potassium and iodine c. calcium and fluorine
b. hydrogen and sulfur d. copper(II) and oxygen

12. Name the following compounds.

a. LiCl c. FeO e. CuF
b. $(NH_4)_3PO_4$ d. $AgNO_3$ f. BaS

13. Using Tables 11–4 and 11–5, write formulas for each of the following compounds.

a. potassium oxide e. chromium(III) sulfide
b. sodium acetate f. calcium phosphate
c. silver sulfate g. iron(II) bromide
d. zinc carbonate h. hydrogen chlorate

14. How many nitrogen atoms are in each compound?

a. $NaNO_3$ b. $(NH_4)_2SO_3$ c. $Al(NO_3)_3$

★ **15.** Find the oxidation number of Mn in $Al(MnO_4)_3$.

CAREER

Chemistry Teacher

Just how elements are attracted to each other and bonded to form compounds did not exactly thrill Ramona Valdez when she was in chemistry class, until she began to see this happen before her very eyes. The first experiment she can remember was leaving a salt solution out to dry. It was through this simple process that she began to understand bonding. Ramona began to enjoy chemistry experiments and new knowledge came easily to her.

Ramona worked as a lab assistant for her chemistry teacher. This led to a job in college working in the chemistry labs and helping a professor with research. Ramona found that she did not enjoy the daily duties of a research chemist. She enjoyed working with people. So she went into chemical education and became a teacher.

As a teacher, Ramona must make daily lesson plans, set up labs, demonstrate experiments, and work with individuals of all backgrounds and interests. Ramona enjoys helping her students discover how chemistry is a part of their everyday lives.

For career information, write
National Science Teachers Association
1742 Connecticut Ave., NW
Washington, DC 20009

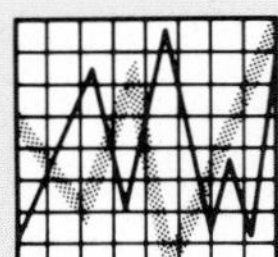

SKILL

Writing Chemical Formulas

Problem: How can you use the crisscross method to write chemical formulas?

Materials

paper and pencil

Background

Oxidation numbers are useful for writing chemical formulas. Tables 11–4 and 11–5 list oxidation numbers for some elements and polyatomic ions. In the examples that follow, oxidation numbers and the crisscross method will be used for writing chemical formulas.

Example 1
What is the formula for a compound of barium and chlorine?
Solution: Barium is in Group 2 and is the more metallic element. Elements in Group 2 tend to lose two electrons when they form compounds. What do you think the oxidation number of barium is? In Table 11–4, the oxidation number for barium is given as 2+. Chlorine is a nonmetal in Group 17. Group 17 elements tend to gain one electron when they form compounds. What is the oxidation number of chlorine? In Table 11–4, the oxidation number of chlorine is given as 1–.

Now write the symbols in the correct order with the oxidation numbers shown as superscripts. Remember, for oxidation numbers of 1+ and 1–, only the positive or negative sign is written.

$$Ba^{2+} \quad Cl^{-}$$

Next crisscross the numbers only and show them as subscripts. The number one is understood and not written.

$$Ba^{2+} \quad Cl^{-}$$
$$Ba \quad Cl_2$$

The correct formula for a compound containing barium and chlorine is $BaCl_2$.

Example 2
What is the formula for a compound composed of magnesium and phosphate?
Solution: Most of the polyatomic ions you will use have negative oxidation numbers. The ammonium ion, NH_4^{+}, is an exception to this rule. First, write the parts of the compound in the correct order and assign oxidation numbers.

$$Mg^{2+} \quad PO_4^{3-}$$

Write the chemical formula for the compound by crisscrossing the superscripts. Since the phosphate ion will be used more than once, it must be placed in parentheses. The parentheses prevent confusion between the subscripts.

$$Mg^{2+} \quad PO_4^{3-}$$
$$Mg_3 \quad (PO_4)_2$$

The correct formula for the compound containing magnesium and phosphate is $Mg_3(PO_4)_2$.

Questions and Conclusions

1. How can you use the crisscross method to write chemical formulas?
2. Use the crisscross method and Tables 11–4 and 11–5 to write the chemical formulas for the compounds described below.
   a. A compound containing ammonium ions and selenate ions is used as a mothproofing agent. The selenate ion is SeO_4^{2-}.
   b. A compound containing oxygen and titanium is used as a white pigment in the production of paint, plastic, and paper. Titanium has an oxidation number of 4+ in this compound.
   c. Potassium chloride is used in fertilizer, photography, and as a salt substitute.
   d. Zinc iodide is used as an antiseptic.

Chapter 11 Review

SUMMARY

1. A compound is formed when two or more elements combine chemically. 11:1
2. A chemical formula is a group of symbols that represent a compound. 11:1
3. Atoms with filled outer energy levels, or energy levels with eight electrons, are chemically stable. 11:2.
4. When atoms bond, they form stable outer energy levels. 11:2
5. The attraction between positive and negative ions is an ionic bond. 11:3
6. Covalent bonds form when atoms share electrons. 11:4
7. Molecules are neutral particles containing covalently bonded atoms. 11:4
8. Bonding in crystals can be due to weak forces, ionic bonds, covalent bonds, or metallic bonds. 11:5
9. Hydrated crystals contain water molecules. 11:6
10. The oxidation number of a bonded atom is the number of electrons gained, lost, or shared. 11:7
11. Binary compounds are named by changing the name of the element that has the negative oxidation number to end in *–ide.* 11:8
12. A polyatomic ion generally acts as a single unit in chemical reactions. 11:9

VOCABULARY

a. anhydrous
b. binary compound
c. chemical formula
d. covalent bond
e. crystal
f. hydrate
g. ion
h. ionic bonding
i. macromolecule
j. molecule
k. oxidation number
l. polyatomic ion
m. subscript

Matching

Match each description with the correct vocabulary word from the list above. Some words will not be used.

1. a group of atoms that act as one
2. a crystal that contains water
3. a charged atom
4. a number in a chemical formula that tells how many of each kind of atom
5. made of two elements only
6. a network crystal formed by covalent bonding
7. formed by sharing electrons
8. shows the combining capacity of an element
9. what the attraction between unlike charged atoms produces
10. a solid with a regular shape

Chapter 11 Review

MAIN IDEAS

A. Reviewing Concepts

Complete each of the following sentences with the correct word or phrase.

1. When atoms form covalent bonds, ____________ may be formed.
2. The elements of Group 17 have ____________ electrons in the outer energy level.
3. A(n) ____________ is a charged atom or group of atoms.
4. The charge on a molecule is ____________.
5. A binary compound contains atoms of ____________ elements.
6. ____________ bonding occurs when ions of opposite charge are attracted to one another.
7. The formula X_3Y shows that for each atom of Y, there are ____________ atoms of X.
8. Nitrate, NO_3^-, is an example of a(n) ____________.
9. Sodium chloride is an example of a(n) ____________ compound.
10. The formula for ammonium hydroxide contains ____________ atoms of hydrogen.
11. A magnesium atom can form an ionic compound by giving ____________ electrons to a nonmetal.
12. In the compound, $CuCl_2$, the oxidation number of copper is ____________.
13. A crystal that is a network of covalently bonded atoms is called a(n) ____________.
14. Water molecules in ice are held together by ____________.
15. The compound iron(II) sulfide, has the formula ____________.

B. Understanding Concepts

Answer the following questions using complete sentences when possible.

16. How does covalent bonding differ from ionic bonding?
17. Name the compounds represented by the following formulas.
    a. $NaCl$ b. NH_4NO_3 c. $Ca_3(PO_4)_2$
    d. $CuSO_4 \cdot 5H_2O$
18. Write formulas for the following compounds.
    a. potassium sulfate
    b. sulfur dioxide
    c. mercury(I) sulfide
19. What kinds of atoms and how many of each are represented by the formula $Mg(NO_3)_2$?
20. What oxidation number does nitrogen have in HNO_3? Chromium in K_2CrO_4?
21. The formula for aluminum carbonate contains how many atoms of oxygen?
22. What is the formula for the binary compound made of the most active metal and the most active nonmetal?
23. Do ionic compounds form molecules? Why or why not?
24. What is the definition of a compound?
25. What are the oxidation numbers of carbon in CO and CO_2?

C. Applying Concepts

Answer the following questions using complete sentences when possible.

26. An atom of an element has electrons distributed in energy levels: 2, 8, 2. What would you expect the oxidation number of this element to be? Why? If its symbol is R, what is the formula of a compound of this element with bromine?

27. How do crystals formed by ionic bonding differ from crystals formed by weak forces?
28. How can iron form the two compounds $FeCl_2$ and $FeCl_3$?
29. What kind of crystal bonding would you expect between members of Group 1 and Group 17? Why?
30. Element X has oxidation numbers of 2+ and 3+. Element Y has oxidation numbers of 2– and 3–. What are formulas of possible compounds of the two elements?

SKILL REVIEW

1. Rocio is doing a science experiment on how temperature affects plant growth. She studies a zone chart that shows how North America is divided into various climate zones. Zone charts are made using data such as temperature range and rainfall for various areas on the continent. How can a zone chart be helpful to Rocio?
2. A thief stole 10 gold bars from a federal reserve bank. The police received a tip that the thief was leaving the country by plane and was carrying the gold bars in a tan duffle bag. Undercover police at the airport spotted two people carrying tan duffle bags. After observing the two suspects carrying the duffle bags, the police easily identified the thief. How were the police able to infer which duffle bag contained the gold?
3. Thallium carbonate is used to make artificial diamonds. Thallium has an oxidation number of 1+ in this compound. What is the chemical formula for thallium carbonate?
4. Gallium forms binary compounds with several Group 15 elements. These compounds are used in semiconductors. The oxidation number of gallium in these compounds is 3+. What is the formula for gallium phosphide?
5. The lanthanoid and actinoid series of elements were once called rare earth elements, partly because they were rarely used. However, many advances in technology and medicine have been made using compounds containing these elements. Generally, the lanthanoids and actinoids have oxidation numbers of 3+. The compound neodymium oxide is used in color TV tubes. What is the chemical formula for this compound?

PROJECTS

1. Do a library report on how the atomic theory has changed from the time of John Dalton until today.
2. Obtain information on the different structures of crystals. Make a poster showing the various crystal structures.

READINGS

1. *Exploring Space and Atoms.* New York: Arco, 1984.
2. Mebane, Robert C. and Thomas R. Rybolt. *Adventures with Atoms and Molecules.* Hillside, NJ: Enslow Printers, 1985.
3. Reesink, Carol J. "Crystals: Through the Looking Glass with Planes, Points, and Rotational Symmetries." *The Mathematics Teacher.* May, 1987, pp. 377–380.

SCIENCE AND SOCIETY

THE PROMISES AND PROBLEMS OF PLASTICS

In Chapter 11 you learned about chemical bonds and how elements combine to form compounds. Many of these compounds form in the natural course of events, such as the photosynthesis of glucose in plants. Later these compounds decompose again, as when glucose is oxidized in our bodies to provide energy. The continuing formation and decomposition of glucose in this way is said to be part of a *natural cycle*.

Background

Natural cycles are very important in providing balance among chemical compounds. They allow resources to be used again and again. They make sure that we do not get too much of a compound we do not want. This is especially true of things we throw away.

We call the things we throw away "garbage." The people who collect and dispose of our "garbage" call it *solid waste*. Most of the solid waste they collect is currently being buried in landfills. There, bacteria act on paper and paper products to decompose them. This decomposition leads to other compounds which can fertilize the soil to grow new trees to make more paper. The glass that we throw away eventually becomes ground up as finely as the sand from which it was originally made. Metals react with oxygen, carbon, and sulfur to reform the compounds that originally formed their ores.

Paper, glass, and metals are all made up of substances occurring naturally on Earth. When they are discarded, they decompose naturally into the substances from which they originally formed. Thus paper, glass, and metals are all a part of natural cycles.

But what about plastics? Unlike paper, glass, and metals, plastics are human-made compounds. Plastics are synthetic polymers. They are made by forcing small molecules to form bonds between them. Thus chemists can form long chains of molecules bonded together. You will learn more about them in Section 14:5.

Plastics are materials of our own creation, and they have given us many conveniences. We wear polyester clothes, package food in polyethylene bags, and drink hot beverages from polystyrene cups. When we discard our polyester clothes, polyethylene bags, and polystyrene cups in the garbage, a problem arises.

FIGURE 1. Many plastics, like polyethylene, may remain undegraded forever, using up limited landfill space.

The problem with these plastics in solid waste is that they are not naturally occurring substances and are not a part of any natural cycle. There is nothing to cause them to decompose into the smaller molecules from which they were formed. This resistance to decay makes these plastics very strong while they are being used. But after we are finished using them, they linger on in the same form.

Therefore, once smaller molecules are used to create a plastic polymer, they remain in that polymer. If you were to dig into your local landfill 50 years from now, you would probably find sand from ground glass and compounds of metallic ores and decomposed paper. The polyethylene bags and polystyrene cups would still be the same, however.

Continued use of these plastics will continue to provide us with many conveniences. Making more of them, however, requires more resources that will not be returned to the natural cycle. Many places are running out of landfill space to dispose of discarded plastics and other solid waste. What can be done? Some cities are building plants to burn solid waste. Burning will indeed decompose plastics, but burning many plastics produces harmful chemicals.

Case Studies

1. One procedure, which shows more promise, is recycling. Recycling already allows us to convert discarded paper, glass, and metal into new paper, glass, and metal products. The technology to do the same with plastics is not as advanced or widely used, however.

2. Faced with limited landfill space for its solid waste, the State of New Jersey in 1987 passed a law requiring all citizens to separate recyclable materials from the rest of their solid waste. The law provides for further action if plastic beverage containers are not being recycled at the same rate as glass or aluminum beverage containers by a given date.

3. Yet another technology would treat plastics so that they would decompose when exposed to water, sunlight, or special chemicals. Like the technology to recycle plastics, this technology is also in the early stages of development.

Developing a Viewpoint

Come to class prepared to discuss these questions.

1. How many solutions to the problem of disposing of plastics can you think of?

2. What would be the costs and benefits of these solutions?

3. Which of these solutions would you be willing to live with?

4. Which do you feel would be the best?

Suggested Readings

John W. Hill. *Chemistry for Changing Times*. 4th ed., Burgess, 1984.

New Jersey P.L. 1987, c. 102.

James R. Chiles. "On Land, at Sea and in the Air, Those Polymer Invaders are Here." *Smithsonian*. November, 1985, p. 76.

Eleanor Johnson Tracy. "Plastic That Won't Clutter the Countryside." *Fortune*. September 1, 1986, p. 48. Article describes a plastic coating which will dissolve in water when treated with an environmentally acceptable reagent.

Stephen Budiansky. "The World of Crumbling Plastics." *U.S. News and World Report*. November 24, 1986, p. 76. This article discusses water-soluble, biodegradable starch-based plastics and plastics that disintegrate from solar ultraviolet radiation.

UNIT 4

Patterns like this spider web appear throughout nature. You have learned that all the elements can be classified into families by their patterns of physical and chemical properties. In the spider web, the pattern is formed from silk that the spider spins. The silk fibers are made of long chain organic molecules called polymers.

1752
Ben Franklin shows lightning to be electricity.

1765
James Watt invents the steam engine.

1776
Declaration of Independence is signed.

1789
George Washington becomes president.

PATTERNS OF MATTER

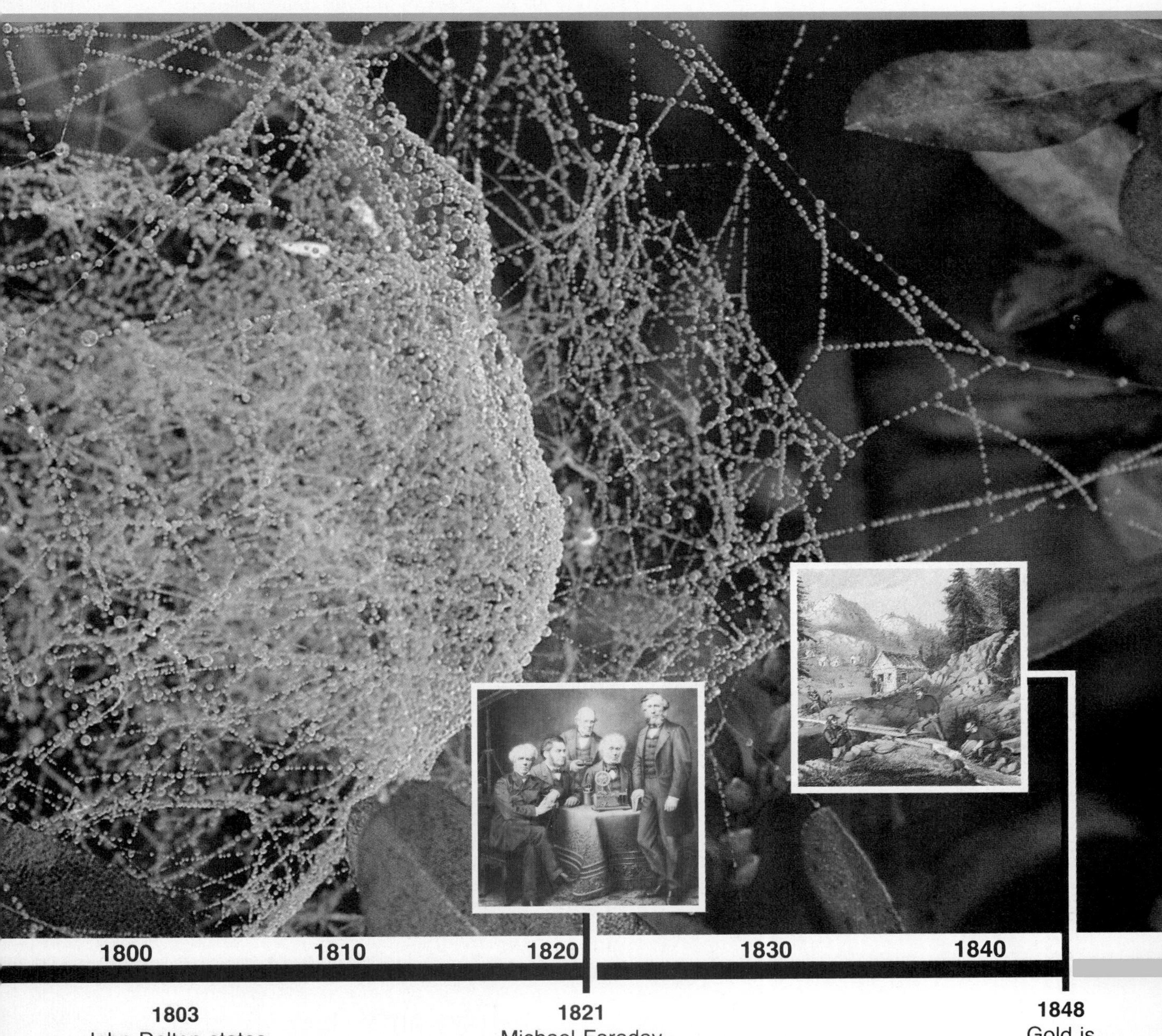

1803
John Dalton states his atomic theory.

1821
Michael Faraday invents electric motor.

1848
Gold is discovered in California.

METALS
GROUPS 1 AND 2
TRANSITION ELEMENTS
METALLURGY

Chapter 12

Elements in Groups 1 Through 12

With the exception of hydrogen, elements in Groups 1 through 12 on the periodic table are metals. Imagine how different your life would be without the metallic elements. Metals are used for the heaviest construction equipment as well as the finest jewelry.

METALS

GOALS

1. You will learn about the properties of metals.
2. You will learn about the metallic bond.
3. You will learn how flame tests can be used to identify metals.

The properties of metals are determined for the most part by the way their atoms bond. In this section, you will learn about the properties common to metals and how the bonding gives them these properties.

12:1 Properties of Metals

Give two properties of metals.

Metals are generally hard and shiny. They conduct heat and electric current. They are malleable and ductile. A **malleable** substance is one that can be rolled or beaten into sheets. A **ductile** substance can be pulled into wires.

Most metals are elements that have three or fewer electrons in the outer energy level of their atoms. Metals tend to give up electrons readily. When metals form bonds with other elements, they usually give up electrons. Thus, they form ionic bonds.

12:2 The Metallic Bond

Metals tend to crystallize in relatively simple patterns. Atoms of metals form regular, orderly, 3-dimensional arrangements through metallic bonds. In **metallic bonding,** the outer electrons of all the atoms are distributed as a common electron cloud. The electrons are shared equally by all the ions.

What is metallic bonding?

INVESTIGATION 12–1

Flame Tests

Problem: Using a flame test, how do you identify a metal?

Materials   

7 test tubes
7 test solutions
distilled water
nichrome wire loop
goggles
test tube rack
hydrochloric acid
two small beakers
laboratory burner
apron

CAUTION: *Handle the hydrochloric acid and the metal solutions with care. Avoid skin contact and do not breathe vapors.*

Procedure

1. Label each of the seven test tubes with one chloride: lithium, potassium, sodium, barium, calcium, strontium, and copper.
2. Place 3 mL of the first test solution into the correctly labeled test tube. Repeat for the other six test solutions. Be sure to put the correct solution into its labeled tube.

FIGURE 12–1.

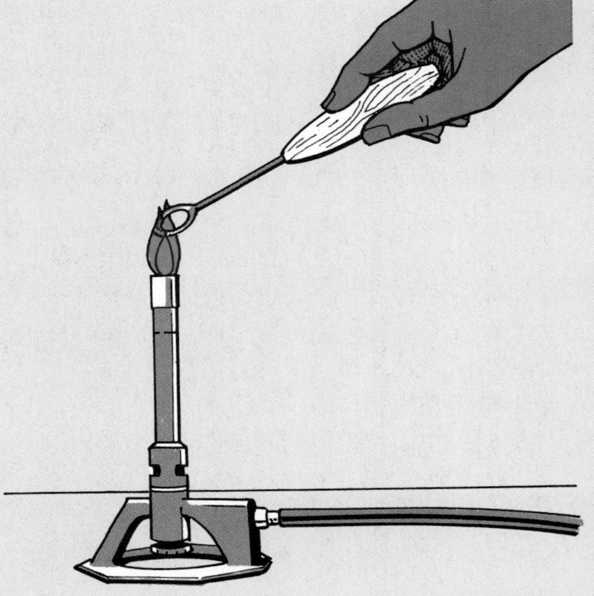

3. Label two small beakers, one "acid" and the other "water." Pour a few milliliters of hydrochloric acid into the acid beaker and a few milliliters of distilled water into the water beaker.
4. Clean the wire loop by dipping it in hydrochloric acid, then in distilled water, and then heating it in the burner flame.
5. Repeat Step 4 until the wire no longer colors the flame.
6. Dip the clean wire into the first test solution. Hold the wire loop at the top of the inner cone of the burner flame, as in Figure 12–1.
7. Record the color of the flame seen in Step 6. Clean the wire as in Steps 4 and 5.
8. Repeat Steps 6 and 7 for the other six test solutions.
9. Obtain an unknown solution from your teacher. Identify the metal in the unknown solution using the flame test.

Data and Observations

Solution	Color
LiCl	
KCl	
NaCl	

Analysis and Conclusions

1. What metal was present in your unknown?
2. How can you be sure that the chloride ion does not cause the color in the flame?
3. Suppose your unknown was a mixture of metal ions. Could you identify two colors in the flame? Try the flame test with a mixture and see.
4. Using a flame test, how do you identify a metal?

The common electrons in a metal help explain some of the properties of metals. Because outer electrons are shared, they are free to move throughout the crystal. This freedom of movement allows metals to conduct electricity. Metals are not brittle because the metallic ions can slide by each other without shattering the crystal. This type of movement explains why metals are both ductile and malleable.

Why are metals not brittle?

12:3 Flame Tests

One way to identify metals is by flame tests. When solutions of these elements are heated in a flame, some of their electrons gain energy. These electrons move to higher energy levels. As they return to their previous state, the electrons lose energy in the form of light. Some metallic elements have a specific color of light that is used to identify the elements.

Some elements such as rubidium and cesium were found through the colors they give off. In fact, *rubidus*

F.Y.I. Robert Bunsen (1811–1899), for whom the Bunsen burner was named, was responsible for the discovery of rubidium and cesium. In November 1860, he and Gustav Kirchhoff, after nearly a year of work, found a trace of cesium in some spring water. They boiled 10 000 gallons to obtain one ounce. In February of 1861, they found rubidium by the color of its spectrum.

Table 12–1

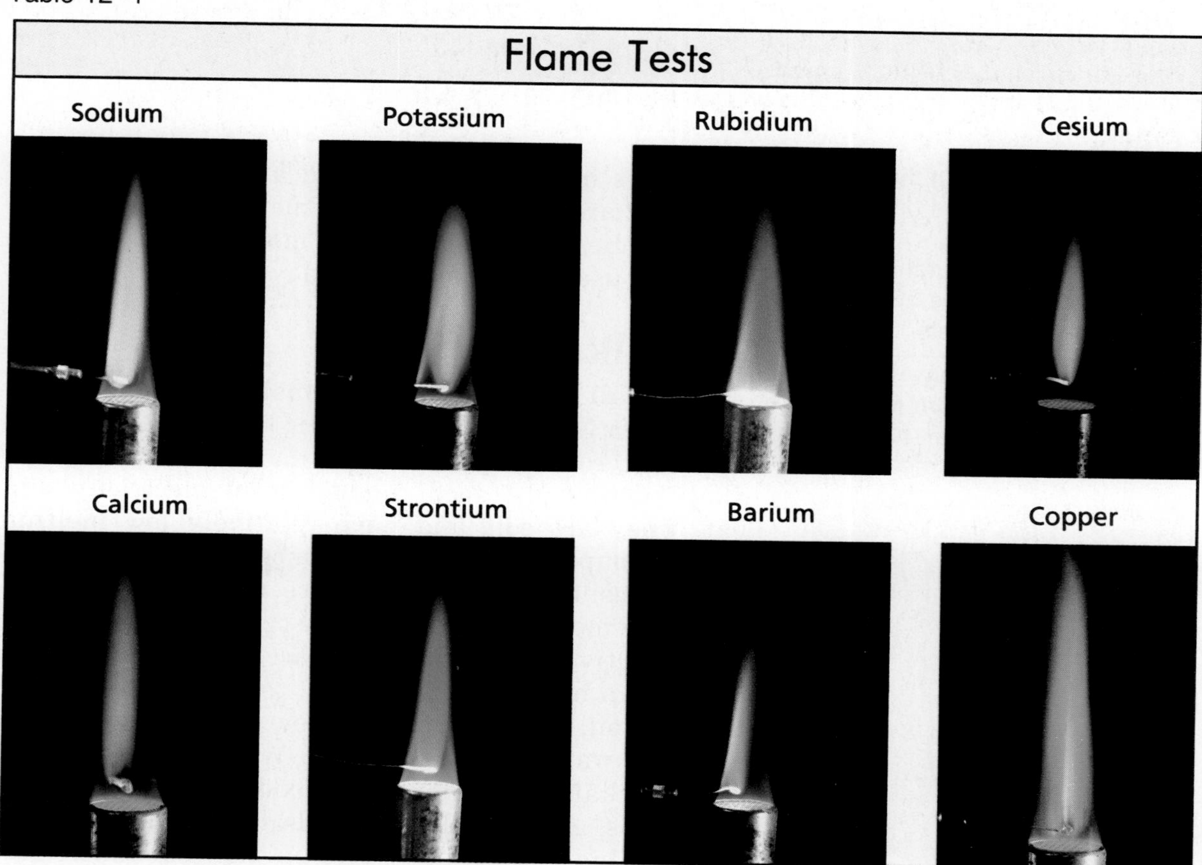

(red) and *cesius* (bluish gray) are the root words for these elements. The names describe the color they give off in a flame test. Flame test colors for various metallic ions are given in Table 12–1.

Review

1. Give three properties of metals.
2. What type of bonds do metals usually form with other elements?
3. How is metallic bonding different from ionic and covalent bonding?
4. Explain why certain metal ions produce colored flames.
5. ★ The sodium flame generally overpowers all other flames. If there is contamination with sodium, the other ions do not show well. A blue glass is used to view the flame. If you view the yellow flame through a blue glass and only violet shows, what could it be? If you view the yellow flame through the blue glass and no color appears, what ion would be present?

GROUPS 1 AND 2

GOALS

1. You will learn about the properties and uses of the alkali metals.
2. You will learn about the properties and uses of the alkaline earth metals.

Elements in Group 1 are called alkali metals. Those in Group 2 are the alkaline earth metals. These families include some of the most active metals. They are also extremely useful metals in everyday life.

12:4 Alkali Metals

FIGURE 12–2. Lithium is floating on oil, which in turn is floating on water. Lithium has the lowest density of any metal.

The **alkali** (AL kuh li) **metals** make up the family of elements in Group 1 of the periodic table. They are usually shiny, reflect light, and are malleable and ductile. Alkali metals are good conductors of electricity and heat. They are soft and have relatively low melting points. Group 1 elements are the most reactive of all the metals. Cesium and rubidium are more reactive than the family members in the earlier periods. Because they are so reactive, the alkali metals are never found as free elements in nature. In pure form, the alkali metals are stored in oil. This is done so they will not react with oxygen or water vapor in the air. When exposed to water, the alkali metals form hydroxides and give off hydrogen gas. All the alkali metals form compounds by ionic bonding. They readily give up their one outer elec-

Table 12–2

Alkali Metals		
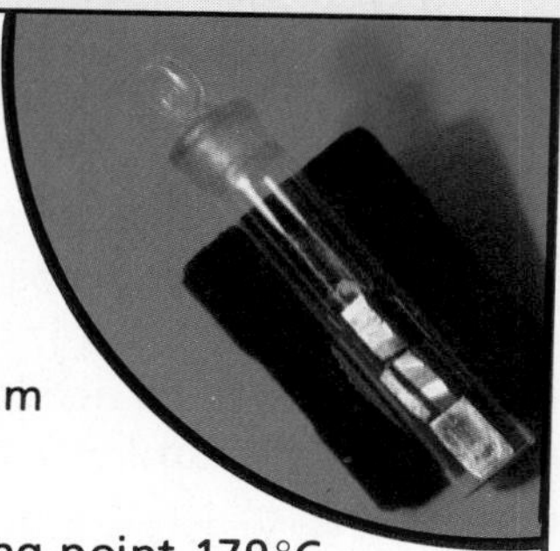 ${}^{7}_{3}Li$ Lithium Melting point 179°C Boiling point 1336°C	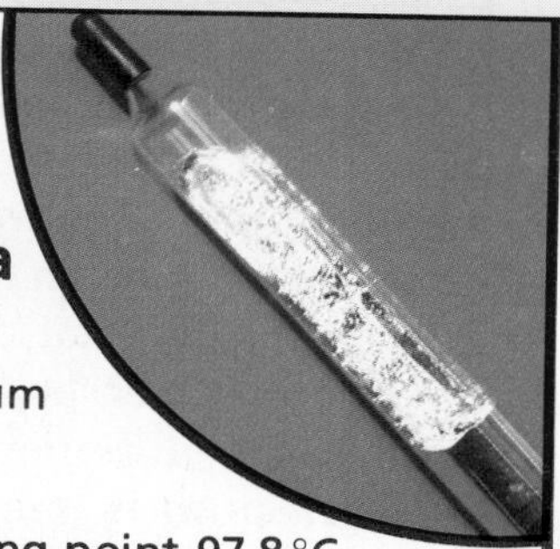 ${}^{23}_{11}Na$ Sodium Melting point 97.8°C Boiling point 883°C	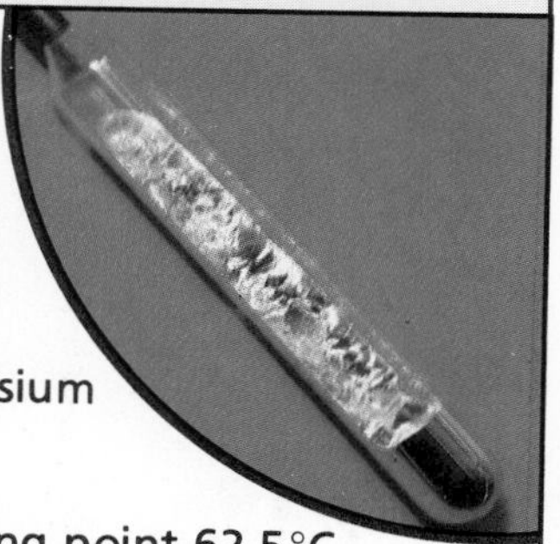 ${}^{39}_{19}K$ Potassium Melting point 62.5°C Boiling point 758°C
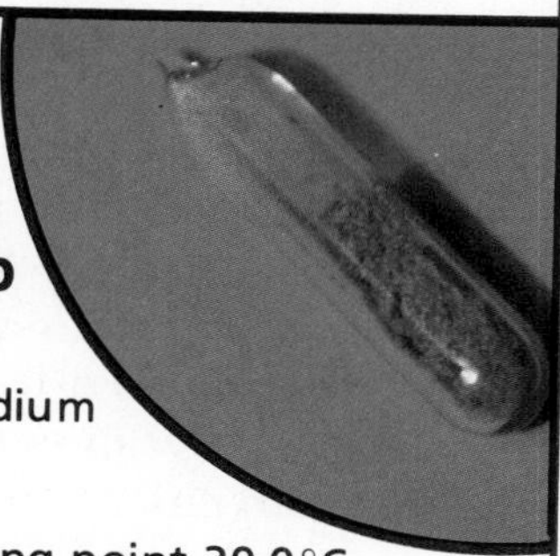 ${}^{85}_{37}Rb$ Rubidium Melting point 39.0°C Boiling point 700°C	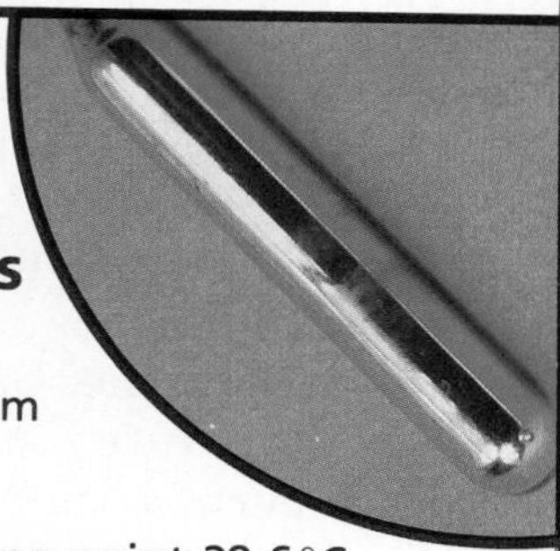 ${}^{133}_{55}Cs$ Cesium Melting point 28.6°C Boiling point 670°C	${}^{(223)}_{87}Fr$ Francium Radioactive element, 223 is the mass number of the most stable isotope.

tron to form ions. As a result, they react easily with the halogens. These Group 17 elements readily accept an electron.

The alkali metals have many common uses. Lithium is valuable in metallurgy and medicines. Sodium is found in table salt, lye, and many other compounds. Potassium is an element necessary for plant growth. Potassium compounds are used in medicine and photography. A proper balance of sodium and potassium is needed for human health. Rubidium and cesium have been used in photocells.

What are the Group 2 elements called?

12:5 Alkaline Earth Metals

The elements in Group 2 of the periodic table are called the **alkaline** (AL kuh lin) **earth metals.** The alkaline earth metals are very reactive. Thus, they are not found free in nature. Most of these elements give up their two outer electrons and form ions. They tend to form compounds by ionic bonding. Some of these metals react with water and give off hydrogen.

Beryllium is found chemically combined with aluminum, silicon, and oxygen in the mineral beryl. The

FIGURE 12–3. The mineral beryl is a source of the element beryllium.

element may be obtained by passing an electric current through melted beryllium chloride. Beryllium forms compounds with all the elements in Group 17.

In nature, magnesium is found chemically combined in mineral deposits and as an ion in seawater. Pure magnesium burns with a very bright flame. For this reason, it is used in some photographic flashbulbs. Since it is strong but not dense, magnesium is used in industry when both strength and light weight are needed. Examples are automobile parts, aircraft, and spacecraft.

What metal is found in the green plant pigment, chlorophyll?

Magnesium is one of the elements in the green plant pigment, chlorophyll (KLOR uh fihl). Some compounds of magnesium are used as medicines. An example is magnesium sulfate, which is sold as Epsom salt. Some antacids (ant AS ids) contain magnesium hydroxide.

Calcium is one of the most abundant elements in Earth's crust. Slightly less than four percent of the mass of Earth's crust is made of calcium compounds. An important example is calcium carbonate, the main component of limestone. Calcium is never found as a free element in nature. It can be prepared by passing an electric current through melted calcium chloride.

CAREER

Chemical Engineer

Tom Sheung was never satisfied with simply watching the world around him. He wanted to know what made fireworks explode in colors and patterns. He wondered why acids ate through some metals. He wanted to know what made dry ice different from regular ice, why some plastics were soft and some hard. He wanted to know how a fire extinguisher put out fires.

The chemistry sets he had as a young boy were interesting, but Tom wanted to understand why and how chemicals react, so he took chemistry and physics in high school. He learned about controlling reactions with temperature, density, and pressure. He began to understand the nature of oxidation, acid-base reactions and polymer formation.

In college Tom studied chemical engineering. He now works for a roofing products company. The "plastic roof" he is researching could save money because it would not need to be replaced as often as other roofing materials.

For career information, write
American Chemical Society
1155 Sixteenth Street NW
Washington, DC 20036

a

b

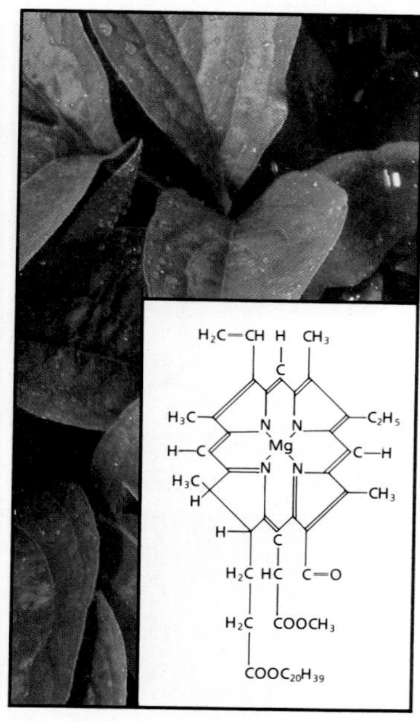

c

FIGURE 12–4. Magnesium is used in photographic flashbulbs because it burns brightly (a). Used in baseball bats (b), magnesium is lightweight and strong. Green plants (c) contain chlorophyll, a compound of magnesium.

Lime is calcium oxide. Lime is mixed with sand, water, and other materials to make plaster and mortar for buildings. Lime is also used in making glass, removing hair from hides, and softening hard water. Calcium compounds are also used in treating soils that are too acid for crops to grow. An important part of bones and teeth, calcium is essential to the diet of humans and other animals. Milk and other dairy products are excellent sources of calcium.

What is lime?

Strontium is the least abundant of the alkaline earth metals in Earth's crust. It is found chiefly combined with oxygen and carbon or silicon. The flame test for

FIGURE 12–5. Travertine is a mineral made of calcium carbonate. The photograph shows travertine deposits at Minerva Spring, Mammoth Hot Springs, Yellowstone National Park.

Table 12–3

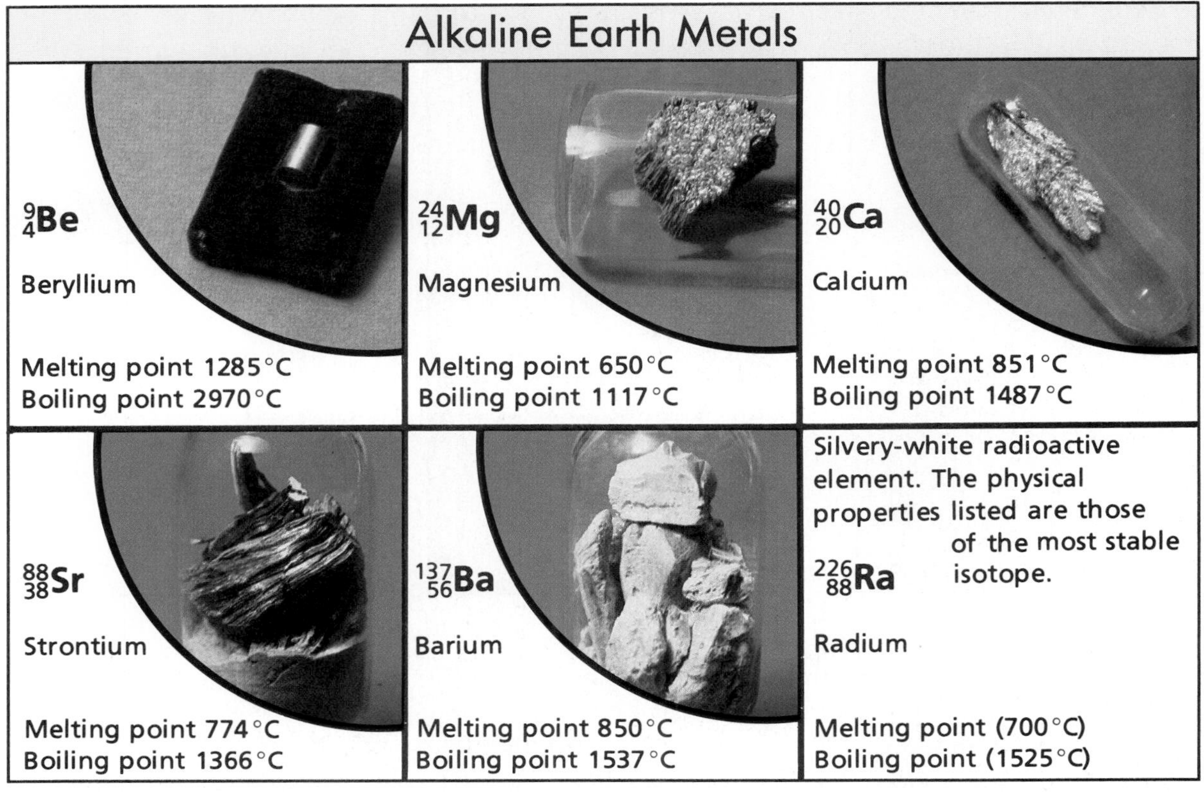

strontium and its compounds is a brilliant shade of red, Table 12–1. For this reason, strontium compounds are often used in fireworks.

Like the other alkaline earth metals, barium is also found combined in nature. It is most commonly found as barium sulfate in the mineral barite. Barium metal has chemical properties similar to calcium and strontium. However, it tends to react faster than calcium and strontium. Barium reacts readily with water, oxygen, and the Group 17 elements. It is often stored under oil or kerosene to keep it from reacting with air. The flame test for barium and its compounds is green, Table 12–1.

Which alkaline earth metal is radioactive?

The compound barium sulfate is used to study the digestive tract. Patients swallow a liquid mixture containing barium sulfate, which absorbs X rays. A doctor can then study X rays of the digestive tract as the chemical moves through it.

Radium is more reactive than barium. In nature, it is found in uranium ores. Radium is also radioactive. It can be obtained as a free element by passing an electric current through melted radium salts. The metal is silvery white but turns black when exposed to air.

F.Y.I. Radium and similar radioactive metals are used to determine the wear resistance of motor oil. Engine blocks and/or piston sleeves are made including a radioactive element. The engine is run with various kinds of oil. After the engine test, the oil is checked to determine how much radioactive material wore off the engine and is in the oil.

Radium is used in medicine to treat cancer. At one time, it was used to make luminous (LEW mi nus) watch dials. These watch dials glow in the dark. It was later found that using radium for this purpose caused cancer in some of the workers making the dials.

Review

6. How many electrons are in the outer energy level of an atom of each of the alkali metals?
7. Why are the alkali metals stored under oil?
8. What are some common uses for calcium and barium?
9. How many electrons are in the outer energy level of each of the alkaline earth metals?
★ 10. All alkali metals and alkaline earth metals form hydroxides. Write the formula of each of these metal hydroxides.

TRANSITION ELEMENTS

GOALS

1. You will learn about the common properties of the transition elements.
2. You will learn about the specific properties of some of the subgroups of the transition metals.

In general the elements in the middle of the periodic table are called the transition elements. Some of these elements are used in catalytic converters on cars. Some are responsible for the colors of many beautiful gems. Some are part of the new superconducting magnets. These elements are metallic.

12:6 Properties of Transition Elements

The **transition elements** form Groups 3 through 12 of the periodic table. Transition elements include some of our most familiar metals. Among them are iron, silver, copper, zinc, and gold. Except for palladium, they all have one or two electrons in their outer energy level. However, some of these elements form compounds using electrons from the next-to-outer level as well. There are certain likenesses among the transition elements because of their electron structure. There is often little difference in properties between one transition metal and its nearest neighbors on the periodic table.

FIGURE 12–6. The colors of many gems are due to compounds of transition elements.

Most of the transition metals are hard and have high melting points. The compounds of transition metals are often highly colored. Some transition metal ions can be

FIGURE 12–7. These brightly-colored solutions contain the cobalt(III) ion bonded to various molecules and negative ions.

identified by their colors in compounds. Some transition metal compounds are used as pigments in paint. You may have heard of "cobalt blue" or "cadmium yellow." These colors refer to specific compounds of cobalt and cadmium.

List four elements that have two oxidation states.

Many transition metals have more than one oxidation state. Iron, for example, forms both iron(II) and iron(III) compounds. Chromium also has oxidation states of 2+ and 3+. Copper exists in copper(I) and copper(II) and gold in gold(I) and gold(III) oxidation states. The compounds formed by the different oxidation states often have characteristic colors. From the color, it is easy to tell which form of the element is in the compound.

12:7 Iron, Cobalt, and Nickel

What is the most used metal?

What metal is in hemoglobin?

The transition elements iron, cobalt, and nickel are important metals. More iron is used than all other metals combined. It is the second most abundant metal and the fourth most abundant of all the elements in Earth's crust. Nearly every animal, vegetable, or mineral material contains iron in some form. Hemoglobin in red blood cells is a compound containing iron.

Table 12–4

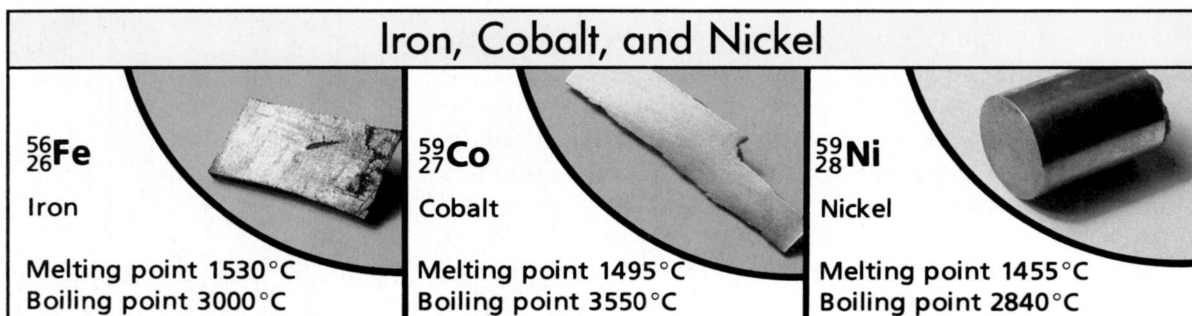

Iron, Cobalt, and Nickel		
$^{56}_{26}Fe$ Iron	$^{59}_{27}Co$ Cobalt	$^{59}_{28}Ni$ Nickel
Melting point 1530°C	Melting point 1495°C	Melting point 1455°C
Boiling point 3000°C	Boiling point 3550°C	Boiling point 2840°C

FIGURE 12–8. Nickel is electroplated onto other metals to make them shiny. Chrome-plated objects have an underlayer of nickel.

Cobalt and nickel are far less abundant than iron. Both are difficult to mine and refine. Cobalt is used to produce special heat-resistant steel for cutting tools. Nickel can be polished to a high gloss and is used to coat other metals to make them shiny. It is also combined with other metals to make them strong. The United States nickel coin is made of nickel and copper.

What elements make up the United States nickel coin?

12:8 Copper, Silver, and Gold

What are the members of the copper family?

The copper family contains three well-known metals, copper, silver, and gold. None of the three is very reactive. Therefore, they are all found free in nature. Copper and silver can be mined as free elements or in ores combined with other elements. Gold is almost always found free.

Copper is a reddish metal and is a good conductor of heat and electricity. It is easily drawn into wires and pounded or rolled into sheets. Copper is most widely used in electrical wiring and plumbing. It is often used to protect other materials, because it forms an unreactive green coating when exposed to air. You have seen this green copper(II) carbonate on many statues and copper roofs. It has formed from the reaction of copper, water, and carbon dioxide in the air.

Gold is a yellow, soft metal that conducts heat and reflects light well. It is often used with other metals in jewelry because it can be shaped easily. Gold combined with copper, nickel, and zinc is "white gold." "Yellow gold" contains silver and copper. Gold has always been valuable, because it is rare. It is used as a base for money systems all over the world. It is also used in arthritis treatment. Gold is not reactive chemically. It dissolves in *aqua regia* only. *Aqua regia* is a mixture of concentrated nitric and hydrochloric acids.

FIGURE 12–9. Gold has been used for ornamental objects since ancient times.

INVESTIGATION 12–2

Transition Metal Compounds

Problem: What can cause transition metal compounds to change color?

Materials 

2 test tubes
laboratory burner
small beakers
distilled water
test materials
test tube holder
droppers
graduated cylinder
goggles
apron

CAUTION: *Handle acids and bases with care; they can cause burns. Cobalt chloride and iron(III) sulfate are poisonous. Wear goggles and an apron.*

Procedure

1. Place a few crystals of cobalt(II) chloride $CoCl_2$, in a test tube. Record the color of the crystals. Heat the tube over the laboratory burner, gently at first, then strongly. Record the color of the solid.
2. Cool the test tube from Step 1. Then add a few drops of water to the tube. Record any changes you observe.
3. Heat the cobalt solution in the test tube from Step 2. **CAUTION:** *Point the open end of the test tube away from other students.* Heat the side of the test tube, as in Figure 12–10. Allow the solution to cool. Record any changes.
4. Add a few drops of hydrochloric acid, HCl, to the solution in the test tube from Step 3. Record any color changes.
5. Place about 3 mL of $Fe_2(SO_4)_3$, iron(III) sulfate, solution in a test tube. Record its color. Add about 1 mL of dilute sodium hydroxide, NaOH, to the iron solution in the test tube. Record any changes in color.
6. Add a few milliliters of HCl to the test tube from Step 5. Record any color changes.

FIGURE 12–10.

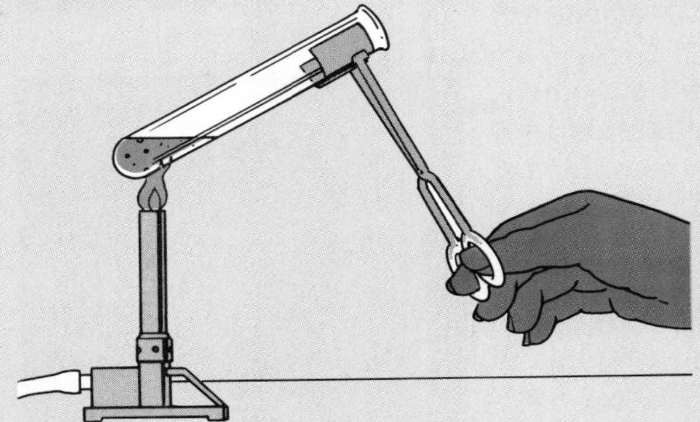

Data and Observations

Substance	Treatment	Observations
1. $CoCl_2$	none heat	
2. $CoCl_2$	water	
3. $CoCl_2$ solution	heat cool	
4. $CoCl_2$ solution	HCl	
5. $Fe_2(SO_4)_3$	none NaOH	
6. $Fe_2(SO_4)_3$ + NaOH	HCl	

Analysis and Conclusions

1. What does heating remove from the original cobalt(II) chloride crystals?
2. What do you think caused the color change in Step 2?
3. Form a hypothesis to explain the color changes of Steps 4 and 5.
4. What can cause transition metal compounds to change color?

Table 12–5

Of all metals, silver is the best conductor of heat and electricity. Silver can also be shaped easily and is used for jewelry and other ornaments. It is a white, soft metal that reflects light well. Silver is sometimes used as a backing for mirrors.

What metal is the best conductor of electricity?

Silver has a 1+ oxidation state. It does not react with oxygen but does darken when exposed to hydrogen sulfide. As with carbon dioxide and copper, silver reacts with hydrogen sulfide in the air and tarnishes. The tarnish on silverware may also come from sulfur compounds in foods. Silver tarnish is a coating of silver sulfide. Silver compounds are used in photography because they turn black when exposed to light. This property of silver makes it useful in making photosensitive (foh toh SEN sut ihv) glass.

What is the oxidation state of members of the zinc family?

FIGURE 12–11. The cadmium rods in nuclear reactors help control the speed of the reaction by absorbing neutrons.

12:9 Zinc, Cadmium, and Mercury

The zinc family is Group 12. These elements all show a 2+ oxidation state. Zinc is a silvery metal that tarnishes by forming zinc oxide with oxygen in air. The tarnish forms a protective coating and prevents further corrosion. For this reason, zinc is often used to coat other metals, such as iron, to protect them from corrosion. This process is called galvanizing. Zinc compounds are used in paint, medicines, fiberboard, and automobile tires. Zinc is an element needed in the diet. At least 15 mg per day is necessary for growth and conversion of carbonic acid to CO_2 and H_2O.

Cadmium is generally obtained during the refining process for zinc. It has many of the same uses, including plating on other metals for protection. Cadmium sulfide is a yellow pigment in paint. It should be used with care because it is poisonous. Cadmium rods are used in

Table 12–6

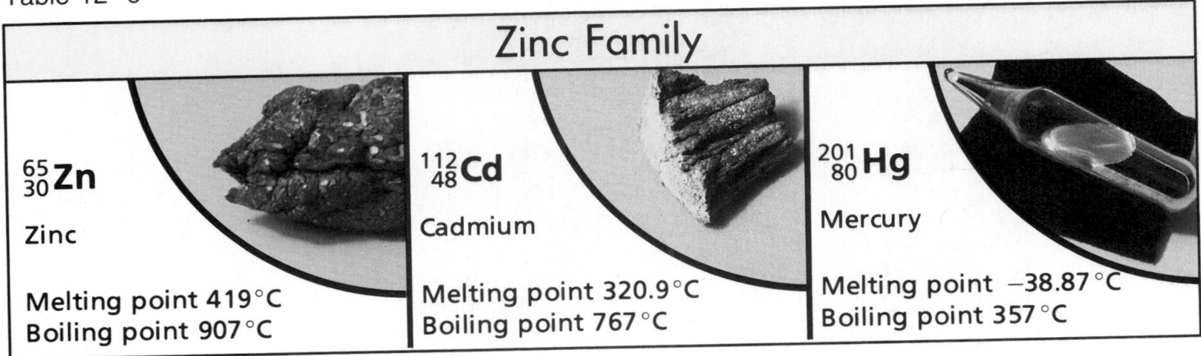

Zinc Family		
$^{65}_{30}$**Zn**	$^{112}_{48}$**Cd**	$^{201}_{80}$**Hg**
Zinc	Cadmium	Mercury
Melting point 419°C	Melting point 320.9°C	Melting point −38.87°C
Boiling point 907°C	Boiling point 767°C	Boiling point 357°C

nuclear reactors to absorb neutrons. The more neutrons absorbed, the slower the nuclear chain reaction.

What is the only metal that is liquid at room temperature?

Mercury is the only metal that is liquid at room temperature. It is a dense, silvery metal that has a low freezing point and a high boiling point. These properties make mercury useful in thermometers, barometers, and electrical switches. Mixtures of mercury with silver, tin, and copper are called amalgams and are used in dentistry for filling teeth. Mercury is poisonous and should not be handled. Because it vaporizes easily, mercury should always be stored in sealed containers. Some people have allergic reactions to mercury. Mercury compounds dumped as waste can be absorbed by plants and animals. These compounds can accumulate in the body. People have died as a result of mercury poisoning. Therefore, make certain that spilled mercury is disposed of properly and quickly.

12:10 Lanthanoids and Actinoids

How many lanthanoid elements are there?

Periods 6 and 7 contain two unusual series of elements called the lanthanoids and the actinoids. The **lanthanoids** are the fourteen elements that begin with

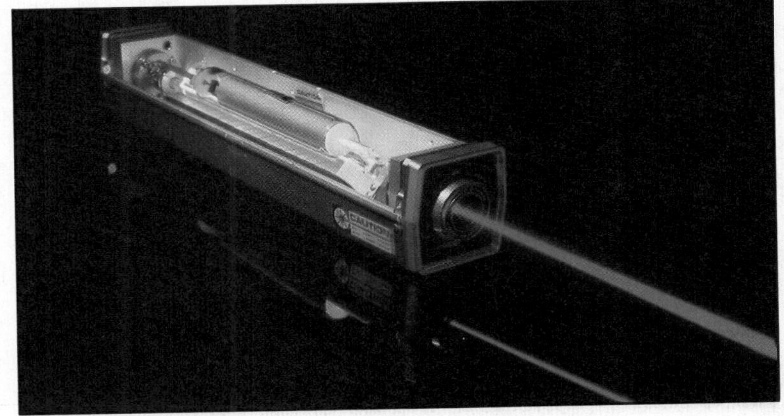

FIGURE 12–12. Compounds of neodymium, a lanthanoid element, may be used in laser glass.

lanthanum on the periodic table. The fourteen **actinoids** begin with actinium and include elements 89–102. All but four actinoids are synthetic.

The lanthanoid elements are bright, silvery metals. Like other metals, they are good conductors. Their main oxidation state is 3+. Some may exhibit 2+ or 4+ in certain compounds. The lanthanoid elements occur together in many minerals. They are very difficult to separate. Lanthanoids were once called rare earth elements. They were called "rare" because scientists believed they were rare in nature. They were called "earth" because their oxides did not dissolve in water or melt. However, they are not rare, but occur in relatively large amounts all over the world.

The lanthanoids generally form compounds that are colored and show some magnetic properties. Most uses of these elements involve mixtures of the metals. Misch metal is a mixture of lanthanoids used in lighter flints. Misch metal or cerium can be added to iron to increase its ductility. A compound of cobalt and samarium forms strong permanent magnets used in audio headsets.

There are also several important lanthanoid compounds. The red color in television picture tubes can be caused by compounds containing yttrium, gadolinium, or europium. Both lanthanum and yttrium are used in new superconducting ceramics (page 498). Lanthanum oxide is used in fiber optics. Some types of laser glass contain neodymium compounds. Neodymium is also mixed with iron and boron to produce the most powerful magnets known.

The actinoids are radioactive and have little use beyond atomic weapons and nuclear power. These uses have created much controversy. Some nuclear reactions of uranium are discussed in Chapter 23.

BIOGRAPHY

Chien-Shiung Wu
1912–

Chien-Shiung Wu grew up in China. Her most famous experiment involved cobalt-60. Her experiment revised one of the basic laws of physics. She showed that while the cobalt nucleus spins in a "left-handed" direction, the electrons it emits are "right-handed."

F.Y.I. In 1788, the mineral ytterbite was discovered. It was eventually found to contain 16 new elements. It took more than 100 years to find them all, contributing to the idea that these elements were "rare earths."

Review

11. What are some uses for iron?

12. Write the formulas for the chlorides of iron. Use its common oxidation states.

13. Write the formulas for all of the nitrates of all members of the copper family. Use all oxidation states.

14. Identify each of the following as a transition element, a lanthanoid, or an actinoid: Dy, Ag, W, Cr, Nd, U, Ni, Pu, Cd, Cf.

★ **15.** What is the formula for the tarnish on silver? For the carbonate of copper? For the oxide of zinc?

METALLURGY

GOALS

1. You will learn about processes used to extract metals from their ores.
2. You will learn about alloys, and how they are used.

Metallurgy is the process of mining and refining metals from their ores. When metal is taken from its ore, the process is called winning the metal. Refining is the purification of metal that has been extracted from the ore. Many different processes are used to win, or separate, metals from their ores.

12:11 Ores

What is an ore?

An **ore** is a mineral or other natural material from which one or more metals can be profitably obtained. Many different processes are used to extract metals. The simplest metals to obtain are those that occur as elements. Gold, for example, was first found and mined as the element.

Sometimes metals occur in a quartz (SiO_2) vein. The quartz is pulverized, and the metals are separated by combining them with other metals.

Ores also give up their metals in various chemical processes. Generally an ore can be reduced to the free metal by the use of coke (processed coal) in a blast furnace. Tin and iron are reclaimed this way, for example. You have already seen that many alkali or alkaline earth metals are obtained by passing an electric current through the melted ore.

FIGURE 12–13. High quality steel is produced in basic oxygen furnaces like this. Molten iron is treated in the furnace with a stream of hot oxygen to remove impurities.

Table 12–7

Some Alloys and Their Uses		
Alloy	**Metals**	**Typical uses**
Wood's metal	Bi, Pb, Sn, Cd	automatic sprinklers
commercial bronze	Cu, Sn	jewelry, screens, nuts, and bolts
German silver	Cu, Zn, Ni	silver platings, jewelry
gold, 14 carat	Au, Cu, Ag	jewelry
solder	Sn, Pb	electrical wire solderings
dentist's amalgam	Ag, Sn, Cu, Hg	dental fillings
nichrome	Ni, Cr	electrical heating elements
monel metal	Ni, Cu, Fe	household appliances
Dow metal	Mg, Al, Mn	aircraft parts
red and yellow brass	Cu, Zn	pipes, hose nozzles ornamental objects, jewelry
wrought iron	Fe, C, Mn	ornamental objects

12:12 Metal Alloys

One of the most interesting properties of metals is their ability to form alloys. In many respects this is the opposite of winning metals from ores. An **alloy** is a material that contains more than one element and has metallic properties.

The first alloy was produced as early as 3000 B.C. People discovered that mixing copper and tin would produce a more durable material that we call bronze. Since that first discovery, hundreds of alloys have been created. Because metals can combine in many different proportions, the possibilities for new alloys are endless.

Forming alloys of metals is an important process, because materials with totally new properties can be produced. Making an alloy is one of the primary ways of changing the properties of metals. For example, pure gold is too soft to be used in jewelry. When copper is mixed with the gold, a much harder material is obtained. Pure gold is said to be 24 karat. A 12-karat gold item is 50% gold. The common alloy used in jewelry is 14 karat. What is the percent of gold in this alloy? Gold used in coins is 22 karat, or 92% gold. White gold in jewelry is an alloy of gold, nickel, copper, and zinc.

The standard kilogram is an alloy of platinum and iridium. This alloy combines properties of both transition metals. Platinum is relatively soft and unreactive. Iridium is one of the hardest metals and one of the least reactive, as well. The alloy is hard and very unreactive. It is important that the standard kilogram be made of an unreactive material. Otherwise, it might lose or gain mass through corrosion.

F.Y.I. The people in the California Gold Rush in 1849 used a panning technique to find the gold. Gold is usually found in veins much like coal. However, in the gold rushes, the everyday miner used a "placer deposit." This was gold deposited in streambeds by glaciers or by water running over exposed gold veins. "Gold panners" would use the running water of a creek to wash the less dense material away from the gold.

FIGURE 12–14. This photo shows a microscopic view of a gold-copper alloy.

Table 12–8

Some Steel Alloys			
Name	**Composition**	**Properties**	**Uses**
Manganese	10–18% Mn	very hard	railroads, armor plate, conveyors
Duriron	12–15% Si	acid resistant	pipes, condensers, containers
Nickel	2–5% Ni	elastic, corrosion resistant	gears, drive shafts, cables
Invar	36% Ni	does not expand or contract	measuring tapes, pendulums
Permalloy	78% Ni	magnetic	cables
Stainless	14–19% Cr 7–9% Ni	strong, corrosion resistant	surgical instruments, knives, flatware
High speed	14–20% W, 4% Cr or 6–12% Mo, 4% Cr	keeps hardness at high temperatures	cutting tools, drill bits, saw blades

TECHNOLOGY: ADVANCES

Metals with a Memory

Imagine an alloy with a memory! Shape-memory alloys (SMAs) are metals composed of various elements such as copper-zinc and nickel-titanium that have an unusual property. When the alloy is heated, it changes back to its original shape. This is due to a physical change in which the alloy's crystalline structure changes from one form to another when the temperature varies.

The technological applications of SMAs are becoming widespread. For example, coupling cylinders made of SMAs are being used in fighter aircraft to join hydraulic tubes. When cooled, the coupling expands and slips easily over the tubes. As the coupling warms, it contracts to its original shape and shrinks to form a sealed joint.

A new anti-scald shower valve makes use of a shape-memory alloy. When scalding hot water streams out of the shower, a spring made of SMA brass expands and triggers a cut-off valve in the shower head. The water pressure decreases and the water trickles out. When cold water is turned on, the shower returns to its normal pressure. When eyeglass frames made of the alloy are bent, hot tap water can be run over them. The wire frames will return to their original shape.

SMAs may become important in the field of medicine. A new device has been developed that delivers small metered doses of medication into the veins using SMAs power. SMAs are also being used in word processors for the blind.

A **steel** is an alloy of iron. All steels contain carbon in varying amounts. The amount of carbon added depends on the use of the steel. Carbon steels become less flexible as more carbon is added. The percentage of carbon in steel ranges from 0.1% to 1.7%. Low-carbon steels, less than 0.2%, are soft. Medium steels contain 0.2% to 0.6% carbon. High-carbon steels contain 0.75% to 1.7% carbon and are the hardest. Steels may contain elements other than iron and carbon. Sulfur, phosphorus, manganese, and silicon are some other elements that may be present. Steel is produced in greater amounts than all other alloys.

Besides iron, what element does steel always contain?

REVIEW

16. What is an ore?
17. What percent gold is 24-karat gold?
18. Would steel used in manufacturing automobile bodies be high- or low-carbon steel? Why?
19. What advantage does silicon provide in steel?
★ 20. Wood's metal is an alloy used in automatic sprinklers of fire safety systems. What property makes it useful in these systems?

PROBLEM SOLVING

Can you interpret a qualitative analysis scheme?

A qualitative analysis scheme is a series of tests used to identify an unknown. The diagram below is a scheme for Hg_2^{2+}, Ag^+, and Pb^{2+}. A precipitate, ppt., is an insoluble substance that crystallizes out of solution. Identify the unknown or the test in the following situations.

1. Hot water is added to a solid unknown. How could you tell if the resulting solution contains Pb^{2+}?
2. How could you tell if an unknown solid contains Hg_2^{2+}?
3. Hot water is added to a solid unknown. A precipitate forms. Ammonia is added to the precipitate, forming a solution. No change occurs when HNO_3 is added.

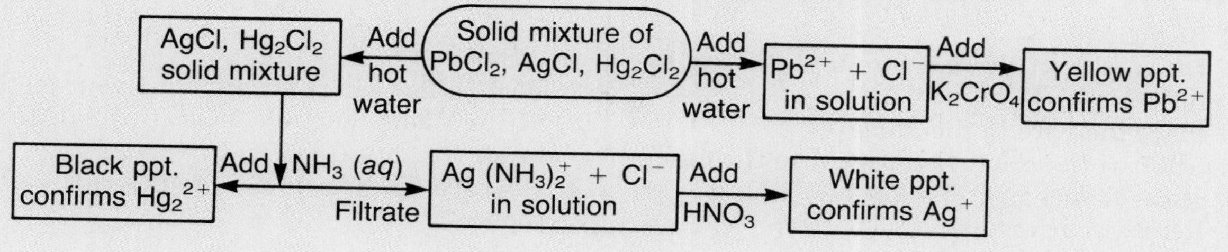

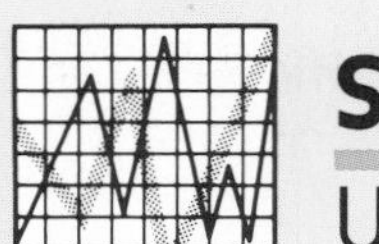

SKILL
Using Flow Charts

Problem: How are flow charts used to describe a procedure?

Materials

paper and pencil

Background

A flow chart is a visual method of giving instructions for a procedure. As a road map simplifies directions for travel, a flow chart helps to simplify what may be an involved or complicated process. With a flow chart, you can order the steps in a process for a desired goal. Flow charts are used to design manufacturing processes as well as computer programs.

Flow charts contain symbols that represent the specific steps in a process. The shape of each symbol used in the flow chart has a special meaning. An oval ⬭ indicates the beginning and the ending of each flow chart. A rectangle ▭ shows that some instruction takes place. A diamond ◇ indicates that a decision must be made. It can be answered yes or no. A parallelogram ▱ shows that something is copied or recorded. Arrows → indicate the direction of the flow. The Sample Procedure below shows how a flow chart can be used for the process of making a flame test for sodium. The steps of the process are listed first. Then the steps are shown in a flow chart.

Sample Procedure

1. Begin.
2. Dip a clean nichrome wire into the test solution.
3. Place the wire in the flame.
4. Observe the color. Compare it to the colors of the flames in Table 12–1.
5. Record your results.

FIGURE 12–15.

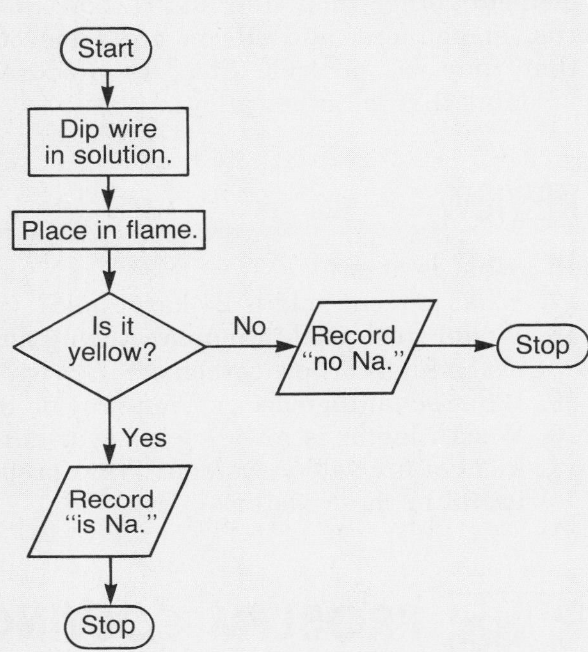

Questions

1. Consider the process of determining whether a substance is a metal. Use the statements below inside the correct symbols to make a flow chart of this process.
   - Start
   - Observe
   - Is it shiny?
   - Yes/No/Stop
   - Does it conduct electricity?
   - Yes/No/Stop
   - List as metal.
   - Stop
2. Write a flow chart for brushing your teeth.
3. Write a flow chart for separating salt from sand.
4. How are flow charts used to describe a procedure?

Chapter 12 Review

SUMMARY

1. Metals generally have three or fewer electrons in the outer energy level. 12:1
2. In metallic bonding, the atoms share all their outer electrons in a common electron cloud. 12:2
3. Flame tests can be used to identify some metallic ions. 12:3
4. Group 1, the alkali metals, are the most reactive metals. 12:4
5. Group 2 elements are called the alkaline earth metals. 12:5
6. Some transition metals form highly colored compounds. 12:6
7. Most transition metals have more than one oxidation state. 12:6
8. Iron is the most widely used metal. 12:7
9. The members of the copper family, gold, silver, and copper, are not very reactive. 12:8
10. Mercury is the only metal that is a liquid at room temperature. 12:9
11. Lanthanoids and actinoids are two series of elements located in Periods 6 and 7 of the periodic table. 12:10
12. An ore is a mineral or other natural material from which a metal can be profitably obtained. 12:11
13. An alloy is a material that contains more than one element and has metallic properties. 12:12
14. Steels are alloys of iron. 12:12

VOCABULARY

a. actinoids
b. alkali metals
c. alkaline earth metals
d. alloy
e. ductile
f. lanthanoids
g. malleable
h. metallic bonding
i. ore
j. steel
k. transition elements

Matching

Match each description with the correct vocabulary word from the list above. Some words will not be used.

1. a combination of elements that has metallic properties
2. Group 1 elements
3. mineral from which a metal can be obtained
4. can be drawn into a wire
5. an alloy of iron
6. All of these elements are radioactive.
7. can be rolled into sheets
8. Group 2 elements
9. elements in Groups 3 through 12
10. All atoms have a common electron cloud.

Chapter 12 Review

MAIN IDEAS

A. Reviewing Concepts

Complete each sentence with the correct word or phrase.

1. ____________ metals are the most reactive metals.
2. Calcium is a(n) ____________ metal.
3. Silver, copper, and ____________ are in the same family.
4. When metals react with other elements, they usually give up electrons and form ____________ bonds.
5. Ores contain ____________ in an unrefined state.
6. Atoms in metals are held together by ____________.
7. "Yellow" gold contains ____________, ____________, and ____________.
8. Transition metals generally have ____________ electrons in the outer energy level.
9. Some metals can be identified by specific colors of light given off in ____________ tests.
10. Alkali metals are stored in oil to keep them from reacting with ____________ and ____________.
11. Photographic flashbulbs often contain the metal ____________.
12. Lime is the compound ____________ ____________.
13. The greater the amount of carbon in steel, the ____________ flexible the steel becomes.
14. Compounds of transition metals are often ____________.
15. Dental amalgams contain the liquid metal ____________.

B. Understanding Concepts

Answer the following questions using complete sentences when possible.

16. What are some uses for the elements in the alkaline earth family?
17. How are the alkali metal family and the copper family different?
18. What metals named in this chapter are used to coat other metals? Why is one metal used to coat another?
19. What are the properties that distinguish metals from nonmetals?
20. Name the following compounds:
    a. RbCl
    b. Fe_2O_3
    c. $CuNO_3$
    d. $Mg(OH)_2$
21. Write formulas for the following compounds.
    a. lanthanum oxide
    b. copper(II) chloride
    c. lithium hydroxide
    d. sodium carbonate
22. Describe a metallic bond.
23. List four transition elements and their oxidation states.
24. What is galvanizing?
25. Give three characteristics of mercury.

C. Applying Concepts

Answer the following questions using complete sentences when possible.

26. What happens to the melting points of the alkali metal elements as the mass number increases? Why do you think this happens?
27. What kind of bonding does each of the following pairs of elements have when forming a compound?
    a. sodium-chlorine
    b. iron-oxygen
    c. magnesium-chlorine
    d. copper-sulfur
28. What properties of magnesium make it a good choice for airplanes and space vehicles?
29. What is the difference between coating metals and alloying them?
30. In at least three ways, compare and contrast the properties of gold and silver.

Chapter 12 Review

SKILL REVIEW

1. What does a rectangular block represent in a flow chart?
2. In what way do flow charts describe a procedure?
3. Prepare a flow chart for determining an element's group and period from the arrangement of electrons in its energy levels. Use elements with atomic numbers 1–20.
4. Why do scientists make inferences?
5. Why is it helpful to answer the questions in the margin as you read your science assignment?

PROJECTS

1. Report to the class on coordination compounds.
2. Set up an experiment to show the difference in reactivity of a number of transition elements with respect to common acids.
3. Find out why ceramic materials are being considered to replace the cast iron engine blocks in cars.

READINGS

1. Barnhardt, Wilton. "The Death of Ducktown." *Discover*. October, 1987, pp. 34–43.
2. Radford, Don. *Looking at Metals*. North Pomfret, VT: David & Charles, 1985.
3. Raymond, Robert. *Out of the Fiery Furnace*. University Park, PA: Pennsylvania State University Press, 1986.

NONMETAL GROUPS
MIXED GROUPS
THE CARBON GROUP

Elements in Groups 13 Through 18

The elements of Groups 13 through 18 are mostly nonmetals. Each of Groups 13 through 17 contains one or more metalloids. Some groups also include metals. Nonmetals make up many everyday objects. The main components of matches, for example, are phosphorus and sulfur. Diamonds and graphite are forms of carbon. Gasoline is a mixture that contains compounds of carbon and hydrogen. Metalloids are found in many electronic devices.

NONMETAL GROUPS

GOALS

1. You will learn about the properties and uses of hydrogen.
2. You will learn about the properties and uses of the halogen family.
3. You will learn about the properties and uses of the noble gases.

Only one family, Group 18, is made up entirely of nonmetals. Except for the metalloid astatine, Group 17 has all nonmetals also. Astatine is so rare that this group will be studied as nonmetals. Hydrogen is sometimes thought of as a family by itself. It and other nonmetals tend to hold their electrons tightly. As a result, they are good insulators. They do not generally conduct heat or electric current well. They are not shiny, malleable, or ductile. Nonmetals tend to gain or share electrons when they react with other substances.

13:1 Hydrogen

Hydrogen is a colorless, odorless, and tasteless gas. It is the lightest of all the elements and was used to fill lighter-than-air vehicles early in their history. Blimps, dirigibles, and balloons used hydrogen until a safe substitute, helium, was found. Hydrogen will burn in the presence of oxygen. This fact has made its use in these vehicles dangerous.

When hydrogen is found free in nature, it is found as the diatomic molecule, H_2. The action of an acid on a metal such as iron or zinc will produce hydrogen. It is

F.Y.I. "Inflammable air," or hydrogen, was discovered by a Swiss, Paracelsus, in the 16th century. It was not until 1781, in England, that Priestly and Cavendish noted that when the "inflammable air" was exploded, water was formed.

also formed from the electrolysis of water and the action of steam on hot iron filings.

FIGURE 13–1. The Hindenburg was one of the largest airships ever built. Its crash in 1937 in New Jersey marked the end of airship passenger service. The hydrogen gas inside ignited, and the ship exploded.

Hydrogen usually has an oxidation number of 1+ in compounds made with other nonmetals. This is because hydrogen shares electrons with the nonmetal to complete both of their outer energy levels. Water, H_2O, and hydrogen chloride, HCl, are examples of this covalent bonding.

In other instances, hydrogen may gain an electron. It then has a 1− oxidation number. Hydrogen gains an electron when it reacts with the active metals in Groups 1 or 2. Calcium hydride, CaH_2, is an example of these compounds. These compounds are highly reactive, because the electrons are not tightly held.

13:2 Halogens

Group 17 on the periodic table is called the halogen family. **Halogen** means "salt-producer." Halogen elements combine with metals to form compounds called salts. For example, tin(II) fluoride, SnF_2, is a salt used in fluoride toothpaste. In the elemental form, all of the halogens are poisonous and will burn the skin. Fortunately, halogens do not occur free in nature. Each occurs combined with at least one other element.

What type of bonds does a halogen form with a metal?

A halogen forms ionic bonds when it combines chemically with a metal. Each halogen has seven electrons in its outer energy level. One more electron is needed to complete the outer energy level. The halogen atom gains one electron from the metal atom and they form an ionic bond.

FIGURE 13–2. The halogen gases have distinctive colors: bromine, red-brown; chlorine, yellow-green; iodine, purple.

Halogens can form covalent bonds with nonmetals. In the gaseous state, the halogens are diatomic molecules, such as Cl_2 and I_2. Two atoms of a halogen share one pair of electrons. The halogens also bond covalently with each other. For example, the covalent compounds iodine monochloride, ICl, and iodine trichloride, ICl_3, are used to prevent skin infections.

Fluorine is the most reactive of all the chemical elements. It is found in nature in the mineral fluorspar, CaF_2. Compounds containing fluorine are called fluorides. Free fluorine is obtained by passing an electric current through melted fluorides. Fluorine is a corrosive, pale yellow gas. It combines with nearly all the elements. However, it does not react with helium, neon, and argon. Wood and many other materials burst into flame when exposed to fluorine gas.

Fluorine reacts explosively with hydrogen to form hydrogen fluoride, HF. A water solution of HF is used to etch glass. Some fluorides are added to drinking water or brushed onto teeth to strengthen them and prevent tooth decay. The "nonstick" material on cooking utensils is a compound made from fluorine and carbon.

Fluorocarbon gases such as Freon are used as the coolant in refrigerators and freezers. They are nonflammable. Fluorocarbon gases have also been used as propellants in spray cans. There has recently been much concern about their use. There is some evidence that fluorocarbons are destroying the ozone layer in the atmosphere. The ozone layer protects us from the sun's ultraviolet radiation.

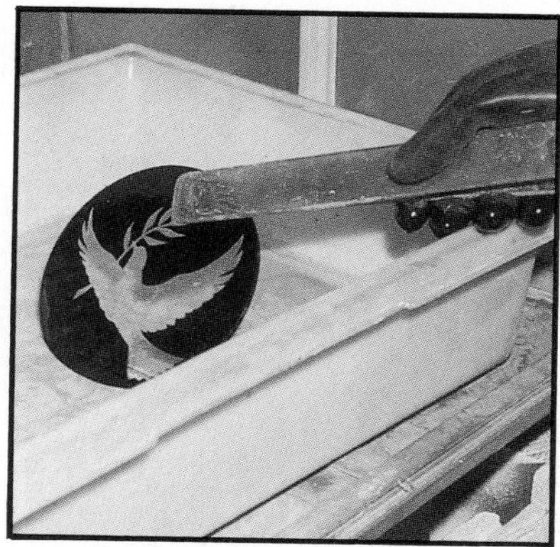

FIGURE 13–3. Hydrofluoric acid is used to etch glass.

Which is the most abundant of the halogens?

Chlorine is the most abundant halogen. It is slightly less active than fluorine. Chlorine is most often found in compounds with sodium, potassium, magnesium, or calcium. The pure element is usually obtained by the electrolysis of melted sodium chloride or saltwater brine. **Brine** is a concentrated salt or ocean water solution.

Many cleaning products and bleaches contain chlorine compounds. Chlorine bleach is used to whiten clothes. Another type of chlorine product is used to bleach flour and paper. Chlorine compounds are also used to disinfect drinking water and swimming pools.

In nature, bromine is found in compounds called bromides. Bromides are generally found in seawater and brine wells. Bromine is prepared by treating seawater, or brine, with chlorine. Chlorine is more reactive than bromine and will replace bromine in compounds. Free bromine is released. At normal room temperature, bromine is a dark red liquid. It is extremely poisonous.

Bromine in the form of silver bromide, AgBr, is used in making photographic film. Bromine is also used in

Table 13–1

Halogen Family

Element	Atomic number	Atomic mass	Melting point (°C)	Boiling point (°C)	Description
fluorine	9	19.0	−218.6	−188.1	Pale yellow gas
chlorine	17	35.5	−101.0	−34.0	Green-yellow gas
bromine	35	79.9	−7.25	59.5	Red-brown liquid
iodine	53	126.9	113.6	185.2	Gray, metallic-looking crystals
astatine	85	(210.0)	302	337	Radioactive solid

FIGURE 13-4. Certain seaweeds, like kelp, absorb iodine from seawater. Iodine can be obtained from seaweed ashes.

Which halogen is radioactive?

making dyes, especially those of deep indigo or purple. One compound is an anti-knock agent in gasoline.

Iodine, like bromine, can be obtained from seawater. Solid iodine can change directly to a gas and then back to solid form without passing through a liquid state. This process is known as sublimation. Iodine is purified by sublimation. The pure vapor is allowed to crystallize on a cool surface.

At room temperature, iodine is a gray, shiny solid. When heated, it becomes a purple vapor. It has some of the physical properties of a metal. Iodine compounds are needed in the human diet and are also used in medicines. Lack of iodine can cause goiter. For this reason, table salt is often "iodized" to be sure people receive enough iodine.

The last member of the halogen family, astatine, is one of the rarest elements in nature. It is found in uranium ore. Astatine has properties similar to iodine. It is, however, a radioactive element. Astatine is usually classified as a metalloid.

CAREER

Cosmetologist

Sandi Patterson's interest in makeup and hairstyles was similar to most of her high school friends. She was always experimenting with different looks, bleaching and highlighting her hair with various products.

It was in her high school chemistry class that Sandi learned about chemicals and their reactions. She learned that people do not all have the same body chemistry and that this can cause makeup and haircare products to act differently for different people. Sandi began to understand the importance of reading labels to determine if a product might cause side effects.

Sandi went to a vocational school the last two years of high school to learn the art of cosmetology. She now works in a salon where she gives permanents, cuts, styles, and colors hair. Sandi also provides makeup analysis and advice to patrons on hair care.

For career information, write
National Hairdressers and
Cosmetologists Association
3510 Olive Street
St. Louis, MO 63103

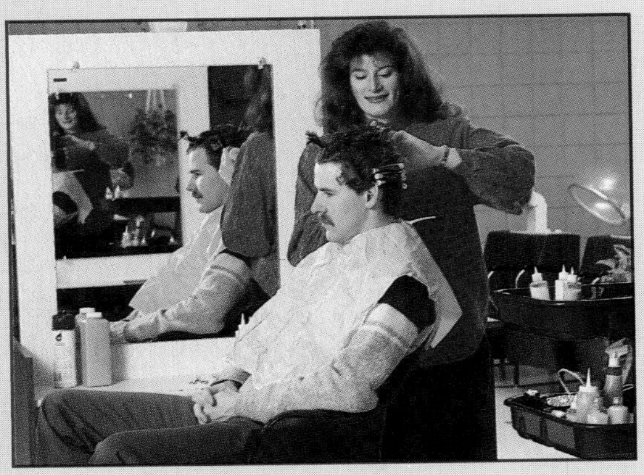

Table 13–2

Noble Gases					
Element	**Atomic number**	**Mass number**	**Melting point (°C)**	**Boiling point (°C)**	**Description**
helium (He)	2	4	−272	−269	All are colorless gases.
neon (Ne)	10	20	−249	−246	
argon (Ar)	18	40	−189	−186	
krypton (Kr)	36	84	−157	−153	
xenon (Xe)	54	131	−112	−108	
radon (Rn)	86	(222)	−71	−62	

13:3 Noble Gases

The elements of Group 18 are known as the noble gases. They do not combine naturally with other elements, and they are found free in nature. Because they are very stable, most of the noble gases were found by chance. Helium was found in an analysis of sunlight before it was discovered on Earth. Argon was found when not all of the sample of a distillation of liquid air could be accounted for.

What is distillation?

Distillation is a process in which liquids are separated by differences in their boiling points. Air is a mixture of gases including oxygen and nitrogen. Each gas has a different boiling point. Air is liquefied by compression and cooling. When it is allowed to warm, each gas boils off at a different temperature. Xenon, neon, and krypton were also found in the distillation of liquid air. The last member of the family, radon, is the most dense gas known. It is radioactive and forms when the nuclei of radium atoms break down.

The density of helium is less than that of air. Its low density makes helium useful as a lifting gas in airships and balloons. Helium can be compressed and cooled to form a liquid. Liquid helium is used in refrigeration. For example, it is used to cool metals to extremely low temperatures. When supercooled, some metals offer no resistance to the flow of an electric current and are called superconductors.

Helium, neon, and argon are used in making lighted signs. Light bulbs are filled with argon to protect the filament and make it last longer. Both krypton and argon are used in fluorescent lighting. Xenon is used in strobe lamps, where short flashes of light are needed for high-speed photography. Radon is used as a radiation source in cancer treatment.

FIGURE 13–5. In 1962, xenon tetrafluoride crystals were prepared. Before that it was believed that the noble gases were inert.

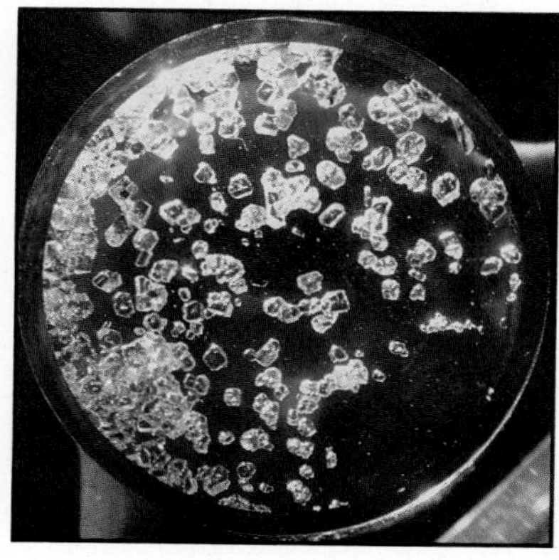

Review

1. Write the chemical formula for a molecule of each of the following: fluorine, chlorine, bromine, and iodine.
2. In what two ways can hydrogen form compounds?
3. Give two uses for noble gases.
4. Name one use for each of the first four elements in the halogen family.
★ 5. Draw a diagram showing the electrons for the compound, BrCl.

MIXED GROUPS

GOALS

1. You will learn about the properties and uses of the boron group.
2. You will learn about the properties and uses of the nitrogen group.
3. You will learn about the properties and uses of the oxygen group.

Mixed groups are those families that contain metalloids. They may also have metals and nonmetals. Metals are located toward the bottom of these groups in the periodic table. Nonmetals are at the top. Metalloids have some of the properties of both metals and nonmetals. They may act like metals in the presence of one element or compound and like nonmetals in the presence of something else. These sections explore the mixed groups. They point out what happens as the atomic numbers in a family increase.

13:4 The Boron Group

Boron is mainly nonmetallic in its chemical properties, even though it has three electrons in its outer energy level. Boron is considered a metalloid. Boron is never found free in nature. Its compounds are mined extensively in the western United States. Common com-

Table 13–3

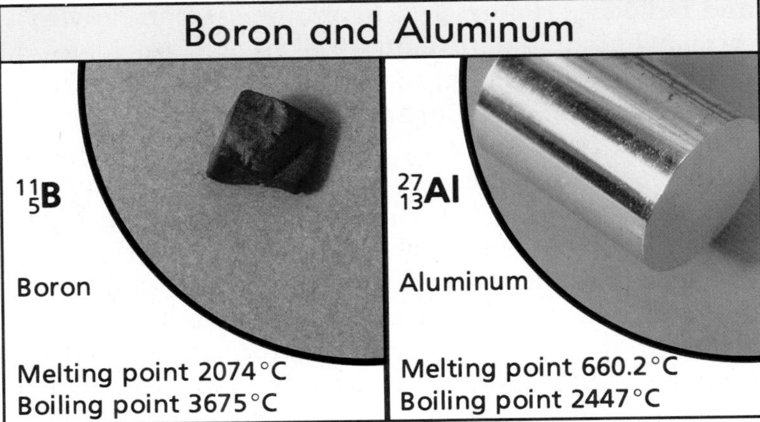

FIGURE 13–6. Aluminum products are used in a variety of ways in homes.

pounds of boron are boric acid, a mild antiseptic, and borax, a water softener. Boron reacts with hydrogen to form boranes. One projected use for these compounds is for high energy fuels for rockets and jet planes.

The other members of Group 13 are aluminum, gallium, indium, and thallium. These elements are all metals. The most important one is aluminum. It is the most abundant metal in Earth's crust. Aluminum ore, bauxite, contains aluminum in the form of its oxide. Aluminum is won from its ore by electrolysis. This process produces aluminum that is 99% pure. Aluminum has a silvery appearance. Like zinc, it forms a protective coating on its surface by combining with oxygen. It is a very light metal, but strong. It is a good conductor of heat and electricity. It is used in kitchen pots and pans, in airplanes, in electrical wire, and as a foil for wrapping and packaging.

Much of the aluminum produced is used in alloys. Duralumin is made of aluminum, copper, manganese, and magnesium. It is less dense than steel, though as strong. These properties make duralumin an excellent material for aircraft construction. Alnico is an alloy of iron, aluminum, nickel, and cobalt. It makes strong magnets. Aluminum compounds are used in medicines and deodorants. They are also used in making pigments and dyes.

The rest of the elements in this family are the metals gallium, indium, and thallium. All three elements find limited use in the electronics industry. They are used as semiconductors. **Semiconductors** are substances that conduct electric current weakly. They will be further discussed in Chapter 22.

F.Y.I. Because aluminum bonds oxygen so tightly, for years bauxite presented chemists with difficult refining problems. Finally, Charles Hall, a 21-year-old Oberlin College student, using earlier research, developed a commercially efficient process. He found a way to dissolve bauxite and then separate the aluminum using an electric current.

FIGURE 13–7. Gallium metal, a member of the boron group, has a melting point of 30°C. It melts below body temperature, 37°C.

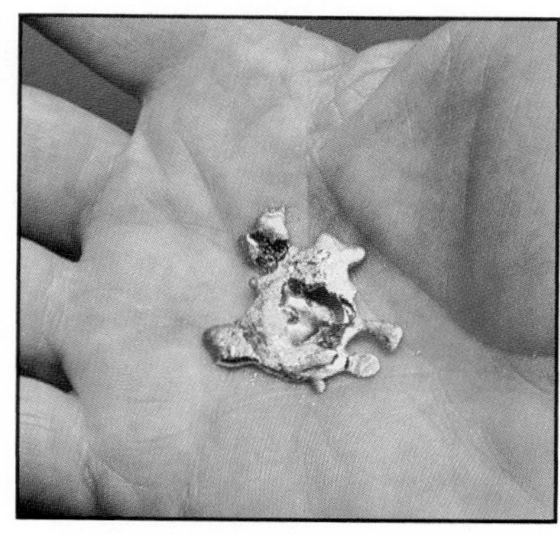

FIGURE 13–8. Nitrogen-fixing bacteria are found on the roots of certain plants. The bacteria change free nitrogen into nitrate ions that are absorbed by the plant.

What element in the nitrogen group is a metal?

What is the formula for atmospheric nitrogen?

13:5 Nitrogen Group

Group 15 on the periodic table is the nitrogen family. Each member of the nitrogen family has five electrons in its outer energy level. Elements in the nitrogen family are not very reactive. One reason for this is that it is unlikely that these elements will gain three electrons or lose five electrons. However, they do share electrons with other atoms.

This family contains elements with a wide range of properties. For example, nitrogen is a gas. Both nitrogen and phosphorus are nonmetals. Bismuth is a metal. Arsenic and antimony are metalloids. The metallic character of elements in this family increases as the atomic number increases.

Nitrogen is required by every living thing. Air is nearly seventy-nine percent free nitrogen. However, most living things cannot get nitrogen directly from the air. Nitrogen for life comes from compounds, usually nitrates (NO_3^-). These are found as minerals in the ground, formed during electrical storms, or made by bacteria.

Nitrogen is usually prepared by the distillation of liquid air. Liquid nitrogen boils at −196°C. It is found free as the diatomic molecule, N_2. Nitrogen forms many compounds that are important to people. One of these compounds is ammonia, NH_3. It is found in many cleaning products. Industry uses nitrogen compounds in the form of nitrates in making fertilizers and explosives. "Laughing gas," an anesthetic (an us THET ihk), is the nitrogen compound N_2O.

Phosphorus is a solid at room temperature. It exists in different molecular forms called allotropes (AL oh

FIGURE 13–9. Nitrogen, phosphorus, and potassium compounds are used in fertilizer to provide essential nutrients for plants.

FIGURE 13–10. White phosphorus is very reactive and is stored under water. It will cause severe burns if it touches the skin. Red phosphorus is much less reactive.

trohps). **Allotropes** are different forms of the same element. They have different properties because they have different arrangements of atoms. The two most common allotropes of phosphorus are white and red phosphorus.

What are the two common allotropes of phosphorus?

White phosphorus is produced from calcium phosphate, $Ca_3(PO_4)_2$. White phosphorus is stored under water, because it bursts into flame in air. Red phosphorus is formed slowly from chains of white phosphorus atoms. At room temperature, red phosphorus has little chemical activity. However, at higher temperatures, it forms many compounds. The ease with which phosphorus burns makes it useful in matches.

Phosphates are an important class of phosphorus compounds. Calcium phosphate is present in bones. Some phosphates serve as water softeners. Ammonium phosphate, $(NH_4)_3PO_4$, is an important fertilizer. It is used because it contains nitrogen and phosphorus. Both elements are needed for plant growth. Phosphorus is also found in deoxyribonucleic acid, DNA, an important compound in the nuclei of cells. Phosphorus compounds provide a means for transferring energy in both plants and animals.

Excessive use of phosphates in detergents contributes to water pollution. Wastewater from the laundry is joined with runoff water from fields fertilized with phosphates and nitrates. These wastes often end up in lakes and rivers. As a result, water plants are fed a diet rich in nutrients. They multiply rapidly and clog the waterways. When these plants die, the supply of oxygen dissolved in the water is used up as they decompose. This process deprives fish and other aquatic life of oxygen. Many soap industries are reducing the amount of phosphate in detergents. This change is helping to reduce this type of pollution.

FIGURE 13–11. Phosphate pollution in bodies of water causes plants to grow at increased rates.

INVESTIGATION 13–1

Metals and Alloys

Problem: What is the melting point of Onion's alloy?

Materials

forceps
Onion's alloy
250-mL beaker
water
hot plate
ring stand
clamp
thermometer in cork
pieces of pure metals

CAUTION: *Metals can be toxic, so handle with forceps. Handle the thermometer carefully; hazards are broken glass and toxic mercury vapor.*

Procedure

1. Using chemistry or physics reference books, look up the melting temperatures of tin, lead and bismuth. Record them in your data table.
2. Make observations of pieces of tin, lead, and bismuth that are in boiling water.
3. You will be melting a piece of Onion's alloy, which is a combination of tin, lead, and bismuth. At what temperature do you think it will melt? Record your prediction.
4. Using forceps, place a piece of Onion's alloy in the beaker. Fill the beaker about one-third full of water.
5. Set the beaker on the hot plate. Using the ring stand and clamp, arrange the thermometer so that the bulb is covered by water but does not touch the beaker or alloy.
6. Heat the water and watch for the alloy to melt. Record the temperature at which the alloy melts.
7. When the alloy has completely melted, turn off the hot plate. Allow the beaker and its contents to cool. When the metal has become solid, remove it from the beaker using forceps, and return it to your teacher.

Data and Observations

Description of metal	Temperature of water	Melting point
Bismuth		
Tin		
Lead		
Onion's alloy		prediction °C

Analysis and Conclusions

1. What is the average melting point of the three pure metals?
2. What is the melting point of Onion's alloy?
3. What is the difference between the average melting point of the three metals and that of Onion's alloy? Between each metal's melting point and that of the alloy?
4. Form a hypothesis about why there is a difference between the melting point of a pure metal and an alloy.

Application

5. Why are alloys such as Onion's alloy used in automatic fire safety sprinkler systems?

Table 13–4

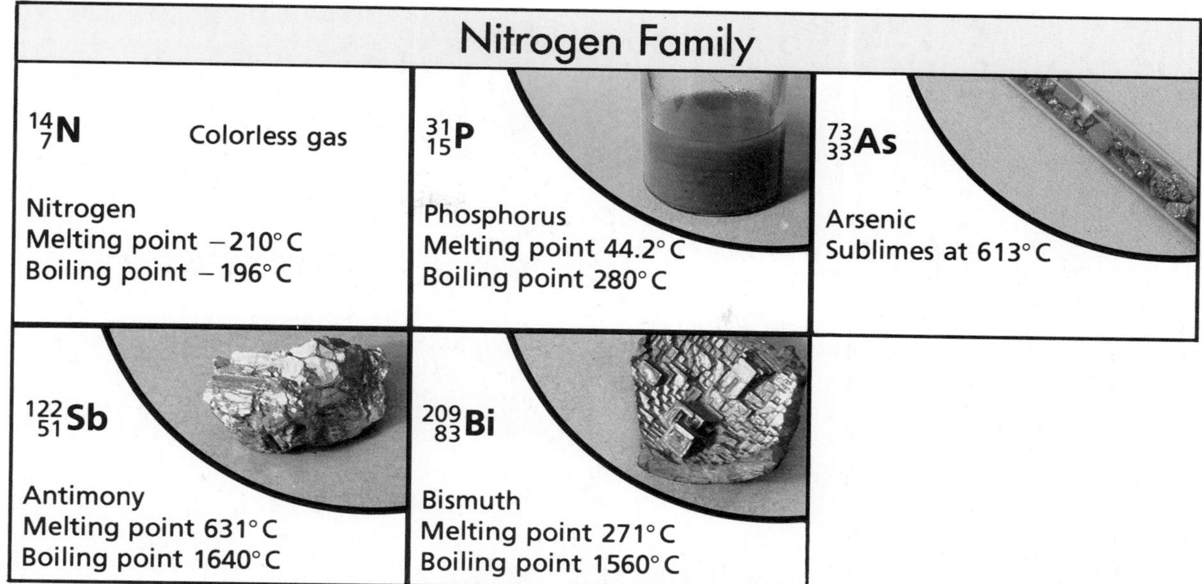

Nitrogen Family		
$^{14}_{7}N$ Colorless gas Nitrogen Melting point −210°C Boiling point −196°C	$^{31}_{15}P$ Phosphorus Melting point 44.2°C Boiling point 280°C	$^{73}_{33}As$ Arsenic Sublimes at 613°C
$^{122}_{51}Sb$ Antimony Melting point 631°C Boiling point 1640°C	$^{209}_{83}Bi$ Bismuth Melting point 271°C Boiling point 1560°C	

Arsenic compounds are widespread in nature. The most common consist of arsenic and sulfur. Two allotropes of the element arsenic exist. Yellow arsenic, a nonmetal made up of molecules of As_4, changes slowly to the more stable metallic gray arsenic, As. Perhaps you know that arsenic is a poison. However, it is also used as a medicine.

What are the two allotropes of arsenic?

Both antimony and bismuth have metallic properties. Bismuth is a true metal. These two elements have properties and compounds similar to phosphorus and arsenic. Bismuth is used in some medicines to soothe and coat the stomach. Antimony and bismuth can be used in alloys with other metals to reduce the melting points and the hardness of these metals. Bismuth is used in automatic sprinkler systems that protect buildings from fire. Heat from a fire melts the alloy plugs in water pipes, and the water is released.

FIGURE 13–12. An arsenic compound is often used to prevent and treat heartworms in dogs.

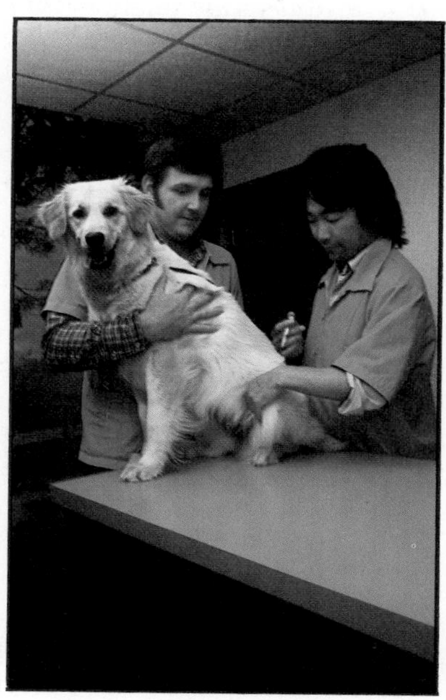

13:6 Oxygen Group

Group 16 on the periodic table is called the oxygen family. Its elements are found in nature, both free and in compounds. Most members form covalent compounds. Each atom has six electrons in its outer energy level. Thus, it can share two electrons with other elements to form compounds.

Oxygen is a gas at room temperature. All other family members are solid. Sulfur and selenium are nonmetals. Tellurium and polonium are metalloids. Polonium, in

Table 13–5

Composition of Dry Air

Substance	Percent	Boiling point (°C)
nitrogen, N_2	78.1	−195.78
oxygen, O_2	20.9	−182.98
argon, Ar	0.934	−185.87
carbon dioxide, CO_2	0.033	−78.477
neon, Ne	0.0018	−246.1
helium, He	0.00053	−268.94
krypton, Kr	0.00012	−153.4
xenon, Xe	0.00009	−108.1
hydrogen, H_2	0.00005	−252.77
methane, CH_4	0.00002	−161.5
nitrous oxide, N_2O	0.00005	−88.48
ozone, O_3	trace	−111.3

addition, is radioactive. It is one of the rarest elements in Earth's crust.

F.Y.I. Oxygen is paramagnetic. If a magnet is placed in liquid oxygen, some of the oxygen will cling to the magnet. Oxygen is the only common gas that is magnetic. This property is a result of two of the six electrons in the outer energy level being unpaired.

Oxygen is one of the most reactive nonmetallic elements. Oxygen forms compounds with nearly every other element. Oxygen compounds compose nearly 50%, by mass, of Earth's crust. About 20% of the total volume of air is diatomic oxygen, O_2. During thunderstorms and electrical discharges, some molecules of O_2 may be changed to triatomic ozone, O_3. A **triatomic** molecule is one that is composed of three atoms. Diatomic oxygen and ozone are allotropes of oxygen.

Without free oxygen, most life on Earth could not exist. Animals need air containing oxygen for respiration. The ozone layer around Earth shields us from some of the sun's radiation. Compounds of oxygen are also extremely important to life. Water, H_2O, is perhaps the most important oxide. Another compound of hydrogen and oxygen is hydrogen peroxide, H_2O_2. It is used as a bleach and to kill germs.

FIGURE 13–13. Io, one of Jupiter's moons, appears yellow because of sulfur deposits.

Oxygen in large amounts is most often prepared by the distillation of liquid air. Liquid oxygen begins to boil at −183°C. It is drawn off into another container. Repeating this process produces an oxygen sample that is almost pure. Oxygen is also produced by the electrolysis of water.

Sulfur, like oxygen, is found both free and combined in nature. Sulfur is generally found in compounds with metals in the form of mineral ores. Most sulfur is obtained from deposits of the free element in the southern and southwestern United States. Sulfur is mined by the Frasch process, Figure 13–14b. This process produces sulfur that is more than 90% pure.

How is sulfur mined?

Sulfur also exists in several allotropic forms. Some allotropes of sulfur consist of eight sulfur atoms joined in a ring. The most common form is orthorhombic (orth oh RAHM bihk) sulfur. Another allotrope of sulfur exists as a long chain of sulfur atoms.

Sulfur unites with some metals to form compounds called sulfides. It also unites directly with oxygen. Sulfur compounds in the air, such as hydrogen sulfide, H_2S, cause tarnish on silver. Products that contain sulfur include insecticides, fertilizers, medicines, and rubber.

Selenium can be found in deposits of free sulfur. It is also an impurity in sulfides and in copper ore. Most selenium is obtained as a by-product from the electrolysis of copper ore in the production of copper. Like sulfur, selenium exists in several allotropic forms. Two of these, crystalline red and crystalline gray, are nonmetals. One, metallic gray, is a metal.

How is selenium used in the garden?

In trace amounts, selenium is needed in the human diet. In larger amounts, it is a poison. It is used in some insecticides. Small amounts of the insecticide are put into the soil or sprayed on plant leaves. The selenium passes through the entire plant without harming it. However, insects eating the plant are poisoned.

When selenium is exposed to light, it gives up electrons and becomes a good conductor of electricity. For this reason, selenium is called a photoconductor. A **photoconductor** is a material that allows electrons to flow when it is struck by light. The brighter the light, the more electrons flow. When the light is turned off, no

a

FIGURE 13–14. Free sulfur is often deposited around hot springs (a). The Frasch process is used for mining sulfur (b).

b

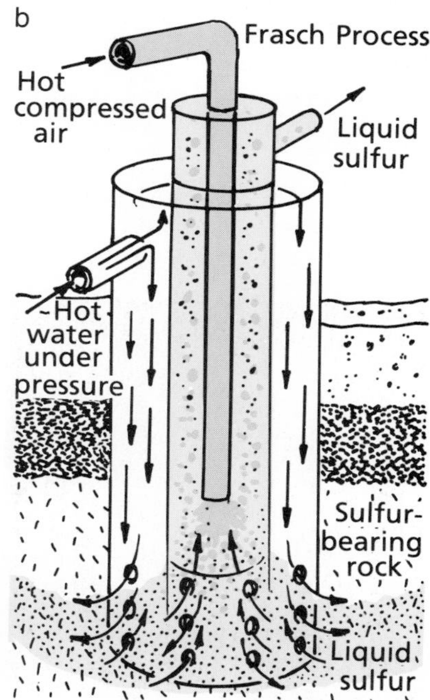

Table 13–6

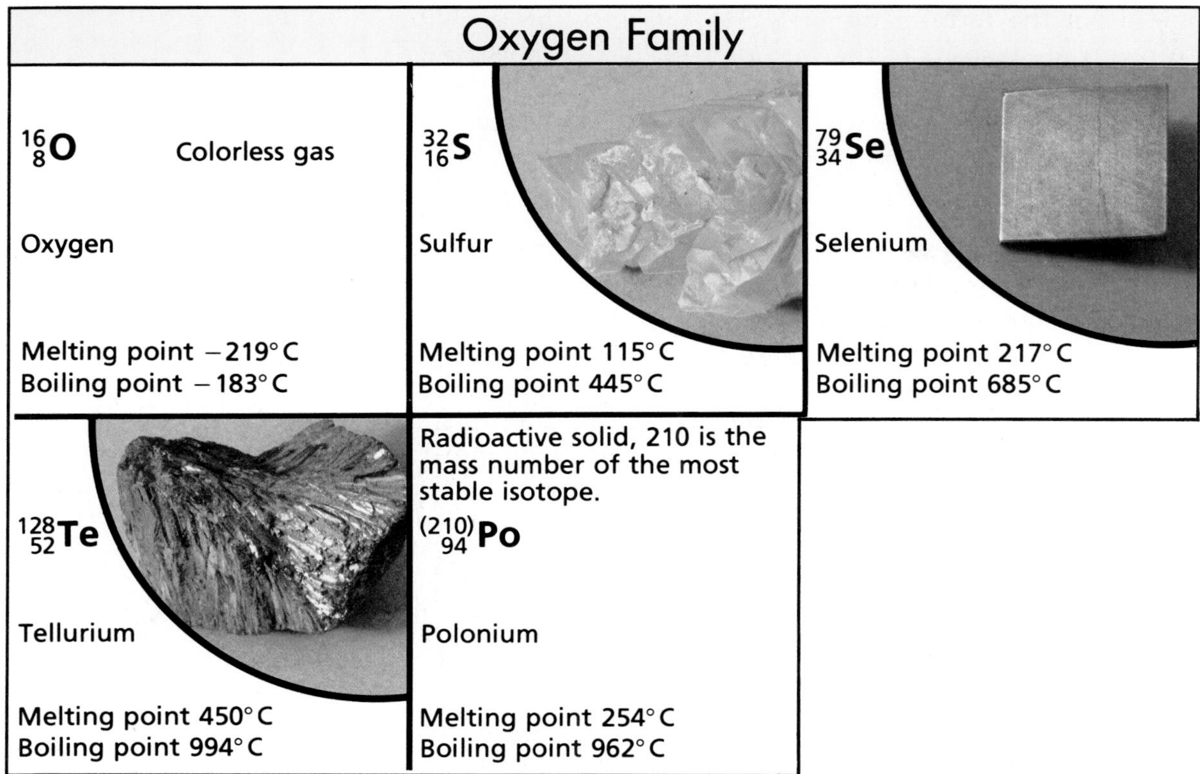

Oxygen Family		
$^{16}_{8}O$ Colorless gas Oxygen Melting point −219°C Boiling point −183°C	$^{32}_{16}S$ Sulfur Melting point 115°C Boiling point 445°C	$^{79}_{34}Se$ Selenium Melting point 217°C Boiling point 685°C
$^{128}_{52}Te$ Tellurium Melting point 450°C Boiling point 994°C	Radioactive solid, 210 is the mass number of the most stable isotope. $^{(210)}_{94}Po$ Polonium Melting point 254°C Boiling point 962°C	

current passes through the substance. Photoconductors make up the photocells used in photographic light meters. They are in "electric eye" cameras that automatically adjust to light intensity. Selenium photocells are also used in counting people as they enter buildings and for setting off burglar alarms. Photocopying machines also use photoconductors.

When added to glass, selenium absorbs the green color due to iron impurities. If a large amount of selenium is used, the glass becomes red. This red glass is used in traffic lights.

List three uses for tellurium.

Selenium was named for the Greek word *selena,* meaning moon. Tellurium was named for *tellus,* the Latin word for Earth. The properties of tellurium are similar to those of selenium. Tellurium can be found free in nature but is usually combined with gold or other metals. Tellurium is useful in making dyes, electrical equipment, and glass. Tellurium, alloyed with iron and other metals, makes these metals easier to machine. It makes a hard alloy with tin. Tellurium is poisonous. If inhaled, the tellurium vapors produce breath that smells like garlic.

INVESTIGATION 13–2

Oxygen in Air

Problem: What is the percent of oxygen in a volume of air?

Materials

candle
pie pan
water
matches
25-mL graduated cylinder
deep pan
cork
steel wool
ring stand
clamp
goggles
apron
beaker or glass

Procedure

Part A

1. Stand a candle in some melted wax in the center of a pie pan.
2. Fill the pie pan two-thirds full of water.
3. Light the candle.
4. Invert a beaker over the lighted candle and into the water. Watch carefully. Record your observations of the candle and water level.

Part B

5. Fill a deep pan with water. Place a piece of steel wool on a cork and float the cork on the water in the pan.
6. Invert a 25-mL graduated cylinder over the cork and steel wool as in Figure 13–15.
7. Clamp the cylinder in place so that the water level is at the 25-mL mark. In a table, record the data, the water level in the cylinder, and observations of the steel wool. Allow the equipment to stand for one week.
8. After one week, again record the date, the level of water in the cylinder, and observations of the steel wool.

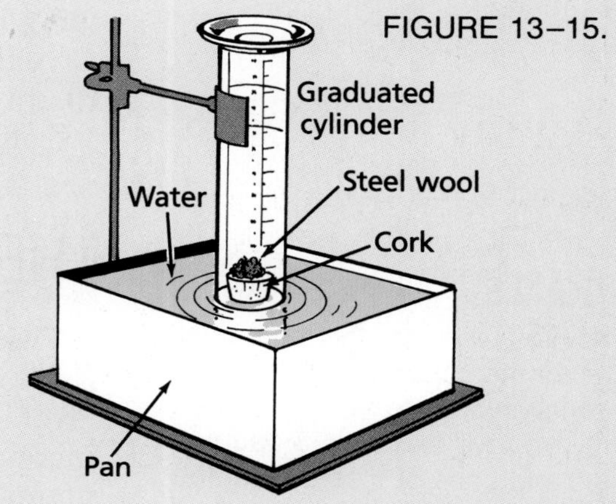

FIGURE 13–15.

Data and Observations

Part A

candle	
H_2O level	

Part B

1st date: 10/12/89	water level: ______mL
description of steel wool:	
2nd date: 10/19/89	water level: ______mL
description of steel wool:	

Analysis and Conclusions

Part A

1. Why did the candle go out?
2. Form a hypothesis about why the level of water in the beaker changed.

Part B

3. How much did the water level rise? What percent of 25 mL is this?
4. Why did the water level rise?
5. How does the change in the steel wool depend on oxygen?
6. Assuming that all oxygen in the cylinder reacted, what is the percent of oxygen in a volume of air?

Review

6. Why is selenium called a photoconductor?
7. Why is there a similarity in the chemical properties of the elements of the oxygen family?
8. Give five examples of how the nitrogen family is useful to people.
9. What are allotropes? Name two elements that can exist as allotropes, and list some of their allotropes.
★ 10. In distilling liquid air would nitrogen or oxygen boil off first? Why?

THE CARBON GROUP

GOALS

1. You will learn the importance of the carbon family in everyday life.
2. You will learn the properties and uses of elements of the carbon family.

The carbon family contains the elements of Group 14. Each element has four electrons in its outer energy level. Like Groups 15, 16, and 17, as the atomic number increases, the metallic properties increase. Carbon is a nonmetal; silicon and germanium are metalloids, with some properties of metals and some of nonmetals; and tin and lead are metals. No other group of elements shows a greater range of properties.

The family as a whole has become increasingly important in the field of technology. The limited electrical conductivity of silicon and germanium make them especially useful in electronics. Many fields, including medicine, biochemistry, and computers are finding new uses for the elements in the carbon family.

13:7 Carbon

Carbon is the second most abundant element in the human body. Diamond and pencil "lead" (graphite) are both carbon. The wood that holds the "lead" is a mixture of carbon compounds. Plastics, foods, fibers, and most fuels contain carbon. Coal and charcoal are mostly carbon. Carbon is present in all living things.

Graphite (GRA fite) is a black allotrope of carbon. Graphite crystals are thin and flat. Carbon atoms in a graphite crystal are bonded in layers that have a hexagonal structure, Figure 13–16a. The bonds between the atoms in each layer are covalent, but weak forces bond the layers together. The structure of graphite crystals makes it easy for the layers of atoms to slip and slide over each other. For this reason, graphite is used as a lubricant.

Why does graphite make a good lubricant?

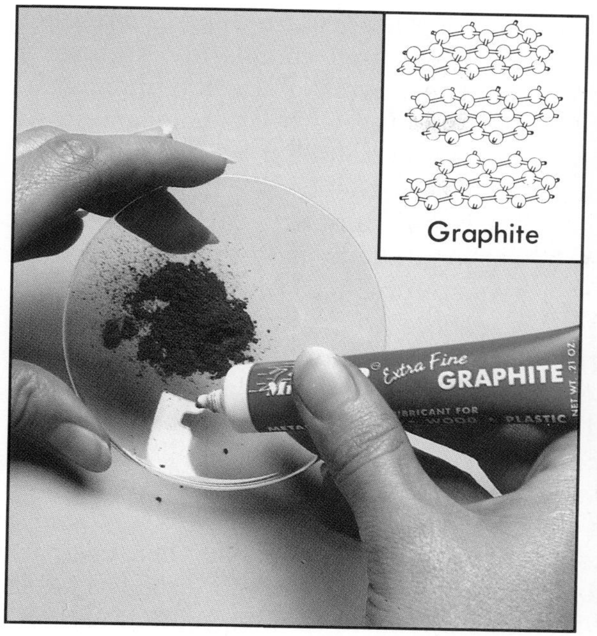

a

b

FIGURE 13–16. Graphite (a) is used as a lubricant. Notice that the graphite structure consists of parallel planes of carbon atoms that can slide over one another. Diamond (b) is one of the hardest substances known. Its structure consists of a network of carbon atoms.

Diamond is another allotrope of carbon. In contrast to graphite, it is clear and colorless. Diamond is one of the hardest substances known. Each carbon atom in a diamond crystal is bonded covalently to four other carbon atoms. The atoms are arranged in a tetrahedral pattern, the four bonds pointed toward the vertices of a tetrahedron, Figure 13–16b. Diamonds are used in cutting tools and in jewelry. What properties of a diamond make it suitable for these two uses?

How are the atoms in diamond arranged?

Carbon shares electrons in its compounds. It has the ability to form long chainlike compounds. These will be discussed in Chapter 14. Carbon burns to form carbon monoxide, CO, and carbon dioxide, CO_2, depending on the amount of oxygen available. Both compounds are colorless, odorless gases. Carbon monoxide is produced

a

b

FIGURE 13–17. Carbon dioxide may be stored in tanks. The gas is dissolved in water and soda syrup to give soft drinks their fizz (a). Large deposits of chalk, calcium carbonate, produced the famous white cliffs of Dover, England (b).

in internal combustion engines, where there is often not enough oxygen to burn the fuel completely. Cigarette smoke also contains high levels of carbon monoxide. Carbon monoxide can combine with the hemoglobin in blood. This prevents the attachment of oxygen molecules to hemoglobin. Thus, the body cells do not get enough oxygen. As a result, inhaling carbon monoxide can lead to death. Carbon dioxide makes up about 0.04% of the air. CO_2 is a waste product of food breakdown in our body cells. We exhale this waste carbon dioxide. Plants convert CO_2 to food, helping to keep the amount of CO_2 in the atmosphere constant. Carbon dioxide is also produced from the burning of wood, coal, oil, and natural gas. Solid CO_2 is known as **"dry ice"** because at normal pressures it sublimes, producing no liquid state. Thus, it cools objects without the mess of melting ice.

What does "carbonated" mean?

Soda drinks are said to be "carbonated" because carbon dioxide is dissolved in them. Carbon dioxide is also used to manufacture carbonates such as sodium carbonate, Na_2CO_3, and sodium hydrogen carbonate, $NaHCO_3$. **Carbonates** are compounds containing CO_3^{2-} ions. Sodium carbonate is useful as a cleanser and in soaps. Or-

What are carbonates?

Table 13–7

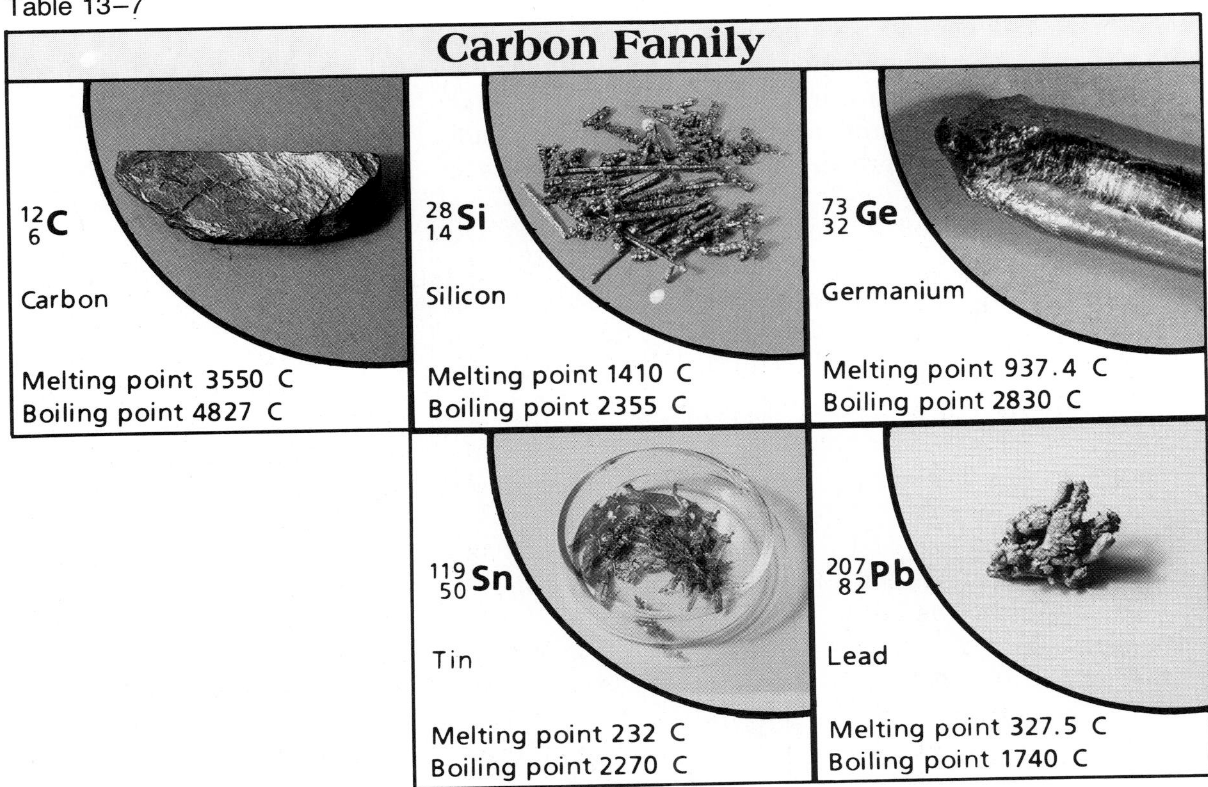

dinary baking soda is sodium hydrogen carbonate. Calcium carbonate, $CaCO_3$, is limestone. When it is heated, it decomposes into lime, CaO, and carbon dioxide. Calcium carbonate is a necessary ingredient for strong bones and teeth.

13:8 Silicon and Its Compounds

Silicon is the second most abundant element on Earth. Together silicon and oxygen make up more than 75% of Earth's crust. The crystal structure of pure silicon is similar to that of carbon in a diamond. Each silicon atom forms covalent bonds with four nearby silicon atoms. As a result, silicon generally is a hard, gray nonmetal. However it may also be found as a brown powder allotrope. Silicon is classified as a metalloid, mainly because of its use as a semiconductor (Chapter 22).

Most silicon is found as silicon dioxide, SiO_2 in sand, flint, quartz, and opal. In nature, silicon is combined with iron, aluminum, magnesium, and other metals. It is found in nearly all rocks, soils, and clays. One of the major reasons for the number of silicon compounds is the fact that silicon, like carbon, forms long chains, often with oxygen atoms.

FIGURE 13–18. Opal is a precious gem containing silicon.

Where is most silicon found?

TECHNOLOGY: ADVANCES

The New World of Ceramics

Ceramics are materials produced by the action of heat on earthen materials. They contain mainly silicon, silicon dioxide, and silicates. Ceramic materials are hard and strong and resist corrosion. They can withstand very high temperatures. They can even be designed to sense changes in temperature, pressure, sound, or humidity. Ceramics are good electrical insulators. They can be made into powerful magnets or tiny components for computers and other electronic equipment.

One important ceramic is silicon nitride. Compared to steel, it can stand up eight times longer under stress. Silicon nitride is lightweight and stays very hard over a wide range of temperatures. It is used to make gears, electric motor parts, and turbine rotors. Sialon, another ceramic, is very resistant to wear and may be used in the future to make aerospace gas-turbine engine parts.

Ceramics of the future may find their greatest use in the auto industry. Most of the major car manufacturers are considering ceramics for engine turbochargers. These materials weigh less and can replace expensive, hard-to-get materials that are in use today.

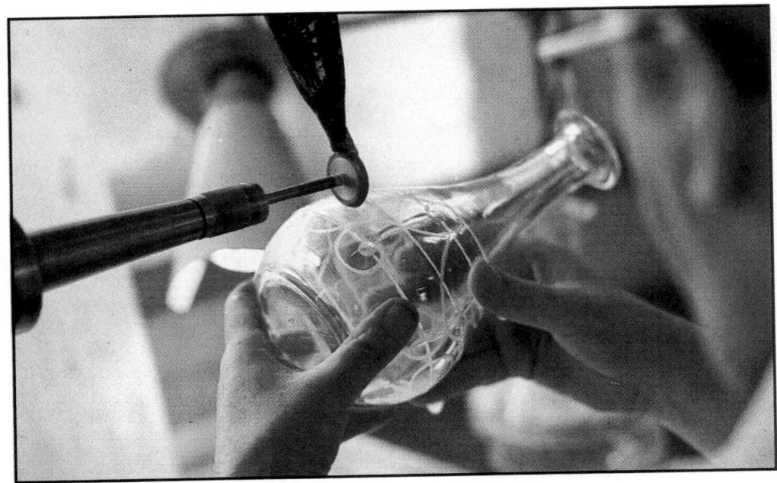

FIGURE 13–19. Silicon compounds are used in grinding wheels, because they are durable, hard, and strong.

F.Y.I. Silicon carbide, an abrasive, has a structure similar to diamond. Silicon and carbon atoms alternate. Each silicon atom is covalently bonded to four carbon atoms and each carbon atom is covalently bonded to four silicon atoms. Each forms a tetrahedron like the carbon atoms in diamond. As a result, SiC is extremely hard.

Silicon has many practical uses. It is used to make transistors found in radios, television sets, and computer chips. A silicon crystal, manufactured with certain impurities, has the ability to convert light energy into electrical energy. One type of steel contains a small percentage of silicon and is used for the cores of electric transformers. Carborundum, SiC, is a very hard substance used in grindstones and sandpaper.

Silicon dioxide, SiO_2, known also as ordinary sand or **silica,** is one of the most common silicon compounds. When silicon dioxide is melted and allowed to cool, it forms a glass. A **glass** is a supercooled liquid. A **supercooled liquid** is a material that appears to be a solid but does not have a regular crystalline structure. When glass is heated, it does not reach a point at which it suddenly becomes liquid. It melts over a wide temperature range. In the same way, as it cools, glass does not reach a point at which it suddenly hardens. As it cools, it simply flows less and eventually reaches a stage where it appears to be a solid.

What are silicates?

Ordinary glass is generally made with silicates. **Silicates** are compounds containing silicon, oxygen, and at least one metallic ion. The glass is made by melting a mixture of sodium carbonate or sodium sulfate, sand, and limestone. It is mainly oxygen and silicon with about 10% sodium, 5% calcium, and a trace of aluminum.

Heat resistant glass, such as Pyrex, is used in laboratories and in baking dishes. It contains boron and aluminum in addition to oxygen and silicon. China glazes, enamels, and porcelain consist of glasses that contain pigments.

a

b

c

FIGURE 13–20. Glass (a) is made from silicon dioxide. The heat resistant glass used in laboratories (b) and bakeware (c) also contains the elements boron and aluminum.

Silica glass is made from SiO_2. This glass is used for making scientific instruments and chemical apparatus. It allows ultraviolet light to pass through. For this reason, silica glass is also used in mercury-vapor lamps and optical instruments. Silicon dioxide is used to make optical fibers, fibers that carry light (Chapter 20).

Silicones are compounds containing long chains of silicon and oxygen bonded to carbon compounds. The silicones are highly elastic and heat resistant. They can be used for electrical insulation and heat insulation. They are also used as water repellants, lubricants, and synthetic motor oils.

What are two properties of silicone compounds?

At one time, asbestos was considered to be a universal insulator for heat. Asbestos cloth is fire resistant. In one form, it was used to coat ceilings and pipes. Asbestos is a fibrous mineral made of long chains of silicates that

FIGURE 13–21. Asbestos is a fibrous silicate mineral. The fibers are now known to cause lung disease.

contain calcium, magnesium, silicon, and oxygen. These chains can be unraveled into fibers. These fibers are now recognized as a health hazard. Few asbestos products are now being produced or used.

Silicon nitride, Si_3N_4, is one of a family of ceramics being developed for use in diesel, jet, and automobile engines. These materials have great resistance to heat and wear. Silicon nitride tools are already being used in machines that cut cast iron and its extremely hard alloys. Because of their strength, these tools permit greater cutting speeds at greater depths of cut.

BIOGRAPHY

Mario Molina
1943–

Mario Molina is a research scientist at the Jet Propulsion Laboratory in California. He was one of the first to warn that the use of chlorofluorocarbons would deplete ozone in the atmosphere. He is part of a team that is studying the ozone "hole" in the atmosphere over Antarctica.

13:9 Germanium, Tin, and Lead

Germanium is the least abundant of the Group 14 elements. In many ways, germanium resembles silicon in the formation of compounds. Germanium is a gray metalloid and does not conduct electricity well. However, when Group 13 or Group 15 elements are introduced into the crystal structure, conductivity is greatly increased. The chief use of germanium is in manufacturing semiconductor devices. It is also used with gold in a low-melting alloy that expands on freezing.

How many isotopes of tin exist in nature?

Tin is a silvery white metal that is very malleable. Ordinary tin, called white tin, is a relatively inert metal. It is used to coat other metals, such as steel, to protect them from corrosion. Gray tin is a nonmetallic powdered allotrope of tin. Tin can be found in nature as at least ten isotopes, Table 10–3.

Tin is used in many different alloys. Chief among these are solder, bronze, pewter, and britannia metal. In compounds, tin is found in the Sn^{2+} or Sn^{4+} oxidation state. Tin compounds are used in the fabric industry to set dye in cloth, to fireproof cotton, and to add weight to silk. Tin(II) fluoride or stannous fluoride, SnF_2, is used to prevent tooth decay.

FIGURE 13–22. Tin compounds may be used in herbicides to prevent build-up of hazardous pollutants in the soil.

Lead is a soft, dense, gray metal. Like tin, it forms compounds with two different oxidation states, 2+ and 4+. In the past, lead was often used in paints, gasoline, and to prevent corrosion. However, lead is now being replaced in many compounds because it is poisonous. For example, where lead oxide was once used as a white paint pigment, titanium oxide is now used. Tetraethyl lead, added to gasoline to prevent engine knock has been nearly eliminated because of the pollutants it forms in automobile exhaust.

FIGURE 13–23. Lead is obtained from a variety of minerals such as galena, crocoite, and mimetite. Because it is highly toxic, its use in common materials such as paint and gasoline has been reduced.

Review

11. What elements are in the carbon family? What are their atomic numbers? Atomic masses?
12. Name the two oxides of carbon. List their physical properties.
13. Why are there such a large number of carbon and silicon compounds?
14. What is a glass? What is the difference between silica glass and ordinary glass?
★ 15. What is the oxidation number of carbon in CO_2? In CO? In CO_3^{2-}?

PROBLEM SOLVING

Minerals in Garden Soil

The table summarizes data on mineral element deficiency and plant growth. Use this table to decide how to treat the soil in the following gardens.

1. Corn plants are short and thin looking. Some of the older leaves are yellowing. However, new growth is dark green.
2. The leaves of a house plant have brown spots. Close examination shows no evidence of insects. The ends of the leaves also look brown.
3. New leaves on soybean plants are lighter in color than normal. What else would you check before treating the soil?

Deficient Element	Appearance of Plant
nitrogen	pale green; older leaves become yellow and dry; stems short and slender
phosphorus	dark green; older leaves and stems similar to N deficiency
potassium	yellow leaves; tip of leaf dies; dead, dry spots in leaf between veins and on edges
calcium	terminal buds die
sulfur	light green young leaves

SKILL
Classifying

Problem: How do scientists determine categories for classification?

Materials

paper and pencil

Background

You routinely classify objects everyday. You may put all your socks in one drawer and your sweaters in another. You store soaps, detergents, and other cleansers separately from food. You may store vegetables and soups on one shelf and spices on another. Putting similar objects together is classification.

Scientists organize information by classifying it. Classifying helps them compare and contrast properties of various groups. For example, elements can be classified as metals, nonmetals, and metalloids. Scientists begin to classify materials by identifying a common property. This property may be size, shape, color, use, behavior, or composition. If you understand the properties used as the basis for classification, you can classify an object from a description. Once classified, materials are easier to study. If you worked in a sports equipment store, how could you classify the equipment? There are several possibilities. You might group the items by use. A baseball bat, a tennis racquet, and a golf club are all used to hit a ball. The balls would form another category. Think of other ways to classify the sports equipment. What about shape? You might classify the items by the sport in which each is used.

The number of groups you have does not matter. What matters is that you can describe the group and determine whether something fits in a group. Most important is that you choose a classification system that will be useful. It may not be very useful, for example, to group bats, golf clubs, and tennis racquets together because they are used to hit balls. Standard classification systems such as the periodic table help scientists all over the world to communicate with each other. The procedure below can be used as a general guideline for classifying objects or ideas.

Procedure

1. Determine a classification for groups of objects or ideas based on observable properties. For the sports equipment, one group could be things that strike other things and another group could be the things struck.
2. Judge each object or idea against the description of the classification. Where, for example, would a bowling ball fit?
3. Group the objects or ideas under the classification.

Questions

1. Classify the following elements into two categories. Label each category.

hydrogen	aluminum	silver
gold	iron	oxygen
fluorine	copper	zinc
bromine	mercury	helium

2. In what other ways can these elements be classified?
3. Use the periodic table to classify the following elements. Label the categories.

radium	plutonium	magnesium
neon	nobelium	xenon
curium	krypton	

4. Biologists classify living things according to a five-kingdom classification. What characteristics are used to classify insects? Is a spider an insect?
5. How do scientists determine categories for classification?

Chapter 13 Review

SUMMARY

1. Hydrogen can form a covalent or an ionic bond. 13:1
2. The halogens are the most reactive of the nonmetal families. 13:2
3. Noble gases form the least reactive family of elements. 13:3
4. Aluminum is the most abundant metal in Earth's crust. 13:4
5. Semiconductors are substances that conduct electricity weakly. 13:4
6. Elements in the nitrogen family are not very reactive. Some exist in allotropic forms. 13:5
7. Some phosphorus and sulfur compounds have been found to pollute the environment. 13:5, 13:6
8. Members of the oxygen family also exist as allotropes. 13:6
9. A photoconductor is a material that allows electrons to flow when struck by light. 13:6
10. Graphite and diamond are two allotropes of carbon. 13:7
11. Carbon and silicon form covalent bonds, while tin and lead have metallic bonding. 13:7, 13:8, 13:9
12. Silicon is the second most abundant element in Earth's crust. 13:8
13. Glasses are supercooled liquids rather than crystals. 13:8
14. Tin is used mainly in alloys and for coating other metals. 13:9

VOCABULARY

a. allotropes
b. brine
c. carbonates
d. distillation
e. dry ice
f. glass
g. halogen
h. photoconductor
i. semiconductor
j. silica
k. silicates
l. silicones
m. supercooled liquid
n. triatomic

Matching

Match each description with the correct vocabulary word from the list above. Some words will not be used.

1. a molecule with three atoms
2. solid carbon dioxide
3. physical separation by boiling point differences
4. any material that looks solid but has no crystal structure
5. compounds containing CO_3^{2-} ions
6. salt water or ocean water
7. Light causes a current in this material.
8. a material that conducts a current, but weakly
9. red and white phosphorus
10. silicon dioxide, or ordinary sand

Chapter 13 Review

MAIN IDEAS

A. Reviewing Concepts

Complete each sentence with the correct word or phrase.

1. Aluminum is separated from its ores by the process of ________________.
2. At room temperature bromine is a ________________.
3. Argon is a by-product of the ________________ of air.
4. When exposed to light, selenium ________________.
5. About twenty percent of air is ________________.
6. One of the hardest substances known is the carbon allotrope, ________________.
7. The O_3 allotrope of oxygen is called ________________.
8. The most metallic member of the nitrogen family is ________________.
9. In calcium hydride, CaH_2, the oxidation number of hydrogen is ________________.
10. Fluorocarbons from spray cans may be destroying the ________________.
11. Silicon and carbon form compounds having ________________ bonds.
12. When carbon burns, ____________ and ____________ may form.

Choose the word or phrase that correctly completes each of the following sentences.

13. All of the halogens have (*5,6,7,8*) electrons in the outer energy level.
14. Halogen atoms form compounds with other elements by (*ionic, covalent, ionic and covalent*) bonding.
15. All elements in the oxygen family need (*2, 4, 6, 8*) electrons to fill their outer energy level.

B. Understanding Concepts

Answer the following questions using complete sentences when possible.

16. Why are the properties of diamond and graphite so different?
17. Why did it take so long to discover the noble gases?
18. What kind of bonding is present in compounds containing nitrogen? How does this compare with bonding between the alkali metal and halogen families?
19. How can you distinguish between metallic and nonmetallic members of a family of elements?
20. What is a diatomic gas? Name three and give their formulas.
21. Iodine is purified by sublimation. What does that mean?
22. Nitrogen has many uses. Name at least one use in three different areas of the economy.
23. There are a number of gases that are produced by the distillation of air. Name four and tell how the distillation works.
24. At room temperature, what are two physical properties of each of the four most common halogens?
25. List five elements that can act as semiconductors.

C. Applying Concepts

Answer the following questions using complete sentences when possible.

26. Rods of glass that are stored on end for a long time have a tendency to warp out of shape. Explain why this happens.

27. How are allotropes different from isotopes?
28. Explain photoconduction. How does it work in "electric eyes"?
29. Draw the bonding model diagrams for H_2S and MgF_2. How are the two compounds different?
30. What relationship exists between atomic number and metallic properties in Groups 15 through 17?

SKILL REVIEW

1. The Mohs' scale is used to classify minerals and rocks according to hardness. Use an earth science book or encyclopedia to find out about the scale. What material is the hardest? How could you use this scale to classify rocks gathered on the moon according to hardness?
2. Prepare a list of at least four properties that could be used to classify a material as a gas.
3. Make a list of all the courses offered at your school. Find out how these courses are classified into subject areas.
4. What do we call the relationship between an event and why it occurred?
5. How was Mendeleev able to predict the existence and properties of undiscovered elements?

PROJECTS

1. Visit a nursery or garden shop. From labels on the pesticides, determine which elements are used most often. Use the labels on the fertilizers to determine what elements are most often used in fertilizers.
2. Portland cement has been an important building material for centuries. Investigate its history and find out how it is being used now with other materials to enhance its usefulness.

READINGS

1. Bamford, C. H., and C. F. Tipper. *Reactions of Solids with Gases.* New York: Elsevier, 1984.
2. "Carbon." *Growing Up with Science.* Westport, CT: H. S. Stuttman, 1984. Vol. 3, pp. 263–265.
3. Torrey, Lee. "Extreme Conditions." *Science Digest.* February, 1986, pp. 54–58, 76–77.

ORGANIC COMPOUNDS
BIOLOGICAL MOLECULES

Carbon and Organic Chemistry

More than eighty percent of all known compounds contain carbon. Millions of different carbon compounds have been discovered. The compounds of carbon with hydrogen, oxygen, and other elements make up the branch of chemistry known as organic chemistry.

ORGANIC COMPOUNDS

Organic compounds are used as fuels. The clothing you are wearing is made of organic substances. Some may be natural substances as in wool and cotton. Others are manufactured. Every living thing contains a large number of organic compounds. Why is there such a wide variety of organic compounds?

GOALS

1. You will learn how organic compounds differ from other compounds.
2. You will learn about the structures, properties, and uses of organic comounds.
3. You will learn how polymers are made and used.

14:1 Organic Compounds

Most compounds that contain carbon are called organic compounds. At one time, people thought organic compounds came only from living things. However, this idea has changed. For many years, chemists have known how to make organic compounds without using plants or animals. **Organic chemistry** is now defined as the study of the properties of carbon compounds.

Several million organic compounds are known to exist. There are four main reasons why there are so many carbon compounds. First, carbon can form four covalent bonds with other carbon atoms. These atoms can then form long chains, which may be straight or branched. Organic molecules may contain one carbon atom or thousands of carbon atoms. Second, the bonds between these carbon atoms can be single, double, or triple covalent bonds. Third, a carbon chain can contain different arrangements of single, double, and triple bonds.

How many bonds can a single carbon atom form?

TECHNOLOGY: ADVANCES

Fiber-Reinforced Plastics

With fiber-reinforced plastics, FRPs, scientists are able to make materials to fit specific designs. FRPs are made by combining fine fibers that have certain characteristics with a base material or matrix having other special properties. There is an almost limitless choice of fiber and matrix materials. Although the matrix is usually a plastic, FRPs have been designed with metal or ceramic matrices. The fibers might be made of glass, graphite, aluminum, or Kevlar. Kevlar is a special kind of synthetic fiber that pound-for-pound is stronger than steel. In addition to FRPs, Kevlar is used to make cables, tires, and mechanical rubber goods. It is also used in bullet-proof vests made for law enforcement personnel.

Fiber-reinforced plastics are lightweight but very strong. Automobile manufacturers use FRPs because they resist corrosion and denting. Tennis rackets, golf clubs, fishing rods, and skis are also made with FRPs. FRPs are also used in high-performance aircraft and space vehicles.

Finally, carbon will bond with atoms of many other elements. Among these are the halogens, the nitrogen family, oxygen, and hydrogen. In fact, there are so many compounds of carbon and hydrogen that they form a class all their own called hydrocarbons. A **hydrocarbon** is a compound that contains only carbon and hydrogen. In nearly all its compounds, carbon is bonded to hydrogen.

What is a hydrocarbon?

Properties of organic compounds depend on the number and types of atoms in the compound. They also depend on the pattern or structure in which the atoms are bonded. It is possible for two compounds to have the same molecular formula but different structures and properties. You will learn in the rest of the chapter how composition and structure affect carbon compounds.

14:2 Formulas for Hydrocarbons

A formula for an organic compound can be written in the same way you write the formula for any other compound. For example, the formula for methane is CH_4. The methane molecule contains one carbon atom and four hydrogen atoms. Natural gas is mostly methane. It is used as fuel in stoves and furnaces. Methane is the simplest hydrocarbon. Ethane, C_2H_6, is another example of a hydrocarbon. How many atoms of carbon and hydrogen are in an ethane molecule?

What is the name of the simplest hydrocarbon?

Table 14–1

Alkane Series of Hydrocarbons			
Name	**Formula**	**Name**	**Formula**
methane	CH_4	pentane	C_5H_{12}
ethane	C_2H_6	hexane	C_6H_{14}
propane	C_3H_8	heptane	C_7H_{16}
butane	C_4H_{10}	octane	C_8H_{18}

BIOGRAPHY

Benjamin Alexander
1921–

Benjamin Alexander is an organic chemist. In the 1960s, he was the chief organic chemist at Walter Reed Hospital. There he worked on the synthesis of organophosphorus compounds. This research was aimed at finding drugs that could be used to treat diseases like leukemia.

The formula for an organic compound can also be written to show its structure. The **structural formula** of a compound shows the pattern or form in which the atoms are bonded. For example, the structural formulas for methane and ethane are given below. A line represents a shared pair of electrons.

```
     H                 H   H
     |                 |   |
  H—C—H            H—C—C—H
     |                 |   |
     H                 H   H
  methane            ethane
```

How many covalent bonds are in each molecule? Remember, each covalent bond is a shared pair of electrons. Notice that in ethane, one covalent bond links the two carbon atoms together. How many hydrogen atoms are bonded to each carbon atom?

In a **saturated hydrocarbon,** all the carbon atoms are joined by single covalent bonds to other carbon or hydrogen atoms. One group of saturated hydrocarbons is the alkane series. The eight simplest compounds in the alkane series are listed in Table 14–1. Note that methane and ethane are members of this group. All of the compounds in the alkane series will burn and can be used as fuel. Several of these compounds are the main components of gasoline. Notice that the names of all compounds in the alkane series end in *-ane.*

What does a structural formula show?

What type of bond exists between carbon atoms in saturated hydrocarbons?

FIGURE 14–1. Shown here are a variety of hydrocarbons. Hydrocarbons with few carbon atoms are used mostly as fuels and solvents. Those with many carbon atoms are used as greases and lubricating oils.

Carbon atoms can be linked with a double covalent bond. In a double covalent bond, four electrons (two pairs) are shared. Ethene (ETH een) is an example of an organic compound with a double covalent bond. Its formula is C_2H_4. Its structural formula has two lines showing the double covalent bond between the carbon atoms.

Carbon atoms also bond with each other by sharing three pairs, or six, electrons. This bond is a triple covalent bond. One example of a compound with a triple bond is ethyne (ETH ine), C_2H_2. The common name for ethyne is acetylene (uh SET uh leen). It is a gas burned in welding torches. The structural formulas of ethene and ethyne are shown below.

```
H       H
 \     /
  C=C
 /     \
H       H
```

ethene

$H-C\equiv C-H$

ethyne

What is an unsaturated hydrocarbon?

What is the shape of a methane molecule?

If a hydrocarbon has one or more double or triple bonds, it is an **unsaturated hydrocarbon.** Both ethene and ethyne are unsaturated. Some vegetable oils such as corn oil and safflower oil are mixtures of mostly unsaturated hydrocarbons. Unsaturated oils contain compounds with double or triple bonds.

You should realize that the structural formulas shown in this book are flat drawings of three-dimensional molecules. In methane, the four single bonds point to the vertices of a tetrahedron, Figure 14–2. Ethene is planar, while ethyne (C_2H_2) is a linear molecule. Double and triple bonds are not very flexible.

FIGURE 14–2. Each carbon-hydrogen bond in methane points toward a vertex of a tetrahedron (a). In (b), the tetrahedral structure is shown with a ball-and-stick model. The scale model in (c) shows the relative volumes of the electron clouds.

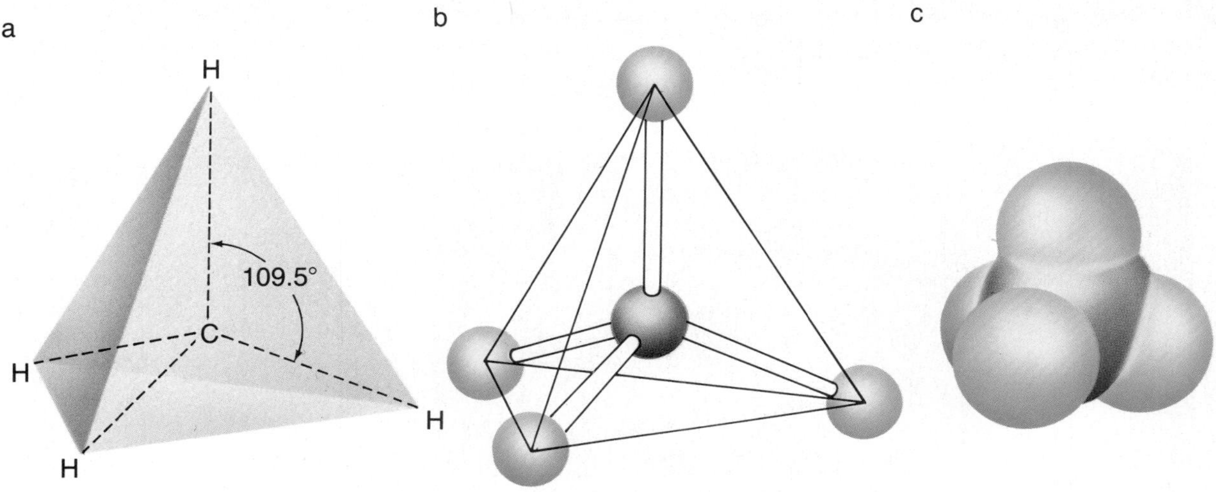

INVESTIGATION 14–1

Organic Molecules

Problem: What are the shapes of molecules with single, double, and triple bonds?

Materials

2 plastic foam balls, 4 cm in diameter
4 plastic foam balls, 2 cm in diameter
6 pipe cleaner pieces, 4 cm long
2 cardboard forms, 109.5° and 121.6°
toothpicks

Procedure

1. In this investigation, the larger balls represent carbon atoms and the smaller balls represent hydrogen atoms. Each pipe cleaner represents a bond. Place the 109.5° form against a 4-cm ball as shown in Figure 14–3a.
2. Insert pipe cleaner bonds halfway into the ball along both edges of the form.
3. Turn the form, and locate a single point that is 109.5° from each of the first two bonds. Be patient and practice until you find a correct point. Temporarily mark the point with a toothpick and have your teacher check its position. When you have found a correct point, replace the toothpick with a pipe cleaner.
4. Repeat Step 3 to locate a fourth bond 109.5° from all three of the other bonds.

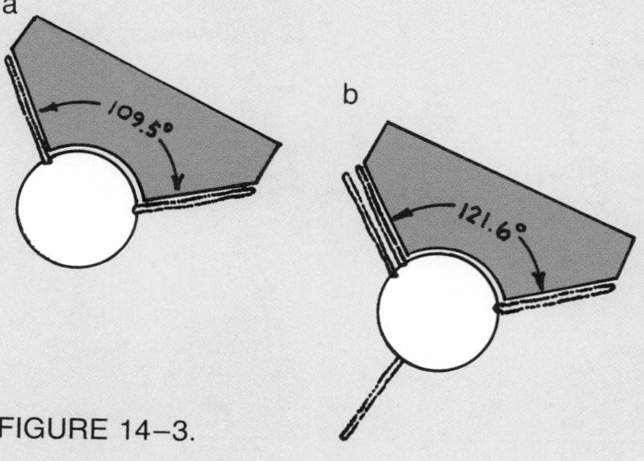

FIGURE 14–3.

5. Place 2-cm balls on each of the pipe cleaner bonds. Draw and describe the model molecule.
6. Insert two bonds side-by-side in one 4-cm ball, forming a double bond.
7. Place the 121.6° form on the ball so that the double bond is against one edge. Insert a pipe cleaner into the ball along the other edge of the form. Place a 2-cm ball on this pipe cleaner.
8. Repeat Step 7, but place the pipe cleaner on the opposite side as in Figure 14–3b.
9. Attach the second 4-cm ball to the double bond. Insert two pipe cleaners into this ball as in Steps 7 and 8 and add the remaining 2-cm balls. Draw and describe the result.
10. Insert three pieces of pipe cleaner side-by-side in one 4-cm ball. Attach the other 4-cm ball to this triple bond.
11. Attach a pipe cleaner and 2-cm ball to each of the 4-cm balls so that all bonds are in a line. Draw and describe the molecule.

Data and Observations

Drawings and descriptions of each of the three molecules.

Conclusions and Applications

1. What are the shapes of molecules with single, double, and triple bonds?
2. After studying the models, how would you compare the ability of single, double, and triple bonds to rotate?
3. In all of these molecules, how many bonds were formed by each carbon atom?
4. What are the formulas and names of the three molecules for which you constructed models?

Also, notice the difference in the endings of the names, ethane, ethene, and ethyne. The ending, or suffix, gives a clue to the structure of the compound. The suffix *-ane* refers to a hydrocarbon in which the carbon atoms all have single covalent bonds. Hydrocarbons with the ending *-ene* have at least one double covalent bond between carbon atoms. The suffix *-yne* means a triple covalent bond is present.

What does the suffix *-ene* tell about a hydrocarbon?

14:3 Isomers

The chemical formulas of two different carbon compounds can be the same. The molecular formulas for both butane and isobutane (2-methylpropane) can be written as C_4H_{10}. Both compounds have four atoms of carbon and ten atoms of hydrogen. However, the two compounds have different structures. As a result, their properties are different. For example, butane has a freezing point of −138.3°C. Isobutane has a freezing point of −159.6°C.

What are isomers?

Butane and isobutane are isomers. **Isomers** are compounds with the same molecular formula but different structures. The carbon atoms in butane are in a straight chain. Isobutane has a branched chain. The branch in isobutane is bonded to the carbon atom at the center of the chain, Table 14–2.

As the number of carbon atoms increases, the number of possible isomers also increases. Drawn below are three isomers of pentane, C_5H_{12}. Are there more than three? There are eighteen isomers for octane, C_8H_{18}. You can begin to see how isomers add to the great number of carbon compounds.

Table 14–2

Properties of Butane and Isobutane		
Name	butane	isobutane (2-methyl propane)
Structural formula	H H H H H—C—C—C—C—H H H H H	H H H H—C——C——C—H H H H—C—H H
Description	colorless gas	colorless gas
Melting point	−138.3°C	−159.6°C
Boiling point	−0.50°C	−11.7°C

```
    H  H  H  H  H
    |  |  |  |  |
 H—C—C—C—C—C—H
    |  |  |  |  |
    H  H  H  H  H
```

pentane

```
          H
          |
       H—C—H
    H     |     H
    |     |     |
 H—C—————C—————C—H
    |     |     |
    H     |     H
       H—C—H
          |
          H
```

2,2-dimethylpropane

```
              H
              |
           H—C—H
    H  H      |     H
    |  |      |     |
 H—C—C—————C—————C—H
    |  |      |     |
    H  H      H     H
```

2-methylbutane

14:4 Additional Compounds

Not all hydrocarbons occur as chains. Many form rings. Both saturated and unsaturated hydrocarbons can form rings. Cyclohexane, C_6H_{12}, and benzene, C_6H_6, are two such compounds. Are these compounds isomers? The structural formulas for these compounds follow.

```
         H H
      H  | |  H
  H    \ | | /    H
        C—C
   \  /     \  /
     C       C
   /  \     /  \
  H     C—C     H
      /  | |  \
     H   | |   H
         H H
```

cyclohexane

```
      H       H
       \     /
        C=C
       /    \
  H—C        C—H
      \\    //
        C=C
       /    \
      H      H
```

benzene

The structural symbol for benzene is ⬡ or ⌬.

Carbon atoms form bonds with other elements. When an atom of some other element replaces one or more hydrogens, a **substituted hydrocarbon** is formed. Tetrachloromethane, CCl_4, is a substituted hydrocarbon. The common name for this compound is carbon tetrachloride. It is formed by replacing the hydrogen atoms in methane, CH_4, with chlorine atoms. Tetrachloroethene, C_2Cl_4, is a compound used in dry cleaning. What is the structural formula for C_2Cl_4?

Chloroform, $CHCl_3$, and iodoform, CHI_3, are also substituted hydrocarbons. Chloroform is used mainly to dissolve organic substances such as grease, oil, and rubber, and as a cleanser. Iodoform is a yellow solid that can be used as a disinfectant.

If one or more hydrogen atoms are replaced by an $-OH$ group, an **alcohol** is formed. Ethanol, C_2H_5OH, is produced by the action of yeasts or bacteria on the sugar in fruits or grains such as wheat and corn. It is the type

How is a substituted hydrocarbon formed?

FIGURE 14–4. Substituted hydrocarbons containing chlorine are found in many paint removers.

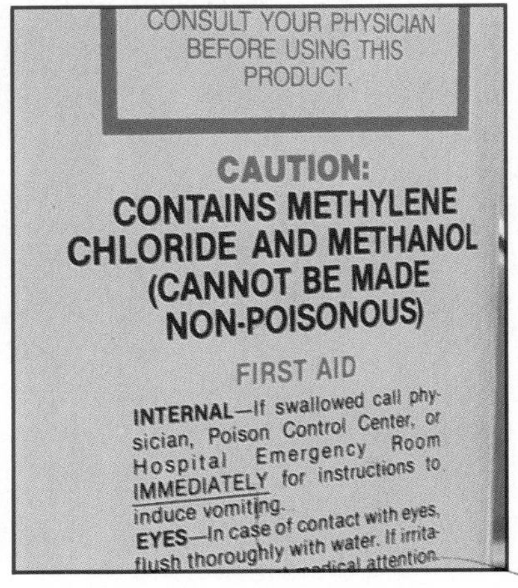

14–3

Common Alcohols		
Name	**Structural formula**	**Uses**
Methanol	$\begin{array}{c} \text{H} \\ \vert \\ \text{H—C—OH} \\ \vert \\ \text{H} \end{array}$	fuel for high-performance engines, solvent, preparation of other compounds
Ethanol	$\begin{array}{ccccc} & \text{H} & & \text{H} & \\ & \vert & & \vert & \\ \text{H—} & \text{C} & \text{—} & \text{C} & \text{—OH} \\ & \vert & & \vert & \\ & \text{H} & & \text{H} & \end{array}$	solvent, preparation of other compounds, germicide, fuel, alcoholic beverages
2-Propanol (isopropyl alcohol)	$\begin{array}{ccccccc} & \text{H} & & \text{OH} & & \text{H} & \\ & \vert & & \vert & & \vert & \\ \text{H—} & \text{C} & \text{—} & \text{C} & \text{—} & \text{C} & \text{—H} \\ & \vert & & \vert & & \vert & \\ & \text{H} & & \text{H} & & \text{H} & \end{array}$	common rubbing alcohol, preparation of other organic compounds, solvent
Phenol	$\langle\bigcirc\rangle\text{—OH}$	preparation of plastics, disinfectant, preparation of other compounds
1, 2-Ethanediol (ethylene glycol)	$\begin{array}{ccccc} & \text{OH} & & \text{OH} & \\ & \vert & & \vert & \\ \text{H—} & \text{C} & \text{—} & \text{C} & \text{—H} \\ & \vert & & \vert & \\ & \text{H} & & \text{H} & \end{array}$	solvent, coolant, antifreeze

What alcohol is in antifreeze?

of alcohol contained in beer, wine, and other alcoholic drinks. Methanol, CH_3OH, is poisonous. Drinking it may cause blindness or death. Antifreeze for car radiators is generally ethylene glycol. It is a substituted hydrocarbon with two –OH groups. Table 14–3 lists the formulas and uses for some common alcohols.

FIGURE 14–5. Organic acids are used in home canning to keep foods from spoiling or changing colors.

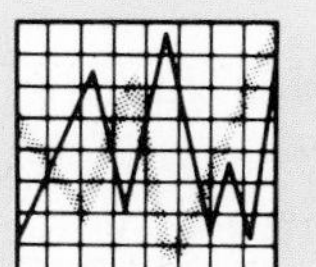

SKILL

Making Models

Problem: How can models show that isomers differ from one another?

Materials

5 plastic foam balls, 4 cm in diameter
10 plastic foam balls, 2 cm in diameter
15 pieces of pipe cleaners, 3 cm long
paper and pencil

Background

Many molecules exist as isomers. Recall that isomers are molecules that have the same chemical formula but different structures. Most organic compounds have isomers. Some large hydrocarbons have thousands of isomers. The different arrangements of atoms and bonds in molecules give them different properties. To understand the properties of a molecule, it is necessary to know the structure of that particular molecule.

Procedure

1. The large balls will be used to represent carbon atoms and the smaller balls, hydrogen. The pipe cleaners represent bonds. Use four large balls and ten small balls to construct a model of butane, C_4H_{10}. Remember that the four bonds of carbon point to the four vertices of a tetrahedron.
2. Draw and describe your model.
3. Remove the end carbon and its three hydrogen atoms. Remove a hydrogen from the center carbon. Place that hydrogen where the end carbon was. Attach the end carbon and its three hydrogen atoms to the center carbon where the hydrogen atom was.
4. Draw and describe the result. The models in Steps 1 and 3 represent the two isomers of butane.
5. Use five large balls, 10 small balls, and 15 pieces of pipe cleaner to construct cyclopentane, C_5H_{10}.

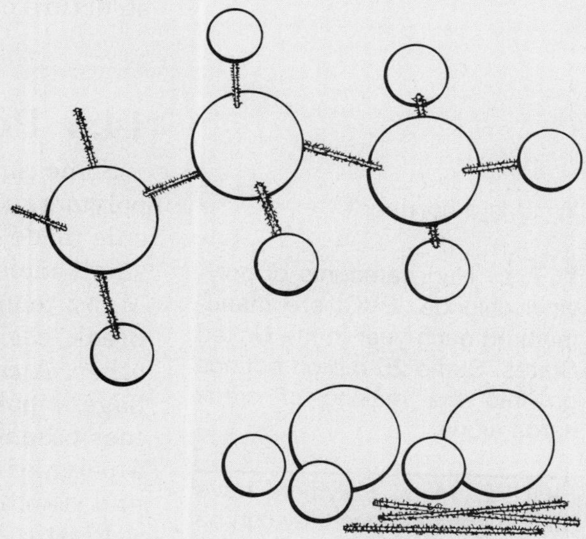

FIGURE 14–6.

6. Draw and describe the result.
7. Rearrange the same set of materials used in Step 5 to form a linear molecule, all carbon atoms in one chain. Recall that alkenes have a double bond. This model represents the alkene called pentene. If the double bond is between the first two carbons, the molecule is called 1-pentene. If the double bond is between carbons two and three, it is called 2-pentene.
8. Draw and describe your model from Step 7.

Questions and Conclusions

1. How are the models of butane and isobutane different?
2. What characteristics do isomers have?
3. How do cyclopentane and 1-pentene differ?
4. Are there other isomers of C_5H_{10}? If so, construct and draw them.
5. How can models show that isomers differ from one another?

Most food colors, flavors, and preservatives are organic compounds. One substance used to preserve food is vinegar. Vinegar contains acetic acid, an organic compound. Acetic acid can slow the growth of some organisms that spoil food. Most organic acids are carboxylic (kar bahk SIHL ihk) acids. A **carboxylic acid** is an organic compound that contains the –COOH group. The structure of this group is —C(=O)—O—H. Note double bond.

What is a carboxylic acid?

14:5 Polymers

What is a polymer?

Some small organic molecules can combine to form polymers (PAHL uh murz). A **polymer** is a giant molecule made of many small molecules linked together. The small molecules are called monomers (MAHN uh murz). Many monomers have double or triple bonds that can break easily so that the molecules can bond to each other. A common plastic used for food wrap and plastic bags is polyethylene. It is made from the alkene monomer ethene, once known as ethylene. Natural rubber is a polymer of smaller hydrocarbon molecules. Wool, silk, and starch are other natural polymers.

F.Y.I. Huge amounts of polyvinyl chloride, PVC, are manufactured each year in the United States. Some 25 million pounds go into the making of credit cards alone.

Plastics and synthetic fibers are polymers. Plastics such as polyvinyls are used to make phonograph rec-

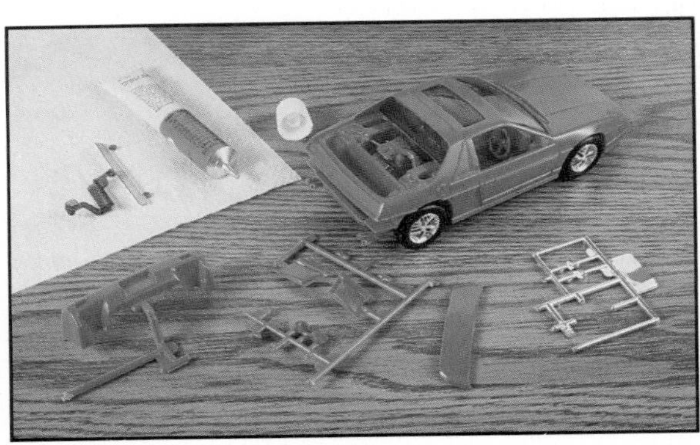

FIGURE 14–7. Polymers have many uses because they can be made into a wide variety of forms.

Table 14–4

Common Polymers

Name	Structural	Uses
Dacron® (a polyester)	$\sim C(=O)-C_6H_4-C(=O)-OCH_2CH_2O-C(=O)-C_6H_4-C(=O)-OCH_2CH_2O\sim$	textiles, arterial grafts
Nylon 66	$\sim C(=O)(CH_2)_4-C(=O)N(H)(CH_2)_6N(H)-C(=O)(CH_2)_4C(=O)-N(H)(CH_2)_6N(H)\sim$	tire cord, textiles, brush bristles, netting, carpet, athletic turf, sutures
polyethylene	$\sim CH_2-CH_2-CH_2-CH_2-CH_2-CH_2\sim$	tubing, prosthetic devices, packaging materials, kitchen utensils, paper coating
polypropylene	$\sim CH(CH_3)-CH_2-CH(CH_3)-CH_2-CH(CH_3)-CH_2\sim$	rope, protective clothing, textiles, carpet
polystyrene	$\sim CH(C_6H_5)-CH_2-CH(C_6H_5)-CH_2-CH(C_6H_5)-CH_2\sim$	containers, boats, coolers, insulation, furniture, models
polyvinyl chloride (PVC)	$\sim CH_2-CH(Cl)-CH_2-CH(Cl)-CH_2-CH(Cl)\sim$	as a rubber substitute, cable covering, tubing, rainwear, gaskets

ords, upholstery, and floor coverings. Acrylics are polymers used in making clear sheets for windows. They are also used in floor wax, paint, and synthetic fibers. Polystyrene foam is used as insulation. Many fabrics contain synthetic fibers such as nylon or polyester that are also polymers. The properties of latex paint that make it wear well are partly due to polymers. Glues such as epoxys and super-strength glues obtain their strength from the chemical bonds of polymers.

Name two synthetic fibers that are polymers.

Molecules of tetrafluoroethene combine to form the Teflon coating for "nonstick" utensils. Teflon resists heat and chemicals. Also, with the proper care, food does not stick to it. Synthetic polymers are often used to replace natural materials because the polymers are more flexible, stronger, and more resistant to chemical change and wear.

Review

1. How do ethene, ethane, and ethyne differ? Draw structural formulas for all three compounds. Which of these is saturated?
2. How many single covalent bonds can a carbon atom form? Double covalent bonds? Triple covalent bonds?
3. In alcohols, what group replaces hydrogen on the hydrocarbon chain?
4. How are polymers formed?
5. ★ There are eight different isomers of $C_5H_{11}Cl$. Draw a structural formula for each isomer.

BIOLOGICAL MOLECULES

GOALS

1. You will learn what values amino acids and proteins have in your body.
2. You will learn how fats and oils, carbohydrates, and vitamins are important to life processes.

In the human body, there are many thousands of organic compounds, probably even millions. Each compound has a specific role to play. Some are used in body structures. These make up cell membranes, bones, skin, and hair, for example. Some molecules such as DNA store and transfer information. Other compounds, like insulin, control processes. Insulin regulates the amount of sugar in the bloodstream. Other compounds are nutrients and sources of energy. You will study five types of biological molecules in the sections that follow.

14:6 Amino Acids and Proteins

What is biochemistry?

Biochemistry is the study of the chemistry of living systems. Living things are mostly water and organic compounds. Several classes of organic compounds are important to the life processes of all living things.

Much of the structure of your body consists of polymers formed from 20 amino acids. Other polymers of the same amino acids carry out many of the life processes of your body. An **amino acid** is an organic compound that has a carboxylic acid (–COOH) group and an amino ($-NH_2$) group in specific locations in its structure.

What is an amino acid?

What is a protein?

A **protein** is one of a major group of polymers formed from amino acids. All living organisms contain proteins.

FIGURE 14–8. We build our own proteins from the amino acids obtained by digesting high-protein foods.

```
                                   S—H
                                   |
H     H      O            H   H—C—H   O
 \    |     //             \      |   //
  N—C—C                    N—C—C
 /    |     \              /      |   \
H     H      OH           H       H    OH
   glycine                   cysteine
```

About one-half of your body mass other than water is made of proteins. Proteins make up cartilage, tendons, and other body tissues. The hemoglobin that transports oxygen through the bloodstream is a protein. An **enzyme** (EN zime) is a protein that speeds up chemical reactions in living systems. Enzymes enable reactions to go fast enough to support life processes.

What is an enzyme?

PROBLEM SOLVING

How do you name organic compounds?

There are rules for naming organic compounds. You may have noticed some patterns for compound names in this chapter. For example, hydrocarbon names have prefixes that tell the number of carbon atoms in a chain. They have suffixes that indicate single, double, or triple bonds. Use the structures and names of compounds illustrated in this chapter to help you name the following compounds.

```
     H  H  H  H  H  H
     |  |  |  |  |  |
1. H—C—C—C—C—C—C—H
     |  |  |  |  |  |
     H  H  H  H  H  H

     H  H
     |  |
2. H—C—C—C≡C—H
     |  |
     H  H

     H  H  H  H  H
     |  |  |  |  |
3. H—C—C=C—C—C—H
     |        |  |
     H        H  H
```

INVESTIGATION 14–2

Textiles

Problem: How do synthetic and natural fiber properties compare?

Materials 

samples of natural and synthetic fabrics, three 2×2-cm pieces each of

wool	nylon	silk	linen
cotton	Orlon	rayon	Dacron

laboratory burner	tongs
graduated cylinder	timer
8 test tubes	beaker
test tube rack	hot plate
dilute HCl	goggles
dilute NaOH	apron
water	

CAUTION: *HCl and NaOH can cause burns. Wash spills with plenty of water. Do the investigation in a well-ventilated room.*

Procedure

1. With tongs, hold one sample of each fabric over the burner flame. Observe what happens. Remove sample from flame, and record which samples continue to burn. Estimate the time it takes each sample to burn completely. **CAUTION:** *Be careful when using an open flame.*
2. Put a second sample of each fabric in a test tube containing 5 mL of dilute hydrochloric acid, HCl. Wait 5 minutes. Record your observations.
3. Put a third sample of each fabric in a test tube containing 5 mL of dilute sodium hydroxide, NaOH. Wait 5 minutes and record your observations.
4. Gently heat the test tubes from Step 3 (with NaOH) in a beaker of hot water. Record any changes that you observe.

FIGURE 14–9.

Data and Observations

Sample	Burner test	HCl	NaOH	Heated NaOH
wool				
cotton				
rayon				
silk				
Dacron				
nylon				
linen				
Orlon				

Analysis and Conclusions

1. In general, did natural or synthetic fabrics hold up better in the tests?
2. Which natural fabric appeared to withstand heat and chemicals the best? Which synthetic fabric was the best?
3. How do natural and synthetic fiber properties compare?

Applications

4. What other tests might help you choose the best fabric for a certain application?
5. If you needed a fabric that did not burn easily, which of those tested would you use?

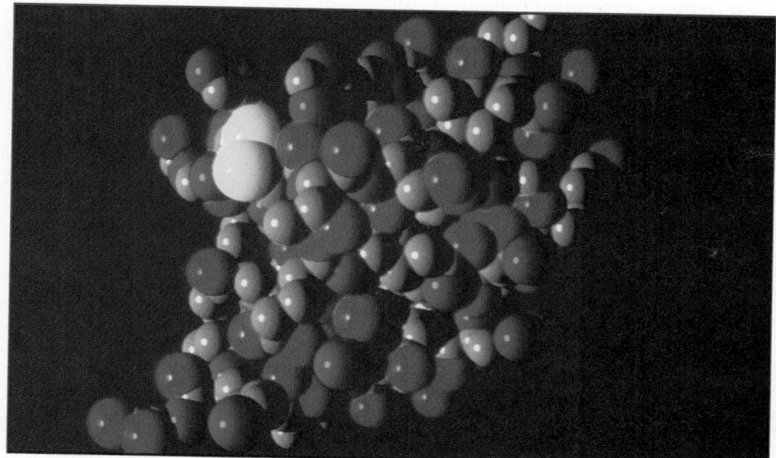

FIGURE 14–10. This molecular model shows the arrangement of atoms in a typical molecule of protein.

Proteins can contain thousands of amino acid groups. For our bodies to make protein, we must take in amino acids. We do this by eating and digesting protein from other sources. Meat, fish, and dairy products are good sources of protein.

What is a peptide linkage?

To make proteins, amino acids form polymers by means of peptide linkages. In a **peptide linkage,** the –COOH (acid) group of one amino acid combines with the $-NH_2$ (amino) group of another. Notice the peptide bonds in the following structure that shows part of a protein.

peptide linkage

peptide linkage

14:7 Carbohydrates, Lipids, and Vitamins

What is a carbohydrate?

A **carbohydrate** is an organic molecule that has hydrogen and oxygen present in a ratio of two hydrogen atoms to one oxygen atom. Starch and sugar are two examples of carbohydrates. The sugar in blood is a simple sugar called glucose, $C_6H_{12}O_6$. Complex sugars consist of two or more simple sugars bonded together. Table

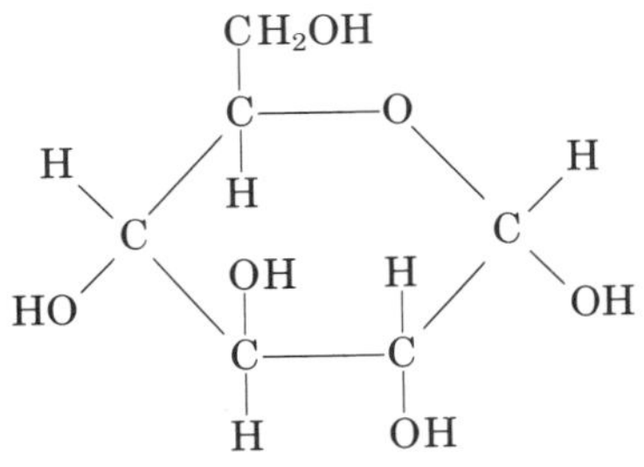

glucose

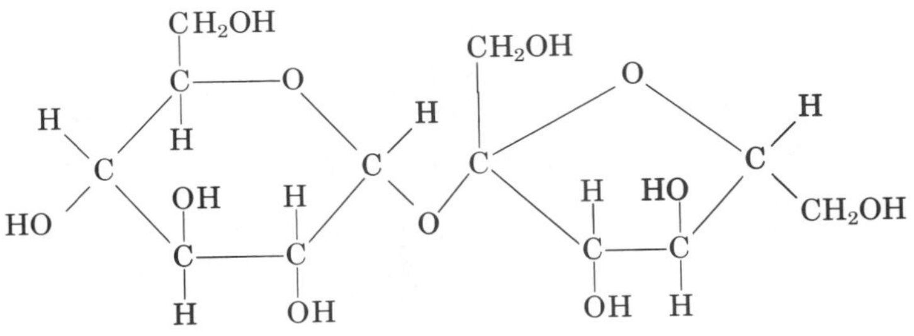

sucrose

sugar is sucrose, $C_{12}H_{22}O_{11}$. Sucrose is a complex sugar containing two simple sugars. Starch molecules are polymers of many simple sugars. Both starch and sucrose are converted to simple sugars in the process of digestion.

Carbohydrates are the chief energy source for most organisms. Energy is released as the carbohydrates combine with oxygen. Carbon dioxide and water are produced.

$$C_6H_{12}O_6 + 6O_2 \xrightarrow{\text{enzymes}} 6CO_2 + 6H_2O + \text{energy}$$

What are lipids?

Lipids are a class of organic compounds commonly called fats and oils. They contain more hydrogen and less oxygen than carbohydrates. Most do not dissolve in water. Cooking oils, fat in meat, and butter are examples of lipids. Fats are formed from fatty acids. Fatty acids are carboxylic acids with 12 to 20 carbon atoms in a chain. In animal fat, the chains are usually saturated. In many oils from plants, the chains are unsaturated. Some plant oils, such as coconut oil, have a high percentage of saturated carbon chains.

What are fatty acids?

F.Y.I. The distinction between fats and oils is usually based on melting point. At room temperature, oils are liquid while fats are solid. Materials rich in unsaturated fatty acids are generally oils. Those that contain saturated fatty acids tend to be fats. Hydrogenation (adding hydrogen to double bonds) converts vegetable oils into fats. This process is used in the manufacture of margarine.

Fats and oils are necessary to maintain the proper functioning of cell membranes. The human body stores excess energy from the breakdown of food by making and storing fat molecules. However, evidence shows that eating excess amounts of saturated fats and oils can contribute to heart disease.

Vitamins form another group of organic compounds important in living systems. A **vitamin** is an organic compound used in small amounts by cells in many of the chemical changes that take place within the body. Chemical structures of vitamins vary greatly. Some, like vitamin C, dissolve in water. Others, like vitamin A, have structures similar to lipids and dissolve in fats or oils.

vitamin A

vitamin C

One of the most important substances in living things is not found in humans. This substance is chlorophyll, found in green plants. The structure of chlorophyll is shown in Figure 12–4c on page 271. All the energy in the food you eat originally came from the sun. With chlorophyll, plants use the energy of the sun to combine carbon dioxide and water molecules into carbohydrates. Oxygen is also produced in the reaction. This process is called photosynthesis.

How do green plants use chlorophyll?

$$6CO_2 + 6H_2O + \begin{matrix}\text{sunlight}\\ \text{(energy)}\end{matrix} \xrightarrow{\text{chlorophyll}} C_6H_{12}O_6 + 6O_2$$

Most animals obtain energy by eating plant materials. Humans then use both the animals and plants for food.

FIGURE 14–11. The sun's energy stored during photosynthesis by green plants is available from the foods we eat. We then use this energy in our daily activities.

Review

6. Explain why starches and proteins are called polymers.
7. Why is it correct to say that the energy in meat comes from the sun?
8. How are fats different from carbohydrates? How are they alike?
9. Define an enzyme and explain why enzymes are needed in the body.
★ 10. Vitamin C and the B vitamins are water-soluble. Vitamins A, D, and E are fat-soluble. Relate this information to the fact that it is easier to take too much of vitamins A, D, and E than B and C.

CAREER

Nutritionist

Dan Lane's mother was always telling him to eat right. In elementary school, he was taught that there were four basic food groups and that he should eat foods from each every day. His high school football and wrestling coaches stressed that he follow special diets to keep his body in good physical condition. Dan never really paid attention to why or what he was told to eat until he took a science course and learned the roles of proteins, fats, and carbohydrates in body chemistry. He found out that vitamins and minerals really are important to one's health. Dan began to understand the statement, "You are what you eat."

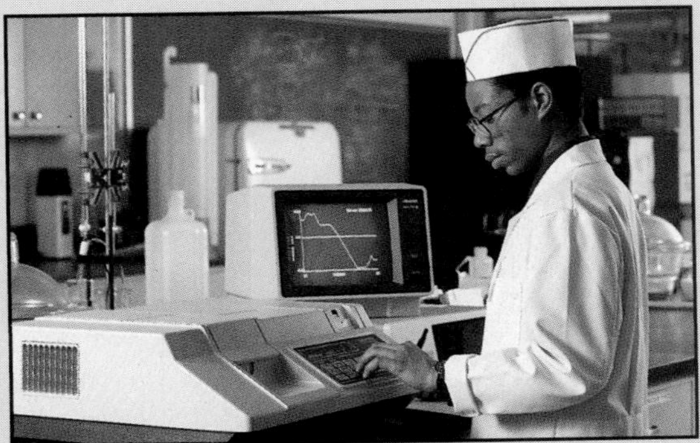

Dan learned even more about nutrition in his high school job as a food preparer in a local hospital. While in college, he studied dietetics and food technology. This gave him a thorough knowledge of food chemistry and its effects on the body.

Today Dan is a food technologist with a salad dressing company. He began his career as a water quality inspector for a dairy products company. His job was to see that the factories followed safe, healthy procedures in food preparation. However, Dan preferred research, so he changed jobs. He now develops new salad dressings. Dan is most proud of a new potato salad dressing he developed that not only tastes good but is also nutritious.

For career information, write
The American Dietetic Association
430 North Michigan Avenue
Chicago, IL 60611

Chapter 14 Review

SUMMARY

1. Organic chemistry is the study of the properties of carbon compounds. 14:1
2. There are many organic compounds because carbon forms four covalent bonds; single, double, or triple bonds; straight or branched chains; and bonds with atoms of other elements. 14:1
3. Carbon may form saturated and unsaturated hydrocarbons by forming single, double, or triple bonds. 14:2
4. A structural formula shows the pattern of bonded atoms. 14:2
5. Isomers have the same molecular formulas but different structures. 14:3
6. Substituted hydrocarbons result when an atom of another element replaces one or more hydrogen atoms. 14:4
7. An alcohol is a compound that contains one or more –OH groups. A carboxylic acid has one or more –COOH groups. 14:4
8. Polymers are giant molecules made of many small molecules linked together. 14:5
9. Biochemistry is the chemistry of living systems. 14:6
10. Amino acids, proteins, carbohydrates, lipids, and vitamins are classes of organic compounds also needed for the proper functioning of the human body. 14:6, 14:7

VOCABULARY

a. alcohol
b. amino acid
c. biochemistry
d. carbohydrate
e. carboxylic acid
f. enzyme
g. hydrocarbon
h. isomers
i. lipids
j. organic chemistry
k. peptide linkage
l. polymer
m. protein
n. saturated hydrocarbon
o. structural formula
p. substituted hydrocarbon
q. unsaturated hydrocarbon
r. vitamin

Matching

Match each description with the correct vocabulary word from the list above. Some words will not be used.

1. connects amino acids to form proteins
2. C_2H_4, C_6H_{14}, or a similar compound
3. hydrocarbon with double or triple bonds
4. supplies body's main source of energy
5. building block of proteins
6. organic compound that contains at least one –OH group
7. study of the properties of the compounds of carbon
8. a protein that speeds up chemical reactions in living systems
9. a synthetic or natural substance composed of many monomers
10. shows the pattern of bonding in compounds

Chapter 14 Review

MAIN IDEAS

A. Reviewing Concepts

Complete each sentence with the correct word or phrase.

1. Fats and oils are classified as ____________.
2. Chloroform, $CHCl_3$, is a ____________ hydrocarbon.
3. Animal fats are generally ____________, while many plant oils are ____________.
4. It is possible for two compounds to have the same formula but different ____________ and ____________.
5. In nearly all its compounds, carbon is bonded to ____________.
6. In a ____________ covalent bond, two pairs of electrons are shared.
7. The suffix *-ene* refers to a hydrocarbon that has at least one ____________ bond.
8. An enzyme belongs to the class of biological molecules called ____________.
9. The sugars, glucose and sucrose, belong to the group of organic molecules known as ____________.
10. Plastics, proteins, wool and silk are ____________.
11. An example of a ring compound is ________________.
12. Unsaturated hydrocarbons have ____________ or ____________ bonds.
13. To make proteins, the acid group of one amino acid combines with the amino group of another amino acid in a ________________.
14. All the energy in the food you eat originally came from the ____________.
15. Organic compounds that are important to the body, needed in small amounts, and given letter names are ____________.

B. Understanding Concepts

Answer the following questions using complete sentences when possible.

16. What is the molecular formula for the three isomers of pentane?
17. How do organic compounds differ from other compounds?
18. What is the difference between a polymer and a monomer?
19. How is it possible for carbon to form so many organic compounds?
20. What is the major difference between saturated and unsaturated compounds?
21. Name five polymers that have practical uses. Give one example of a use of each polymer.
22. Name four classes of molecules important in living systems.
23. Write structural formulas for two saturated and two unsaturated hydrocarbons.
24. Write the chemical reaction for the production of glucose by photosynthesis.
25. What is the main energy source for organisms?

C. Applying Concepts

Answer the following questions using complete sentences when possible.

26. Our bodies manufacture protein. If this is true, why must we have protein in our diet?
27. Propane, propene, and propyne are all 3-carbon hydrocarbons. Show how they are different by drawing their structural formulas.
28. Explain why an alcohol is a substituted hydrocarbon.

29. All our food energy comes from the sun. Why is this statement true?
30. Draw structural formulas for all the isomers of C_4H_9Cl.

SKILL REVIEW

1. Give two reasons why models are useful in studying science.
2. List two industrial uses for models.
3. How are models useful to the automotive industry?
4. Ammonium sulfate is used in fertilizers, for water treatment, and as a food additive. What is the formula for this compound?
5. Describe the shape that should enclose the following statements in a flow chart.
   a. Start
   b. Add 5 mL H_2O to 2 g NaCl in a test tube.
   c. Does all the NaCl dissolve?
   d. Add NaCl in 1-g portions until some solid remains at the bottom of the test tube.
   e. Record mass of NaCl and volume of H_2O.
   f. Stop.

PROJECTS

1. Some polymers such as polyethylene and polyvinyl chloride are addition polymers. Others like polyester and nylon are condensation polymers and contain copolymers. Research and explain these differences.
2. Prepare a vitamin table to display in class. List several vitamins and include their common name, chemical name, formula, recommended daily allowance, and common sources.

READINGS

1. "Chemistry, Organic." *Science and Technology Illustrated.* Chicago: Encyclopedia Britannica, 1984, pp. 674–677.
2. Meade, J. "Amino Acids." *Prevention.* June, 1986, pp. 97–100.
3. Whyman, Kathryn. *Chemical Changes.* New York: Franklin Watts, 1986.
4. Zubrick, James W. *The Organic Chemistry Laboratory Survival Manual.* New York: Wiley, 1984.

SCIENCE AND SOCIETY

FORMALDEHYDE DEBATE

In Section 14:4, you learned about substituted hydrocarbons. Another type of substituted hydrocarbon can be formed by replacing two hydrogen atoms by a single oxygen atom. When this is done, an aldehyde is formed. The simplest aldehyde is formaldehyde. It is formed when two hydrogen atoms in a molecule of methane are replaced by a single oxygen atom, H—C—H.

$$\begin{array}{c} H-C-H \\ \| \\ O \end{array}$$

Background

Formaldehyde has been used to preserve biological specimens, manufacture insulation for homes as well as plywood and particleboard, and keep the permanent press in clothing. Many complaints of headaches, sore throats, and fatigue have been blamed on the use of formaldehyde in construction materials. For this reason, home insulation made with formaldehyde is no longer used. Steps have also been taken to reduce the use of formaldehyde in plywood and particleboard. However, 777 000 clothing workers continue to be exposed to relatively high levels of formaldehyde. The Environmental Protection Agency (EPA) of the United States has determined that formaldehyde is a "probable human carcinogen" or cancer-causing substance. Rats in laboratory studies developed nasal cancer after exposure to formaldehyde. Also, in some human studies, an association between formaldehyde and respiratory cancer has been shown.

Case Studies

Consider the following people:

1. Joe and Florence McGraw, an elderly couple living on a limited income from their retirement in a mobile home whose plywood walls expose them to high levels of formaldehyde. EPA's data show that up to 1170 people now living in mobile homes and up to 630 people living in conventional homes will get cancer from exposure to formaldehyde if steps are not taken to reduce their exposure.

2. The president of the Formaldehyde Institute of America, who argues that the EPA data are not good enough to make a decision. If formaldehyde is a carcinogen, there should be a high incidence of cancer in the industry that has manufactured

FIGURE 1. Formaldehyde is used in the glues and binders of many wood products. It is also used in oil-based paints and carpets.

FIGURE 2. Garment workers are exposed regularly to formaldehyde that outgases from permanent press fabrics.

formaldehyde for the 90 years that it has been in common use.

3. The president of the International Ladies Garment Workers Union (ILGWU), who is concerned that the union members are being exposed to unnecessary health risks. EPA data show that up to 4662 garment workers will get cancer if all present garment workers are exposed for 40 years to the maximum amount of formaldehyde permitted by the Occupational Safety and Health Administration (OSHA). OSHA sets safety standards for the workplace.

4. The president of a large garment manufacturing firm, who is concerned that replacing formaldehyde with another chemical in garment manufacturing will increase costs. The business is already suffering from cheaper imported garments. The president contends that the level of formaldehyde in the air in his or her factory is only one-sixth the OSHA limit.

5. A member of Congress whose district contains a large formaldehyde manufacturing plant. Closing the plant will mean the loss of many jobs in the community in which it is located.

6. A spokesperson for the Natural Resources Defense Council, which has previously sued the EPA over inaction on formaldehyde. The study showing the incidence of nasal cancer in rats exposed to formaldehyde was released in 1979. Only after "limited evidence" that humans could be affected was gathered did the EPA act.

Developing a Viewpoint

Members of your class are to conduct a simulated hearing to gather the testimony of the people in the case studies. Class members who are playing the people listed should study the articles in the suggested reading list that pertain to their part of the testimony. In addition to the witnesses and the EPA director and panel, class members are needed to represent the moderator of the hearing, reporters, and interested citizens. The main purpose of the hearing is to gather information from all sides of the issue and make recommendations to the EPA's office of toxic substances. The panel should give reasons for the recommendations they make and note the consequences of these recommendations.

Suggested Readings

Ashford, Nicholas A., William Ryan, and Charles C. Caldart. "Law and Science Policy in Federal Regulation of Formaldehyde." *Science*. November 25, 1983, pp. 894–900.

Marshall, Elliott. "EPA Indicts Formaldehyde, 7 Years Later." *Science*. April 24, 1987, p. 381.

"Beware, 'Sick Building Syndrome.'" *Newsweek*. January 7, 1985, pp. 58–60.

UNIT 5

We constantly experience chemical reactions. From the split-second explosions of spectacular fireworks to the slow corrosion of metals and marble statues, our world is filled with change. Thousands of chemical reactions occurring every second inside our bodies keep us alive. All of these reactions change matter from one form to another.

1859
Charles Darwin publishes theory of natural selection.

1865
Lewis Carroll writes *Alice in Wonderland*.

1869
Dimitri Mendeleev publishes his first periodic table.

INTERACTIONS OF MATTER

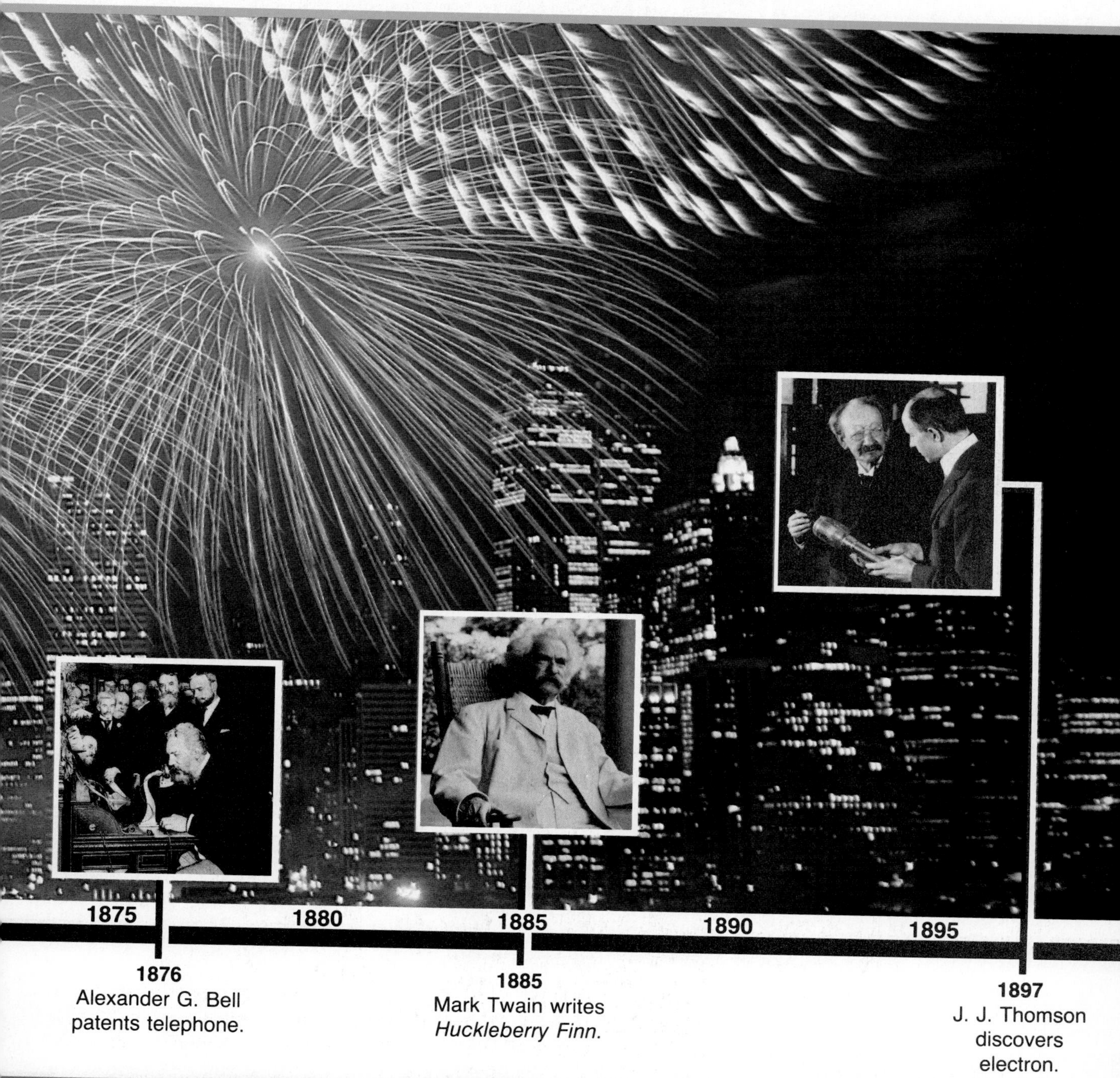

1876
Alexander G. Bell patents telephone.

1885
Mark Twain writes *Huckleberry Finn.*

1897
J. J. Thomson discovers electron.

SOLUTION THEORY
PARTICLES IN SOLUTION
SOLUBILITY AND CONCENTRATION

Solutions

Most of the materials you encounter everyday are mixtures. Many of them are solutions. The air you breathe and the water you drink are solutions. The oceans are solutions of many substances in water. The fluids that flow through your body are solutions, as are the coins you put into a vending machine. Stainless steel tableware is a solid solution of iron and other elements. How solutions form, why water dissolves some substances and not others, why seawater conducts electric current and distilled water does not are some of the topics discussed in this chapter.

SOLUTION THEORY

Recall that solutions are homogeneous mixtures. To mix evenly, the particles in a solution must be the size of atoms, ions, or molecules. When solid air fresheners sublime, their particles form a solution with air. Dust particles thrown into the air, however, form a suspension. The dust particles are too large to mix evenly. Fog is produced by water droplets in the air. The droplets are large enough to scatter light. The fog is a colloid, not a solution. However, when water evaporates into air, it forms a solution. In these sections, you will study types of solutions and the process of making a solution.

GOALS

1. You will learn the different types of solutions.
2. You will learn how substances dissolve.
3. You will learn how to speed the rate of solution.

15:1 Types of Solutions

Recall from Chapter 9 that a **solution** is a homogeneous mixture in which one substance is dissolved in another substance. In a solution, two or more substances are uniformly mixed. The solution formed is the same in all parts. In a sugar-water solution, molecules of sugar are spread evenly throughout the molecules of water. In a gold-silver solution, atoms of gold and silver are uniformly distributed.

What is a solution?

Define solute and solvent.

The **solute** (SAHL yewt) is the substance being dissolved. The **solvent** is the substance in which a solute is dissolved. In the sugar-water solution, sugar is the solute and water is the solvent. In the gold-silver solution, either substance could be considered the solute and the other the solvent. The substance present in the largest amount is usually called the solvent.

The most common solutions are those in which the solvent is a liquid. The solute can be a solid, liquid, or gas. Water is the most common solvent. A solution with water as the solvent is called an **aqueous solution.** Unless some other solvent is named, assume a solution is aqueous. A salt solution is salt dissolved in water.

What is an aqueous solution?

Gaseous solutions are formed by dissolving solids, liquids, or gases in gases. Air is a gaseous solution. All mixtures of gases are solutions. Solid solutions are formed by dissolving solids, liquids, or gases in solids. Sterling silver is a solution of copper in silver. A solid solution like sterling silver is an alloy. Most of the alloys studied in Chapter 12 are solid solutions.

15:2 Solution Process

When sugar is added to water, a solution forms. The dissolving action takes place on the surface of the crystal, Figure 15–1. Water molecules surround the surface molecules of sugar. The sugar molecules are held together only by weak bonding forces. The sugar molecules are attracted more to the water molecules than to

Table 15–1

Types of Solutions		
Solvent	**Solute**	**Example**
liquid	liquid	antifreeze (ethylene glycol in water)
	solid	sugar-water
	gas	carbonated soft drink
gas	liquid	humidity (water in air)
	solid	mothballs (naphthalene in air)
	gas	air (oxygen in nitrogen)
solid	liquid	dental amalgam (mercury in silver)
	solid	steel (carbon in iron)
	gas	gas stove lighter (palladium-hydrogen electrode)

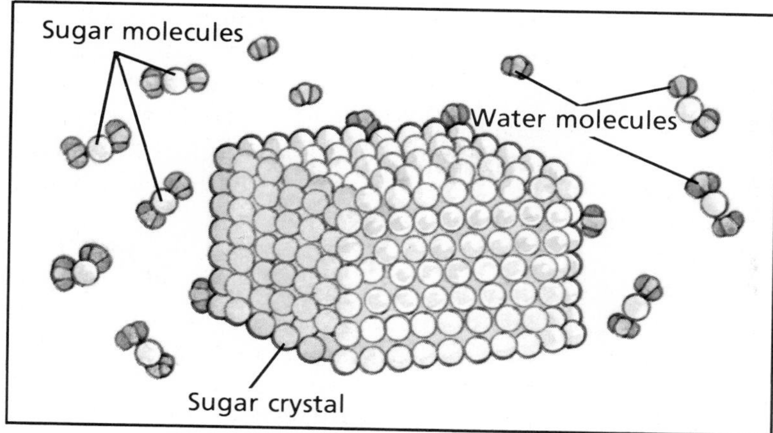

FIGURE 15–1. As sugar dissolves, sugar molecules are pulled away from the crystal by the water molecules.

How does a crystal of sugar dissolve in water?

each other. Surrounded by water molecules, surface sugar molecules are carried away from the crystal surface by molecular motion. As the outer layer of molecules is dissolved, the next layer is exposed to water. This process continues until all the sugar molecules are separated from each other and mixed evenly throughout the solution.

15:3 Rate of Solution

Suppose you stir some lemonade after adding sugar to it. Does the stirring help the sugar dissolve? Will granulated sugar dissolve faster than a sugar cube? Learning the answers to these questions tells you something about what affects the rate at which a solute dissolves.

TECHNOLOGY: APPLICATIONS

The Bends

A deep sea diver faces dangers other than people-eating sharks. One condition that threatens a diver is the bends, or decompression sickness. When a diver breathes compressed air from a tank, a greater amount of nitrogen dissolves in the blood than would dissolve at the surface. If the diver ascends too fast, the nitrogen will form bubbles in the blood vessels as the pressure decreases. Gas bubbles may block the flow of blood. This results in the bends. The bends may cause paralysis, unconsciousness, or even death. To avoid the bends, many divers use a helium-oxygen mixture instead of nitrogen and oxygen, because helium is less soluble in the blood than nitrogen. Divers also learn to ascend more slowly.

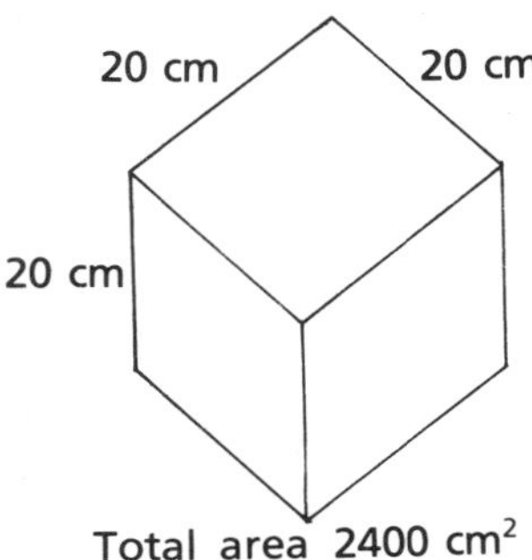

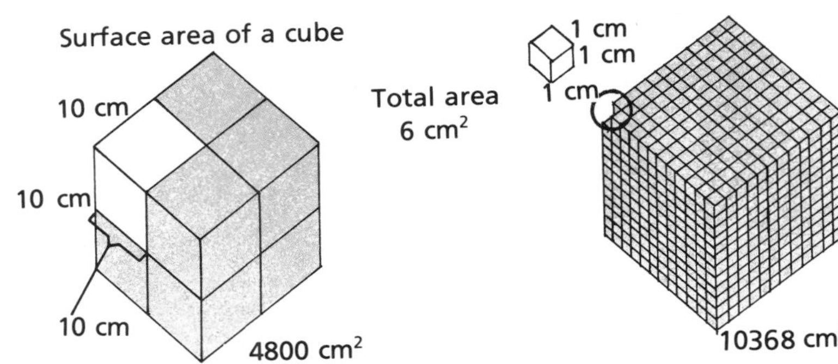

FIGURE 15–2. As a crystal is cut into smaller pieces, the total surface area of the crystal increases. Smaller crystals dissolve faster because a greater surface area is exposed.

When a solution is stirred, particles of the solute move away from the crystal surface at a faster rate. This exposes more particles to the solvent sooner. Thus, the solute dissolves at a faster rate.

What factor causes granulated sugar to dissolve faster than a cube of sugar?

If a large crystal is crushed, the small pieces have more total surface area exposed to the solvent than the single, large crystal. Surface area is the total outside surface of an object. Granulated sugar will dissolve faster than a sugar cube. The increased surface area brings more of the sugar particles into contact with the water. Thus, more particles can move away from the surface in a shorter period of time than with a single cube.

Energy is also a factor in the solution process. Many substances absorb energy as they dissolve. Energy is needed to break the bonds holding the particles of a solid together. Adding energy increases the particle motion and causes the particles to separate faster. Particle motion in the solvent also increases, moving solute par-

FIGURE 15–3. Instant ice packs, used by athletes, work by absorbing thermal energy.

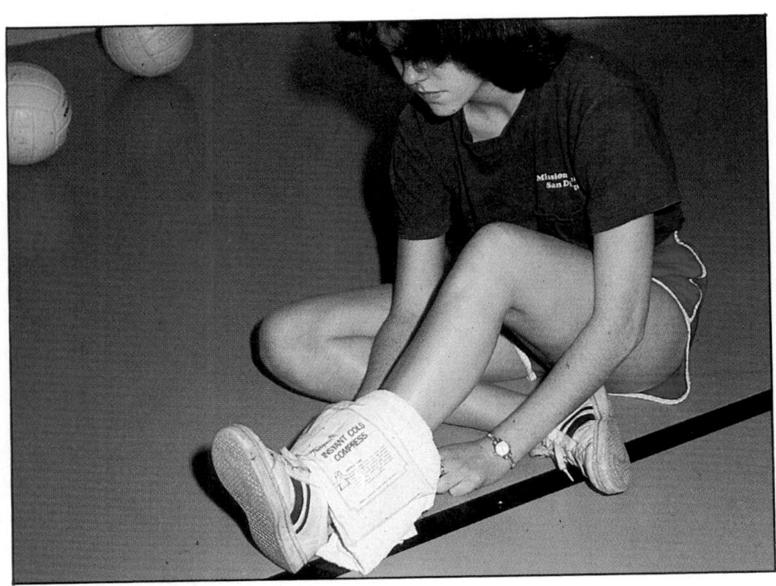

ticles away from the solid surface faster. Therefore, solids often dissolve faster in hot solvents. For example, sugar dissolves faster in hot tea than in iced tea. Hot water, not cold, is used to dissolve gelatin.

To summarize, three ways to increase the rate at which a solute dissolves in a liquid are (1) stir or shake the solution, (2) expose more surface by crushing a solid solute, and (3) warm the solution.

Adding energy usually increases the amount of solid that can dissolve in a liquid. However, the opposite is true for solutions of gases in liquids. When tap water is heated, bubbles of air rise to the surface and escape from the water. More gas can be dissolved in a cold liquid than in a hot one. The amount of dissolved gas can also be increased by raising the pressure on the solution. Cooling a gas or increasing the pressure on it will move the gas particles closer together. If more particles are in a smaller space, more can form bonds with the solvent. Before a bottle of soda pop is open, the gas inside is under pressure. What happens when the cap is removed from a warm bottle of soda pop that has been shaken? Gas that has been in solution rushes out of the bottle and usually takes some of the liquid along with it.

Does stirring speed or slow the rate at which a gas dissolves in a liquid? Carbon dioxide gas is dissolved in many kinds of beverages. If you stir a carbonated beverage, gas molecules come out of solution and rise to the surface of the liquid. Thus they can escape. When you stir or shake soda pop, does the gas stay in solution?

FIGURE 15–4. As a bottle of soda is warmed or the pressure is reduced, the gas comes out of solution.

F.Y.I. When sulfuric acid is dissolved in water, a large amount of energy is released as heat. Because this acid is more dense than water, the heat effect is diluted if the acid is added slowly to water with stirring. If water is added to the acid, the water may remain on top of the acid, the temperature will rise, the water will vaporize, and an explosion may result. Thus, always add acid to water.

Review

1. You are given a 5-gram sample of rock salt and a 5-gram sample of table salt. Which will dissolve faster in 100 mL of water? Why?
2. What causes an open can of soda to get "flat" after standing at room temperature?
3. Why is hot water used to wash most dirty clothes?
4. Which dissolves faster, one kilogram of rock salt in a pond or one kilogram in a moving stream? Why?
5. ★ Power plants may dump their cooling water into surrounding lakes or rivers. The water in the lakes and rivers becomes warmer. In the past, before the dumping was regulated, some types of fish died as a result. Explain.

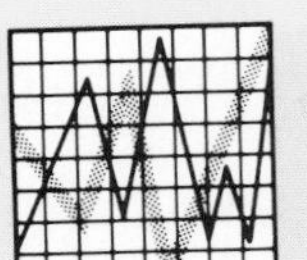

SKILL

Designing an Experiment

Problem: How do you design an experiment to test a hypothesis?

Materials

paper and pencil

Background

One of the most difficult tasks in science is designing an experiment that can test a hypothesis. While developing a hypothesis, you should organize your ideas on how to conduct an experiment that will test the hypothesis. The guidelines that follow describe how to design an experiment. The experiment described is based on one designed by two scientists at the University of Tennessee at Chattanooga.

Procedure

1. Describe the problem. These scientists wanted to find out what factors influenced the amount of dye that clings to an eggshell. It is important that you describe the problem clearly so you can focus your efforts.
2. Identify the variables in the situation to be studied. In this case, some of the variables studied included the concentrations of dye and vinegar, the presence of salt in the dye solution, and the eggshell condition.
3. Select a variable to test. Think about what will happen if you change a factor. Consider what experimental conditions will be required to test the variable selected. Choose a variable that can be tested using the equipment available to you.
4. Propose a hypothesis. Do not make your hypothesis so broad that you cannot test it. A possible hypothesis for this research is "the greater the concentration of vinegar in the dye solution, the greater the amount of dye that clings to the eggshell."
5. Outline the experimental procedure. From your hypothesis, you should be able to determine the dependent and independent variables. In the hypothesis stated in Step 4, the dependent variable is the amount of dye that clings to eggshell. The independent variable is the concentration of vinegar in the dye solution. Plan how you will change the independent variable. You could vary the concentration of vinegar by a set amount. Decide how many different tests are needed. For example, will two different vinegar concentrations give enough data? Will twelve different concentrations give you more data than you need?
6. Identify the constants. In this case, the dye concentration, the amount of salt in the dye solution, and eggshell condition are constants. Plan a way to control these variables. For example, boil all the eggs at the same time in distilled water.
7. Plan how to analyze your data. Design your experiment so that the data obtained is in a form that can be used to determine whether the hypothesis is correct. Think about what you want to measure, how you will make the measurements, and how you will use these measurements. The data obtained from this experiment will be from observations of colored eggs. The eggs could be ranked in order of least intense color to most intense color.

Questions

1. Suggest another hypothesis for the egg dyeing problem.
2. List three other variables that should be constants in this experiment.
3. Why should you begin planning your experiment as you develop your hypothesis?
4. How do you design an experiment to test a hypothesis?

PARTICLES IN SOLUTION

Some stains can be removed by water. Other stains can only be removed by mineral oil or a similar organic liquid. These organic liquids do not usually conduct electricity. Other liquids do. These sections discuss the properties of the liquids that cause these events to happen.

GOALS

1. You will learn how "like dissolves like."
2. You will learn the difference between polar and nonpolar molecules.
3. You will learn the characteristics of solutions that conduct electricity.

15:4 Solvents

No known solvent will dissolve everything. Water is probably closest to being a universal solvent. It can dissolve many gases, liquids, and solids. However, even water will not dissolve all substances. Grease and carbon tetrachloride, CCl_4, are two materials that do not dissolve in water.

F.Y.I. Liquids that dissolve in each other are miscible. Oil and gasoline are miscible. Oil and water are immiscible.

Generally, a solvent will dissolve a solute that is chemically like the solvent. Usually, organic solvents will dissolve organic solutes. Inorganic solvents will dissolve inorganic solutes. Remember, organic compounds contain carbon. Both grease and carbon tetrachloride are organic materials. Carbon tetrachloride, a liquid organic solvent, readily dissolves grease. Benzene, another liquid organic solvent, dissolves grease and CCl_4. Water, however, is inorganic. Water dissolves many inorganic substances, such as table salt, but will not dissolve grease, salad oil, or CCl_4.

What kinds of solutes will a solvent dissolve?

General rules for solution are not always followed. For example, ethanol is an organic compound. However, water and ethanol can mix. Water also dissolves sugar, another organic substance.

FIGURE 15–5. Vinegar, in salad dressing, does not dissolve in oil. This dressing must be shaken to blend the vinegar with the oil.

Organic solvents are used for dry cleaning because most soil on clothing is organic. Be careful when you choose a solvent to remove some foreign matter from your clothes. A solvent that will remove chewing gum may also dissolve nylon. In addition, many organic solvents are flammable and have toxic vapors. Care should be exercised in using any solvent.

15:5 Polar Molecules

Water dissolves many substances because water molecules are polar. A **polar molecule** is positively charged at one end and negatively charged at the other end.

CAREER

Dry Cleaning Operator

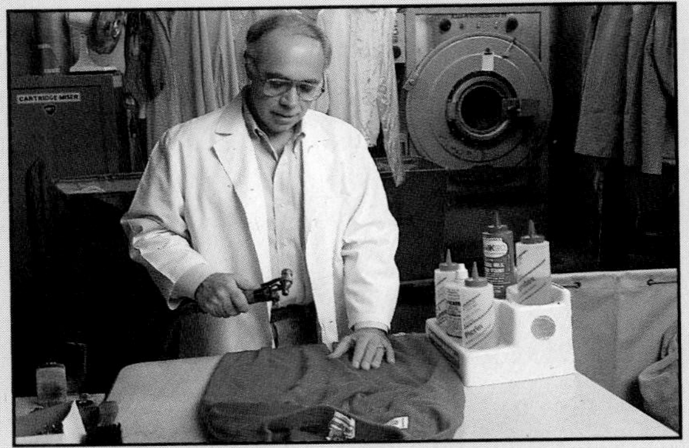

Josh Stein's job as a dry cleaning operator came about gradually. After working at a fast food restaurant in high school, Josh began working for a hospital as a driver, delivering linens and equipment throughout the city.

Josh became good friends with some of the people on his route, especially the owner of Lee's Dry Cleaning. Josh had a knack for fixing equipment and helped Mr. Lee whenever his dry cleaning machines broke down. Thus, Josh learned how the business operated. When Mr. Lee decided to retire, he asked Josh if he was interested in buying the dry cleaning operation.

Over a six month period, Mr. Lee taught Josh the dry cleaning business: what chemical solvents were used and how, what safety precautions and equipment were necessary, and how to deal with his customers and employees. Mr. Lee told Josh that, above all, he should be neat and courteous at all times. Josh's Dry Cleaning is now a booming success.

For career information, write
Service Employees International Union
2020 K Street NW
Washington, DC 20006

Hydrogen and oxygen are covalently bonded by pairs of shared electrons. Oxygen atoms have a greater attraction for electrons than do hydrogen atoms. The oxygen end of the molecule attracts the shared pair more than the hydrogen end. The oxygen end of the molecule becomes negatively charged, and the hydrogen end becomes positively charged.

What is dissociation?

Most inorganic substances are composed of polar molecules or ions. Sodium chloride, NaCl, an inorganic substance, is an ionic compound. When sodium chloride is placed in water, the positive ends of the water molecules cluster around a negative chloride ion. This chloride ion is then carried away by the water molecules through particle motion in the solution, Figure 15–6. In a similar way, the negative ends of other water molecules pull the positive sodium ions into solution. In this way, the ions in salt quickly spread throughout the solution. When an ionic compound dissolves in water and comes apart to form ions, the process is called **dissociation** (dis oh see AY shuhn).

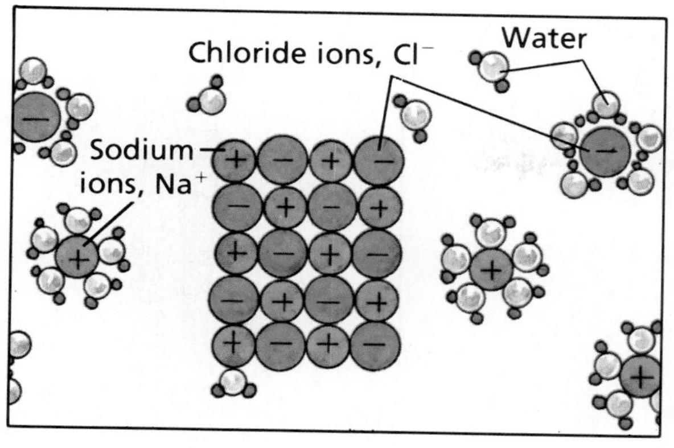

a

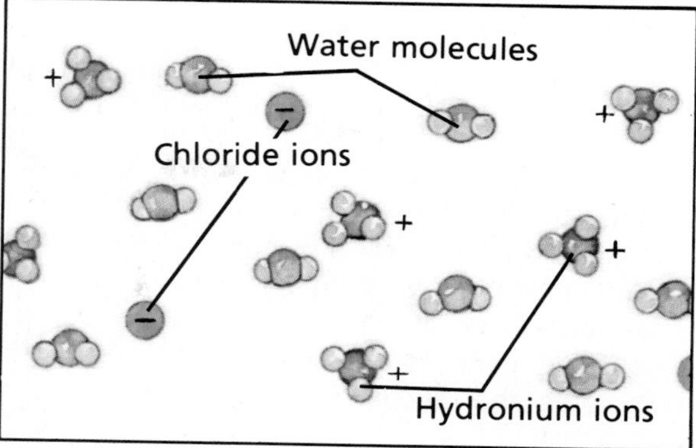

b

FIGURE 15–6. As sodium chloride dissolves (a), the positive ends of water molecules attach to the negative chloride ions. The negative ends of water molecules pull the positive sodium ions from the crystal. When an acid solution forms (b), the positive hydrogen ion from the acid attaches to a water molecule.

Some inorganic polar molecular compounds such as hydrogen chloride dissolve in water and form ions. Certain polar organic compounds, such as sugar and ethanol will also dissolve in water. However, these molecules do not break up into ions. The solution of sugar is described in Section 15:2.

Most organic compounds do not dissolve in water. Organic molecules usually do not form ions and most are not polar enough to be affected by the polar water molecules.

Why do most organic compounds not dissolve in water?

15:6 Solutions as Conductors

Electric current in a wire is a flow of electrons. An electric current can be passed through a solution containing ions. In a solution, the electric current is a movement of ions. A conductor allows electricity to flow readily. Ions in solution, like the electrons in copper wire, are conductors of electricity.

How is electric current passed through a solution?

Pure water is not a good conductor of electricity. However, tap water can be because it contains many ions from the minerals and salts that are dissolved in it.

Water conducts an electric current when it contains ions. In general, inorganic compounds that dissolve in water dissociate or ionize and release ions. The apparatus in Figure 15–8 is used to determine whether a substance forms ions when it dissolves in water. Organic compounds, with some exceptions, do not produce ions and do not conduct electricity.

Potassium bromide, KBr, is an inorganic ionic compound that dissociates in water. The ions present, K^+ and Br^-, make the solution a conductor. A substance that conducts electric current when in a water solution is called an **electrolyte** (ih LEK troh lyt). Potassium bromide is one example.

FIGURE 15–7. Oil and other petroleum products are organic. They rise to the surface and do not mix with the water that they pollute.

a

b

FIGURE 15–8. A molecular substance like sugar (a) does not contain ions. Thus the bulb does not light. A sodium chloride solution (b) contains ions. The movement of these ions completes the circuit and the bulb lights.

What is a nonelectrolyte?

Sugar in solution does not form ions. Therefore, the solution does not conduct electricity. Because the sugar solution does not conduct electricity, sugar is called a nonelectrolyte. A **nonelectrolyte** is a substance that does not conduct an electric current when dissolved in water. An alcohol-water solution does not conduct a current because alcohol is an organic compound that does not ionize. Alcohol is a nonelectrolyte.

Review

6. Explain briefly what is meant by "like dissolves like."
7. You can clean up spilled honey with water. Why?
8. What is a polar molecule? Give an example.
9. What is dissociation?
10. ★ Would a solution of iodine (I_2) in ethanol conduct electricity? Explain your answer.

SOLUBILITY AND CONCENTRATION

GOALS

1. You will learn about solubility and concentration.
2. You will learn the differences among saturated, unsaturated, and supersaturated solutions.
3. You will learn what happens to the boiling and freezing points of solutions as the solute concentration increases.

One teaspoon of sugar in a glass of lemonade might be too sweet for some but not sweet enough for others. More and more sugar could be placed in the glass. The lemonade will become sweeter and sweeter, and eventually no more sugar will dissolve. This section will deal with what substances dissolve, in what proportions they dissolve, and what happens to the solution when they dissolve.

15:7 Solubility Rules

Solubility is a measure of the amount of solute that can be dissolved in a specific amount of solvent at a given temperature. Table salt is soluble in water, and iodine is soluble in ethanol. When table salt is added to water, the salt dissolves readily to form a saltwater solution. However, only a very tiny amount of table salt dissolves in ethanol. In contrast, iodine crystals do not dissolve in water. When iodine crystals are added to ethanol, however, the iodine dissolves readily, coloring the liquid brown. The solution of iodine in ethanol is known as tincture of iodine.

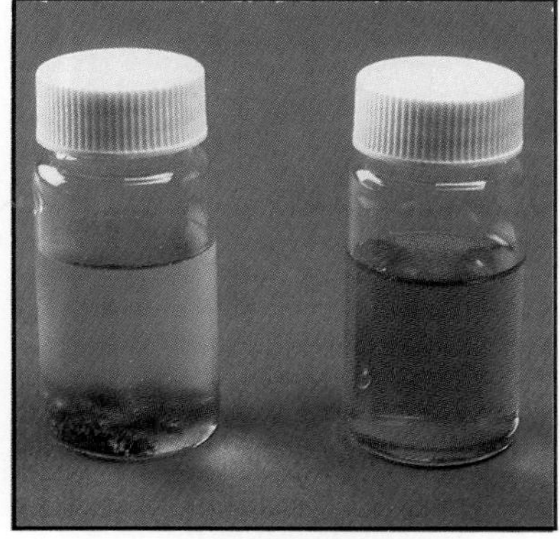

FIGURE 15–9. Iodine is insoluble in water but it dissolves in alcohol.

It is often difficult to determine whether a compound will dissolve. It may not be practical to try to find out. Chemists have determined some solubility rules that can be used to predict whether an inorganic compound will dissolve in water, Table 15–2. These rules are based upon observations that have been made during laboratory experiments.

How are solubility rules used?

For example, is sodium carbonate soluble in water? Using the table, we can see that all compounds of sodium are soluble. Therefore, sodium carbonate is soluble in water. Is calcium carbonate soluble in water? Ca^{2+} does not appear in the list of ions that are soluble. However, carbonate, CO_3^{2-}, does appear in the list of insoluble ions. Except for Na_2CO_3, K_2CO_3, and $(NH_4)_2CO_3$, all carbonates are insoluble. Therefore, calcium carbonate is insoluble.

Table 15–2

Solubility of Common Compounds in Water
Common compounds that contain the following ions are soluble. (a) sodium (Na^+), potassium (K^+), ammonium (NH_4^+) (b) nitrates (NO_3^-) (c) acetates ($C_2H_3O_2^-$), except silver acetate, which is only moderately soluble (d) chlorides (Cl^-), except silver, mercury(I), and lead chlorides; $PbCl_2$ is soluble in hot water (e) sulfates (SO_4^{2-}), except barium and lead sulfates; calcium, mercury(I), and silver sulfates are slightly soluble
Common compounds that contain the following ions are insoluble. (a) silver, (Ag^+), except silver nitrate and silver perchlorate (b) sulfides (S^{2-}), except those of sodium, potassium, ammonium, magnesium, barium, and calcium (c) carbonates (CO_3^{2-}), except those of sodium, potassium, and ammonium (d) phosphates (PO_4^{3-}), except those of sodium, potassium, and ammonium (e) hydroxides (OH^-), except those of sodium, potassium, ammonium, and barium

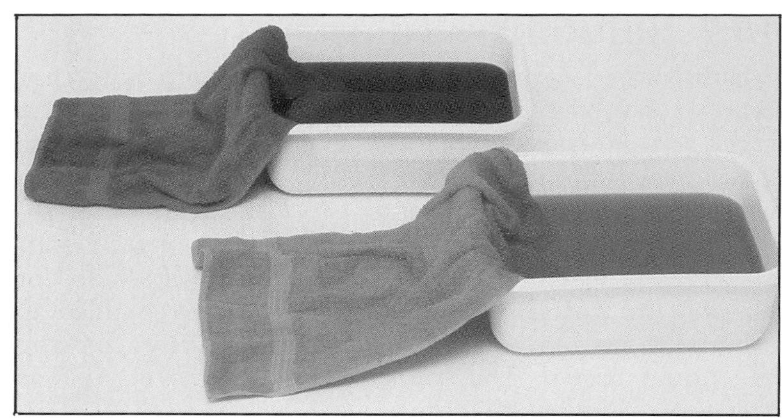

FIGURE 15–10. A concentrated dye solution contains more solute (dye) per volume of solution than a dilute solution. Thus, it produces a more intense color than the dilute solution.

You should notice from the table that most of the common inorganic compounds are soluble in water. Is barium carbonate soluble? How about iron(II) sulfate?

15:8 Determining Concentration

As with the lemonade, to some people a cup of tea may be "strong." To others the same cup of tea may be "weak." These terms are not precise. Other terms that might be used for "strong" and "weak" are concentrated and dilute. Concentrated means there is a large amount of solute dissolved compared to the amount of solvent. Dilute means there is little solute dissolved in a solution compared to the amount of solvent. "Dilute" and "concentrated" are not precise statements of concentration either. It is difficult to determine what is concentrated and what is dilute unless measurements are made.

What is solution concentration?

Concentration is the amount of solute in a unit volume of solvent. A solution may be described by giving its concentration as a ratio of so many grams of solute in each liter of solution (g/L).

$$\textit{concentration}\ (\text{g/L}) = \frac{\textit{mass of solute}\ (\text{g})}{\textit{volume of solution}\ (\text{L})}$$

For example, a solution may contain 50 grams of KBr in one liter of water. Its concentration could be expressed as 50 g/L. The K^+ and Br^- ions are spread evenly throughout the solution. In 100 mL of solution, there would be 5 grams of KBr. If you evaporated the water from 100 mL of the KBr solution, five grams of KBr would remain in the evaporating dish.

FIGURE 15–11. Many canned fruit drinks are solutions of fruit juice and water. The law requires that the label clearly state the percent by volume of fruit juice each contains.

Concentration can also be expressed as a percent of solute in the solution. If the solute is a liquid, the concentration is often expressed as a volume percent. A glass of orange drink, which is ten percent fruit juice by volume, contains 10 milliliters of fruit juice for every 100 milliliters of orange drink. What percent of the drink is added water?

When the solute is a solid, it may be more convenient to express the concentration in terms of percent by mass. A 15 percent solution by mass of sugar in water means that there are 15 grams of sugar in 100 grams of solution. To make a 15 percent sugar solution, 15 grams of sugar would be dissolved in 85 grams of water. Remember, the density of water is 1.0 g/mL. Therefore, 15 grams of sugar are dissolved in 85 milliliters of water to form the 15 percent solution by mass.

BIOGRAPHY

Ellen Swallow Richards
1842–1911

The first woman to receive a degree from the Massachusetts Institute of Technology, Ellen Richards plotted the amount of dissolved chlorine in that state's water supplies. This analysis, which involved 100 000 samples, was a model for other states. Her data was used to find causes of pollution and improper sewage disposal.

EXAMPLE Concentration

A sugar solution contains 76 g of sucrose in 1.0 L of solution. How many grams of sucrose are in 25 mL of solution?

Given: $\textit{concentration} = 76 \text{ g/1.0 L}$
$\textit{volume of solution} = 25 \text{ mL} = 0.025 \text{ L}$

Unknown: *mass of solute*

Basic Equation: $\textit{concentration} = \dfrac{\textit{mass of solute}}{\textit{volume of solution}}$

Solution: $\textit{mass of solute} = \textit{concentration} \times \textit{volume of solution}$
$= 76 \text{ g/L} \times 0.025 \text{ L} = 1.9 \text{ g}$

EXAMPLE Percent by Volume

A fruit drink contains 44 mL of fruit juices and 156 mL of water. What is the percent by volume of fruit juice in the drink?

Given: $V_{fruit\ juice} = 44 \text{ mL}$
$V_{water} = 156 \text{ mL}$

Unknown: *percent by volume*

Basic Equation: $\%_{volume} = \dfrac{V_{solute}}{V_{total}} \times 100\%$

Solution: $V_{total} = V_{fruit\ juice} + V_{water}$
$= 44 \text{ mL} + 156 \text{ mL} = 200 \text{ mL}$

$$\%_{volume} = \frac{V_{fruit\ juice}}{V_{total}} \times 100\%$$

$$= \frac{44 \text{ mL}}{200 \text{ mL}} \times 100\% = 22\%$$

PRACTICE PROBLEMS

1. A liter of vinegar contains 53 mL of acetic acid. What is the percent by volume of acetic acid in the vinegar?
2. Directions in a laboratory investigation ask for 500 g of a 12% by mass aqueous NaOH solution. How many grams of NaOH and how many milliliters of water are needed to make this solution?

15:9 Saturated Solutions

What is one way of stating the solubility of a substance?

The solubility of a substance is often reported as the greatest amount of that substance that will dissolve in 100 grams of water at a certain temperature. The graph in Figure 15–12 shows the solubilities of four salts at various temperatures. What is the solubility of KBr at 10°C and at 50°C? Be sure to include the units in your answer.

You have learned that the solubility of most solids is increased by raising the temperature of the solution. Look at Figure 15–12 again. Temperature does not affect the solubility of all compounds by the same amount. At 20°C, about 38 grams of both potassium nitrate, KNO_3, and sodium chloride, NaCl, will dissolve in 100 grams of water. However, if the temperature is raised to 80°C, more than 150 grams of KNO_3 will go into solution, while only about 40 grams of NaCl will dissolve.

At room temperature, 25°C, 100 milliliters of water will hold about 102 grams of sodium chlorate, $NaClO_3$.

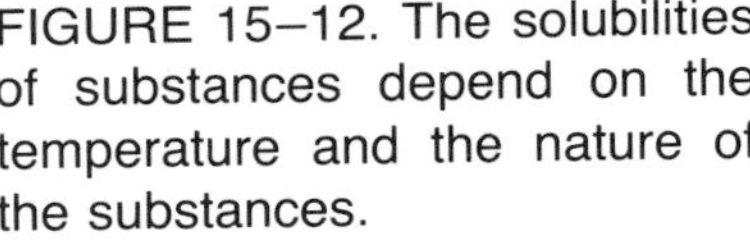

FIGURE 15–12. The solubilities of substances depend on the temperature and the nature of the substances.

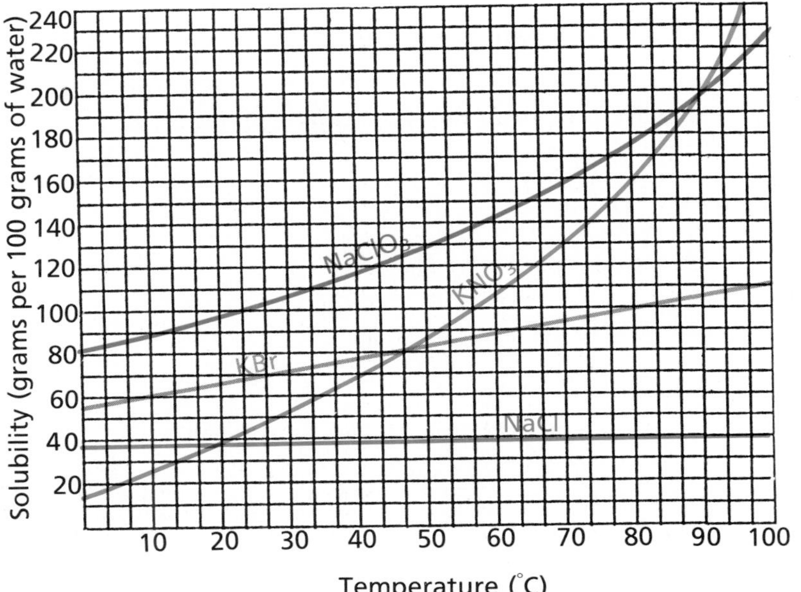

If any more $NaClO_3$ is added to the solution, it falls to the bottom of the container undissolved. The solution is said to be saturated. **Saturated** means that all the solute the solution can hold at a certain temperature is dissolved. However, if the same solution is warmed to 100°C, the same amount of water can hold about twice as much $NaClO_3$. According to Figure 15–12, at 100°C a solution containing 102 g $NaClO_3$ is unsaturated. **Unsaturated** means that more solute can be dissolved in the solution at that temperature.

Suppose the solution containing 102 g $NaClO_3$ is cooled slowly to 10°C so that no crystals form. This solution is now supersaturated. **Supersaturated** means that the solution contains more solute than is normal for that temperature. According to Figure 15–12, at 10°C only 88 grams of $NaClO_3$ will dissolve in 100 milliliters of water. The supersaturated solution contains 102 grams of $NaClO_3$. A supersaturated solution is unstable. If a $NaClO_3$ crystal were dropped into the solution, the excess solid would crystallize.

One way to determine whether a solution is saturated is to add more solute to it. A saturated solution contains all the solute it is predicted to contain at that temperature. Even if you add additional solute, no more will go into solution. The amount of dissolved solute in a saturated solution does not increase.

If a solution is unsaturated, additional solute will dissolve. However, if the solution is supersaturated, the excess solute in solution will crystallize immediately.

FIGURE 15–13. A solute crystal placed in this supersaturated solution of sodium acetate causes the excess solute to crystallize out immediately.

What is meant by a supersaturated solution?

What happens when additional solute is added to an unsaturated solution?

PROBLEM SOLVING

Solution Viscosity

Assume you have several solutions of different viscosities, such as sugar water, molasses, and motor oil. You also have a 250-mL graduated cylinder, a stopwatch, and a marble. Devise a method for comparing the viscosities of these solutions. How could you use one solvent and solute to prepare a set of standards for measuring the viscosity of an unknown solution?

INVESTIGATION 15–1

Solubility of a Salt

Problem: What is the solubility of sodium chloride in water?

Materials 

2 250-mL beakers
thermometer
iron ring
ring stand
balance
hot plate
goggles
stirring rods
filter paper
funnel
evaporating dish
water
table salt, $NaCl$
apron

Procedure

1. Place 20 mL of water in a beaker.
2. Add salt to the water slowly with constant stirring. Keep adding salt until a small amount of salt lies on the bottom of the beaker. The solution is now saturated with salt. Check and record the temperature of the solution.
3. Set up a filtration system, as shown in Appendix B:4. Read the filtering instructions given there. Filter the salt solution. This separates the solution from the undissolved salt. Keep the filtrate, that is, the salt solution with no undissolved salt.
4. Using the balance, find the mass of a clean, dry evaporating dish. Record the mass in the data table.
5. Pour the filtrate (salt solution containing no undissolved salt) into the evaporating dish. Find the mass of the dish and solution. Record the mass.
6. Warm the dish and solution until all the liquid has evaporated. See Figure 15–14. **CAUTION:** *Be sure to wear goggles and an apron. Solution may spatter as it dries.*
7. Allow the dish and the residue it contains to cool. Find the mass of dish and dry residue. Record.

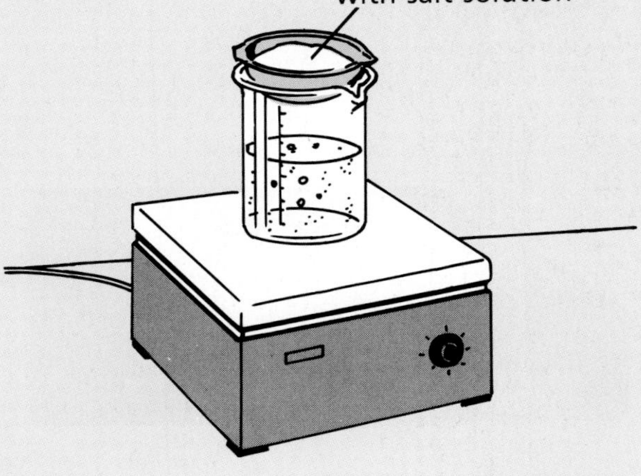

FIGURE 15–14.

Evaporating dish with salt solution

Data and Observations

temperature
mass of dish and solution
mass of dish
mass of solution
mass of dish and residue
mass of residue

Analysis and Conclusions

1. Calculate the mass of the salt solution that was in the evaporating dish.
2. Calculate the mass of the salt residue.
3. Calculate the difference between your answers to Questions 1 and 2.
4. Calculate the grams of salt that dissolved in one gram of water by dividing grams of salt by grams of water.
5. What is the solubility of $NaCl$ in water, based on 100 g of water?

15:10 Effects of Solute Particles

A radiator in a car usually contains antifreeze mixed with water. Antifreeze prevents water in the cooling system from freezing. Directions for making ice cream tell you to add salt to the ice around the ice cream container to lower the ice-water temperature.

When you dissolve a solid in a liquid, the liquid's boiling point is raised. The increase depends on the number of solute particles added. In general, the more particles added, the higher the boiling point. The solute particles interfere with the rapid evaporation of solvent particles at the boiling point. More energy is needed to cause the solvent to evaporate at the same rate. Thus, the boiling point is raised.

An increase in the number of particles in solution lowers the freezing point. The solute particles interfere with crystal formation of the solvent. The temperature must be lower to allow the solvent to crystallize. Thus, the freezing point of the solution is lowered. The addition of a solute to a pure liquid raises the boiling point of the liquid and lowers its freezing point.

F.Y.I. Salts are used to deice roads because they lower the freezing point of water. Some nine million tons of salt are used on American highways each year, at a cost of over $200 000 000.

What happens to the freezing point of a solution when more solute particles are added?

Review

11. Which of the following compounds are soluble in water?

a. sodium nitrate
b. silver phosphate
c. barium chloride
d. ammonium chloride
e. aluminum hydroxide
f. magnesium carbonate

12. If any of the compounds in Problem 11 are soluble in water, what ions, if any, will be present in the solution?

13. By using Figure 15–12, determine the solubility of each of the following compounds at the specified temperature.

a. KBr at 50°C
b. $NaClO_3$ at 70°C
c. KBr at 100°C
d. NaCl at 100°C

14. An aqueous solution of potassium nitrate contains 36 g in 1.0 L of solution. How many grams of potassium nitrate are in 75 mL of this solution?

★ **15.** A 15% solution by volume of grapefruit drink contains how many milliliters of water in 100 mL of grapefruit drink? How many milliliters of water and how many milliliters of grapefruit juice are in 500 mL of the drink?

INVESTIGATION 15–2

Distillation

Problem: How does a solution change when boiled?

Materials   

2 250-mL beakers
teaspoon
stirring rod
water
table salt, NaCl
ice
2 large test tubes
apron
1-hole rubber stopper
gas delivery tube
clamp
ring stand
laboratory burner
2 evaporating dishes
goggles

CAUTION: *Use care around an open flame.*

Procedure

1. Fill a beaker half full of water. Add a rounded teaspoon of salt. Stir until the salt dissolves.
2. Fill a large test tube about one-fourth full of the salt solution. Clamp the test tube to the ring stand. Insert the rubber stopper with delivery tube as in Figure 15–15. Place the test tube so you can heat the solution with a burner.
3. Place a clean, dry test tube in a beaker of ice. Arrange the equipment so that the free end of the delivery tube fits into this test tube. The end of the delivery tube should be below the level of ice in the beaker but not touching the bottom of the test tube.
4. Gently heat the solution in the test tube until it boils. Keep it boiling, but do not allow the water to enter the delivery tube. Record your observations of what is happening.
5. Continue the boiling until half of the original solution is gone. The liquid should boil off and then condense in the test tube in the ice. Allow the solution to cool.
6. Pour the liquids in the two test tubes into separating dishes. Carefully evaporate the liquids to dryness as shown in Figure 15–14, page 358. Record you observations.

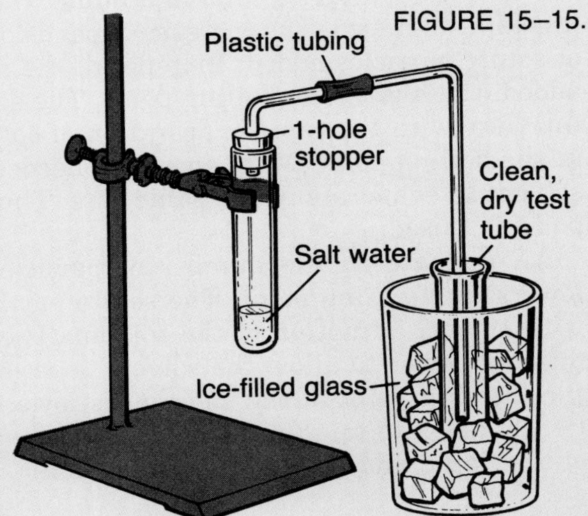

FIGURE 15–15.

Data and Observations

Steps 4 and 5
Step 6

Analysis and Conclusions

1. Suggest a hypothesis to explain how the liquid formed in the test tube in the ice.
2. Which liquid left a solid when it evaporated? Was it the original or the condensed liquid?
3. What do you think the solid is?
4. How does a solution change when it is boiled?

Applications

5. Describe one practical use for this type of separation.

Chapter 15 Review

SUMMARY

1. Solutions are homogeneous mixtures consisting of a solute dissolved in a solvent. 15:1
2. The dissolving of a crystal takes place on its surface. 15:2
3. Warming, crushing the solute, or stirring increases the rate of solution for a solid solute. 15:3
4. The solubility of a gas in a liquid can be increased by lowering the temperature or increasing the pressure. 15:3
5. Organic solvents usually dissolve organic solutes. Inorganic solvents usually will dissolve inorganic solutes. 15:4
6. Ionic compounds in aqueous solution dissociate into ions; some molecular compounds also form ions as they dissolve. 15:5
7. Substances that conduct electric current when dissolved in water are electrolytes. 15:6
8. Solubility is a measure of the amount of solute that can be dissolved in a specific amount of solvent at a given temperature. 15:7
9. The concentration of a solution may be expressed by volume or mass percent or grams of solute per volume of solution. 15:8
10. Solutions may be saturated, unsaturated, or supersaturated. 15:9
11. Dissolving a solid in a liquid raises the boiling point of the liquid and lowers its freezing point. 15:10

VOCABULARY

a. aqueous solution
b. concentration
c. dissociation
d. electrolyte
e. nonelectrolyte
f. polar molecule
g. saturated
h. solubility
i. solute
j. solution
k. solvent
l. supersaturated
m. unsaturated

Matching

Match each description with the correct vocabulary word from the list above. Not all words will be used.

1. contains more solute than predicted to dissolve
2. has positively and negatively charged areas
3. dissolved in water
4. the amount of solute in 1 L of solution
5. conducts electricity in aqueous solution
6. the substance dissolved
7. ionic compounds break apart in water
8. contains maximum amount of solute for a given temperature
9. can accept more solute
10. the substance in which another substance is dissolved

Chapter 15 Review

MAIN IDEAS

A. Reviewing Concepts

Complete each sentence with the correct word or phrase.

1. A gas will become more soluble in a liquid when the temperature is ________________ or when the pressure is ________________.
2. ____________ conduct electricity in a solution.
3. The addition of a solid solute raises the ________________ point of a liquid.
4. The most common solvent is ________________.
5. Dry cleaning solvents are usually ________________ compounds.
6. A solution that will accept more solute is ________________.
7. One hundred mL of a 10% by volume solution of orange juice contains ____________ mL of water.
8. Adding alcohol to water will ________________ the freezing point.
9. A solvent with ________________ bonds is needed to dissolve an ionic substance.
10. ________________ is the process in which ionic compounds form ions in solution.

Choose the word or phrase that correctly completes each of the following sentences.

11. *(Ethanol, Sugar, Oil)* will not dissolve in water.
12. If you could dissolve 5 kg of salt in a liter of water, the solution would probably be *(saturated, unsaturated, supersaturated)*.
13. Most *(nitrate, silver, sulfate)* compounds do not dissolve in water.
14. *(Alcohol, Sodium chloride, Sugar)* will produce ions when it dissolves in water.
15. In a solution of KBr in water, KBr is the *(solute, solvent, alloy)*.

B. Understanding Concepts

Answer the following questions using complete sentences when possible.

16. If a solution of NaCl contains 50.0 g in 1.00 L, how much salt would 50.0 mL of this solution contain?
17. From the graph in Figure 15–12, estimate how many grams of KNO_3 will dissolve in 100 mL of water at 30°C. How does this compare with the amount that will dissolve at 40°C?
18. A 100-mL solution contains 50 g of solute. How could you use this solution to make 100 mL of solution that contained only 30 g of the solute?
19. A solution contains 52 g of solute in 260 mL of solution. What is the concentration in grams per liter?
20. What is the major difference between saturated, unsaturated, and supersaturated solutions of the same solute?
21. A solution contains 15 g of $NaNO_3$ in 185 g of water. What is the mass percent of the $NaNO_3$ solution?
22. A solution contains 25 mL of ethanol in 125 mL of water. What is the volume percent of the solution?
23. Why is salt mixed with the ice in making homemade ice cream?
24. What is the general "rule of thumb" about what dissolves what?
25. Which of the following are soluble in water:
    a. $FeSO_4$
    b. $AgCl$
    c. $CaCO_3$
    d. $Na_2Cr_2O_7$

C. Applying Concepts

Answer the following questions using complete sentences when possible.

26. You need to dissolve a large crystal of $CuSO_4$ in water as quickly as possible. What could you do to speed the process?

27. A solution conducts electricity. What do you know about the solution?

28. Using diagrams, discuss how a crystal of KBr dissolves in water.

29. You have a test tube containing a solution of $NaClO_3$. You also have one crystal of $NaClO_3$. How can you tell whether the solution is saturated, unsaturated, or supersaturated?

30. A can of soda has been shaken up during a ride home from the market. How could you open the can without spraying everyone? Use what you know about the solubility of gases in liquids.

SKILL REVIEW

1. Why is it important to list all the variables in a problem before stating the hypothesis?
2. Tim wanted to find out if ice cubes freeze faster starting with hot tap water than when starting with cold tap water. Identify at least four variables that should be considered in designing an experiment to solve this problem.
3. Patty and Juanita were planning an experiment in which they would be comparing the average response time of boys and girls in their class. The test involved pushing a button after seeing a light flash. Twenty girls and twenty boys were to be tested on five trials each. Patty and Juanita hypothesized that there would be no difference in average response time between the two groups of students. Suggest a way they could analyze the data they obtain.
4. How is Figure 15–1 a model of the dissolving process?
5. How is it possible to separate the solute from the solvent in a saltwater solution?

PROJECTS

1. Find out how to make a "silica garden." Prepare one.
2. Grow a large crystal of alum from a saturated solution.

READINGS

1. Challand, Helen J. *Activities in the Physical Sciences.* Chicago: Childrens Press, 1984.
2. Fialkov, Yu. *Extraordinary Properties of Ordinary Solutions.* Chicago: Imported Pubns., 1985.
3. "Solvent." *Science and Technology Illustrated.* Chicago: Encyclopedia Britannica, 1984, pp. 2984–2985.

CHEMICAL EQUATIONS
KINDS OF CHEMICAL REACTIONS
MASS AND ENERGY IN CHEMICAL REACTIONS

Chemical Reactions

Chemical reactions occur all around us. Some of them take years and some take less than a second. The browning of fruits and vegetables is caused by a chemical reaction. Growth is a process that involves a wide variety of chemical reactions. When we think, chemical reactions take place in our brains. The different kinds of chemical reactions and how they are caused will be the major topics of this chapter.

CHEMICAL EQUATIONS

Just as secretaries use shorthand to take down dictation, chemists use a shorthand to show changes that take place during a chemical reaction. This shorthand makes use of symbols and formulas and is called a chemical equation. A chemical equation represents a chemical reaction.

GOALS

1. You will learn how to write a chemical equation.
2. You will learn how to balance a chemical equation.

16:1 Writing Equations for Reactions

A **chemical equation** shows changes that take place during a chemical reaction. Using word equations, you can describe the chemical reaction between silver nitrate and table salt. Silver nitrate plus sodium chloride produces silver chloride plus sodium nitrate. However, it is faster to write the shorthand form.

What is the importance of a chemical equation?

$$AgNO_3 + NaCl \rightarrow AgCl + NaNO_3$$

The chemical equation above is made of symbols and formulas. A symbol stands for an element. A formula shows the elements present in a compound and their ratio.

What is shown in a formula?

In the chemical equation above, the arrow means "yields" or "produces." Each of the substances to the left

CAREER

Water Treatment Technician

Have you ever dived into a pool and found you could not even open your eyes because the chlorine was so strong? Or have you traveled somewhere and found you could not drink the water because it tasted so odd? Water differs depending on its source and how it is treated.

Someone must control the water we use daily to make sure it is safe to use. This is the job of a water treatment technician like Angela Loloma. Angela must see that solid materials, organisms, and chemicals that may be harmful are removed. Technicians may add fluoride to drinking water to protect teeth. They may repair pumps, take samples of wastewater from industries, or run lab tests to determine if water is contaminated. At times, Angela tests the water leaving nuclear power plants to make sure it is not too warm for fish in the surrounding waters. Wherever there is the possibility for water contamination, there is a job for a water treatment technician.

For career information, write
The National Environmental
Training Association
148 S. Napoleon Street
P. O. Box 346
Valparaiso, IN 46383

of the arrow is called a **reactant.** Each substance to the right of the arrow is called a **product.**

$$\underset{\text{reactants}}{AgNO_3 + NaCl} \underset{\text{yield}}{\rightarrow} \underset{\text{products}}{AgCl + NaNO_3}$$

FIGURE 16–1. The physical states of substances in chemical reactions are indicated by specific symbols.

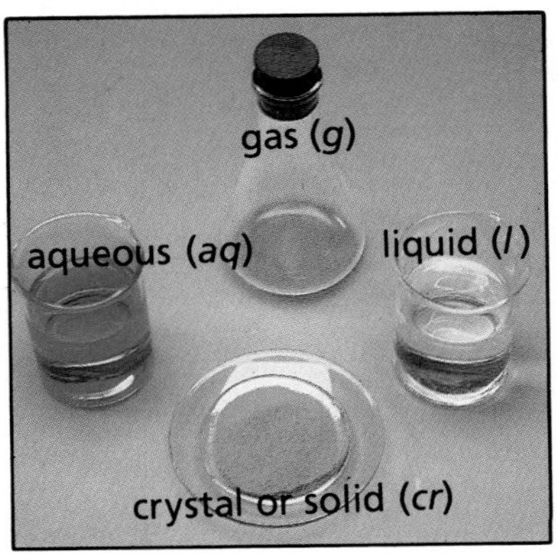

The states (solid, liquid, or gas) of the reactants may decide whether a reaction will take place. For example, when solid sodium chloride and silver nitrate are mixed, no reaction takes place. It is only when these substances are present in solution that they react to produce a white solid. To indicate the states of the reactants and products in an equation, state symbols are used. These state symbols are shown in Table 16–1.

Thus, the silver nitrate-sodium chloride reaction equation when written correctly, shows that $AgNO_3$ and NaCl will react in aqueous solution.

$$AgNO_3(aq) + NaCl(aq) \rightarrow AgCl(cr) + NaNO_3(aq)$$

AgCl is insoluble in water, Table 15–2, page 353, and crystallizes out of solution as a white solid. When an

Table 16–1

State Symbols	
(*cr*) crystal or solid	(*g*) gas
(*l*) liquid	(*aq*) aqueous (water) solution

insoluble substance crystallizes out of solution, it is called a **precipitate.** Rain and snow are precipitates because they fall out of solution in air.

Substances may also be released as gases during a chemical reaction. The following equation shows that hydrogen gas forms from a reaction between solid magnesium and hydrochloric acid solution.

$$Mg(cr) + 2HCl(aq) \rightarrow MgCl_2(aq) + H_2(g)$$

16:2 Balancing Equations

You may have noticed the 2 in front of HCl in the last equation of Section 16:1. That 2 was used to balance the equation. Equations are balanced to show that atoms are not lost or created during a reaction, just rearranged. A balanced chemical equation shows the same number of each kind of atom on both sides of the arrow (*yields* sign). Numbers, called **coefficients,** are used in front of the symbols and formulas, such as 2HCl. These numbers keep the numbers of atoms in balance. They show the relative amounts of each element or compound in the reaction. To balance a chemical equation, you first write the correct formula for each reactant and product. Then you use the coefficients to balance the number of atoms on each side of the equation. Do not change correctly written formulas. If you change a formula, you indicate a different substance. The equation for the reaction would no longer be correct.

Why must all equations be balanced?

How are coefficients used in chemical equations?

a

b

TRAITÉ
ÉLÉMENTAIRE
DE CHIMIE,
PRÉSENTÉ DANS UN ORDRE NOUVEAU
ET D'APRÈS LES DÉCOUVERTES MODERNES;
Avec Figures:
TOME PREMIER.
A PARIS,
Chez CUCHET, Libraire, rue & hôtel Serpente.
M. DCC. LXXXIX.

FIGURE 16–2. Antoine Lavoisier and his wife and colleague, Marie-Anne, were early French chemists (a). Their belief in careful measurement led to the law of conservation of mass in chemical reactions. The illustration on the right (b) is a photograph of the cover of Lavoisier's famous chemistry textbook in which he emphasized the importance of measurements.

F.Y.I. Sometimes in chemical equations for reactions in aqueous solution only a "net ionic equation" is shown. For example, if $AgNO_3(aq)$ reacts with $KCl(aq)$, $AgCl(cr)$ is formed. K^+ and NO_3^- remain in solution. They are called "spectator ions." Thus, the equation would show:
$Ag^+(aq) + Cl^-(aq) \rightarrow AgCl(cr)$

FIGURE 16–3. Divers use magnesium torches for underwater cutting operations. Even underwater, magnesium burns rapidly, producing heat and light.

To write a balanced chemical equation follow these steps.

1. Write a word equation.

   Example 1
   Carbon plus oxygen yields carbon dioxide.

   Example 2
   Magnesium plus oxygen yields magnesium oxide.

2. Write correct symbols and formulas for the substances in the reaction. Put the reactants on the left side of the equation. Put the products on the right. Include state symbols. Include plus signs and an arrow.

   Example 1 $C(cr) + O_2(g) \rightarrow CO_2(g)$
   Example 2 $Mg(cr) + O_2(g) \rightarrow MgO(cr)$

3. Check the number and kinds of atoms on each side to see whether the equation is balanced.

   Example 1 $C(cr) + O_2(g) \rightarrow CO_2(g)$
   There is one C atom and two O atoms on each side. It is balanced.

   Example 2 $Mg(cr) + O_2(g) \rightarrow MgO(cr)$
   There are two O atoms on the left and one on the right. The equation is unbalanced.

4. If the numbers of atoms are not in balance, use coefficients to balance the equation.

   In Example 2, since two O atoms are on the left, two are needed on the right.

   Example 2 $Mg(cr) + O_2(g) \rightarrow \underline{2}MgO(cr)$
   Now the Mg atoms are not in balance.

   There are two Mg atoms on the right, so two are needed on the left.

   Example 2 $\underline{2}Mg(cr) + O_2(g) \rightarrow 2MgO(cr)$
   The equation is balanced.

   Sometimes it is necessary to use several steps to balance the equation. Remember, it is balanced when the numbers of each atom on both sides of the arrow are equal. *Never change a formula to balance an equation.*

EXAMPLES Balancing an Equation

1. Chlorine gas contains diatomic molecules of chlorine, Cl_2. When chlorine combines with sodium, sodium chloride is formed. Write the balanced equation for this reaction.

Solution:

a. Write the word equation.
Sodium plus chlorine gas yields sodium chloride.

b. Write the formula equation.
$Na(cr) + Cl_2(g) \rightarrow NaCl(cr)$

c. Balance the formula equation using coefficients.
$\underline{2}Na(cr) + Cl_2(g) \rightarrow \underline{2}NaCl(cr)$
The Cl_2 requires that the right side be 2NaCl. Thus, a 2 in front of Na on the left balances the equation.

2. Aluminum sulfate and barium chloride react in aqueous solution to form barium sulfate and aluminum chloride. The barium sulfate is insoluble, and aluminum chloride is soluble. Write the balanced equation.

Solution:

a. Write the word equation.
Aluminum sulfate plus barium chloride yields aluminum chloride plus barium sulfate.

b. Write the formula equation.
$Al_2(SO_4)_3(aq) + BaCl_2(aq) \rightarrow AlCl_3(aq) + BaSO_4(cr)$

c. Check the number and kinds of atoms on each side.

Al (2 on left, 1 on right)	Cl (2 on left, 3 on right)
SO_4 (3 on left, 1 on right)	Ba (1 on left, 1 on right)

d. Use coefficients to balance the equation. Put a 2 in front of $AlCl_3$.
$2Al_2(SO_4)_3(aq) + BaCl_2(aq) \rightarrow \underline{2}AlCl_3(aq) + BaSO_4(cr)$
Al balances, but there are six Cl on the right.
$Al_2(SO_4)_3(aq) + \underline{3}BaCl_2(aq) \rightarrow 2AlCl_3(aq) + BaSO_4(cr)$
The Cl balances, but now there are three Ba on the left.
$Al_2(SO_4)_3(aq) + 3BaCl_2(aq) \rightarrow 2AlCl_3(aq) + \underline{3}BaSO_4(cr)$
There are three Ba and three SO_4 on each side. The equation is now balanced.

BIOGRAPHY

Jane Marcet
1769–1858

Jane Marcet wrote her first book, *Conversations on Chemistry,* for the people who liked to attend science demonstrations at the Royal Institute in London. The book's dialogue and excellent science made it quite popular. Thousands of copies were sold in England and the United States.

Review

1. Write the word equation for the following reaction.
$AgNO_3(aq) + KBr(aq) \rightarrow AgBr(cr) + KNO_3(aq)$
a. What are the reactants?
b. What are the products?
c. In what state is each of the substances?

2. Write the word equation for the following reaction.
$Cu(NO_3)_2(aq) + Mg(cr) \rightarrow Mg(NO_3)_2(aq) + Cu(cr)$
   a. What are the reactants?
   b. What are the products?
   c. In what state is each of the substances?
3. What is a precipitate? Use Table 15–2 to determine which of the following substances would be a precipitate if formed in an aqueous solution.
   a. Ag_2S
   b. Na_3PO_4
   c. $PbSO_4$
   d. NH_4Cl
4. Iron rusts in oxygen to form solid iron(III) oxide. The formula for this compound is Fe_2O_3. Write a balanced chemical equation for the reaction.
★ 5. Write a balanced equation for the following reaction: the formation of ammonia gas from nitrogen and hydrogen gases.

KINDS OF CHEMICAL REACTIONS

GOALS

1. You will learn four types of chemical reactions.
2. You will learn the difference between catalysts and inhibitors.

A huge number of chemical reactions is possible. To study these reactions, it is helpful to organize what we know about them. In the sections that follow, chemical reactions have been classified by the forms of the equations for the reactions. Many chemical reactions can be placed in one of four categories. These are synthesis, decomposition, single displacement, and double displacement reactions.

What is a synthesis reaction?

16:3 Synthesis Reactions

The word synthesis means "putting together." A **synthesis reaction** occurs when two or more elements or compounds unite to form one compound. The formation of carbon dioxide from the elements carbon and oxygen is a synthesis reaction.

$$C(cr) + O_2(g) \rightarrow CO_2(g)$$

The formation of calcium carbonate and the burning of white phosphorus in air are both synthesis reactions.

$$CaO(cr) + CO_2(g) \rightarrow CaCO_3(cr)$$

$$P_4(cr) + 5O_2(g) \rightarrow 2P_2O_5(cr)$$

Notice that all of these reactions have the same general form.

$$A + B \rightarrow C$$

FIGURE 16–4. Rust occurs as the result of a chemical reaction between iron and oxygen.

16:4 Decomposition Reactions

Hydrogen peroxide is an unstable compound. Upon standing, it breaks down to form water and oxygen. The oxygen released is a diatomic molecule, O_2.

$$2H_2O_2(l) \rightarrow 2H_2O(l) + O_2(g)$$

A **decomposition reaction** is the breakdown of one substance into two or more other substances. It is the opposite of a synthesis reaction.

What happens in a decomposition reaction?

Oxygen can also be made by carefully heating a compound called potassium chlorate. This compound decomposes to form two substances, potassium chloride and oxygen.

$$2KClO_3(cr) \rightarrow 2KCl(cr) + 3O_2(g)$$

CO_2 is produced from baking soda when $NaHCO_3$ decomposes.

$$2NaHCO_3(cr) \rightarrow Na_2CO_3(cr) + CO_2(g) + H_2O(g)$$

Recall from Chapter 12 that some metallic elements are obtained in pure form from electrolysis reactions. Electrolysis is used to decompose salts to obtain pure elements. Pure barium is obtained by the decomposition of molten barium chloride.

$$BaCl_2(cr) \rightarrow Ba(cr) + Cl_2(g)$$

Electrolysis also can be used to separate hydrogen and oxygen from water.

$$2H_2O(l) \rightarrow 2H_2(g) + O_2(g)$$

FIGURE 16–5. When copper wire is placed in a silver nitrate solution (a), the formation of copper(II) nitrate turns the solution blue as silver metal forms on the wire (b).

a

b

16:5 Displacement Reactions

There are two types of displacement reactions. In one type, an active element may replace a less active element in a compound. For example, if a copper wire is placed in a solution of silver nitrate, silver metal forms on the wire. The copper displaces the silver in silver nitrate and sets the silver free. Copper(II) nitrate is also formed in the reaction.

$$Cu(cr) + 2AgNO_3(aq) \rightarrow 2Ag(cr) + Cu(NO_3)_2(aq)$$

In this **single displacement reaction,** one element displaces another from a compound.

The element beryllium can be obtained in pure form through a single displacement reaction between beryllium fluoride and magnesium.

$$BeF_2(cr) + Mg(cr) \rightarrow MgF_2(cr) + Be(cr)$$

INVESTIGATION 16–1

Reactions That Produce Gases

Problem: How do you know a gas is formed in a reaction?

Materials

- 2 test tubes
- graduated cylinder
- test tube holder
- matches
- wooden splints
- dropper
- hydrogen peroxide, H_2O_2
- yeast
- baking soda, $NaHCO_3$
- acetic acid, CH_3COOH
- goggles
- apron

CAUTION: *Hydrogen peroxide and acetic acid can irritate skin and eyes. Wear goggles and apron.*

Procedure

Hydrogen Peroxide

1. Measure 5 mL of 3% hydrogen peroxide with the graduated cylinder. Pour the liquid into the test tube.
2. Sprinkle yeast on the surface of the hydrogen peroxide. Make and record observations of the reaction.
3. Light a wooden splint. Blow out the flame. Then immediately insert the glowing splint into the mouth of the test tube. Record your observations. Note that yeast acts as a catalyst and increases the rate at which H_2O_2 decomposes.

FIGURE 16–6.

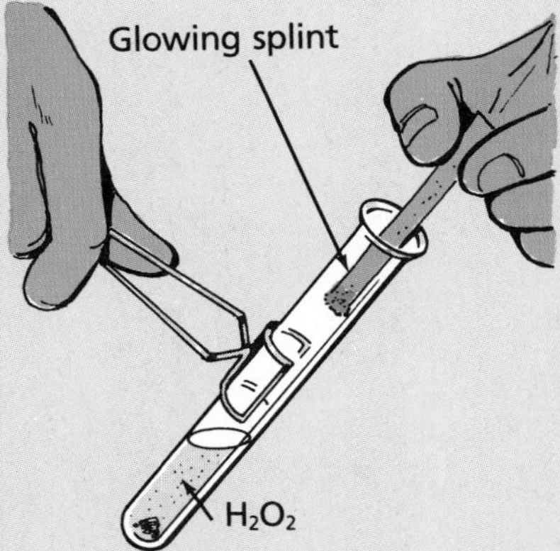

Baking Soda

4. Place one-half inch of $NaHCO_3$ in a clean, dry test tube.
5. Pour or drop a few milliliters of acetic acid onto the baking soda. Make and record your observations.
6. Light a wooden splint. Blow out the flame. Then immediately insert the glowing splint into the mouth of the test tube. Record your observations.

Data and Observations

H_2O_2 + yeast
splint test
$NaHCO_3$ + acetic acid
splint test

Analysis and Conclusions

1. What observation indicates that a gas formed?
2. When the splint begins to burn, what gas is present?
3. Which substance, H_2O_2 or $NaHCO_3$, produced oxygen?

Applications

4. When sodium hydrogen carbonate decomposes, carbon dioxide gas forms. Can you suggest a reason why carbon dioxide is used in fire extinguishers?

The halogens displace each other based on their relative activities. Their relative activities correspond to their places on the periodic table. The most active halogen is fluorine. Chlorine displaces bromine and iodine. Bromine displaces iodine. Bromine can be displaced from a bromide salt by reacting the salt with chlorine.

$$2KBr(aq) + Cl_2(g) \rightarrow 2KCl(aq) + Br_2(l)$$

FIGURE 16–7. Silver chloride is a precipitate formed in a double displacement reaction.

The reaction between silver nitrate and sodium chloride is called a double displacement reaction.

$$AgNO_3(aq) + NaCl(aq) \rightarrow AgCl(cr) + NaNO_3(aq)$$

When water solutions of these two substances are mixed, a white solid forms. This precipitate is silver chloride. In the reaction, silver and sodium ions replace each other. The sodium nitrate formed in the reaction is soluble in water. If the silver chloride were removed by filtration and the filtrate evaporated, the residue would be sodium nitrate. In a **double displacement reaction,** the positive part of one compound unites with the negative part of another compound. Displacement reactions are like dancers. In a single displacement reaction, one atom "cuts in." In double displacement, the dancers switch partners.

What happens in a double displacement reaction?

EXAMPLE Double Displacement Equation

Sodium hydroxide, NaOH, and iron(III) chloride, $FeCl_3$, react to form sodium chloride, NaCl, and iron(III) hydroxide, $Fe(OH)_3$. The NaOH, $FeCl_3$, and NaCl are present as aqueous solutions. $Fe(OH)_3$ is a precipitate. Write a balanced equation showing this reaction.

Solution:

a. Write the formulas for the reactants and products.

$$NaOH(aq) + FeCl_3(aq) \rightarrow NaCl(aq) + Fe(OH)_3(cr)$$

b. Check to see whether the atoms on both sides of the arrow are in balance. Chlorine, hydrogen, and oxygen do not balance. Three chlorine atoms are needed on the right. Therefore, place a 3 in front of NaCl.

$$NaOH(aq) + FeCl_3(aq) \rightarrow \underline{3}NaCl(aq) + Fe(OH)_3(cr)$$

Now three sodium atoms are on the right. To have three sodium atoms on the left, place a 3 in front of NaOH.

$$\underline{3}NaOH(aq) + FeCl_3(aq) \rightarrow 3NaCl(aq) + Fe(OH)_3(cr)$$

Now there are the same number of each kind of atom on the left and right. The equation is balanced.

FIGURE 16–8. Iron(III) hydroxide is formed in a double displacement reaction.

INVESTIGATION 16–2

Displacement Reactions

Problem: Which metal is most active, which is least active?

Materials

5 metal salt solutions
10 test tubes
forceps
goggles
10 metal strips
test tube rack
apron

CAUTION: *Copper and lead solutions are poisonous. Silver nitrate is poisonous and stains skin. Rinse spills with plenty of water.*

Procedure

1. Label the test tubes from 1 to 10. Following the order in the data table, pour a few milliliters of the specified solution into the correctly numbered tube. For example, copper(II) sulfate goes into tubes 1 and 2, and iron(III) sulfate goes into tubes 3 and 4.
2. Place strips of Al metal into tubes 1, 3, and 5, with $CuSO_4$, $FeSO_4$, and $Pb(NO_3)_2$. Wait a few minutes. Using forceps, pull the metal strip out of the solution and observe it. Replace it in the solution. Record all your observations.
3. Place iron metal strips or nails into tubes 2 and 7, with $CuSO_4$ and $Al_2(SO_4)_3$. Wait a few minutes. Observe and record as in Step 2.
4. Place strips of Cu metal into tubes 4, 6, and 9, with $FeSO_4$, $Pb(NO_3)_2$, and $AgNO_3$. Wait a few minutes. Observe and record as in Step 2.
5. Place strips of Pb metal into tubes 8 and 10, with $Al_2(SO_4)_3$ and $AgNO_3$. Wait a few minutes. Observe and record as in Step 2.

FIGURE 16–9.

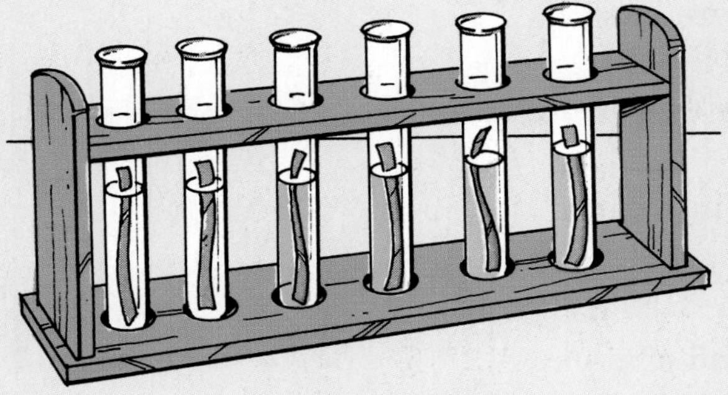

Data and Observations

Test tube	Solution	Metal	Observations
1	$CuSO_4$	Al	
2	$CuSO_4$	Fe	
3	$FeSO_4$	Al	
4	$FeSO_4$	Cu	
5	$Pb(NO_3)_2$	Al	
6	$Pb(NO_3)_2$	Cu	
7	$Al_2(SO_4)_3$	Fe	
8	$Al_2(SO_4)_3$	Pb	
9	$AgNO_3$	Cu	
10	$AgNO_3$	Pb	

Analysis and Conclusions

1. In which test tubes did a reaction occur? How do you know?
2. What type of reaction took place?
3. Write an equation for each reaction.
4. An active metal will replace one that is less active. From your observations, which metal is most active and which is least active?
5. List the five metals in order of activity from lowest to highest.

16:6 Catalysts and Inhibitors

The time taken for a reaction to occur can vary greatly. The chemical change that occurs when silver tarnishes may take place over a few months. The formation of silver chloride from silver nitrate and sodium chloride solutions takes place in an instant. In some cases, a reaction may be too slow to be of use.

Since the decomposition of a dilute solution of hydrogen peroxide is a slow process, manganese dioxide may be added. The MnO_2 speeds the reaction, so the oxygen is formed faster. However, the MnO_2 is unchanged. In this case, MnO_2 acts as a catalyst. A **catalyst** speeds up a reaction without being permanently changed itself.

FIGURE 16–10. The catalytic converter on an automobile contains a metallic catalyst.

Most of the reactions inside your body occur with catalysts present. Recall from Chapter 14 that proteins that act as catalysts in cell reactions are called enzymes. The way that many catalysts speed up reactions is not understood.

What are enzymes?

TECHNOLOGY: APPLICATIONS

Enzymes

Enzymes are the catalysts of living things. All enzymes are proteins, made up of amino acids. They are very specific. Each enzyme can speed up only one type of chemical reaction or similar group of reactions. A German chemist, Emil Fischer likened the way enzymes work to a lock and key. An enzyme has an area on it like a lock. The substrate, the compound on which the enzyme works, fits into the lock like a specially designed key. The chemical change takes place when the lock and key fit together at the active site.

Through research, scientists have found that diseases such as PKU and Tay-Sachs are the result of missing enzymes. Enzyme replacement may be the cure of the future.

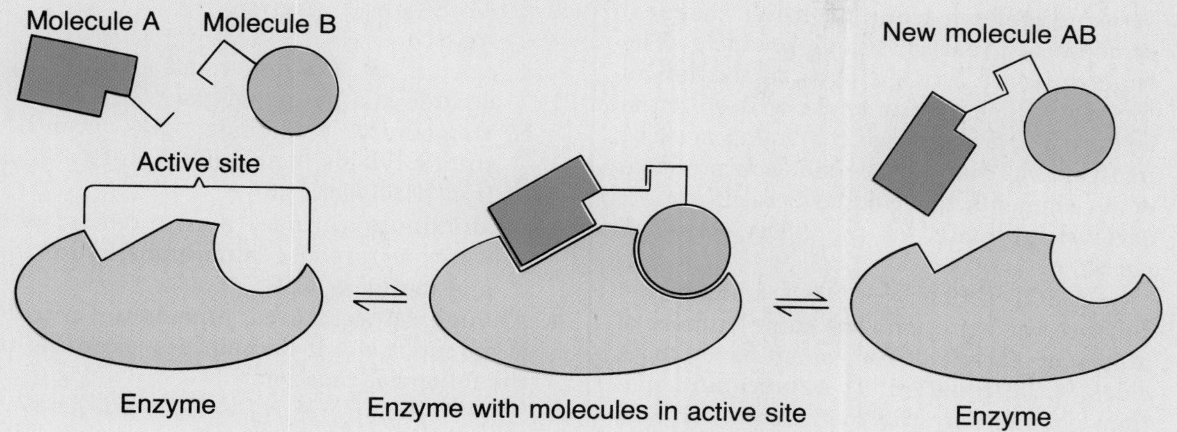

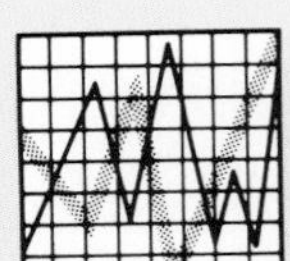

SKILL

Writing Balanced Chemical Equations

Problem: How do you write a balanced chemical equation?

Materials

paper and pencil

Background

A chemical reaction is a process by which one or more substances is changed into one or more different substances. A chemical reaction may be represented by a chemical equation. A balanced chemical equation shows what changes take place. It also shows the relative amounts of the various elements and compounds that take part in these changes.

Procedure

Consider the following reaction: sodium sulfate reacts with barium chloride to form barium sulfate and sodium chloride.

1. Determine exactly which are the reactants and which are the products. *Rewrite the above word equation and label the reactants and the products.*

   Sodium sulfate and barium chloride, reactants, yield barium sulfate and sodium chloride, products.

2. Write a skeleton equation using chemical symbols for reactants and products. The **reactants** are written first, to the left of the arrow. The **products** are written to the right of the arrow. Each compound must be neutral. The sum of the oxidation numbers of its elements must equal zero. *Write the skeleton equation for the above chemical equation.*

   $Na_2SO_4 + BaCl_2 \rightarrow NaCl + BaSO_4$

3. Balance the equation. The same number of atoms of each element must be on both sides of the equation. To balance an equation, change only the coefficients. NEVER change the subscripts in the formulas. *Write the balanced equation for the reaction in the previous step.*

   $Na_2SO_4 + BaCl_2 \rightarrow \underline{2}NaCl + BaSO_4$

   Scan the equation to check if it is balanced or list the number of each type of atom in the balanced equation, as follows.

	Reactants	Products
sodium, Na	2	2
sulfate, SO_4	1	1
barium, Ba	1	1
chloride, Cl	2	2

Questions

1. How do you write a balanced chemical equation?
2. In the lead storage battery used in automobiles, the following reaction takes place when the battery is discharging. Lead metal and lead dioxide react with sulfuric acid and form solid lead sulfate and water. List the reactants and the products of this reaction.
3. Balance each of the following reactions.
   a. $Zn + AgNO_3 \rightarrow Zn(NO_3)_2 + Ag$
   b. $CaSO_4 + K_2CO_3 \rightarrow K_2SO_4 + CaCO_3$
   c. $Al_2(SO_4)_3 + AgNO_3 \rightarrow Al(NO_3)_3 + Ag_2SO_4$
   d. calcium plus water yields calcium hydroxide and hydrogen gas
   e. ammonium hydroxide plus iron(III) sulfate yields ammonium sulfate plus iron(III) hydroxide
   f. aluminum carbide, Al_4C_3, reacts with water to produce aluminum hydroxide and methane, CH_4.
4. At high temperatures, ammonium nitrate is an explosive. It decomposes according to the following reaction.

   $NH_4NO_3 \rightarrow N_2 + H_2O + O_2$

   Balance the equation for this reaction.

FIGURE 16–11. Preservatives in food slow the growth of organisms that spoil food.

Scientists also study substances that slow down reactions. These materials are called inhibitors. An **inhibitor** is a substance that may tie up reactants or catalysts, thus slowing down a reaction. For example, traces of Fe^{3+} ions in hydrogen peroxide can cause it to decompose. However, if a phosphate is added, it ties up the Fe^{3+} and slows the rate of decomposition.

What is an inhibitor?

When inhibitors are added to foods, they are called **preservatives.** These inhibitors slow down the decay of food by retarding the processes that cause foods to spoil. Calcium propionate is one such inhibitor.

F.Y.I. Some medicines are designed to inhibit enzyme activity. These medicines contain a compound that destroys or deactivates an enzyme in bacteria. The enzyme inhibitors thus kill the bacteria and stop an infection.

Review

6. Complete and balance the following.
   a. $Na(cr) + \_\_\_\_ \rightarrow Na_2O(cr)$
   b. $K(cr) + Br_2(l) \rightarrow \_\_\_\_$

7. Write and balance the equation for the formation of magnesium from the electrolysis of molten magnesium chloride.

8. Complete and balance the following equations. Use the tables on pages 251, 254, and 353 to find the oxidation number of elements, charges on polyatomic ions, and the solubilities.
   a. $NaBr(aq) + AgNO_3(aq) \rightarrow \_\_\_\_NO_3(aq) + AgBr(cr)$
   b. $Ca(NO_3)_2(aq) + K_2SO_4(aq) \rightarrow Ca\_\_\_\_(cr) + K\_\_\_\_(aq)$
   c. $KCl(aq) + Pb(NO_3)_2(aq) \rightarrow K\_\_\_\_(aq) + Pb\_\_\_\_(cr)$

d. $Ca(OH)_2(aq)$ + $Fe(NO_3)_3(aq)$ → Fe____(cr) + Ca____(aq)
e. $MgSO_4(aq)$ + $Na_3PO_4(aq)$ → ____ + ____
f. Hydrogen sulfide plus mercury(II) chloride in water yields ____ plus ____

9. Recall that many reactions can be classified as one of four types. Which type of reaction is represented by each equation?
a. $3KOH(aq) + AlCl_3(aq) \rightarrow Al(OH)_3(cr) + 3KCl(aq)$
b. $2HgO(cr) \rightarrow 2Hg(l) + O_2(g)$
c. $SO_3(g) + H_2O(l) \rightarrow H_2SO_4(l)$
d. $CaBr_2(aq) + Cl_2(g) \rightarrow CaCl_2(aq) + Br_2(l)$
e. $2Al(cr) + 3Cu(NO_3)_2(aq) \rightarrow 2Al(NO_3)_3(aq) + 3Cu(cr)$

★ **10.** Balance the following equation for a chemical reaction.
$CeO_2 + KI + HCl \rightarrow KCl + CeCl_3 + H_2O + I_2$

MASS AND ENERGY IN CHEMICAL REACTIONS

GOALS

1. You will learn how the law of conservation of mass can be used to calculate the masses of reactants and products in chemical reactions.
2. You will learn how to calculate molecular and formula masses.
3. You will learn about the loss and gain of energy in chemical reactions.

One of the values in using chemical equations is that they help in finding mass relationships in chemical reactions. A manufacturer may want to know how much bromine can be produced from 1000 kg of sodium bromide. Also the amount of chlorine necessary to produce the bromine may be unknown. The use of chemical equations helps solve both of these problems. In the following sections, you will see how.

16:7 Conservation of Mass

What is the law of conservation of mass?

In ordinary chemical changes, no matter is lost. *The mass of all substances before a reaction equals the mass of all the substances after the reaction.* This statement is called the law of conservation of mass. As iron rusts, it combines with oxygen to form red iron(III) oxide. The mass of the oxide is equal to the combined mass of the iron and oxygen. No mass is lost or gained in the reaction. In the same way, mass is conserved when hydrogen and oxygen react to form water. The mass of the water is equal to the total mass of hydrogen and oxygen that combine.

a

b

FIGURE 16–12. A flashbulb before (a) and after (b) use illustrates that mass is conserved in a chemical reaction.

Because every sample of an element has the same average atomic mass, conservation of mass is easy to see from balanced equations. Balanced equations describe what occurs during a reaction. The same numbers and kinds of atoms are present after the reaction as before. The atoms are simply rearranged. Because the numbers and kinds of atoms are unchanged, the mass must be the same. Thus, no mass is lost.

F.Y.I. The law of conservation of mass applies to physical and chemical changes. In these changes, the amount of mass converted to energy is too small to measure. In nuclear reactions, however, measurable amounts of mass are converted to energy.

16:8 Molecular and Formula Mass

What is molecular mass?

Molecular mass is the sum of the average atomic masses of the atoms in a molecule. Carbon dioxide, for example, is a molecular compound. That is, it is made up of individual particles called molecules. Carbon dioxide has the formula CO_2. Its molecular mass is found by adding the atomic masses of one carbon atom and two oxygen atoms. The atomic mass of carbon to two significant digits, from the periodic table on pages 228–229, is 12. The atomic mass of oxygen is 16. The molecular mass for CO_2 can be found as follows.

$$\begin{array}{rr} \text{1 C atom} & 1 \times 12 = 12 \\ \text{2 O atoms} & 2 \times 16 = \underline{32} \\ \text{molecular mass of } CO_2 & = 44 \end{array}$$

For the purposes of this text, all atomic masses can be rounded to the nearest whole number.

Many compounds do not exist as molecules. Formulas for ionic compounds represent the ratio of elements in the compound and not the actual number of atoms. Table salt, for example, is found as an ionic crystal with the simplest formula of NaCl. For this compound, a formula

What is formula mass?

mass is found. A **formula mass** is the sum of the masses of the atoms or ions present in the formula of a compound. Formula mass is calculated exactly the same way as molecular mass.

EXAMPLE Finding Formula Mass

Find the formula mass of sodium nitrate.

Solution:

a. Write the formula for the ionic compound.

$$NaNO_3$$

b. Find the number and kind of each atom and find the atomic mass of each kind of atom. Add the atomic masses of all the atoms in the formula.

1 Na atom	1×23	$= 23$
1 N atom	1×14	$= 14$
3 O atoms	3×16	$= \underline{48}$
formula mass of $NaNO_3$		$= 85$

When is the term molecular mass used?

The term molecular mass can be used only with molecular compounds or elements that form molecules such as O_2, P_4, or S_8. Formula mass is a more general term. It can be used for any compound, molecular or ionic, or for any element that forms molecules.

PRACTICE PROBLEMS

1. Find the formula mass of $Ca(C_2H_3O_2)_2$.
2. Find the formula mass of silver phosphate.

16:9 Mass Relationships in Equations

When carbon burns in air to form carbon dioxide, the equation is the following.

$$C(cr) + O_2(g) \rightarrow CO_2(g)$$

Suppose 12 g of carbon combine with 32 g of oxygen. Because no mass is lost or gained in a chemical reaction, 44 g of CO_2 are formed. If only 6.0 g of carbon were used up in the reaction, how many grams of CO_2 would form? The atomic and molecular masses can be used to find the answer. The equation for the formation of CO_2 shows that one atom of C combines with one molecule of O_2 to yield one molecule of CO_2. The ratio between the atomic mass of C and the molecular mass of CO_2 is

12 to 44. If 12 g of C are used, 44 g of CO_2 form. If 6.0 g of C are used, 22 g of CO_2 form. The ratio of the atomic and molecular masses is used to obtain the answer.

$$\frac{44}{12} \times 6.0 \text{ g} = 22 \text{ g}$$

How many grams of CO_2 could be produced if 24 g of C reacted with enough oxygen?

Hydrogen gas burns in oxygen to form water. The equation for the reaction is the following.

$$2H_2(g) + O_2(g) \rightarrow 2H_2O(g)$$

How much water is formed when 32 grams of oxygen react with hydrogen? The molecular mass of H_2O can be used to predict the answer. The equation shows that two molecules of H_2 combine with one molecule of O_2 to yield two molecules of H_2O. The molecular mass of O_2 is $2 \times 16 = 32$.

The molecular mass of H_2O is 18 (16 + 1 + 1). However, the coefficient 2 in front of water in the equation shows that two water molecules are formed when one molecule of oxygen combines with hydrogen. Therefore, the molecular mass of water, 18, is multiplied by 2.

$$2 \times 18 = 36$$

The ratio between the mass of O_2 and the mass of H_2O is

$$O_2 \text{ to } H_2O = 32 \text{ to } 36.$$

Thus, 36 grams of water are formed from 32 grams of oxygen. How many grams of hydrogen react with 32 grams of oxygen? If 8 grams of oxygen were used, how much H_2O would form? How much H_2 would be needed?

What is an exothermic reaction?

16:10 Energy and Reactions

Energy is either absorbed or released during a chemical change. In some reactions such as burning, energy is released. If thermal energy is released, the reaction is called **exothermic** (ek soh THUR mihk). If thermal energy must be added during a reaction, the reaction is **endothermic** (en doh THUR mihk).

The burning of magnesium is an exothermic reaction. Some energy is needed to start the reaction. However, the energy given off when magnesium bonds with oxygen is more than enough to keep the reaction going.

$$2Mg(cr) + O_2(g) \rightarrow 2MgO(cr) + \text{thermal energy}$$

FIGURE 16–13. Many chemical reactions are exothermic. The thermal energy released is used for warmth or converted to mechanical work.

PROBLEM SOLVING

Identifying Precipitates

Many double displacement reactions take place in aqueous solution. Generally, one product will precipitate and one will stay in solution. How do you know which product is the precipitate?

Use Table 15–2 to make a solubility table. Put positive ions down the left column and negative ions across the top. Use symbols to indicate if the compound is soluble, insoluble, or slightly soluble. There will be some blanks in your table. Write balanced chemical equations for the following reactions. Use state symbols to indicate precipitates and other products in solution.

1. $Pb(NO_3)_2(aq) + Li_2SO_4\ (aq) \rightarrow$
2. $ZnBr_2\ (aq) + AgNO_3\ (aq) \rightarrow$
3. $BaCl_2\ (aq) + K_2S\ (aq) \rightarrow$

What is the energy effect in an endothermic reaction?

The reaction between ammonium thiocyanate and barium hydroxide is an endothermic reaction. Energy is absorbed as the two solids react. The temperature of the reaction flask decreases. In fact, ice may form on the outside of the flask. A small amount of energy is released as the products form. However, a net amount of energy is absorbed to keep the reaction going. Thus, the reaction is endothermic.

Review

11. Using the periodic table on pages 228–229, find the formula mass for each of the following compounds.
    a. Na_2SO_4
    b. $CaCO_3$
    c. NH_4NO_3
    d. $MgCl_2$
    e. copper(II) sulfate
    f. silver bromide
    g. potassium phosphate
    h. calcium nitride
12. What is the difference between an endothermic and an exothermic reaction?
13. If 24 g of carbon combine with 32 g of oxygen to form carbon monoxide gas, how many grams of carbon monoxide are formed? The equation for the reaction is $2C(cr) + O_2(g) \rightarrow 2CO(g)$.
14. How many grams of sodium are formed from the electrolysis of 58 grams of molten sodium chloride? The equation for the reaction is $2NaCl(l) \rightarrow 2Na(cr) + Cl_2(g)$.
15. ★ In the reaction of $AgNO_3$ and KCl in aqueous solution, AgCl is formed as a precipitate. If 37 g of KCl are completely used, how much AgCl is formed?

Chapter 16 Review

SUMMARY

1. **1.** Chemical equations are used to describe chemical changes. 16:1
2. **2.** An insoluble substance that crystallizes out of solution during a chemical reaction is called a precipitate. 16:1
3. **3.** A balanced equation contains the same number of each kind of atom on both sides of the arrow. 16:2
4. **4.** Reactions that can be represented by chemical equations include
   a. synthesis reactions, 16:3
   b. decomposition reactions, 16:4
   c. single displacement reactions, and 16:5
   d. double displacement reactions. 16:5
5. **5.** Catalysts speed chemical reaction; inhibitors retard them. 16:6
6. **6.** Mass is conserved in a chemical change. 16:7
7. **7.** A formula mass is the sum of the masses of the atoms or ions present in the formula of a compound; a molecular mass is the sum of the masses of atoms in a molecule. 16:8
8. **8.** The mass of a substance involved in a chemical reaction can be found by using molecular mass or formula mass. 16:8, 16:9
9. **9.** Energy is released or absorbed in a chemical change. 16:10

VOCABULARY

a. catalyst
b. chemical equation
c. coefficients
d. decomposition reaction
e. double displacement reaction
f. endothermic
g. exothermic
h. formula mass
i. inhibitor
j. molecular mass
k. precipitate
l. preservative
m. product
n. reactant
o. single displacement reaction
p. synthesis reaction

Matching

Match each description with the correct vocabulary word from the list above. Some words will not be used.

1. a reaction that releases thermal energy
2. speeds up a reaction
3. a solid resulting from a reaction in solution
4. used to balance equations
5. reduces the speed of a reaction
6. two or more substances produce one substance
7. a more active element replaces a less active element
8. a reaction that absorbs thermal energy
9. a substance formed in a chemical reaction
10. a shorthand description of a chemical reaction

Chapter 16 Review

MAIN IDEAS

A. Reviewing Concepts

Complete each of the following sentences with the correct word or phrase.

1. ________________ is the decomposition of a compound by electricity.
2. The molecular mass of H_2 is ________.
3. A reaction that gives off thermal energy is ________________.
4. The molecular mass of CO_2 is ________.
5. In a chemical change, ____________ is conserved.
6. $2KClO_3(cr) \rightarrow 2KCl(cr) + 3O_2(g)$ is an example of a ________________ reaction.
7. In Question 6, KCl and O_2 are ________________.
8. $AB + CD \rightarrow AD + BC$ represents a ________________ reaction.
9. The compound of hydrogen and oxygen with a molecular mass of 34 is ________________.
10. The formula mass of $NaNO_3$ is ______.
11. In the decomposition of H_2O_2, MnO_2 acts as a ________________.
12. A substance that retards spoilage or similar reactions is an ____________.
13. Bromine can displace ____________ in a chemical reaction.
14. If $AgNO_3(aq)$ reacts with $KCl(aq)$, the precipitate that forms is __________.
15. The reaction in Question 14 is an example of a ________________ reaction.

B. Understanding Concepts

Answer the following questions using complete sentences when possible.

16. How does a balanced equation demonstrate the law of conservation of mass?
17. How do endothermic reactions differ from exothermic reactions?
18. Why are formulas not changed when balancing equations?
19. Balance the following equations.
    a. $Na_2S(aq) + AgNO_3(aq) \rightarrow NaNO_3(aq) + Ag_2S(cr)$
    b. $H_2(g) + N_2(g) \rightarrow NH_3(g)$
    c. $KClO_3(cr) \rightarrow KCl(cr) + O_2(g)$
    d. $CuSO_4(aq) + Al(cr) \rightarrow Cu(cr) + Al_2(SO_4)_3\ (aq)$
    e. $Na(cr) + H_2O(l) \rightarrow NaOH(aq) + H_2(g)$
20. What type of reaction is represented by each equation in Question 19?
21. In Question 19, which reaction(s) form(s) a precipitate?
22. Find the molecular or formula mass for each of the following substances.
    a. Na_3AlO_3 d. $Ca_3(PO_4)_2$
    b. Fe_2O_3 e. H_2SiF_6
    c. $ZnCO_3$ f. $(NH_4)_2SO_4$
23. Write an equation for the synthesis of XY_3 from X and Y_2.
24. If 2 g of H_2 unites with 80 g of Br_2, what mass of HBr is formed?
25. N_2 is made by heating $NH_4NO_2(cr)$. $H_2O(g)$ is also formed. Write a balanced equation for the reaction.

C. Applying Concepts

Answer the following questions using complete sentences when possible.

26. In the electrolysis of NaBr, how much Br_2 is obtained from 103 g of NaBr?
27. In the production of $PbBr_2$ from solutions of $Pb(NO_3)_2$ and KBr, how much $PbBr_2$ is formed from 83 g of $Pb(NO_3)_2$?
28. What is the difference between a catalyst and an inhibitor?
29. Carbon dioxide can be produced by the action of an aqueous solution of hydrogen chloride on solid sodium carbonate. Write a balanced equation for the reaction. How much hydrogen

chloride would be needed to react with 53 g of sodium carbonate?

30. What is the difference between molecular mass and formula mass?

SKILL REVIEW

1. The process of photosynthesis can be summarized as the reaction between carbon dioxide and water to form glucose ($C_6H_{12}O_6$) and oxygen gas. Write a balanced equation for this reaction.
2. Sulfur dioxide and iron(III) oxide are pollutants that form when coal is burned. These pollutants are the products of a reaction between the iron pyrite, FeS_2, in the coal and oxygen in the air. Write a balanced equation for the reaction.
3. One type of fire extinguisher uses the following chemical reaction to produce carbon dioxide to smother a fire.
$$NaHCO_3 + H_2SO_4 \rightarrow Na_2SO_4 + CO_2 + H_2O$$
Balance this equation.
4. List three methods that can be used to solve a problem.
5. An engineer wants to know which of three different alloys will have the least amount of corrosion when exposed to road salt and winter weather conditions. She places strips of the three alloys in a test chamber and sprays them with a salt solution. She also adjusts the temperature in the room to 0°C. List three constants that the engineer should use in this test.

PROJECTS

1. Find the Haber process in a reference book. Determine what catalysts and other factors are used to speed the reaction.
2. Research the difference between a contact catalyst and a homogeneous catalyst. Give examples of each.

READINGS

1. Bylinsky, Gene. "The Magic of Designer Catalysts." *Fortune*. May 27, 1985, p. 82–84.
2. Preuss, Paul. "Industry in Ferment." *Science 85*. July/August, 1985, pp. 42–46.
3. Whyman, Kathryn. *Chemical Changes*. New York: Gloucester Press, 1986.

ACIDS AND BASES
MEASURING ACIDITY
REACTIONS OF ORGANIC ACIDS

Chap

Acids, Bases, and Salts

Inorganic compounds can be classified as acids, bases, or salts. Some of these compounds are corrosive and should be handled with great care. Others are present in foods. Still others are produced by the body and are vital to the living process. The manufacture of acids is one of the largest chemical industries in the world. Acids, bases, and salts are all important compounds.

ACIDS AND BASES

GOALS

1. You will learn the properties, uses, and preparations of common acids.
2. You will learn the properties and uses of some common bases.
3. You will learn how acidic and basic anhydrides form acids and bases.

Acids and bases have many properties that are similar and many that are completely different from each other. In many ways they are like the opposite sides of a coin, connected yet different. The following sections point out the differences and similarities of acids and bases and provide one definition of each.

17:1 Common Acids

What is an acid?

Acids have a sour taste, react with metals, and contain hydrogen. Almost all acids are formed from nonmetals. By one definition, an **acid** is a substance that produces hydronium ions in water solution. A **hydronium ion** is an H_3O^+ unit. Many acids are poisonous and corrosive to the skin. For this reason, extreme care should be used when handling these acids.

Common acids play an important part in daily life. Vinegar contains acetic acid. Buttermilk contains lactic acid. We eat citric acid in lemons, oranges, and grapefruit. Hydrochloric acid in the stomach aids digestion. Carbonic acid helps keep blood at the right acidity level. Three acids are of major importance in industry and in the laboratory. They are sulfuric acid, nitric acid, and hydrochloric acid.

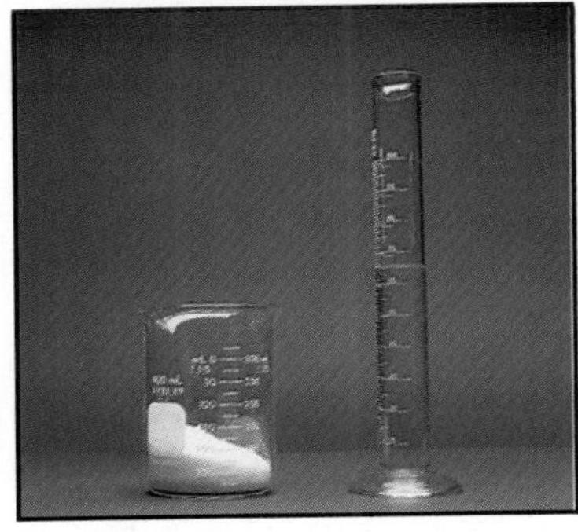

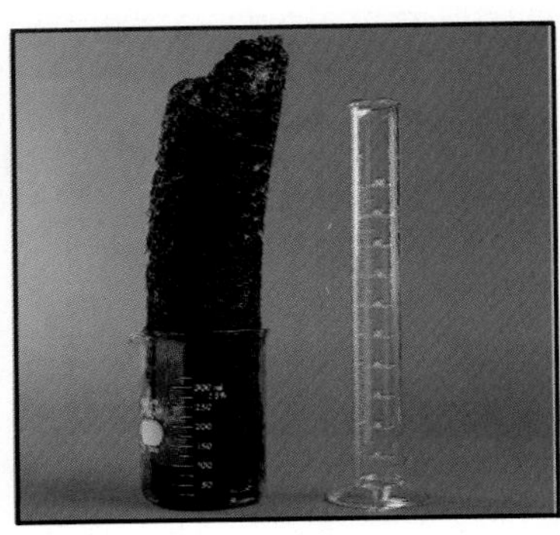

FIGURE 17–1. Concentrated sulfuric acid is a powerful dehydrating agent, capable of removing the components of water from sugar molecules, leaving behind only carbon.

What is the purpose of a dehydrating agent?

Sulfuric acid, H_2SO_4, is an oily, thick liquid. The production of sulfuric acid is greater than that of any other chemical in the United States. It is used in the manufacture of paints, plastics, and fertilizers. It is also used to make other acids and as a dehydrating agent. Dehydrate means to remove water. A wooden stick placed in sulfuric acid turns black as the acid removes water from it, leaving only carbon. Sulfuric acid can burn skin and damage clothing. Always handle it with care.

Sulfuric acid can be produced in the laboratory. First sulfur dioxide is produced by burning sulfur.

$$S(cr) + O_2(g) \rightarrow SO_2(g)$$

The gas is dissolved in water and the solution produced is treated with hydrogen peroxide.

$$SO_2(g) + H_2O(l) \rightarrow H_2SO_3(aq)$$

$$H_2SO_3(aq) + H_2O_2(aq) \rightarrow H_2SO_4(aq) + H_2O(l)$$

TECHNOLOGY: APPLICATIONS

Etching with Acids

Etching is the process of producing an image on metal or glass by the corrosive action of acid. To etch glass, melted wax is first used to coat the glass. Next, lines are drawn with a sharp needle. The glass is then immersed in a hydrofluoric acid solution for a few minutes. The acid dissolves lines into the glass where the needle has exposed the glass. The glass is washed with water and the wax is removed. Acid is also used to frost glass. Glass is frosted by removing the smooth surface with hydrofluoric acid.

The technique for metal etching is similar to that for glass. A metal plate is prepared with a mixture of wax, gum, and resin. The design is dissolved into the metal plate by the acid. The image may then be transferred to paper.

Acids are used in lithography, a printing process, mirror making, and photography. Acid etching is important in both art and industry.

FIGURE 17–2. Sulfuric acid in a car battery often corrodes the terminals.

Dilute sulfuric acid will react with zinc to produce hydrogen gas in a single displacement reaction, as do most dilute acids.

$$Zn(cr) + H_2SO_4(aq) \rightarrow ZnSO_4(aq) + H_2(g)$$

Dilute and concentrated sulfuric acid act in very different ways with copper. Warm concentrated sulfuric acid reacts with copper to produce copper(II) sulfate, water, and sulfur dioxide.

$$Cu(cr) + 2H_2SO_4(l) \rightarrow CuSO_4(aq) + SO_2(g) + 2H_2O(l)$$

Dilute sulfuric acid and copper do not react.

Nitric acid, HNO_3, is oily but not as thick as sulfuric acid. Nitric acid should be handled with care because it is corrosive. If it touches the skin, it combines with protein in the skin, and a yellow stain results. Nitric acid can also be produced in the laboratory. It is produced by heating sodium nitrate with concentrated sulfuric acid.

$$NaNO_3(cr) + H_2SO_4(l) \rightarrow NaHSO_4(cr) + HNO_3(g)$$

The gas is immediately condensed. Dilute nitric acid does not always produce hydrogen when it reacts with metals. Sometimes it produces NO, NO_2, or nitrates that are important in agriculture and explosives. This chemical property makes HNO_3 different from most dilute acids. The other acids usually do produce hydrogen in reaction with active metals.

Hydrochloric acid, HCl, is made by dissolving hydrogen chloride gas in water. The hydrogen chloride gas is formed by heating sodium chloride with concentrated sulfuric acid.

$$NaCl(cr) + H_2SO_4(l) \rightarrow NaHSO_4(cr) + HCl(g)$$

Hydrochloric acid fumes can harm the lungs and will destroy skin. Muriatic acid, used as a cleaning agent for bricks and metal, is another name for hydrochloric acid.

F.Y.I Svante Arrhenius, who offered the first acid-base theory, was nearly dismissed from the University of Stockholm because of what were considered radical ideas. Eventually he won the Nobel Prize for the work that his professor did not consider satisfactory.

Table 17–1

Acids in Some Common Substances		
Substance	**Acid present**	**Formula**
aspirin	acetylsalicylic acid	$CH_3COOC_6H_4COOH$
citrus fruit juice	ascorbic acid (vitamin C)	$\overline{OCOC(OH):C(OH)C}HCHOHCH_2OH$
sour milk	lactic acid	$CH_3CHOHCOOH$
soda water	carbonic acid	H_2CO_3
vinegar	acetic acid	CH_3COOH
apples	malic acid	$HOOCCH_2CH(OH)COOH$
spinach	oxalic acid	$HOOCCOOH \cdot 2H_2O$

What is the role of HCl in the pickling process?

This acid is used in large quantities in the steel industry for pickling. The pickling process removes oxides and other impurities from the steel surface. Hydrochloric acid is also present in the stomach. It assists in the digestion of food.

There are many other important acids. Organic acids contain hydrogen, carbon, and oxygen. Most organic acids are carboxylic acids and contain the –COOH group. Formic acid, HCOOH, was first produced by distilling ants. Acetic acid, CH_3COOH, is in vinegar. It is produced by a chemical change in ethanol. Propanoic acid is used as an inhibitor to slow spoilage in foods such as bread. As you have seen in Chapter 14, amino acids, which also contain nitrogen, are essential to life.

17:2 Common Bases

What is a base?

All bases have properties that make them alike. Bases usually taste bitter and feel slippery. However, taste and touch are not safe methods to identify a base. Strong bases are poisonous and corrosive to skin. Bases break down fats and oils. By one definition, a **base** is a substance that produces hydroxide ions, OH^-, in water solution.

Sodium hydroxide, NaOH, is one of the strongest bases. Lye is the common name for NaOH. It is a corrosive chemical. Because it breaks down oil and grease, it is used in drain cleaners and soap making. Sodium hydroxide is prepared commercially by the electrolysis of saltwater brine.

$$2NaCl(aq) + 2H_2O(l) \rightarrow 2NaOH(aq) + H_2(g) + Cl_2(g)$$

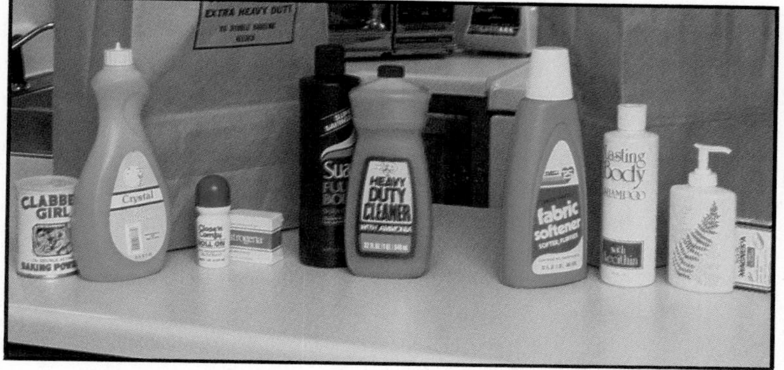

FIGURE 17–3. Many materials around the house contain bases. Check labels for bases in your home.

In the laboratory, it can be prepared by reacting calcium hydroxide with sodium carbonate in water solution.

$$Ca(OH)_2(aq) + Na_2CO_3(aq) \rightarrow 2NaOH(aq) + CaCO_3(cr)$$

Ammonia, NH_3, is another important base. It is a gas at room temperature. Household ammonia is actually a solution made by dissolving ammonia in water, $NH_3(aq)$. Ammonia is a useful cleaning agent found in window and other cleaners. It is also useful in the preparation of fertilizers. Ammonia is prepared in the laboratory by heating a mixture of ammonium chloride and calcium hydroxide.

How is ammonia made in the laboratory?

$$2NH_4Cl(cr) + Ca(OH)_2(cr) \rightarrow CaCl_2(cr) + 2H_2O(l) + 2NH_3(g)$$

Most organic bases are related to ammonia in structure and properties. One class of organic bases is called amines. These compounds contain hydrocarbon chains and nitrogen. Amines are used as solvents and reactants in the preparation of dyes, medicines, and fibers. Another important class of organic bases are the amides. They differ from amines in that they contain oxygen in addition to nitrogen.

Table 17–2

Common Bases and Their Uses

Name	Formula	Use
aluminum hydroxide	$Al(OH)_3$	deodorant, antacid
ammonium hydroxide	NH_4OH	household cleaner
calcium hydroxide	$Ca(OH)_2$	leather production, manufacture of mortar and plaster
magnesium hydroxide	$Mg(OH)_2$	laxative, antacid
sodium hydroxide	$NaOH$	drain cleaner, soap making

17:3 Ions in Acids and Bases

re water?

Pure water contains both water molecules and ions. About one in every 500 000 000 water molecules breaks up to form ions. The ions formed are hydronium, H_3O^+, and hydroxide, OH^-, ions.

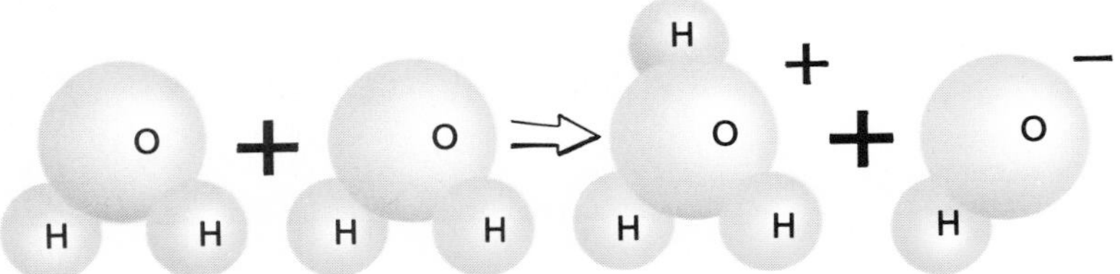

17–4. Two water molecules can split to form hydronium ion and hydroxide ion. Water acts like an acid in producing H_3O^+ (*aq*) ions and like a base in producing OH^- (*aq*) ions.

In pure water, there are equal numbers of these ions. However, the ratio changes if an acid or base is added to the water. An acid increases the amount of hydronium ions. The hydronium ions are produced when the hydrogen in the acid combines with water molecules. For example, the equation for the addition of hydrogen chloride to water is

$$HCl(g) + H_2O(l) \rightarrow H_3O^+(aq) + Cl^-(aq)$$

The addition of a base increases the amount of hydroxide ions in water. When sodium hydroxide dissolves, it dissociates. It adds sodium and hydroxide ions to water.

$$NaOH(aq) \rightarrow Na^+(aq) + OH^-(aq)$$

Why are alcohols not classified as bases?

Not all compounds that contain an OH group are bases. Recall from Section 14:4 that alcohols contain a hydroxyl (–OH) group. However, alcohols do not break down to form hydroxide ions. Therefore, they are not classified as bases. The ammonia molecule, NH_3, does not contain a hydroxide ion, but it is a base. When it dissolves in water, it forms hydroxide ions by removing an H^+ from a water molecule.

$$NH_3(g) + H_2O(l) \rightleftarrows NH_4^+(aq) + OH^-(aq)$$

Some metal hydroxides, such as zinc hydroxide or aluminum hydroxide, can act as acids or bases. Reaction conditions determine how each of these compounds will react.

Acids and bases may be classified as strong or weak. A strong acid or base breaks up completely into ions when added to water. Sodium hydroxide dissociates completely to form Na^+ and OH^- in water. A weak acid or base does not break up completely when added to wa-

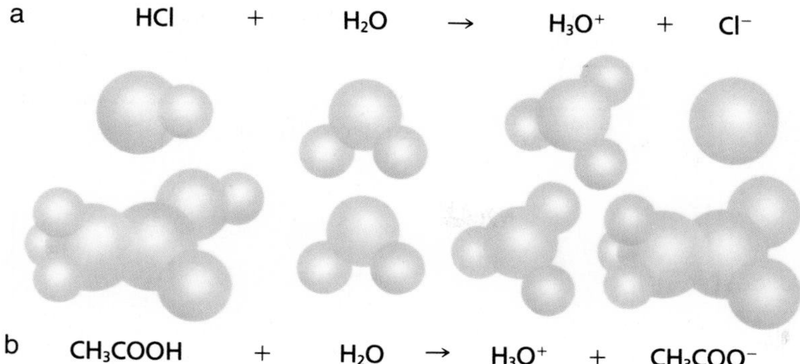

FIGURE 17–5. When added to water, a strong acid breaks up completely into ions (a). Many of the molecules of a weak acid will not break apart (b). Thus, fewer hydronium ions will be produced.

ter. Most of the particles of a weak acid or base exist in water in their molecular form rather than as ions. Acetic acid, a weak acid, exists as both molecules and ions in water.

The terms weak and strong acid or base have nothing to do with the concentration of the acid or base in the solution. We can have dilute solutions of strong acids and concentrated solutions of weak acids. If a conductivity apparatus is placed in hydrochloric acid and acetic acid solutions of equal concentration, the bulb in HCl will be brighter, Figure 17–6. The amount of conductivity is due to the number of ions in solution. The number of H_3O^+ or OH^- ions in solutions of equal concentration determines the relative strength of acids and bases. The solution of HCl in water contains more ions than the water solution of CH_3COOH.

What determines the strength of an acid or a base?

a

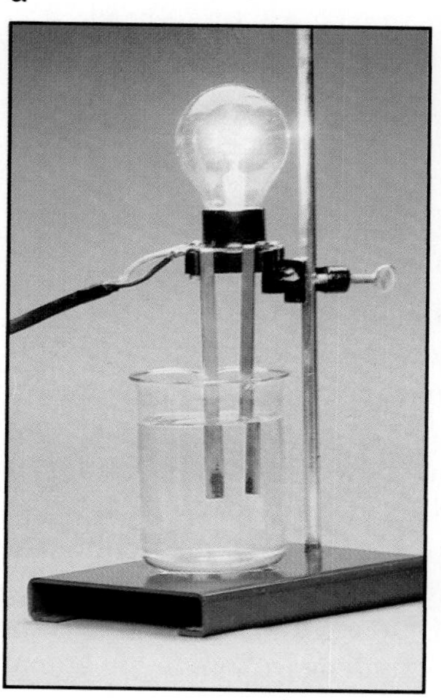

b

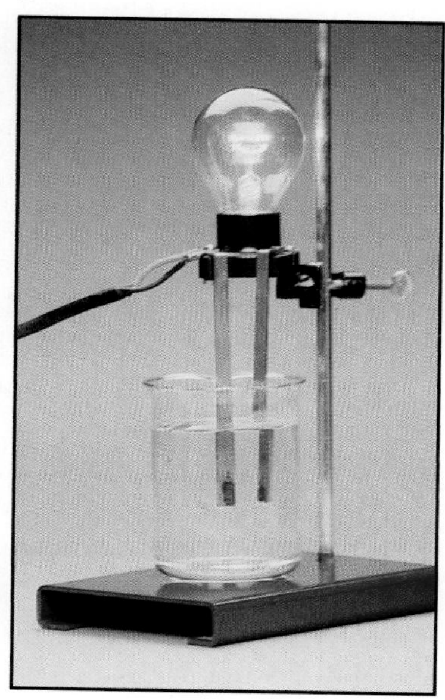

FIGURE 17–6. A conductivity apparatus can be used to distinguish strong and weak acid solutions. The apparatus is placed in hydrochloric acid (a) and in acetic acid (b) solutions of equal concentration. The light in the hydrochloric acid, the strong acid, is brighter.

Table 17–3

Strength of Some Acids and Bases		
	Strong	**Weak**
Acids	nitric acid, HNO_3 hydrochloric acid, HCl hydrobromic acid, HBr	acetic acid, CH_3COOH citric acid, $C_7H_8O_6 \cdot H_2O$ carbonic acid, H_2CO_3 oxalic acid, $C_2H_2O_4$
Bases	sodium hydroxide, $NaOH$ calcium hydroxide, $Ca(OH)_2$ potassium hydroxide, KOH	ammonia, NH_3, (NH_4OH) iron (III) hydroxide, $Fe(OH)_3$ aluminum hydroxide, $Al(OH)_3$

17:4 Anhydrides

When magnesium is burned, white magnesium oxide is formed. If the oxide is added to water, it produces a basic solution.

$$MgO(cr) + H_2O(l) \rightarrow Mg(OH)_2(aq) \rightarrow Mg^{2+}(aq) + 2OH^-(aq)$$

What is a basic anhydride?

Magnesium oxide is a basic anhydride. An anhydride contains no water. A **basic anhydride** is a metallic oxide that forms a base when added to water. Most metallic oxides are basic anhydrides.

Sulfur dioxide gas, SO_2, combines with water. A solution of sulfur dioxide is acidic.

$$SO_2(g) + H_2O(l) \rightarrow H_2SO_3(aq) \rightarrow 2H^+(aq) + SO_3^{2-}(aq)$$

What is an acidic anhydride?

Sulfur dioxide is an acidic anhydride. An **acidic anhydride** is a nonmetallic oxide that forms an acid when added to water. Most nonmetallic oxides are acidic anhydrides.

Review

1. What property of a base makes sodium hydroxide useful in making soap and cleaning drains?
2. Write an equation to show how dissolving hydrobromic acid, HBr, in water increases the hydronium ion concentration.
3. Write an equation to show how dissolving $Ca(OH)_2$ in water increases the hydroxide ion concentration.
4. Identify each of the following as a basic or acidic anhydride.
   a. MgO b. SO_3 c. CO_2 d. K_2O
5. ★ Acids with more than one hydrogen ionize in steps. Show the steps in the ionization of H_2SO_4.

CAREER

Research Chemist

While José Herrara was working on his degree in biochemistry, he worked part-time for a drug company. He had an opportunity to see many aspects of how new drugs are developed, tested, and produced. José is now a research chemist for this company.

José works with other chemists, pharmacologists, and technicians. Together they research new drug treatments for various medical problems, such as leukemia. José and his coworkers must plan their research carefully. They must test new drugs thoroughly before they can be approved by the government for use.

José is very proud of his work. He knows that his hard work can help people in pain and possibly save lives.

For career information, write
American Chemical Society
1155 16th Street NW
Washington, DC 20036

MEASURING ACIDITY

Often chemists, doctors, and other people of science need to know how acidic or how basic a solution is. Chemists have devised ways to test and report the relative amount of hydronium ion in a solution. From this, the relative amount of OH^- can also be found.

GOALS

1. You will learn what pH of a solution is and how it is found.
2. You will learn how salts are produced through neutralization.
3. You will learn how titration is used to determine acid-base concentration.

17:5 pH of a Solution

The acidity of a solution can be expressed using the pH scale. The **pH** of a solution shows its acidity in terms of its hydronium ion concentration. The pH scale ranges from 0 to 14. Solutions above 7 are basic. Solutions below 7 are acidic. A neutral solution has a pH of 7. A neutral solution is neither acidic nor basic. Pure water is neutral and has a pH of 7.

Concentrated solutions of strong acids have a pH near 0. Concentrated solutions of weak acids can have a pH range of 2 to 5. A concentrated solution of a strong base has a pH near 14. Concentrated solutions of weak bases can have a pH range of 9 to 12. A low pH value indicates a high hydronium ion concentration. A high pH indicates a high hydroxide ion concentration.

FIGURE 17–7. A pH meter is used to give an accurate pH reading.

pH Values of Some Common Substances

pH	Substance	pH	Substance	pH
1.6	carrots	5.0	blood	7.35
2.8	urine	6.0	sea water	8.4
3.0	milk	6.5	milk of magnesia	10.5
3.5	pure water	7.0	household ammonia	11.1

17:6 Determining pH

In the laboratory, the pH of a solution can be determined using a pH meter, Figure 17–7. This instrument shows pH by measuring the electrical potential difference, the voltage (Chapter 21), between electrodes placed in the solution.

Sometimes, however, a pH meter is not available. Then acidity or basicity can be determined by using indicators. Acid-base **indicators** are usually organic compounds that are different colors in acidic or basic solutions. **Litmus paper** is one indicator you can use to test for an acid or base. Blue litmus paper will turn red in an acidic solution. Red litmus paper will turn blue in a basic solution. A neutral solution will not change the color of either paper.

What are acid-base indicators?

Phenolphthalein (feen ul THAY leen) is another indicator used to detect an acid or base. Phenolphthalein is colorless in an acidic solution and bright pink in a basic solution. Many indicators are more specific than litmus or phenolphthalein. Methyl orange can be used to detect the presence of a strong acid. It changes from red to yellow in the pH range of 3.2 to 4.4.

Some everyday materials contain indicators. For example, red cabbage juice has different colors over the

FIGURE 17–8. This indicator paper (a) can show approximate pH over a wide range. It is more specific than litmus paper. Litmus (b) is an indicator that turns red in an acid and blue in a base.

a

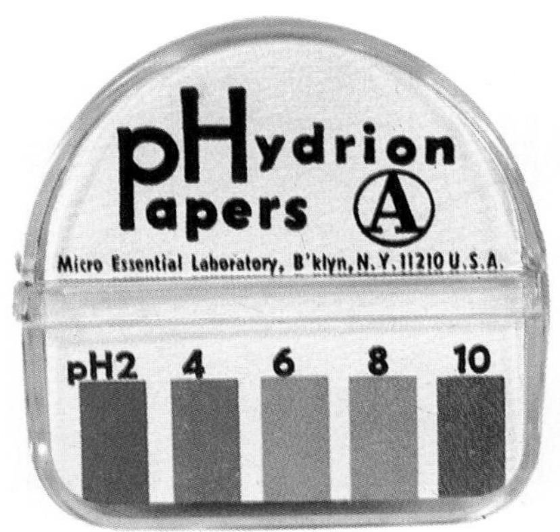

b

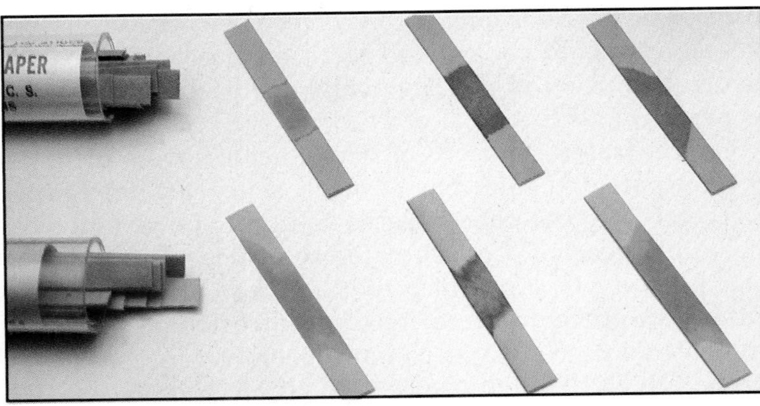

a

b

FIGURE 17–9. Methyl orange and bromthymol blue are two common pH indicators. Methyl orange (a) is shown, from left to right, at pH = 2, 4, and 6. Bromthymol blue (b) is shown at pH = 5, 7, and 9.

entire pH range. The colors of a red rose, a red dahlia, and a blue cornflower are produced by the same substance at different pHs. You may have noticed how the color of tea changes when lemon juice is added.

A good indicator should change colors over a narrow pH range. Some pH test papers are made from mixtures of indicators in order to get a material that will change color over the entire pH scale.

17:7 Neutralization and Salts

If an acid is added to a base, a chemical reaction called **neutralization** (new trah lih ZAY shuhn) can take place. In neutralization, both the acidic and the basic properties are destroyed. Neutralization explains why bases are used to counteract acids that are spilled on skin or clothing. Baking soda in water is a common base used to neutralize acids. Antacids contain bases used to reduce excess stomach acid. In neutralization, hydronium ions from the acid combine with hydroxide ions from the base. As a result, water is formed. The remaining ions form a salt.

What is formed in an acid-base neutralization reaction?

$$\begin{array}{ccccc} H_3O^+(aq) & + & OH^-(aq) & \rightarrow & 2H_2O(l) \\ \textit{hydronium ion} & + & \textit{hydroxide ion} & \rightarrow & \textit{water} \end{array}$$

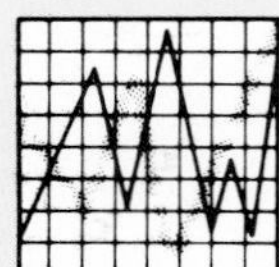

SKILL

Using Various Indicators

Problem: How do indicators differ in testing acids and bases?

Materials   

distilled water
stirring rods
12 large test tubes
test tube rack
red and blue litmus
phenolphthalein
bromthymol blue
methyl orange
methyl red
medicine dropper
dilute NaOH solution
dilute HCl solution
goggles
apron

CAUTION: *Acids and bases can cause burns. Rinse spills immediately. Phenolphthalein may be toxic.*

Procedure

1. Pour 5 mL of distilled water into each of four large test tubes.
2. With a stirring rod, put a drop of distilled water on red and blue litmus paper. Put two drops of phenolphthalein into one of the test tubes, two drops of bromthymol blue into the second test tube, two drops of methyl orange into the third, and two drops of methyl red into the fourth. Record your observations.
3. Pour 5 mL of the dilute hydrochloric acid solution into each of four test tubes. Repeat Step 2 using the hydrochloric acid in place of distilled water. Record your observations. Save these solutions to use in Step 5.
4. Pour 5 mL of the dilute sodium hydroxide solution into each of four test tubes. Repeat Step 2 using the sodium hydroxide solution in place of distilled water. Record your observations. Save these four solutions to use in Step 6.
5. To each test tube from Step 3 that contains hydrochloric acid solution, adds NaOH solution a drop at a time. Swirl or stir gently after each drop. Add drops until the indicator changes. Record the number of drops needed to change each indicator.
6. To each of the test tubes from Step 5 that contain the sodium hydroxide solution, add hydrochloric acid solution a drop at a time. Swirl or stir gently after each drop. Add drops until the indicator changes. Record the number of drops needed to change the indicator.

Data and Observations

Prepare a table that lists the indicators across the top. Down the left side of the table use the following headings:

Water (Steps 1, 2)
Acid (Step 3)
Original color (Step 5)
Number of drops of base added (Step 5)
New color (Step 5)
Base (Step 4)
Original color (Step 6)
Number of drops of acid added (Step 6)
New color (Step 6)

Questions and Conclusions

1. What was the purpose of using the distilled water?
2. Based on the number of drops of base added, write the order in which the indicators changed color in acidic solution (Step 5).
3. Based on the number of drops of acid added, write the order in which the indicators changed color in basic solution (Step 6).
4. Which of these indicators would best show a neutral solution?
5. How do indicators differ in testing acids and bases?

FIGURE 17–10. Dangerous acid spills can be controlled by neutralization with a base, producing a harmless salt and water.

What is a salt?

Thus, neutralization produces water and a salt. A **salt** is a compound formed from the positive ion from a base and the negative ion from an acid. For example, when NaOH is neutralized by HCl, a salt is formed. The salt is sodium chloride.

$$HCl(aq) + NaOH(aq) \rightarrow NaCl(aq) + H_2O(l)$$

Most salts contain a metal and a nonmetal. In sodium chloride, sodium is the metal and chlorine is the nonmetal. The metal comes from the base and the nonmetal from the acid. Some salts, such as ammonium chloride, contain the ammonium ion, which is made up of only nonmetals. Examples include ammonium chloride, NH_4Cl, and ammonium sulfide, $(NH_4)_2S$. Others contain a polyatomic ion of oxygen and another nonmetal. For example, sodium nitrate, $NaNO_3$, contains nitrogen and oxygen in addition to sodium, a metal.

Sulfuric acid reacts with sodium hydroxide to form water and sodium sulfate. Sodium sulfate is a salt.

$$H_2SO_4(aq) + 2NaOH(aq) \rightarrow Na_2SO_4(aq) + 2H_2O(l)$$

Salts are also formed when metals react with acids. For example, iron filings added to hydrochloric acid produce iron(II) chloride, a salt. Hydrogen gas is also formed.

$$Fe(cr) + 2HCl(aq) \rightarrow FeCl_2(aq) + H_2(g)$$

The action of an acidic anhydride and a basic anhydride may also produce a salt. Sodium oxide and sulfur dioxide react to form sodium sulfite.

$$Na_2O(cr) + SO_2(g) \rightarrow Na_2SO_3(cr)$$

When solution concen[illegible] is given as the number of [illegible]es in a liter, the quantity is called molarity. A solution of NaOH, for example, that contains 40 g NaOH in a liter of solution is said to be 1.0 molar or 1.0*M*. That means it has one mole of NaOH per liter. A 2.0*M* solution would have 2.0 moles, or 80 g, of NaOH in one liter. "Molar" is a more specific description of the concentration of a solution.

17:8 Titration

Chemists and medical technicians, as well as others, often need to know the concentration of an acidic or basic solution. Recall that concentration of a solution may be given as the number of grams of substance in a liter of solution. It may also be given by volume percent or by weight percent.

Titration is a process that makes use of a solution of known concentration to determine the concentration of another solution. Generally the concentration is found in grams per liter or moles per liter. A **mole** is the formula mass of a substance expressed in grams. For example, a mole of H_2 is 2 g and a mole of HNO_3 is 63 g. If we know the number of grams or moles per liter of solution, we can know how much of a substance enters into a reaction. When we know the concentration of a solution exactly, it is called a **standard solution.**

What is a standard solution?

The most common titrations are those that use an acid-base neutralization reaction. Let us use an example to explain the process. Suppose we wish to find the concentration of a solution of NaOH, a base. We have an acid, HCl, that we know contains 36 g/L.

What is a titration endpoint?

A buret is filled with standard solution, HCl. A second buret is filled with the NaOH solution, Figure 17–11. A buret is a long glass tube marked off usually in 1 mL or 0.1 mL divisions. An indicator such as phenolphthalein or a pH meter is used to find the endpoint of the reaction. The **endpoint** is the point at which the indicator changes color. This is close to the point where neutralization has occurred. A small amount of the NaOH solution is run into a beaker. Because a solution of NaOH is basic, phenolphthalein will turn bright pink. The acid is then slowly run into the beaker until the color disappears completely. The endpoint is reached when one drop of base will turn the indicator pink and a drop of acid will turn it colorless. Both burets are read and the concentration is determined.

FIGURE 17–11. Burets are precision-made pieces of glassware used to measure volumes of solutions accurately. Here, a basic solution in the flask (containing phenolphthalein), is being titrated with acid solution from a buret.

EXAMPLE Titration Calculation

50 mL of a solution of HCl, which is 36 g/L, exactly neutralizes 80 mL of NaOH solution. What is the concentration of the NaOH solution?

Solution:

1. Write the equation.

$$NaOH(aq) + HCl(aq) \rightarrow NaCl(aq) + H_2O(l)$$

From the balanced equation, you can see that one formula mass of NaOH is neutralized by one formula mass of HCl. That is, 36 g of HCl uses 40 g of NaOH.

2. Find the amount of HCl in 50 mL of 36 g/L solution.

$$36 \text{ g/L} \times 0.050 \text{ L} = 1.8 \text{ g HCl}$$

3. Find the amount of NaOH in 80 mL of solution. From the chemical equation, we know that 36 g HCl reacts with 40 g NaOH. This is used as a ratio to find out how many grams of NaOH are needed to react with the 1.8 g HCl.

$$\frac{\text{grams for 1 formula mass NaOH}}{\text{grams for 1 formula mass HCl}} = \frac{40 \text{ g NaOH}}{36 \text{ g HCl}} =$$

$$\frac{\text{grams in 80 mL NaOH solution}}{\text{grams in 50 mL HCl solution}} = \frac{? \text{ g NaOH}}{1.8 \text{ g HCl}}$$

$$\frac{40 \text{ g NaOH}}{36 \text{ g HCl}} = \frac{? \text{ g NaOH}}{1.8 \text{ g HCl}}$$

$$\frac{40 \text{ g NaOH}}{36 \text{ g HCl}} \times 1.8 \text{ g HCl} = 2.0 \text{ g NaOH}$$

Thus, there are 2.0 g NaOH in 80 mL of the solution.

4. Find the number of grams of NaOH in a liter of solution.

$$2.0 \text{ g} \div 0.080 \text{ L} = 25 \text{ g/L}$$

The concentration of the NaOH solution is 25 g/L.

BIOGRAPHY

Gerty Cori
1896–1957

Born in Prague, Czechoslovakia, Gerty Cori shared the Nobel Prize with her husband for their work on sugar metabolism. She helped to isolate a compound that is part of the metabolism of sugar. Her research shows that glycogen in muscle is metabolized to lactic acid.

Review

6. Classify each substance in Table 17–4 as acidic, basic or neutral.
7. What salt is prepared from the neutralization of sulfuric acid with potassium hydroxide? Write a balanced equation for the reaction.
8. What salt is formed when zinc replaces hydrogen in hydrochloric acid? Write a balanced equation for the reaction.
9. Write balanced equations for the neutralization of
   a. lithium hydroxide by phosphoric acid, and
   b. calcium hydroxide by nitric acid.

★ 10. In a titration, 50 mL of KOH is neutralized by 25 mL of an HNO_3 solution that contains 63 g/L. Find the concentration of the KOH solution.

INVESTIGATION 17–1

An Acid-Base Titration

Problem: How do you prepare sodium chloride by neutralization?

Materials   

2 droppers
2 graduated cylinders
4 100-mL beakers
evaporating dish
hot plate
goggles
NaOH solution
HCl solution
2 stirring rods
indicator paper
phenolphthalein
apron

CAUTION: *NaOH and HCl are toxic and corrosive. Rinse spills immediately with water.*

Procedure

1. Later in this investigation you will use a dropper to measure solutions. You need to know how many drops from the dropper make one milliliter. To find out, pour some water into a graduated cylinder so that it is exactly at some line on the cylinder. Use a dropper to add enough water to make *exactly* one more milliliter. Hold the dropper straight up and down, and count the drops as you add them. Record this number.
2. You will do the rest of the investigation with a partner. Label one of your droppers NaOH and the other HCl. Write this information in the data table along with the number of drops in a milliliter for your partner's dropper.
3. Obtain 2 small, clean, dry beakers. Label one NaOH and the other HCl. Add about 3 mL of the correct solution to each beaker.
4. Add 2 to 3 drops of phenolphthalein to the NaOH solution. Record your observations.
5. Repeat Step 4 using HCl solution instead of NaOH. Use a clean stirring rod.
6. Label a third small beaker as the reaction beaker. Using the proper dropper, add 2 mL of HCl solution to the reaction beaker. Record the number of drops. Now add 2 to 3 drops of phenolphthalein to the reaction beaker.
7. Using the other dropper, add NaOH drop-by-drop, with constant stirring, to the HCl solution in the reaction beaker. Count the drops as you add them. As the pink color appears in the beaker, add NaOH more slowly. Stop adding when one drop makes the pink color stay for at least 30 seconds. Record the total number of drops of NaOH added. Using indicator paper, check the pH of the solution. Record it in the data table.
8. Since equal amounts of HCl and NaOH were added, the solution in the reaction beaker should be a neutral salt solution. To recover the salt from the solution, pour it into an evaporating dish. Arrange as in Figure 15–14, page 358. Heat to dryness.

Data and Observations

Step 1. One mL = ____ drops; use for ____.
Step 2. One mL = ____ drops; use for ______.
Step 4.
Step 5.
Step 6. ____ drops HCl
Step 7. ____ drops NaOH, pH = ____

Analysis and Conclusions

1. What was the total amount of HCl used to make the neutral solution? Total NaOH?
2. How do the amounts of HCl and NaOH compare?
3. Write the equation for the reaction between hydrochloric acid and sodium hydroxide.
4. What is the residue in the evaporating dish?
5. Why was phenolphthalein used?
6. How do you prepare sodium chloride by neutralization?

REACTIONS OF ORGANIC ACIDS

Organic acids react with alcohols. The reactions are similar to acid-base reactions. Many of the familiar odors and flavors in everyday life are the result of these reactions.

GOALS

1. You will learn about esterification and some common esters.
2. You will learn about some organic salts.

17.9 Esters

An organic reaction that is similar in form to neutralization is esterification. **Esterification** is a reaction in which an alcohol combines with an acid. The product is called an ester.

$$\text{alcohol} + \text{acid} \rightleftharpoons \text{ester} + \text{water}$$

The double arrow has a special meaning in a chemical equation. It is used to show that in a particular reaction not all the reactants are converted to products. When the reaction begins, alcohol and acid form an ester and water. Later, the ester and water begin to re-form the reactants. The two reactions continue in a balance.

FIGURE 17–12. The pleasing aromas of many perfumes are the result of esters.

What is esterification?

If acetic acid combines with methanol, an ester called methyl acetate is formed. Notice that a water molecule is split out between the –COOH group and the –OH group.

$$\underset{\text{acetic acid}}{CH_3-C(=O)-O-H} + \underset{\text{methanol}}{H-O-CH_3} \rightleftharpoons \underset{\text{methyl acetate}}{CH_3-C(=O)-O-CH_3} + \underset{\text{water}}{H_2O}$$

Esters are a class of substances that are responsible for many of the characteristic odors and flavors of flowers and fruits. Fats and oils are esters, as are natural waxes such as beeswax. Aspirin is both an ester and a carboxylic acid. Table 17–5 lists a number of esters and their familiar odors or flavors. Some of these substances are added to processed fruits and fruit products, such as jam and candies.

What substance is produced along with an ester?

Table 17–5

Name of Ester	Odor/Flavor	Name of Ester	Odor/Flavor
ethyl formate	rum	ethyl butyrate	pineapple
isobutyl formate	raspberry	methyl butyrate	apple
n-pentyl acetate	banana	pentyl butyrate	apricot
n-octyl acetate	orange	methyl salicylate	wintergreen

F.Y.I. Isotopes of oxygen are used to determine whether the oxygen in the ester bond is from the OH (hydroxyl) group of the alcohol or the OH of the acid. For example, the oxygen might be "tagged" by using $^{18}_{8}O$ instead of the usual $^{16}_{8}O$. The ester could then be analyzed to see whether the ester contained the "tagged" oxygen or whether it was in the water molecules.

Polyesters are polymers made from an acid with two –COOH groups and an alcohol that has two –OH groups. This allows the formation of a long chain.

$$\underset{\text{terephthalic acid}}{HO{-}\overset{\overset{\displaystyle O}{\|}}{C}{-}C_6H_4{-}\overset{\overset{\displaystyle O}{\|}}{C}{-}OH} + \underset{\text{ethylene glycol}}{HO{-}\underset{H}{\overset{H}{C}}{-}\underset{H}{\overset{H}{C}}{-}OH} \longrightarrow$$

$$\left[{-}\overset{\overset{\displaystyle O}{\|}}{C}{-}C_6H_4{-}\overset{\overset{\displaystyle O}{\|}}{C}{-}O{-}\underset{H}{\overset{H}{C}}{-}\underset{H}{\overset{H}{C}}{-}O{-}\right] + 2H_2O$$

one unit of the polymer,
polyethylene terephthalate (PET),
a polyester

17:10 Soaps and Detergents

What is a soap?

When heated in water, esters break down to form their original alcohols and acids. However, if the esters are heated in a strong base such as NaOH or KOH instead of water, the ester forms an alcohol and a soap. This process of soap formation is called **saponification.**

A **soap** is a salt of a fatty acid. Soaps contain a sodium or potassium ion attached to the fatty acid. A fatty

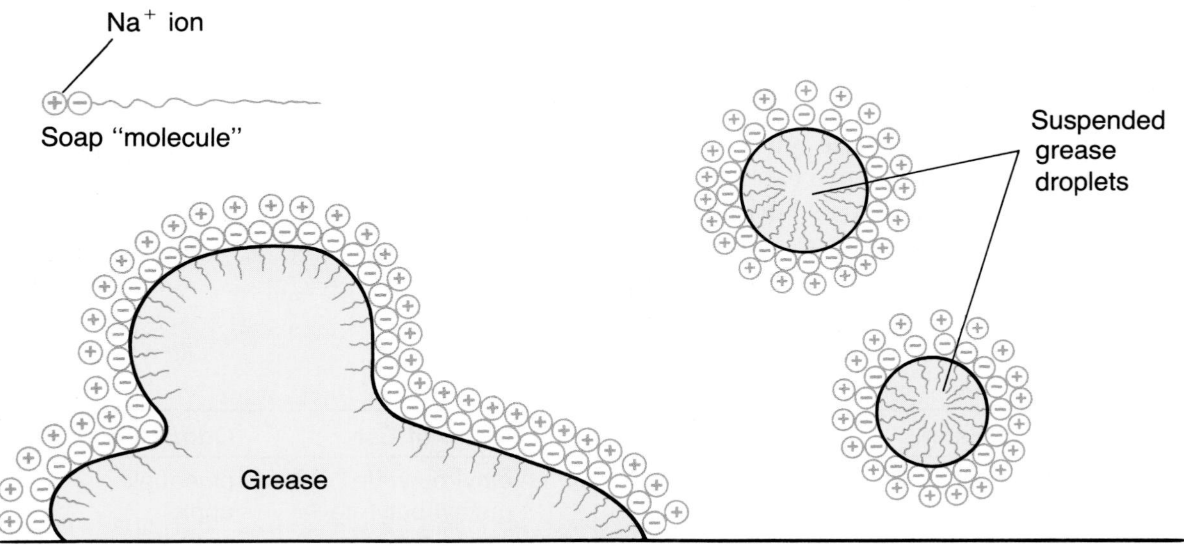

FIGURE 17–13. The cleansing action of soap is due to its ability to form grease-soap droplets that are soluble in water.

acid is a carboxylic acid. It consists of a long hydrocarbon chain attached to a –COOH group. Soap dissolves in water and increases the cleaning ability of water. The hydrocarbon part of the soap dissolves grease and oil. When you wash grease or oil off your hands with soapy water, the soap "cuts" or dissolves the grease. The ionic part of the soap dissolves in water. The water then washes the grease away.

Synthetic detergents are organic compounds that have a structure similar to soap. Detergents also make water do a better cleaning job. Like soap, they are long carbon chains with a metal ion at one end of the chain. They are also organic salts. Unlike soap, synthetic detergents work well in hard water. Hard water contains minerals that form "soap scum," insoluble compounds with soap. This does not happen with detergents.

Why do detergents work better in hard water than soap does?

Review

11. What is an ester?
12. Give two uses of esters.
13. What is saponification?
14. Name one advantage of using detergent instead of soap.
★ 15. Write the equation for the formation of ethyl formate from ethanol and formic acid, HCOOH.

PROBLEM SOLVING

How can you make natural indicators?

Look at the photograph on the first page of this chapter. What caused some of the hydrangeas to be blue and some pink? Reread Section 17:6. Cabbage juice can be used to prepare an indicator that changes color over the entire pH range, as shown below. How could you prepare other natural indicators? How could you tell if a plant would make a good source for an indicator? How could you find out what the pH range for the natural indicator is?

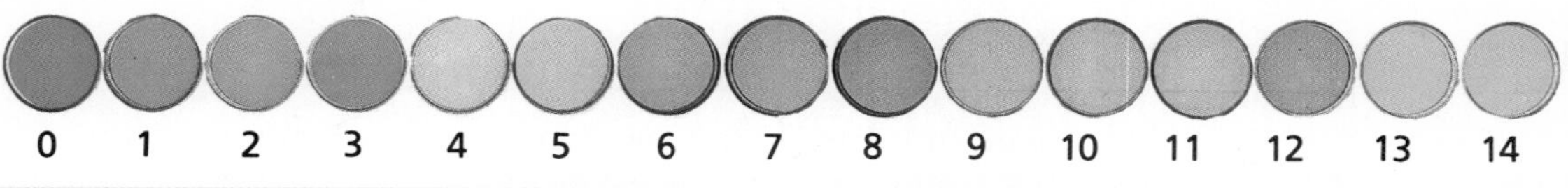

INVESTIGATION 17–2

Soap and Detergent

Problem: How well do soap and detergent work in hard water?

Materials

250-mL beaker
hot plate
stirring rod
balance
wooden spoon
paper towels
10–12 test tubes
test tube rack
dropper
apron
lard
NaOH solution
salt, NaCl
tap and distilled water
commercial soap
detergent
kerosene
graduated cylinder
goggles

CAUTION: *Handle sodium hydroxide and kerosene with care. Kerosene will burn; keep away from flames. Wash up NaOH spills with water. Notify your teacher of kerosene spills.*

Procedure

1. Place 40 g of lard in a beaker and add 10 mL of NaOH solution. Warm the mixture *gently* for about 30 minutes. Stir to prevent spattering.
2. Let the solution stand for a few minutes to cool. Then stir in 10 g of salt.
3. Using the spoon, skim off the soap and rinse with very cold water. Place the soap on a towel to dry.
4. Prepare a soap solution by placing some of your soap in a test tube about half full of distilled water. Shake the test tube. Label this tube as your solution (MY).
5. Obtain a commercial soap solution (COM) and a detergent solution (DET) from your teacher. Label the test tubes.
6. Label nine clean, dry test tubes 1 through 9. In tubes 1, 2, and 3, place 5 mL of distilled water and 5 mL of kerosene. In tubes 4, 5, and 6, place 10 mL of tap water. In tubes 7, 8, and 9, place 10 mL of distilled water.
7. Add 5 drops of your soap solution to tubes 1, 4, and 7. Add 5 drops of commercial soap solution to tubes 2, 5, and 8. Add 5 drops of detergent to tubes 3, 6, and 9. Shake each test tube 10 times. Record all of your observations.

Data and Observations

Test tube	Test solution	Cleaning solution	Observations
1	kerosene and water	your soap	
2	kerosene and water	commercial soap	
3	kerosene and water	detergent	
4	tap water	your soap	
5	tap water	commercial soap	
6	tap water	detergent	

Analysis

1. In kerosene, how did the soaps compare to the detergent?
2. Overall, which of the three cleaning solutions made the best suds?

Conclusions and Applications

3. If you were washing dishes in tap water, which cleaning solution would you use?
4. How well do soap and detergent work in hard water?

Chapter 17 Review

SUMMARY

1. Acids have a sour taste, react with metals, and produce H_3O^+ in an aqueous solution. 17:1
2. Most organic acids contain the –COOH group. 17:1
3. Bases have a bitter taste, feel slippery, and produce OH^- in an aqueous solution. 17:2
4. Acids increase the hydronium ion concentration of a solution; bases increase the hydroxide ion concentration of a solution. 17:3
5. The relative number of H_3O^+ or OH^- ions produced in solution determines the strength of an acid or base. 17:3
6. An acidic anhydride forms an acid when added to water. 17:4
7. A basic anhydride forms a base when added to water. 17:4
8. The acidity of a solution is rated on the pH scale. 17:5
9. Solutions with a pH of 7 are neutral; those with a pH below 7 are acidic; and those with a pH above 7 are basic. 17:5
10. Indicators are different colors in acidic and basic solutions. 17:6
11. A neutralization reaction produces water and a salt. 17:7
12. Titration is a process that is used to find the concentration of a solution. 17:8
13. Esters are formed from alcohols and organic acids. 17:9
14. Soaps are made from esters and a strong base. 17:10

VOCABULARY

a. acid
b. acidic anhydride
c. base
d. basic anhydride
e. endpoint
f. esterification
g. hydronium ion
h. indicators
i. litmus paper
j. mole
k. neutralization
l. pH
m. phenolphthalein
n. salt
o. saponification
p. soap
q. standard solution
r. titration

Matching

Match each description with the correct word from the list above. Some words will not be used.

1. produces OH^- in solution
2. a process used to find the concentration of a solution
3. determines the pH of a solution by color
4. a measure of the concentration of H_3O^+ ions
5. the salt of a fatty acid
6. the reaction of an organic acid with an alcohol
7. a nonmetallic oxide that produces an acid when dissolved in water
8. produces H_3O^+ in water solution
9. a product of a neutralization reaction
10. a solution whose concentration is known

Chapter 17 Review

MAIN IDEAS

A. Reviewing Concepts

Choose the word or phrase that correctly completes each of the following sentences.

1. Acids in food taste *(sour, sweet, bitter, salty)*.
2. An acid solution could have a pH of *(2, 7, 11)*.
3. *(Phenolphthalein, Benzene, Litmus)* is not an indicator of pH.
4. An oxide of a metal usually is a(n) *(acidic anhydride, basic anhydride)*.
5. The pH of a dilute NaOH solution is *(greater than 7, less than 7)*.
6. An example of a basic anhydride is *(carbon dioxide, sulfur dioxide, calcium oxide)*.
7. Soaps are products of esters and *(water, strong acids, strong bases)*.
8. Neutralization reactions produce a salt and *(a gas, light, water)*.
9. As the amount of HCl in water increases, the pH of the solution *(increases, decreases, remains the same)*.
10. The pH of a hydrochloric acid solution would be *(greater than, equal to, less than)* the pH of a solution of citric acid of equal concentration.

Complete each of the following sentences with the correct word or phrase.

11. A base produces ________________ when dissolved in water.
12. A hydrogen ion combines with a water molecule to form ________________.
13. Esterification is an organic reaction similar to ________________.
14. CO_2 is an example of a(n) ________________ anhydride.
15. When an active metal reacts with dilute H_2SO_4, ________________ gas is formed.

B. Understanding Concepts

Answer the following questions using complete sentences when possible.

16. What kind of reaction is shown by the following equation?
    $HCl(aq) + NaOH(aq) \rightarrow NaCl(aq) + H_2O(l)$
17. From what acids and bases are these salts formed?
    a. Na_2SO_4 b. NaCl c. $NaNO_3$
18. How are acids and bases detected?
19. List three important industrial acids. What are the primary uses of each?
20. Classify each substance as an acid, a base, or a salt.
    a. HNO_2 c. KOH e. $Ca(OH)_2$
    b. HCOOH d. CaI_2 f. $Fe(NO_3)_3$
21. Name two common household bases. Give their uses.
22. How is pH related to the hydronium ion concentration?
23. Write a balanced equation for each of the following reactions.
    a. potassium hydroxide + sulfuric acid
    b. nitric acid + sodium hydroxide
    c. calcium hydroxide + hydrochloric acid
    d. zinc + hydrochloric acid
24. Name the salt produced in each reaction in Problem 23.
25. How can the endpoint be found in an acid-base titration?

C. Applying Concepts

Answer the following questions using complete sentences when possible.

26. Explain the process of titration to determine the concentration of a base.
27. If 50 mL of H_2SO_4 that is 49 g/L in solution exactly neutralizes 40 mL of NaOH solution, what is the concentration of the NaOH solution?

28. What is a neutralization reaction?
29. What are the parent acids and bases for the following salts?
    a. sodium sulfate
    b. calcium nitrate
    c. ammonium chloride
    d. potassium phosphate
30. Why is it necessary to have a large number of indicators? How has the pH meter helped?

SKILL REVIEW

Use this table to answer questions 1–3.

Indicator	Acid Color	Range	Base Color
Cresol Red	red	1.0–2.0	yellow
Phloxine B	colorless	2.1–4.1	pink
Methyl orange	red	3.2–4.4	yellow
Methyl red	red	4.8–6.0	yellow
Bromocresol purple	yellow	5.2–6.8	purple
Phenolphthalein	colorless	8.0–10.0	pink
Alizarin yellow R	yellow	10.0–12.0	red
Methyl blue	blue	10.6–13.4	pale violet

1. A solution turned red when methyl red, methyl orange, or cresol red was added. What is the approximate pH of this solution?
2. A solution is known to be basic. Which of the following indicators would you not need to use to determine the pH of the solution: methyl red, bromocresol purple, phenolphthalein, alizarin yellow R?
3. If you wanted to determine the pH of a solution containing an unknown, with what indicator would it be best to start your testing?
4. An important type of single displacement reaction involves the reaction between a metal oxide and carbon. This type of reaction is used industrially to separate metals from their ores. Carbon dioxide is a by-product. Write a balanced equation for the production of iron metal from iron(III) oxide, using this process.
5. Describe how a flow chart could be used to determine what indicators to use to find the pH of an unknown.

PROJECTS

1. Use information from garden books, farm publications, your local garden store, or florists. Make a list of plants that require acidic soil and those that require basic soil. Find out what methods can be used to make soil basic or acidic.
2. Given five common household liquids, devise an activity that would determine their relative pH. How do different concentrations of the solutions affect their pH?

READINGS

1. Hobson, Phyllis. *Making Soaps and Candles.* Pownal, VT: Storey Communications, 1984.
2. Mitgutsch, Ali. *From Sea to Salt.* Minneapolis: Carolrhoda Books, 1985.
3. "pH." *Science and Technology Illustrated.* Chicago: Encyclopedia Britannica, 1984, Vol. 20, pp. 2446–2447.

SCIENCE AND SOCIETY

ACID RAIN: A CONTINUING DEBATE

Balladeers and poets used to sing the praises of "cool clear water." "As pure as the driven snow" is a phrase still heard to describe a person who is virtuous. Yet in many areas the water is clear because it supports no life and the snow has a pH value of 4. They are both a result of what is commonly known as acid rain, more correctly known as acid precipitation.

Background

Pure water has a pH of 7. Normal rain water in the United States has a pH of 5.7 because of CO_2 in the air. Acid rain, however, has a much lower pH. Oxides of sulfur and nitrogen are mainly responsible for this. The burning of high-sulfur coal produces sulfur dioxide. The process starts with solid sulfur or iron sulfide and oxygen gas and goes through a series of chemical reactions, eventually producing sulfuric acid.

The burning of fossil fuels in internal combustion engines is also at fault. At the high temperatures in these engines, nitrogen in the air reacts with oxygen. This leads to the production of nitrogen oxides. These oxides, combined with those formed during the burning of coal, react with water in the atmosphere to produce acid precipitation.

In the lakes and other aquatic environments in the Northeastern United States and Canada, damage to fish and other wildlife from acid precipitation has been studied for two decades. As far back as 1982, 51% of the upland lakes in the Adirondack area had a pH value under 5 and the rain falling there had a pH of 4.

The actual effect on animal and plant life depends on several things other than the acidity of the precipitation. One of these is the buffering capacity of the surrounding rock and soil. If the rain falls on an area made mostly of limestone, which is alkaline, the rocks and the soil neutralize the acid and little damage results. If, however, it falls on an area consisting mostly of granite, which is acidic, damage occurs because there is no buffering. The metallic ions in the rock, such as aluminum and magnesium, are dissolved by the added acid and get into the water and damage the life there. Much of the damage is done to immature or larval creatures. Algae and other plants at the base of the food chain may also be destroyed.

Case Studies

1. The damage done to buildings and monuments is more visible to the general public. One can see corrosion of metals, flaking of paints and erosion of building materials. A New Yorker over the age of forty can tell you that the obelisk in Central Park, called Cleopatra's Needle, had clearly visible heiroglyphics during his or her childhood. Now it is a smooth stone. Anyone who travels through a New England graveyard can see that the marble tombstones, even relatively new ones, are unreadable. Only the granite ones have lasted. Acid erodes marble and has little effect on granite.

2. The same oxides that cause damage to buildings have also been blamed for forest decline or damage to trees. The majority of scientists, both in the United States and Canada, who have been studying the problem for many years believe that it is severe. Yet in September of 1987, the United States government released an interagency report implying that there has been very little damage to lakes, no damage to forests, no effects on health, and no visible effect on buildings or building materials.

3. Many scientists in both countries have attacked the report as misleading. One of the main points being attacked is the definition of an acidified lake. The report considers a lake acidified if it has a pH of 5 or below. This is the level at which sport fishes are affected. The reason they chose these fishes is that their existence has an economic impact on an area. Using that definition, only about 10% of the lakes in the Northeast are affected. Critics feel that the definition should be changed to a pH of 5.5 or even 6 because those levels affect many of the other animals and plants in the food chain. The report also omitted any Canadian data. Because wind patterns carry much of our pollution into Canada, critics want that data examined.

Developing a Viewpoint

The average citizen in the United States is faced with a dilemma. Whom do you believe? Scientists and government agencies issue conflicting reports. Economics plays an important part in decisions made by all parties involved in the acid rain problem. The vast reserves of coal in the eastern United States form an abundant source of energy to support many industries. If this coal were not allowed to be used in these industries the economic effect would be very large. Much of the electricity generated in the Ohio River Valley is made in coal-burning power plants. If these plants were forced to use more expensive, low-sulfur coal or to clean the emissions from the high-sulfur coal, the cost of electricity and goods manufactured using electricity would increase. Would you be willing to pay more for the products you use to reduce acid precipitation?

Hold a mock town meeting to hear different viewpoints concerning the problem of acid precipitation. The viewpoints represented should include those of coal miners, coal company owners, representatives from coal-fired power plants, environmentalists, fishing enthusiasts, conservationists, and historians.

Suggested Readings

Begley, Sharon. "On the Trail of Acid Rain." *National Wildlife*. February-March, 1987, pp. 6–12.

Burns, John F. "A Rage When the Trout Go Belly Up (Acid Rain and Muskoka Lake, Ontario)." *New York Times*. April 23, 1987. p. A4(L) col. 1.

Burns, John F. "Canada Wants Off the Back Burner." (Canadian-U.S. Relations), *New York Times*. March 29, 1987, p. E3(L) col. 5.

Peterson, Ivars. "Acid Rain Linked to Damaged Lakes." *Science News*. March 22, 1986, p. 182(1).

Shabecoff, Philip. "Government Acid Rain Report Comes Under Sharp Attack." *New York Times*. September 22, 1987, p. 19(N).

Taylor, Robert E. "Acid Rain Damage to Lakes Minimal, EPA Advisors Find." *Wall-Street Journal*. March 26, 1987, p. 49(W), p. 51(E).

"EPA Backs Off Acidity View (EPA, Acidity of Lakes)." *New York Times*. March 26, 1987, p. 11(N), p. A19(L) col. 1.

UNIT 6

Some artists never hold a brush. They belong to a growing group of modern artists who use the whole electromagnetic spectrum, both as paint and canvas. These artists create their images on computer screens. The images can then be stored on videotape or reproduced on paper or film.

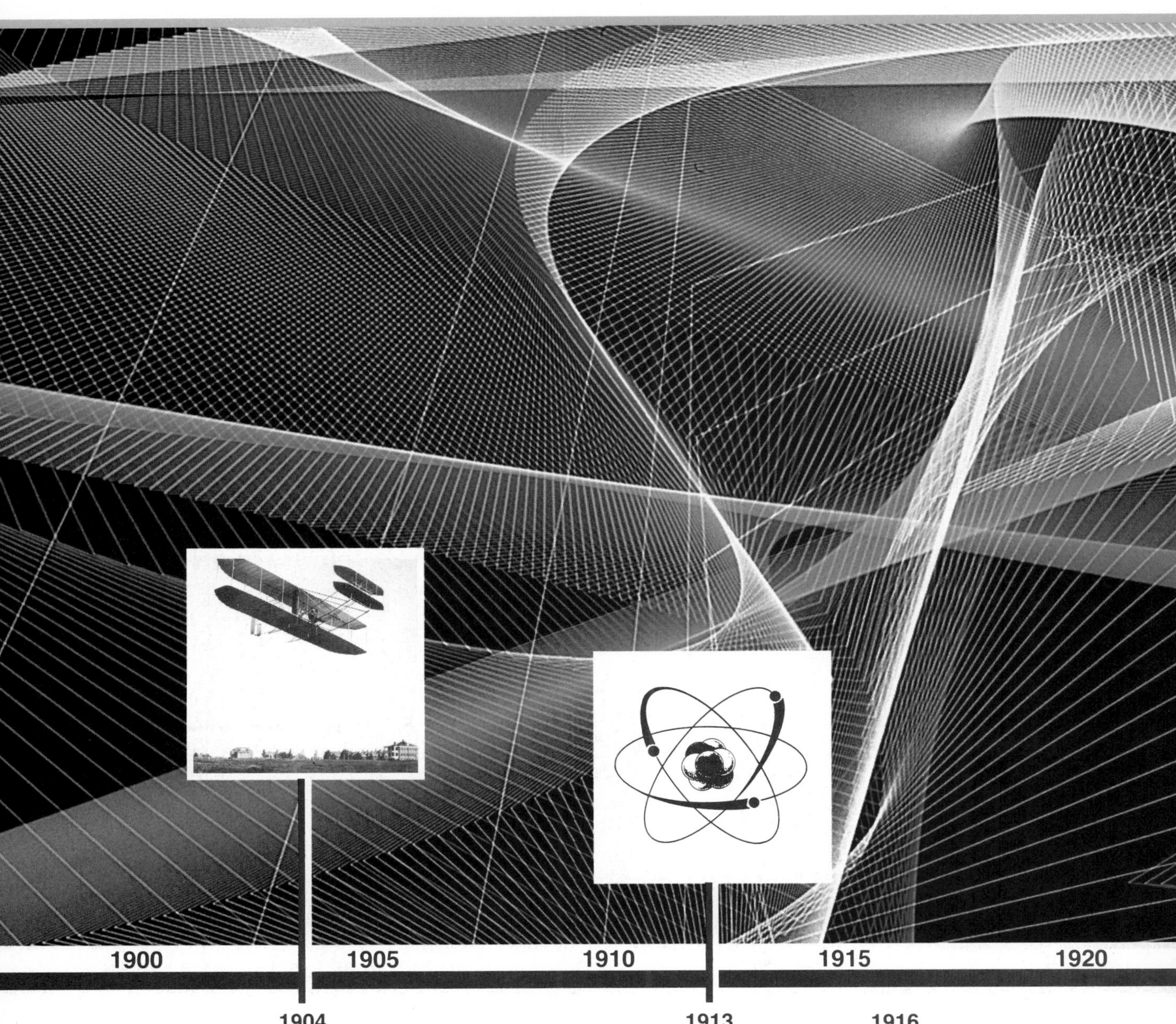

1900	1905	1910	1915	1920

1904
Orville and Wilbur Wright fly their first plane.

1913
Neils Bohr devises planetary model of atom.

1916
Albert Einstein publishes general theory of relativity.

WAVES, LIGHT, AND SOUND

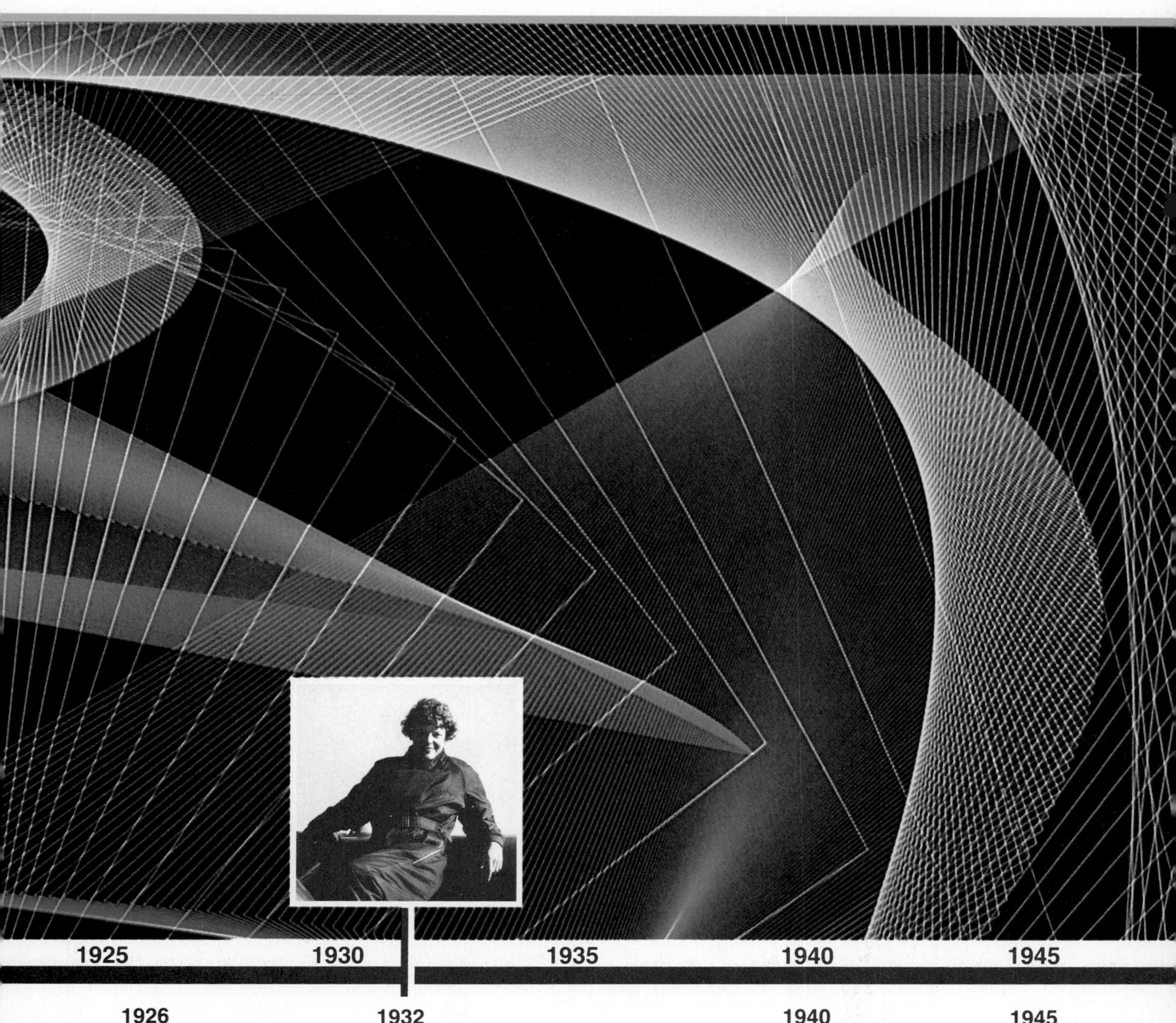

1925	1930	1935	1940	1945

1926
A. A. Milne writes *Winnie the Pooh.*

1932
Amelia Earhart flies solo over Atlantic.

1940
First nuclear chain reaction is produced.

1945
World War II ends.

DESCRIBING A WAVE
WHAT IS SOUND?
MUSIC
CONTROLLING SOUND

Chapter 18

Waves and Sound

Have you ever seen a storm on a large lake or ocean? Then you know how much damage waves can do. The damage is the result of energy transferred from the wind to the shore by the wave. Water waves are only one kind of wave. Sound, light, radio, microwaves, and X rays are all examples of waves. In this chapter we will start learning about waves with perhaps the most common wave phenomenon in our experience, sound.

DESCRIBING A WAVE

You can describe a piece of matter by giving its mass, volume, and other physical or chemical properties. To describe a wave you need a whole different set of terms.

GOALS

1. You will learn the terms that describe or characterize a wave.
2. You will be able to calculate frequency, wavelength, or velocity given the other two.

18:1 Wave Characteristics

Have you ever dropped a stone into a pond? The stone creates a series of ripples or waves. The waves move across the water, but the water itself does not move along with the waves. Only the water surface moves up and down in a regular way.

What is a wave?

A **wave** is a rhythmic disturbance that carries energy. Waves transfer energy from one place to another. If a leaf is floating on the water, the waves will make it move up and down. The leaf is given kinetic energy. The energy of a wave does work on anything in its path. Loud sound waves can shake windows and even break glass. Light waves from the sun are the largest source of energy on Earth.

F.Y.I. Water waves are special kinds of waves called surface waves. They have characteristics of both transverse and compressional waves.

A water wave has many properties that all waves have. Figure 18–1 is a diagram showing water waves at one moment in time. The "hill top" of a wave is called the **crest,** and the "valley" is the **trough.** Locate these

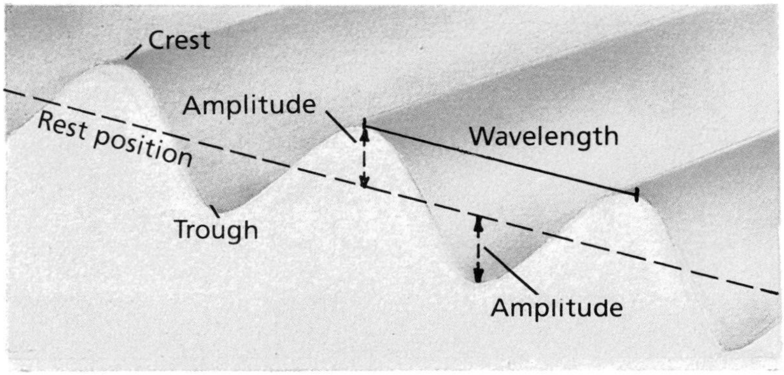

FIGURE 18–1. The parts of a transverse wave are labeled on this cross section of a water wave.

wave parts on Figure 18–2. One **wavelength** is the distance between a point on one wave and the same identical point on the next wave. Wavelength can be measured from crest to crest, or from trough to trough, or between any two corresponding points.

What is a transverse wave?

Amplitude is the greatest distance the particles in a wave rise or fall from their rest position. The energy carried by the wave depends on the amplitude. The larger the amplitude, the greater the wave energy.

What controls the amplitude of a wave?

Some waves are transverse waves. In a **transverse wave,** matter moves at right angles to the direction the wave travels. Suppose you and a friend hold the ends of a rope. If you shake your end up and down, a wave will travel along the rope. The rope itself moves only up and down. One up and down motion of the rope at one point is called a vibration.

F.Y.I. The distance traveled by a wave can be measured from any identical point on two successive waves.

Waves are reflected off boundaries. When a wave is reflected from a surface, it usually changes its direction. If you suddenly move your end of the rope up and down, a wave pulse will travel down the rope. When it reaches your friend's hand, it will be reflected and return to you.

18:2 Frequency of a Wave

The **frequency** is a count of the number of waves that pass a given point in one second. As the number of waves that pass a given point in one second increases, the frequency increases. The frequency of a wave is measured in a unit called a hertz. One hertz (Hz) is one wave per second. The frequency of the note "middle C" is 262 Hz. How many times per second does this sound vibrate? 262

How is the frequency of a wave expressed?

The frequency and wavelength of waves at a given velocity are related. A wave with a long wavelength has a low frequency. Few crests pass a given point in a second. As the wavelength decreases, the frequency increases.

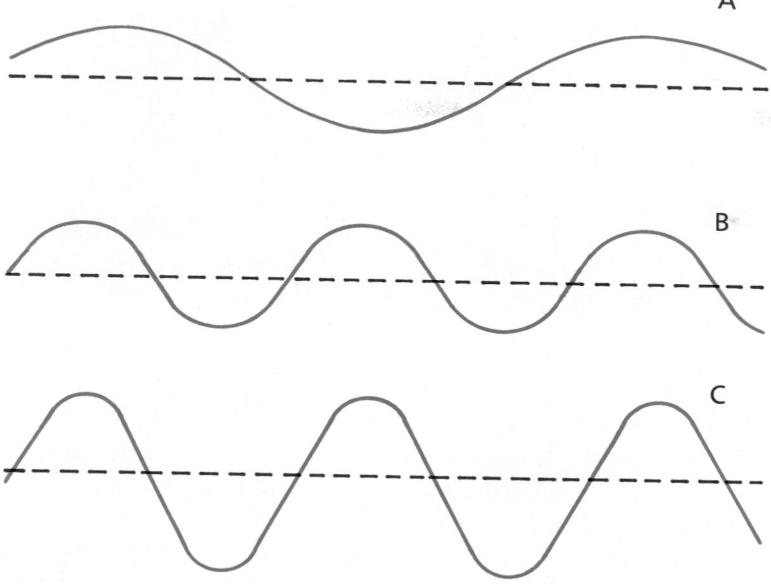

FIGURE 18–2. Waves A and B have equal amplitudes but different wavelengths. Waves B and C have equal wavelengths but different amplitudes.

18:3 Velocity of a Wave

The wave velocity is the distance traveled by any point on the wave in one second. The velocity of a wave depends mainly on the material through which it is passing. For example, the velocity of waves along a rope is lower in heavy thick rope than in a thin light rope. The velocity of a wave is equal to the product of its frequency and wavelength.

How are frequency, wavelength, and velocity related?

$$\text{velocity} = \text{wavelength} \times \text{frequency}$$
$$v = \lambda \times f$$

The symbol for the Greek letter "lambda" is λ. It is the symbol for wavelength. You can calculate any one of the three values in the equation above if you know the other two.

EXAMPLE Calculating the Velocity of a Wave

A tuning fork has a frequency of 256 hertz. The wavelength of the sound produced by the fork is 1.32 meters. Calculate the velocity of the wave.

Given: wavelength of wave $\lambda = 1.32$ m
frequency of wave $f = 256$ Hz

Unknown: velocity of wave (v)

Basic Equation: $v = \lambda \times f$

Solution: $v = \lambda \times f$
$v = 1.32 \text{ m} \times 256 \text{ Hz} = 338 \text{ m/s}$

INVESTIGATION 18–1

Frequency of Vibration

Problem: What affects the frequency of a pendulum?

Materials

ring stand and clamp
string, 1 meter
large washer or other weight
meter stick
timing device

Procedure

1. Tie one end of the string to the washer. Attach the clamp to the ring stand and place it on the table as shown in Figure 18–3.
2. Tie the string to the clamp so the string measures 60 cm from washer to clamp.
3. Pull the washer to the side so it is about 15 cm from the rest position.
4. Release the washer so it swings back and forth. Count the number of to and fro vibrations of the pendulum in 30 seconds. Record the data in the table.
5. Repeat Steps 2 and 3 with the pendulum 40 cm long and the washer pulled 10 cm from the rest position. Record your data.
6. Repeat Steps 2 and 3 with the pendulum 20 cm long and the washer pulled 6 cm from the rest position. Record your data.
7. If time allows, run a second trial for each pendulum length and average your data.

Data and Observations

Pendulum Length	Vibrations in 30 Seconds	Frequency of Pendulum
60 cm		
40 cm		
20 cm		

FIGURE 18–3.

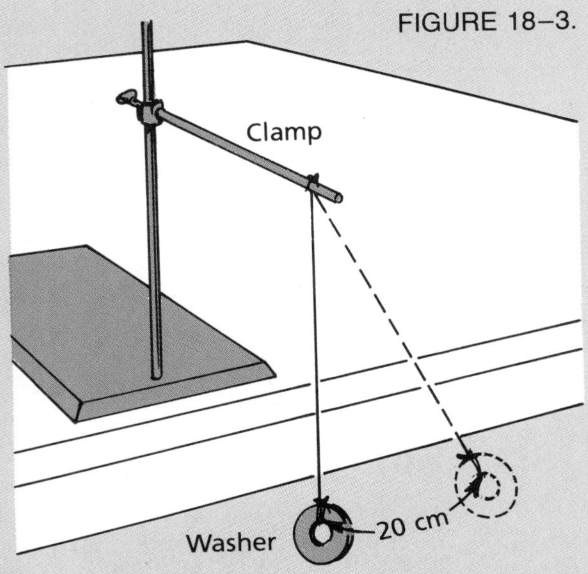

Analysis

1. Which pendulum length has the highest frequency of vibration?
2. Which pendulum length has the lowest frequency of vibration?
3. The amplitude of the pendulum is the distance of the washer from the rest position. What is the initial amplitude of the pendulum in each trial?

Conclusions

4. Review the definitions of kinetic and potential energy in Chapter 5. Where in its swing does the pendulum have the greatest kinetic energy?
5. When does the pendulum have the greatest potential energy?
6. What affects the frequency of vibration of the pendulum?
7. What appears not to affect the frequency of vibration?

EXAMPLE Calculating the Frequency of a Wave

A wave has a wavelength of 1.20 meters. Its velocity is 0.75 meters per second. What is the frequency of the wave?

Given: wavelength of wave $\lambda = 1.20$ m

velocity of wave $v = 0.75$ m/s

Unknown: frequency of wave (f)

Basic Equation: $v = \lambda \times f$

Solution: $v = \lambda \times f$ so $f = v/\lambda$

$$= (0.75 \text{ m/s})/(1.2 \text{ m}) = 0.63 \text{ Hz}$$

PRACTICE PROBLEMS

1. What is the velocity of a wave with a frequency of 760 Hz and a wavelength of 0.45 m?
2. A wave has a velocity of 330 m/s. Its wavelength is 15 m. Calculate the frequency of the wave.

Review

1. What is the amplitude of a rope wave? What determines it?
2. What do you mean when you say that a certain tuning fork has a frequency of 512 hertz?
3. How does increasing the frequency of the wave change the wavelength? The velocity of the wave does not change.
4. A wave has a velocity of 345 m/s. Its frequency is 2050 Hz. Find its wavelength.
5. ★ a. Draw two transverse waves on a piece of paper. Use a ruler to give both the same wavelength. Make one with an amplitude twice the other.
   b. Now draw two more transverse waves having the same amplitude. Make one with a wavelength twice the other.

WHAT IS SOUND?

GOALS

1. You will distinguish between transverse and compressional waves.
2. You will learn to describe sound.
3. You will understand the Doppler effect.

Have you ever considered the many ways humans use sound? Think about the tremendous variety of sounds that are produced, and the ability of the ear and mind to distinguish one from another. Yet we know that sound is only a wave, a rhythmic disturbance of the air that carries energy.

TECHNOLOGY: ADVANCE

Focusing a Camera With Sound

Some cameras made by the Polaroid Land Company find the distance to the subject of the photograph in the same way bats find the distance to their prey. The camera emits a short burst of ultrasound, measures the time it takes the pulse to return to the camera, and adjusts the lens accordingly.

The ultrasound is produced and detected by the same unit, called a transducer. It has a 3-millimeter thick, gold-plated plastic foil that is 38 mm in diameter. An electrical signal causes it to vibrate at a frequency of 50 kHz for just 16 cycles. The electronic circuits then listen for the returning echo. Ultrasound waves that bounce off the subject and return to the camera vibrate the foil, producing a tiny electrical signal. Echoes from subjects as close as 40 cm and as far as 10 m can be detected. The electronic circuits can measure the distance to an accuracy of a few centimeters, allowing precise control of the focus of the camera.

The ultrasound device has uses outside of cameras. One was used in a human-powered airplane that flew over the English Channel. It measured the altitude of the plane above the water. Some have been used to help people who are visually impaired avoid dangers. What uses could you think up for this device?

18:4 Compressional Waves

F.Y.I. Some fish use sound for defense or to attract a mate. By vibrating their swim bladder or rubbing parts of their skeleton together, they can produce squeaks, whistles, coughs, and grinding noises.

Waves in a rope are transverse waves. You can also produce transverse waves in a coil spring by shaking it from side to side. You can produce a different kind of wave in a coil spring by pinching together several coils and releasing them. The disturbance you created in the spring moves forward along the spring. Coils of the spring move forward and backward with a rhythmic motion. At times, some of the coils in the spring wave are compressed or squeezed close together. These areas are called compressions. At other times, these same coils are moved apart. These areas are called rarefactions. This type of wave is called a compressional wave. In a **compressional wave,** matter vibrates in the same direction as the wave travels. Compressional waves are sometimes called longitudinal waves.

How is a compressional wave different from a transverse wave?

Figure 18–4 shows the relationship between a transverse wave and a compressional wave. The crest of the transverse wave corresponds to the greatest compression of the compressional wave. The trough corresponds to the greatest rarefaction. Like transverse waves, compressional waves have wavelengths, frequencies, amplitudes, and velocities. The greater the amount of compression of each wave, the greater the amplitude, and hence the greater the energy carried by the wave.

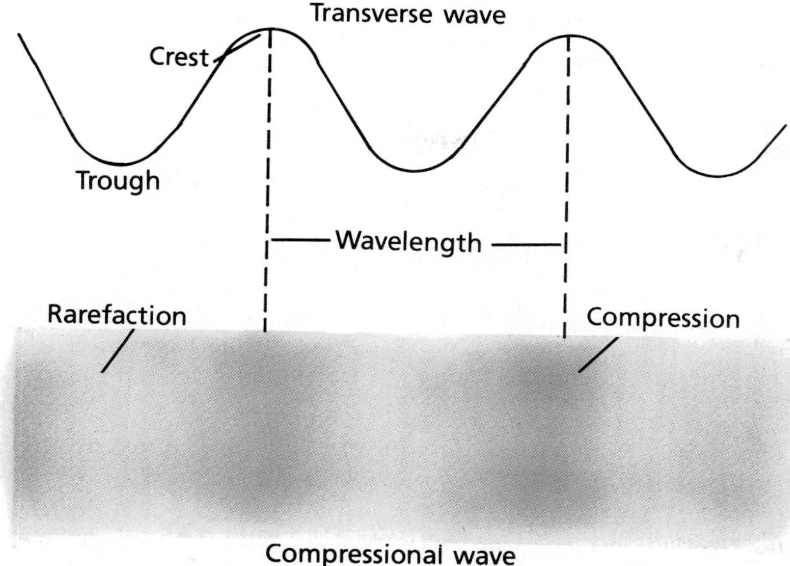

FIGURE 18–4. A sound wave is a compressional wave traveling through matter. The diagram compares compressional and transverse waves. The amplitude of a compressional wave depends on the amount of compression.

Sound waves are compressional waves produced by vibrating matter. The frequency of sounds that can be heard by most people are between 20 Hz and 20 000 Hz. Large animals, such as elephants, can hear sounds below 20 Hz. Sounds above 20 000 Hz are called ultrasound. Some animals can hear ultrasound. For example, a dog can hear sounds with frequencies over 25 000 Hz. Ultrasounds have many uses. They can be used to produce pictures of hidden parts of an object without damaging the object. For example, they can be used to form an image of a baby in the womb without danger to either mother or unborn child.

FIGURE 18–5. Sound waves A and B have equal amplitudes but different wavelengths. Sound waves B and C have equal wavelengths but different amplitudes.

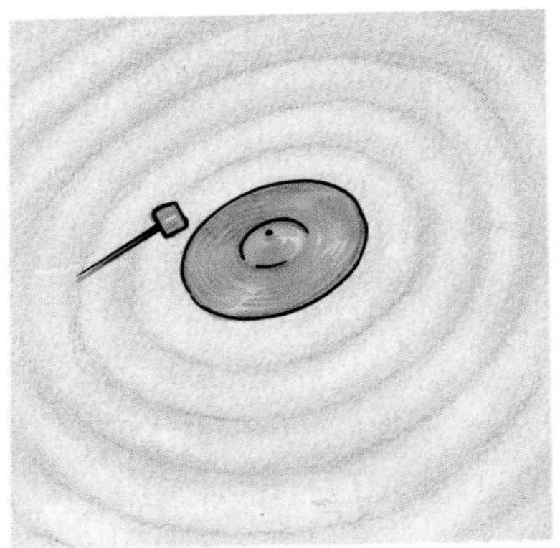

FIGURE 18–6. Sound waves are produced when objects, such as a cymbal, vibrate.

How are sound waves made?

What affects the velocity of sound?

F.Y.I. The increase in air pressure caused by regular conversation is only one-fifth of one-millionth of normal atmospheric pressure.

On what does the intensity of a sound depend?

How are intensity and loudness related?

FIGURE 18–7. The sound of a jet engine may have an intensity of 140 decibels.

18:5 Velocity of Sound

Sound is transmitted through matter. Without matter there can be no transmission of sound. The **velocity of sound** depends on the matter that carries it. The velocity of sound at 0°C in dry air is about 332 m/s. Sound travels faster through warm air than through cold air. The velocity of sound increases about 0.6 m/s for each Celsius degree rise in temperature. At 20°C sound travels through air at 344 m/s. Sound travels much faster through liquids and solids than through gases. The velocity of sound in some common materials is shown in Table 18–1.

As is true for any motion, the velocity of a wave is the distance the wave travels divided by the time required. You can find out how far sound travels in a given time. For example, you can discover how far away a thunderstorm is by measuring the time interval between the time you see the lightning and the time you hear the thunder. Suppose you find that the thunder arrived 3 seconds after the lightning that caused it. Using $d = v \times t$, you find that d = (344 m/s)(3 s) = 1032 m, or about 1 km.

Table 18–1

Velocity of Sound Through Various Substances at 0°C

air	332 m/s	iron	5103 m/s
water	1454 m/s	stone	5971 m/s
wood	3828 m/s		

18:6 Loudness and Pitch

Sound can be as soft as a whisper or so loud that it hurts your ears. The **intensity** of a sound depends on the amplitude of the waves. A loud sound produces a sound wave with large amplitude.

Two people may hear the same sound with a different loudness. **Loudness** describes a person's response to sound intensity. The ear is more sensitive to sounds with frequencies between 300 Hz and 3000 Hz. These sounds have the greatest loudness for a given intensity. The ear perceives sounds having very low or very high frequencies as less loud than sounds of the same intensity with medium frequencies. Ultrasounds can have high amplitude and intensity, but because they cannot be heard, they have no loudness.

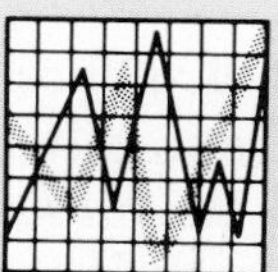

SKILL

Interpreting Diagrams

Problem: How do you get information from a diagram?

Materials

textbook

Background

A good diagram can often explain a complex idea better than several paragraphs of words. To get the most from diagrams, you should do the following things.

1. Study the entire diagram first.
2. Read the caption.
3. Read the labels and identify the parts.
4. Find the part of the text that the diagram illustrates. Go over the text. Locate each part on the diagram as it is referred to in the text.
5. Visualize dimensions. Distances are often indicated between arrows.

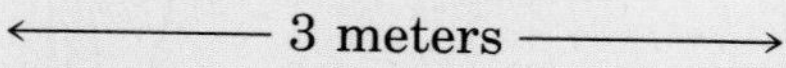

The heads of the arrows indicate where the measurements start and end.

Procedure

A. Figure 18–8

1. What is the purpose of the diagram in Figure 18–8?
2. Identify the text to which the diagram is relates.
3. What do the dark blue areas of the compressional wave represent?
4. What are the white areas?
5. How would you measure one wavelength of a compressional wave?

B. Figure 18–9

6. What is the purpose of the diagram in Figure 18–9?
7. What does the caption tell you about the amplitudes of waves A and B?
8. How is this indicated in the diagram?
9. What does the caption tell you about the wavelengths of B and C?
10. How could you tell this from the diagram?
11. How can you tell whether A and B have the same or different wavelengths?
12. How do the amplitudes of B and C compare? How can you tell from the diagram?

FIGURE 18–8.

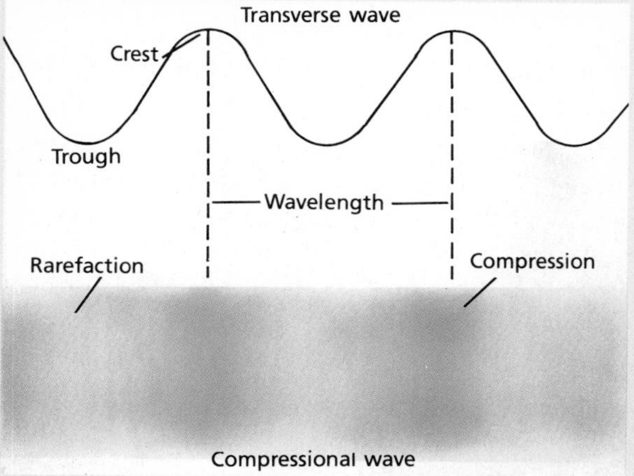

FIGURE 18–9.

What unit is used when measuring loudness?

Loudness is measured using the unit **decibel,** abbreviated dB. The loudness scale is different from other scales you have studied. For example, normal conversation has a loudness of about 60 dB. A sound with loudness of 70 dB is perceived as being twice as loud as a 60 dB sound. An 80 dB sound is four times as loud as the 60 dB sound. The quietest sound that can be heard is 0 dB. When loudness reaches 120 dB, a person feels pain. Figure 18–10 shows several representative sounds and their loudness.

How are the pitch and frequency related?

The pitch of a sound is related to its frequency in somewhat the same way that loudness is related to intensity. A measurement of the frequency of a sound is a measurement of the number of compressions arriving

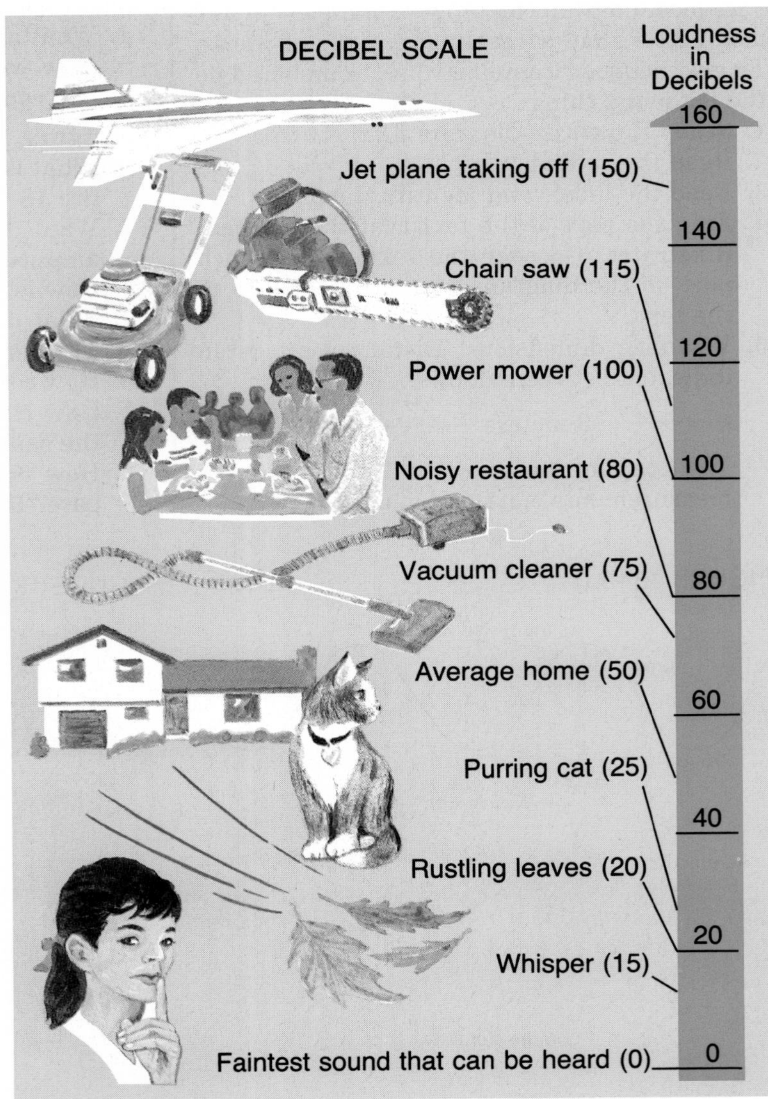

FIGURE 18–10. The illustration gives examples of familiar sounds in various decibel ranges.

F.Y.I. The thermal energy equivalent of the sound emitted over a 90 minute period by a crowd of 50 000 people at a football game is only enough to warm one cup of coffee.

each second. The **pitch** is the way a person hears the frequency. When you sing up a musical scale, the pitch of each note becomes higher. Sounds with higher pitches have higher frequencies.

18:7 The Doppler Effect

The **Doppler effect** is a change in wave frequency caused by the motion of the sound source or the motion of the observer. For example, sound from the siren of an approaching police car is higher than when the car is going away. The motion of the car toward you crowds the sound waves together. The compressions are closer together, increasing the frequency and causing the observer to hear a higher pitch. When the police car is moving away, the compressions are farther apart. The frequency and pitch of the waves is lower. This change in pitch of a moving sound source is an example of the Doppler effect.

The Doppler effect also occurs when the observer is moving and the source of sound is not. While riding in a car have you ever passed someone operating a lawnmower? As you approach, the sound waves strike your ears more frequently. Thus, the pitch is higher. After passing, you notice that the pitch is lower. This happens because the sound waves from the lawnmower now strike your ears less frequently.

Bats make use of the Doppler effect to find their prey. A bat emits a series of high frequency sounds. When the sound is reflected off a flying object, its frequency is changed. By registering the Doppler effect, the bat can tell the direction the object is moving.

BIOGRAPHY

Philip Morrison
1915–

Dr. Morrison is professor of physics at the Massachusetts Institute of Technology. For many years he has been interested in cosmological problems. He was among the first to search for extraterrestrial life. With his wife Phyllis, he is the author of several books on science and host of the TV series "Ring of Truth."

What is the Doppler effect?

Shorter wavelength, higher pitch

Longer wavelength, lower pitch

FIGURE 18–11. The observer on the left hears a higher pitched sound than the observer on the right.

CAREER

Recording Engineer

Eric Suttman spent most of his free time during his freshman year in high school at his neighbor's house setting up a recording studio. It was his first experience at learning about acoustics and working with sound equipment to produce special effects.

While attending college he formed his own production company to produce and record jingles for local businesses. He specialized in operating and working with microphones, sound and video tapes, and light and sound effects. He is now a self-employed recording engineer with his own recording studio. He usually has three or four projects going at a time. In a typical week one might find him in charge of the music at a wedding, recording the band at a local restaurant, or operating the sound system at a concert hall.

For career information write
The National Association
of Broadcasters
1771 N. Street NW
Washington, DC 20036

Review

6. How are sound waves different from water waves?
7. a. Draw two sound waves that differ in frequency.
   b. Draw two sound waves that differ in amplitude.
8. a. How is the intensity of sound different from its loudness?
   b. How is the frequency of a sound different from its pitch?
9. Describe two ways that the Doppler effect can cause you to hear sounds at a pitch higher than the pitch the sound source is producing.
10. ★ A "fishfinder" sends out a pulse of ultrasound and measures the time needed for the sound to travel to a school of fish and back to the boat. If a school is 16 m below the surface, how long would it take sound to make the round trip in the water?

GOALS

1. You will learn the meaning of tone quality.
2. You will learn about musical instruments.
3. You will learn how two sound waves can interact.

MUSIC

Music, just like any other sound, is produced by vibrations. To make a sound musical, however, both the pitch and a new sound characteristic, tone quality, must be carefully chosen. Musical instruments have been developed and changed over thousands of years to allow musicians to achieve the sounds they desire.

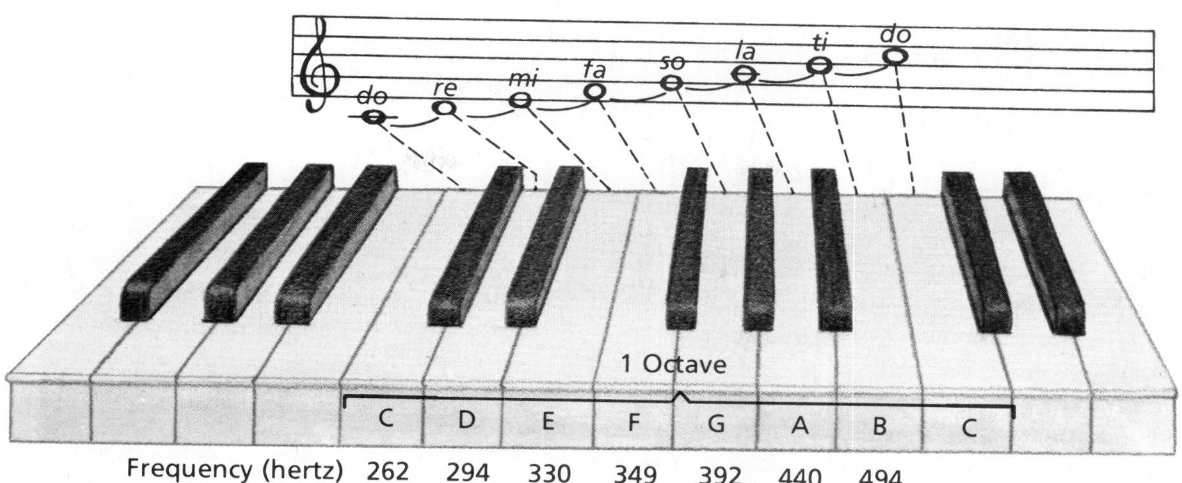

FIGURE 18–12. An octave contains eight notes of increasing frequency. Two notes that are one octave apart have a frequency ratio of 2 to 1.

18:8 Musical Sounds

Most of the sounds that we call music are based on a musical scale. A musical scale is a series of notes that are related to one another by certain ratios of frequencies. The most common kind of musical scale has eight notes. The range between the first and last notes is called an octave. The frequency of the last note is exactly twice the frequency of the first note. If the first note is middle C, 262 Hz, then the frequency of the last note, C above middle C, is 524 Hz. The frequencies of the notes between the two C's are shown in Figure 18–12.

F.Y.I. Unlike most drums, a kettledrum plays notes of different pitch, with a range of about one octave. To change the pitch, the drummer changes the tension of the drumhead.

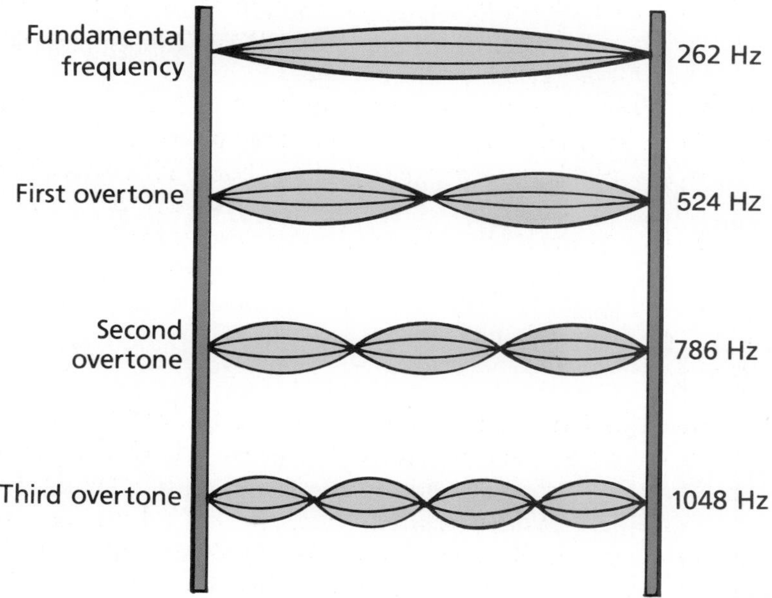

FIGURE 18–13. The diagram shows some of the ways a string, such as on a guitar, can vibrate to produce different overtones. Keep in mind that a string may vibrate in all these ways at once.

INVESTIGATION 18–2

Musical Pitch

Problem: What affects the pitch of sound?

Materials

rubber band
400-mL beaker
8 test tubes
water
test tube rack
dropper
metric ruler
pencil

Procedure

A. The Rubber Band

1. Stretch the rubber band across the top and bottom of the beaker.
2. Pluck the center of the band with your finger. Note the pitch of the sound.
3. Have a classmate pull down on both sides of the band to tighten it slightly. Pluck the band and note any change in pitch.
4. Continue to tighten and pluck the band 3 more times. Record pitch changes.
5. Lay the pencil under the band, but on top of the beaker so that about 2/3 of the band is on one side. Pluck first one side of the band, then the other. Note the relative pitches of the two sides.

B. Vibrating Air Column

6. Number the test tubes 1 through 8. Place the tubes in the rack.
7. Leave test tube 1 empty. Add water to test tubes 2 through 8 so that each tube has a little more water than the preceding tube, Figure 18–14.

FIGURE 18–14.

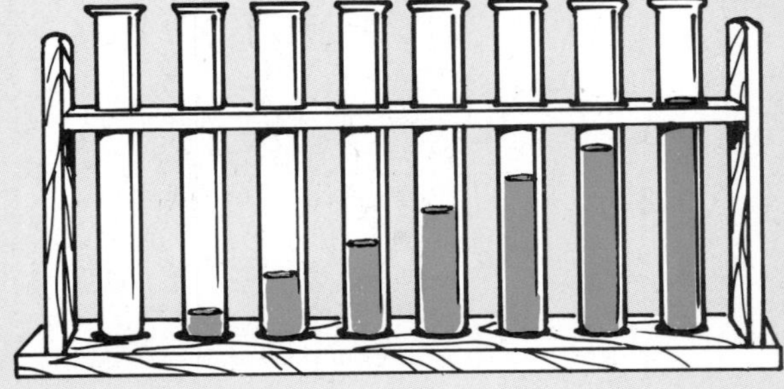

8. Blow across the top of each test tube and listen to the tone produced. Note whether the pitch increases or decreases.
9. Use the dropper to add or remove water from each test tube so that they sound like the notes of a musical scale.
10. Measure the length of the air column above the water in each test tube. Record your observations in the table.

Data and Observations

Test Tube	Length of Air Column	Increased or Decreased Pitch
1		
2		

Analysis

1. How did tightening the rubber band in Step 3 change its pitch?
2. How does the length of the rubber band in Step 5 affect its pitch?
3. How did changing the length of the air column affect the pitch produced?

Conclusions and Applications

4. What are the effects of tension and length on the vibration frequency of a rubber band?
5. What causes the sound you hear when you blow across the top of the test tubes?
6. What is the interval between the lowest and highest notes of the scale called? In what way are the frequencies of these two notes related?
7. How are the lengths of the air columns for the lowest note of the scale and for the highest note related?

Notes that are pleasing when sounded together are said to be in **harmony.** The ratios of the frequencies of tones that are in harmony are small whole numbers. For example, two notes an octave apart have frequencies in the ratio 2 to 1, or $2/1$. The notes E and C are harmonious and are in a ratio 330 to 262 or $5/4$.

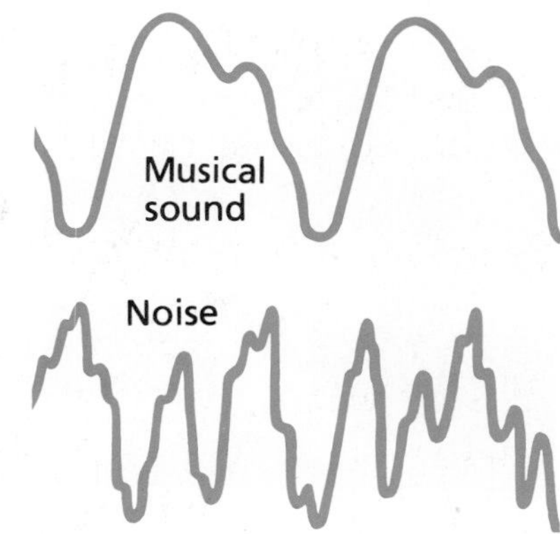

FIGURE 18–15. Musical sounds have regular, repeating patterns. Noise has no regular wave pattern.

When are sounds in harmony?

Vibrations of matter cause sounds, but the sounds you hear depend on more than the matter vibrating. **Tone quality** describes the differences among sounds of the same pitch and loudness. Musical instruments also have different tone qualities. You can tell the difference between sounds of the same pitch made by a piano, guitar, and violin. Each instrument has a special tone quality. Tone quality varies because the sound from each instrument is made up of a different combination of wave frequencies. The tone with the lowest frequency is called the fundamental frequency. Tones with higher frequencies are called overtones. The sound of the human voice or of an instrument consists of the fundamental and several overtones. The number and intensity of overtones produce the tone quality. When you speak or sing, you control the tone quality by changing the shape of your mouth and throat cavities.

What is tone quality?

Hiss through your teeth to make the letters "s" or "f". The sound has no definite pitch. Such a sound is called **noise.** Figure 18–15 shows a graph of noise. The wave pattern is irregular. It does not repeat.

What is noise?

18:9 Musical Instruments

If you hit the head of a drum, the drum will vibrate. The vibrations cause changes in air pressure. You hear these pressure changes as sound. The vibrations could also be caused by a triangle, xylophone, or cymbal. Vibrations in these instruments produce sounds directly. They are called percussion instruments.

The violin, guitar, harp, and piano produce sounds because at least one string vibrates. For this reason they are called stringed instruments. A guitar player plucks the string near one end. The wave pulse travels down the string to the end. There it is reflected back to the other end. The back and forth motion continues, resulting in a regular vibration of the string. The vibration is called a standing wave because the locations of the crests and troughs are always in the same place. The greater the velocity of the pulse on the string, the greater the frequency of the standing wave, and the higher the pitch.

What is a standing wave?

FIGURE 18–16. This tiny violin produces sounds of very high pitch because it has very short strings.

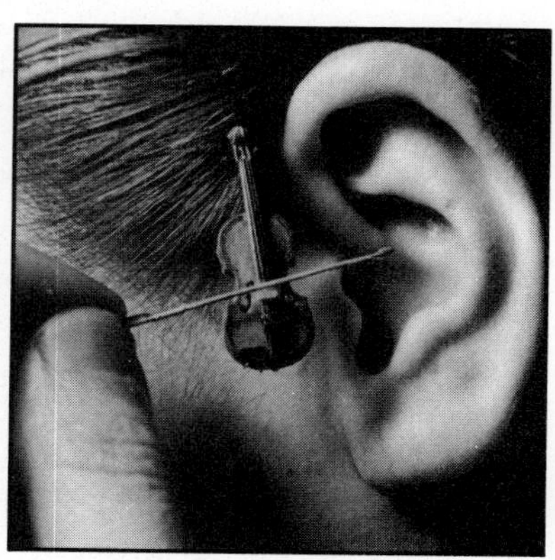

FIGURE 18–17. Electronic instruments allow composers and musicians an almost unlimited choice of pitch and tone quality.

A string, vibrating by itself, produces too faint a tone to be heard. In stringed instruments the string is connected to a soundboard and causes it to vibrate. The soundboard amplifies the sound's loudness. The size and shape of the soundboard, its connection to the string, and other factors control the tone quality of the stringed instrument.

In some instruments, such as electric guitars, the vibration of the string is picked up and amplified electronically. The signals are sent to large loudspeakers, which vibrate at the same frequencies as the strings.

In wind instruments, such as a flute, trumpet, or clarinet, the vibrations take place in a column of air in a tube. The musician produces a series of pulses at one end of a tube. The tone quality of a wind instrument depends on the size of the mouthpiece, the size of the tube, and the material out of which it is made.

The speed of sound in the tube cannot be varied, but the length of the tube can. The longer the tube, the longer it takes the pulse to make the round trip, and the lower the pitch. Pipe organs have a large number of tubes of different lengths, one for each note.

How is the pitch of a wind instrument changed?

In a flute, clarinet, saxophone, or oboe there are holes along the sides of the air tube. As the instrument is played, these holes are opened and closed, changing the length of the vibrating column of air.

In a trombone the length of the air column is changed by moving a slide back and forth. The length of the air column in a trumpet or French horn is varied by valves that add tubes of different lengths to the air column.

In recent years electronic devices have been developed that put together, or synthesize, the fundamental and overtone frequencies that can create any tone quality desired. The tone quality can be similar to a traditional instrument, or it can be a totally new sound.

18:10 Interference

How are beats produced?

Have you ever heard two instruments playing slightly different notes? The loudness of the sound you hear varies in a regular way. This variation is known as beating. Beats are the result of compressions and rarefactions of two slightly different waves reaching your ears together. If the compressions come together they result in a greater compression. The waves reinforce each other, and the sound intensity is greater. **Reinforcement** occurs when the compressions and rarefactions of two or

Describe how reinforcement and cancellation affect sound.

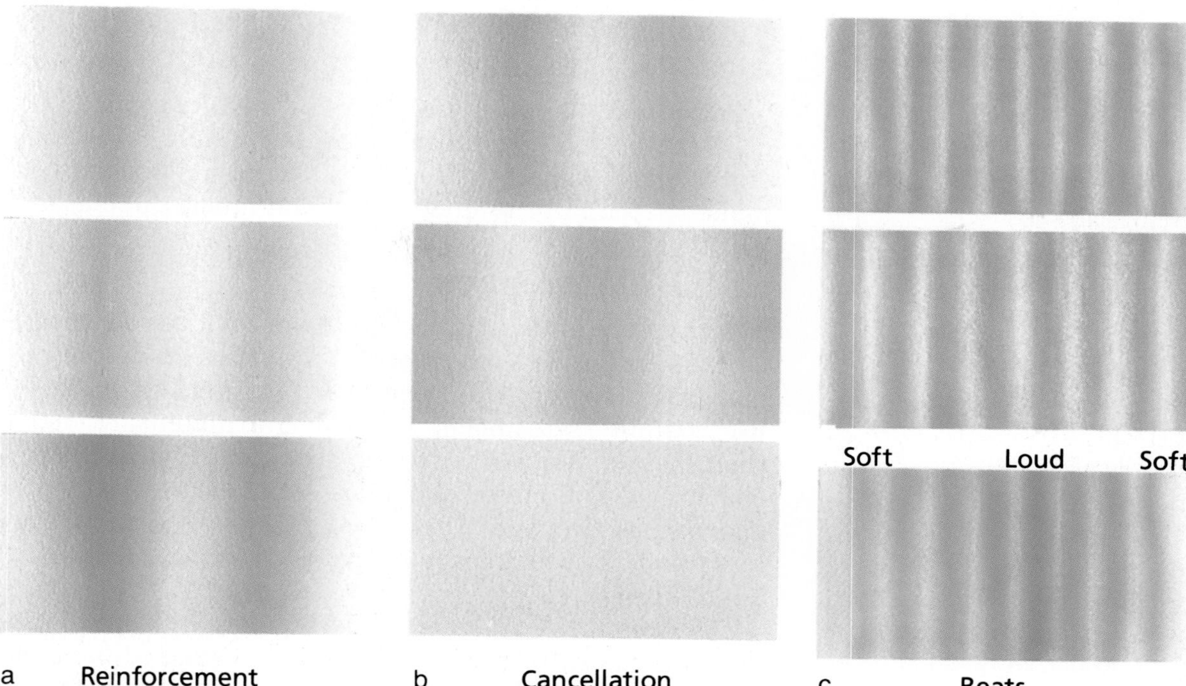

FIGURE 18–18. In (a) the sound compressions reinforce each other to produce a louder sound. In (b) compressions combine with rarefactions to leave no sound wave. In (c) two waves of slightly different frequencies produce sound that varies in loudness.

more waves come together. **Cancellation** occurs if a compression of one wave arrives at the same time as a rarefaction of another wave. The waves partially cancel each other, and a smaller sound intensity results.

The ability of two or more waves to add together to form a new wave is called **interference.**

Review

11. A clarinet and a trumpet play the same note at the same loudness. What characteristic lets you tell one instrument from the other?

12. The frequencies of the notes "E" and "C" are in a ratio of 5/4. Find the note that has a frequency almost exactly 5/4 as much as "F".

13. What is the difference between noise and musical sounds?

14. How can interference produce a sound with less loudness?

★ **15.** Suppose you replaced the air in a wind instrument with helium gas. The velocity of sound in helium is three times that in air. Would the pitch of the instrument go up or down? Why?

CONTROLLING SOUND

GOALS

1. You will learn the meaning of acoustics and the role of a person trained in acoustics.
2. You will understand methods of reducing the loudness of sounds.

Sound may be good, but you can have too much of a good thing. Too loud a sound can harm human hearing and damage objects. Too many sound reflections can make speech hard to understand and music unpleasant.

18:11 Acoustics

What is acoustics?

Acoustics is the study of the science of sound. Scientists and engineers who work in acoustics study the human voice and hearing, and how to protect them. They use computers to model musical instruments to make them better. They also study the ways in which different objects and materials affect sound. Acoustical engineers try to design auditoriums and communication systems so that speakers, singers, and orchestras can be heard clearly.

F.Y.I. The time it takes a sound to die away is the reverberation time. For lecture halls, it should be under 1 second; for music halls, between 1 and 2 seconds. The time in the dome of the Taj Mahal is 12 seconds!

The time it takes sound to reach your ears depends on the distance it travels. When sound is reflected inside a large room, some paths can be much longer than others. A single sound can be heard as a continuous sound that slowly dies away. The result of many different reflections of sound in a large room is called **reverberation.**

In what way can reverberations be controlled?

Some reverberation is good. It makes the sound louder, and the sound seems to come from all directions, not just from the source. If there is too much reverberation, however, speech will become hard to understand. Soft surfaces, such as carpets, drapery, upholstery, and ceiling tile with many small holes, reduce the reverberation. Reverberation can also be controlled by designing the shape of the room to reduce reflections.

FIGURE 18–19. This auditorium has good acoustic properties. It has both hard surfaces and soft materials.

a

b

FIGURE 18–20. Workers in certain industries may have to use hearing protection (a). Loud noises and excess noise may cause hearing loss, even when people are having fun (b).

18:12 Noise Pollution

You probably know about different kinds of pollution such as from smoke, litter, or harmful chemicals. Have you ever considered noise pollution? In today's world, there are many sounds that people find annoying, unpleasant, and even harmful. Frequently people call any sound that bothers them "noise."

The energy transmitted in a sound wave can damage objects. Sudden, sharp sounds such as those caused by thunder and explosions can break windows and crack plaster in buildings. Pressure changes caused by loud sounds can damage your ear, harming your hearing. Exposure to loud noise over a long period of time can cause permanent hearing loss. Loud sounds can also put a person under stress, producing both physical and mental problems. The government has issued regulations to protect the hearing of workers exposed to loud sounds. Table 18–2 lists the maximum daily exposure to sounds of various levels.

List ways that loud sounds can be harmful?

Table 18–2

Occupational Safety and Health Administration Recommended Noise Exposure Limits

Sound level	Maximum daily exposure
90 dB	8 h
95 dB	4 h
100 dB	2 h
105 dB	1 h
110 dB	0.5 h

What actions can reduce noise pollution?

How can noise pollution be reduced? One method is to reduce the intensity of the sound created. New jet engines are designed to produce less noise. Truck tires can be built to reduce the noise they make. The second method is to prevent sound from reaching you. Airplane takeoff patterns can be changed to take the planes away from populated areas. Walls can be built along busy highways to block the noise. Noisy machines can be soundproofed. Finally, people working in a noisy environment can wear hearing protection. Frequently all three methods are used to reduce noise pollution.

Review

16. What kinds of work do acoustical engineers do?

17. List three methods used to control echoes and reverberation in auditoriums.

18. What two factors contribute to hearing loss produced by sounds?

19. Suppose a friend has a job working with a rock band. At his job location the sound level is 100 dB. Use Table 18–2 to determine how many hours a day he can work. If he has to work longer, suggest how he can preserve his hearing.

★ **20.** Large cathedrals have reverberation times as long as five seconds. Would these churches be good places to go to hear a speech? Why or why not?

PROBLEM SOLVING

Cool Music

Karl plays saxophone in the school band. During the football season, the band tunes up in the gym, then goes on to the field to play. The band director warned the musicians that after their instruments had been in the cold air for awhile, they might need to be retuned. On his way out to the field, Karl pondered how and why the pitch would change, and how to adjust the length of his saxophone to fix it. What would you tell him?

Chapter 18 Review

SUMMARY

1. A wave is a rhythmic disturbance that carries energy. 18:1
2. Frequency is the number of waves per second. 18:1
3. Velocity of a wave equals frequency times wavelength. 18:2
4. In a compressional wave such as sound, matter vibrates in the same direction as the wave travels. 18:4
5. The velocity of sound increases as temperature increases. 18:5
6. The intensity of a sound depends on the amplitude of the waves, while its loudness is the way intensity is heard. 18:6
7. The Doppler effect is a change in frequency caused by motion of the sound source or the motion of the observer. 18:7
8. Noise has no definite pitch or wave pattern. 18:8
9. Most musical instruments contain a vibrating part and an air column or sounding board that amplifies the sound and changes its quality. 18:9
10. The ability of two or more waves to add together to form a new wave is called interference. 18:10
11. Acoustics is the study of the science of sound. 18:11
12. Uncontrolled sound can cause health problems. 18:12

VOCABULARY

a. acoustics
b. amplitude
c. cancellation
d. compressional wave
e. crest
f. decibel
g. Doppler effect
h. frequency
i. harmony
j. intensity
k. interference
l. loudness
m. noise
n. pitch
o. reinforcement
p. reverberation
q. tone quality
r. transverse wave
s. trough
t. velocity of sound
u. wave
v. wavelength

Matching

Match each description with the correct vocabulary word from the list above. Some words will not be used.

1. the number of vibrations each second of the source of a wave
2. the distance between two wave troughs
3. two waves that meet and produce either a larger or smaller wave
4. a rhythmic disturbance that carries energy
5. change in frequency caused by moving source
6. vibration in matter made up of compressions and rarefactions
7. the way a person hears the intensity of a sound
8. the unit that measures the intensity of sound
9. result of many reflections of sound in a large room
10. sound with no definite wave pattern

Chapter 18 Review

MAIN IDEAS

A. Reviewing Concepts

Choose the word or phrase that correctly completes each of the following sentences.

1. A sound wave is a *(transverse wave, compressional wave, reverse wave, standing wave).*
2. The ratio of frequencies of two notes an octave apart is *(5/4, 4/3, 3/2, 2/1).*
3. The characteristic of a wave that is measured in hertz is its *(amplitude, velocity, wavelength, frequency).*
4. An instrument that produces sound by the vibration of a reed is in the group called *(percussion, stringed, wind, electronic)* instruments.
5. Interference causes this wave characteristic to change: *(amplitude, velocity, wavelength, frequency).*

Complete each of the following sentences with the correct word or phrase.

6. A(n) ____________ is reflected sound.
7. A muffler on a car reduces ____________ pollution.
8. A flute player changes the length of a(n) ____________ of air by opening and closing holes.
9. Interference between sound waves can cause regular changes in loudness called ____________.
10. ____________ is the study of sound and its control.

Determine whether each of the following sentences is true or false. If it is false, change the underlined word to make the sentence true.

11. Transverse waves can be formed with a coil spring.
12. The hertz is a unit of sound intensity.
13. If the speed of a wave is unchanged, the wavelength will become shorter as the frequency decreases.
14. The Doppler effect involves a change in the pitch of a sound.
15. Carpets and draperies are good reflectors of sound.

B. Understanding Concepts

Answer the following questions using complete sentences when possible.

16. How is a compressional wave different from a transverse wave?
17. In a science fiction movie, a nearby spaceship explodes. You hear the explosion. Is this realistic? Explain.
18. The note "A" has a frequency of 440 Hz. What is the frequency of the same note one octave lower?
19. Suppose you are sitting in the bleachers, 150 m from home plate on a day when it is 20°C. How long after the batter hits the ball do you hear the "crack" of the ball and bat?
20. Bats use the Doppler effect to detect prey. If an ultrasound bounces off an insect flying away from the bat, would the frequency be increased or decreased?
21. A tuning fork has a frequency of 440 hertz. The wavelength of the sound produced by the fork is 0.77 meters. Calculate the velocity of the wave.
22. A submarine starts its propellers. A ship 450 m away is monitoring sounds and hears the noise. How long does it take the sound to reach the ship?
23. What is the loudness (in decibels) of the sound of normal conversation?
24. If the sound of the conversation becomes twice as loud, what will it be in decibels?
25. What is the intensity of sound that can cause pain in the ear?

C. Applying Concepts

Answer the following questions using complete sentences when possible.

26. The marching band tunes the wind instruments in the band room, then goes outside into very cold weather. Would the pitch of wind instruments be affected? How and why?
27. In music a "major triad" chord consists of three notes. The ratio of the second to the first is $5/4$ (a major third interval) while the ratio of the third to the second is $6/5$ (a minor third interval). If the first note is F, find the second and third notes.
28. Suppose your friend is 500 m away along a railroad track while you have your ear to the tracks. He drops a stone on the tracks. How long will it take the sound to reach your ear? How long will the sound take to travel through the air at 20°C?
29. How many times louder is a noisy restaurant than an average home?
30. Suppose your class invites a person to give a speech. When you test out the sound system in the gym you find there are so many echoes the speaker cannot be understood. What could be done?

PROJECTS

1. Design and carry out an experiment to show the effects of various kinds of materials on sound. Record the problem, procedure, observations, and conclusions.
2. Prepare a report on the use by bats of both echo timing and the Doppler shift to locate their prey.
3. Prepare a report on the use of ultrasound to produce images of the human body.

SKILL REVIEW

1. What is illustrated in Figure 18–1?
2. What does the caption tell you about the frequencies of the waves in Figure 18–18c?
3. Find the text sentence(s) that describe Figure 18–15.
4. What is another question you might want to ask about the rubber band experiment in Investigation 18–2?
5. How could you separate a mixture of salt and pepper?

READINGS

1. Ardley, Neil. *Sound and Music.* New York: Franklin Watts, 1984.
2. Brandt, Keith. *Sound.* Mahwah, NJ: Troll Associates, 1985.
3. Gilbert, S. "How a Wave Works." *Science Digest.* August, 1986, p. 31.
4. Kendall, Alan. *Musical Instruments.* Topsfield, MA: Merrimack Publishing Circle, 1986.

ELECTROMAGNETIC RADIATION
LIGHT AND COLOR
WAVE PROPERTIES OF LIGHT

Light

Light, like sound, provides us with a "window" on our world. We receive much of the information about our surroundings from the light that reaches our eyes. Yet, light is only one form of radiation that carries energy to us by means of waves. In this chapter, we will explore many of those forms.

ELECTROMAGNETIC RADIATION

Radio waves, light, and X rays may seem very different from each other. Yet they are all forms of waves, and have many of the same properties as water and sound waves. Radio, light, and X rays are all transverse electromagnetic waves with different wavelengths. In this section we will learn about the many different forms of electromagnetic waves.

GOALS

1. You will become familiar with the names of radiation in the electromagnetic spectrum.
2. You will learn the sources and uses of radiation in the spectrum.

19:1 The Electromagnetic Spectrum

What are some characteristics of electromagnetic waves?

What do the following have in common: radio, television, microwave ovens, heat lamps, light, tanning lamps, X-ray machines? They all use electromagnetic waves.

Electromagnetic waves are transverse waves, like waves on a rope. The transfer of energy by electromagnetic waves is called **radiation.** Electromagnetic waves carry energy through "empty space" at the tremendous velocity of 300 000 kilometers per second. Sunlight, for instance, is an electromagnetic wave that carries energy from the sun through space to Earth. Electromagnetic waves can move through matter too, although at slower speeds.

INVESTIGATION 19–1

Compressional and Transverse Waves

Problem: How do compressional and transverse waves move?

Materials

large spring or Slinky

Procedure and Observations

1. Place the spring on a smooth level surface. Have a partner hold the opposite end firmly. Stretch the spring only until the coils are no more than 1 cm apart.
2. Suddenly move your end of the spring sideways about 20 cm, then quickly return it to its original position. A pulse should travel along its length. Practice until you can do this easily. Observe the direction in which the pulses move, and the direction in which the coils of the spring move. Make a sketch of the pulse.
3. Reach a short distance down the spring and gather the coils toward you. Quickly release them. Again, practice may be needed to form a good pulse. Observe the direction in which the pulse moves, and the direction in which the coils of the spring move. Make a sketch of the pulse.
4. Have your partner send sideways pulses to you at the same time you produce sideways pulses in the same direction. Carefully observe the pulses when they come together and after they pass through one another. Describe your observations. Sketch the pulse when the two pulses come together.
5. Repeat making sideways pulses, but you and your partner make pulses in opposite directions. Describe your observations. Sketch the pulse when the two come together.

Analysis

1. What kind of wave was produced in Step 2?
2. What kind of wave was produced in Step 3?

Conclusions and Applications

3. How could you show that energy is transferred from one end of the spring to the other?
4. When two sideways pulses made in the same direction meet, what is the size of the resulting pulse?
5. What is the size of the pulse made when two sideways pulses formed in the opposite direction meet?
6. How do compressional and transverse waves differ?

FIGURE 19–1.

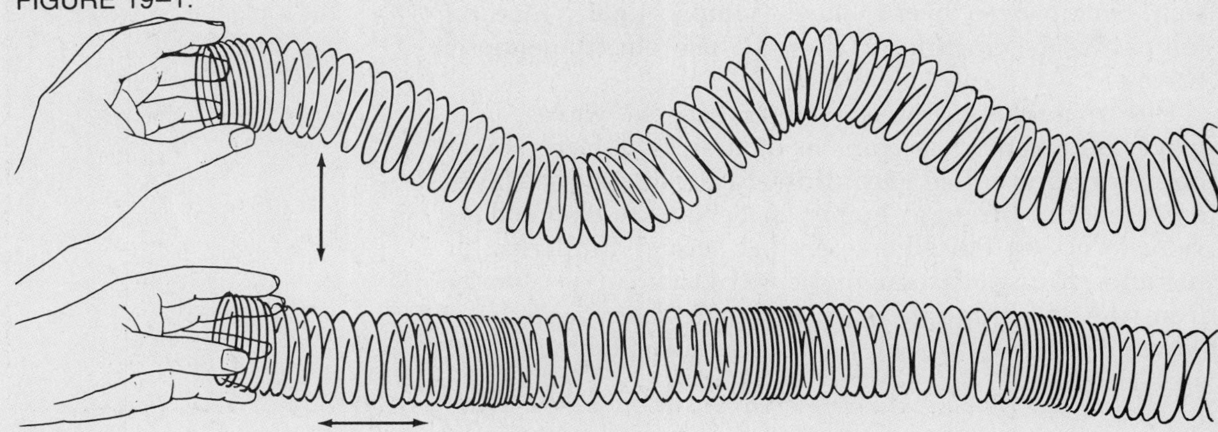

How do electromagnetic waves differ?

A property that differs from one kind of electromagnetic wave to another is wavelength. The arrangement of electromagnetic waves in order of their wavelengths is called the **electromagnetic spectrum,** Table 19–1. Radiation in the spectrum ranges from the very short wavelength gamma rays on one end to long wavelength radio waves on the other. The only portion of the spectrum that can be detected by our eyes is light. The other radiation is invisible, but has many uses.

In some ways, electromagnetic radiation behaves like particles, not waves. Radiation carries energy and momentum. When radiation collides with matter it behaves just like a particle. The particle of radiation is

Table 19–1

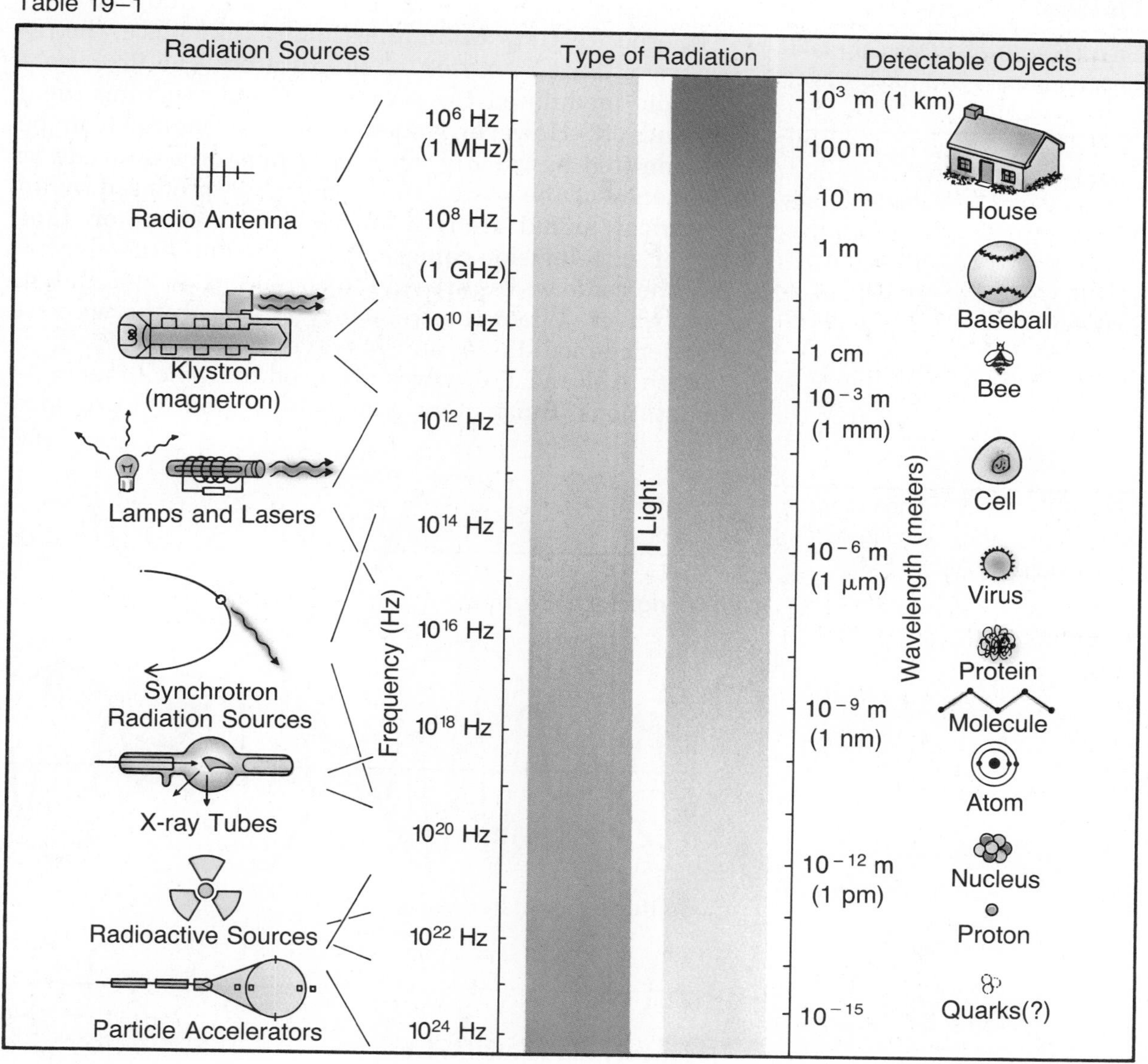

FIGURE 19–2. Cellular telephones in cars use radio waves to communicate.

called the photon. The photon has energy and momentum. It has no mass and travels at the velocity of an electromagnetic wave, 300 000 km/s in a vacuum. The energy and momentum of the photon depend on its wavelength. The shorter the wavelength, the higher the energy.

19:2 Radio and Microwaves

What are the properties of radio waves?

How are AM and FM radio waves different?

Radio waves have wavelengths longer than about 10 cm. They are the electromagnetic radiation with the longest wavelength, therefore the lowest energy. The main use of radio waves is to communicate. Radio and TV broadcasting and cordless and cellular telephones are examples of radio waves used to transmit information.

In order to allow communication to take place, the radio wave must be varied, or **modulated.** The first users of radio modulated the waves by simply turning them on and off. However, much more information can be transmitted by rapidly varying either the amplitude or frequency of the wave. The variation is produced by an electrical signal from a microphone, record or tape player, or television camera. When the amplitude is varied, the radio waves are said to be amplitude-modulated, AM, waves. When the frequency is varied, the wave is frequency-modulated, an FM wave.

Both AM and FM waves are used by radio broadcasting stations. But motors, automobiles, and lighting also

FIGURE 19–3. The diagram shows the same varying current modulated as AM or FM.

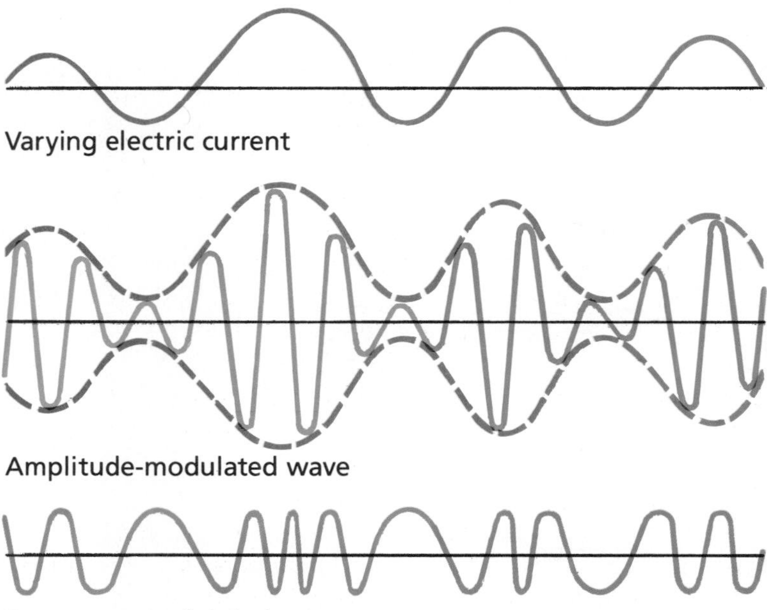

TECHNOLOGY: APPLICATIONS

Photographic Film: Light and Chemistry

All photographic film uses chemical compounds made of silver and one of the halogens. They are called silver halides for short. The tiny crystals of silver halides are embedded in a layer of gelatin, called the emulsion. The emulsion then is put on a plastic backing. When light strikes the silver halide, it breaks the chemical bond, releasing metallic silver in a microscopic-sized particle. The free halogen escapes from the emulsion. The film now contains microscopic clumps of metallic silver where light struck it, and silver halide where there was no light.

Next the film is developed into a negative. The developer converts the microscopic clumps of silver into grains large enough to be seen. The action of the developer is stopped with an acid bath, and the remaining silver halide is removed with a fixer, or hypo solution. The film is finally washed and dried.

A positive print is then made. White light shines through the negative film onto a sheet of paper coated with photographic emulsion. Light strikes the paper where it passes through the clear areas of the negative, the areas where no light hit the original scene.

produce radio waves. When these waves are detected by our receivers, we hear them as "static" or "interference." The radio waves produced by these disturbances change the amplitude of the waves we want to detect. FM receivers are made to be insensitive to changes in amplitude. For this reason, FM broadcasts usually have less static.

Compare the broadcast frequencies of TV, AM radio, and FM radio.

In television broadcasting, the picture is changed into an electrical signal called the video signal. The sound becomes the audio signal. The television station broadcasts the video signal using AM and the audio signal using FM methods. Thus, TV broadcasting is both AM and FM.

Each commercial radio station broadcasts waves at a specific wavelength and frequency. AM stations use waves with frequencies between 540 and 1620 kilohertz. One kilohertz is one thousand hertz. FM stations broadcast at frequencies between 87 and 108 megahertz. One megahertz is one million hertz. Television channels two through six use frequencies from 54 to 87 megahertz. Channels seven through thirteen broadcast between 174 and 216 megahertz, and channels 14 through 82 use the frequencies between 470 and 890 megahertz.

Perhaps you have listened to shortwave radio broadcasts from stations thousands of kilometers away. Shortwave stations broadcast using waves of shorter wavelength, or higher frequency, than AM stations, but

FIGURE 19–4. Shortwave broadcasts reflect from the ionosphere and strike Earth at great distances from the transmitter.

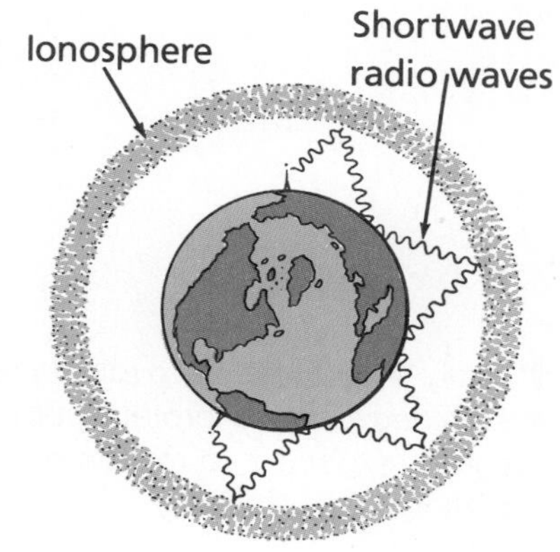

a

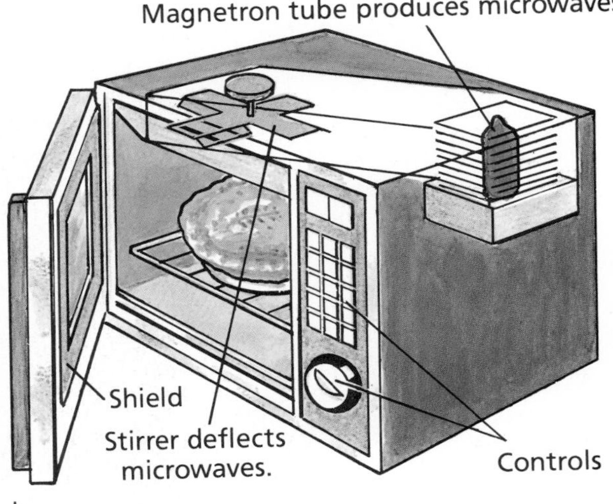

b

FIGURE 19–5. Microwaves can be used to transmit information by television or telephone (a) as well as to cook food (b).

lower than TV stations. Radio waves in this range are reflected when they reach Earth's ionosphere. The ionosphere is a layer of plasma, or electrically charged particles, in the atmosphere starting about 80 kilometers above Earth's surface. Shortwave broadcasts can be received at great distances from the station because of this reflection.

Microwaves have wavelengths between 10 centimeters and 0.3 millimeters. Microwaves are often used to send telephone messages, television programming, and computer information across the country or from Earth to a satellite and back. Dish-shaped antennas are used to transmit a narrow beam of microwaves to another dish. A single beam can carry as many as one-thousand telephone conversations or over one-hundred television signals at one time.

What is microwave radiation?

Microwaves can also be used to carry energy. In a microwave oven, the energy travels from the source of the radiation to the food in the oven. When absorbed, the radiation causes the molecules in the food to rotate and vibrate more. That is, the radiant energy is converted into thermal energy. As this kinetic energy increases, the temperature rises, and the food cooks. Microwaves are directly absorbed by the food, not by the container. Glass or paper cooking dishes are used because they allow microwaves to pass through. Metal containers, however, reflect the waves, and cannot be used.

F.Y.I. A microwave oven has a shielded door to protect people from exposure to microwave radiation.

19:3 Infrared Radiation

Electromagnetic radiation with wavelengths just longer than light is called infrared. **Infrared radiation** has wavelengths between 200 micrometers (0.2 mm) and 0.7 micrometers (0.0007 mm). Infrared radiation is produced by all hot objects. When an object absorbs infrared radiation, the molecules vibrate, increasing the temperature of the object. For this reason, infrared radiation is often used to dry and warm things. For example, infrared lamps are used in fast food restaurants to keep cooked food warm.

The amount of infrared radiation produced by an object depends on its temperature. The higher the temperature, the more radiation. Tumors in the human body are often warmer than the tissue around them. They can be detected by the infrared radiation they give off.

BIOGRAPHY

Ignacio Tinoco, Jr.
1930–

Dr. Tinoco combines chemistry, physics, and biology when he studies DNA and RNA. He uses polarized radiation in a technique in which light and matter interact. He also uses nuclear magnetic resonance, NMR, the interaction of magnetic fields and atomic nuclei. In this way he can "see" nucleic acids at the atomic level.

19:4 Visible Radiation

Light, or **visible radiation,** has wavelengths between about 0.7 and 0.4 micrometers. Light is produced by very hot objects. For example, in an ordinary incandescent lamp the tungsten wire is at about 2400°C. Light is often detected by its effects on molecules and solids. In green plants, light causes a series of chemical reactions called photosynthesis. In the eye, rods and cones contain large molecules that change shape when a tiny amount of light strikes them.

There are so many applications of light that a special science, **optics,** is devoted to the study of light and its uses.

19:5 Ultraviolet Radiation

How is ultraviolet radiation different from light?

Ultraviolet radiation has wavelengths shorter than light. It therefore has higher energy. It is produced by very hot objects such as the sun, or by special lamps called "black lights." When sunlight strikes your body, the ultraviolet radiation enables cells in your skin to produce vitamin D. This vitamin is needed for healthy

a

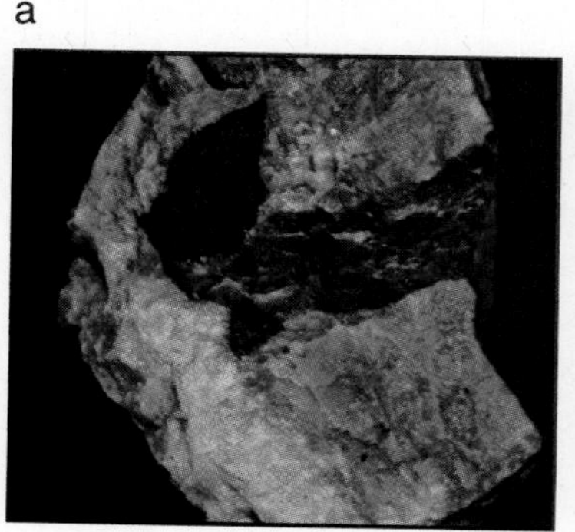

b

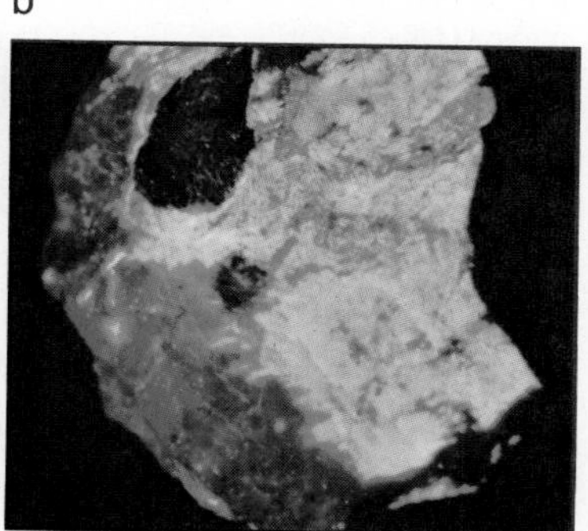

FIGURE 19–6. Many rocks (a) contain minerals that fluoresce (b) under ultraviolet radiation.

F.Y.I. The eyes of many insects are sensitive to ultraviolet radiation, but not sensitive to the red and yellow parts of the spectrum. Yellow lamps that are visible to us are invisible to them, and lights in the violet or ultraviolet range attract them.

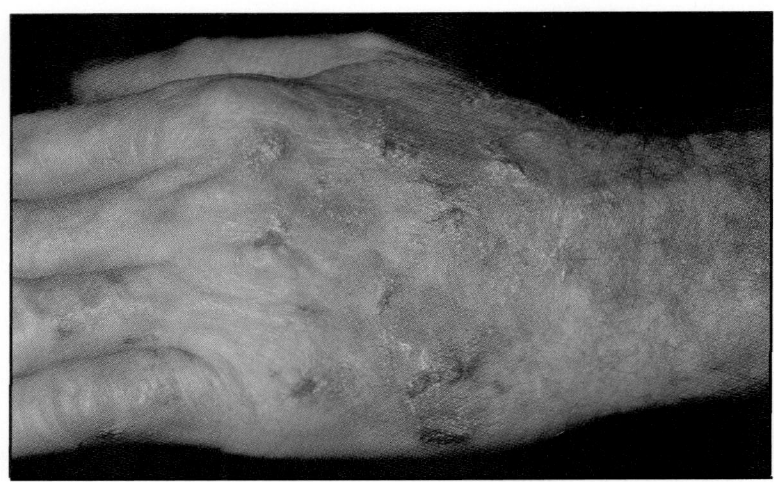

FIGURE 19–7. Excess exposure to the sun's ultraviolet radiation can cause skin cancer.

bones and teeth. Ultraviolet radiation can also kill living cells. For this reason, hospitals often use ultraviolet lamps to kill harmful bacteria.

Why is overexposure to sunlight dangerous?

Overexposure to ultraviolet radiation can be harmful. Frequent overexposure to sunlight is known to cause skin cancer. Sunscreen lotions contain substances that absorb ultraviolet radiation and thereby provide some protection for the skin. A layer of ozone, a form of oxygen, in the atmosphere shields us from most of the ultraviolet radiation produced by the sun. Scientists have recently found that Freon, used in spray cans, may be destroying this ozone layer. As a result, skin cancer may become more of a problem for us. Ultraviolet radiation also causes the breakdown of many paints and plastics.

19:6 X Rays and Gamma Rays

How is the energy carried by X rays and gamma rays different from other electromagnetic radiation?

X rays and **gamma rays** are electromagnetic waves with the shortest wavelengths, less than 0.1 micrometer, and the highest energy. In an X-ray source, electrically charged particles are given large kinetic energy. These particles then crash into other matter, where some of their kinetic energy is changed into X-ray radiation. The remainder becomes thermal energy. Gamma rays are produced in the center, or nucleus, of radioactive atoms.

Where is gamma radiation produced?

In 1895, the German scientist W. K. Roentgen accelerated charged particles into glass. He noticed that a fluorescent-coated plate near the glass glowed with green light. He did not know what kind of radiation made the plate glow, so he called the unknown radiation, X rays.

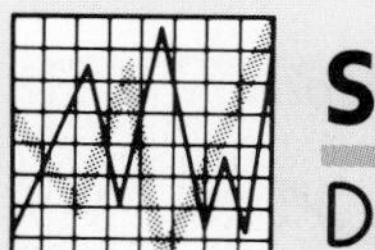

SKILL
Drawing Conclusions

Problem: How do you draw conclusions from experimental data?

Background

A conclusion is a judgment based on interpreting observations and answering questions. Scientists do not base their conclusions on just one set of data. The experiment is repeated many times to be sure the same results occur every time.

It is especially important not *to draw conclusions that are not supported by your data.*

Materials

shiny white, red, blue, and green paper
red, green, and blue gelatin filters
flashlight

Procedure

1. Darken the room as much as possible.
2. Turn on your flashlight and aim it at the white paper. Observe and record the color of the paper in the table.
3. Repeat Step 2 with the red, blue, and green pieces of paper.
4. Place the red filter in front of the beam of the flashlight. Shine the filtered beam on the white, red, blue, and green papers and record the colors you see.
5. Repeat Step 4 using the blue filter and then the green filter.

Data and Observations

Filter / Paper	none	red	green	blue
white				
red				
blue				
green				

Analysis and Conclusions

1. Why did the papers look white, red, blue, and green respectively in the white light?
2. How did the filters affect the flashlight beam?
3. How did using a filter affect the way the different papers looked?
4. Using your observations, explain how the color of the light shining on an object affects the way we see that object. *Support your conclusions by stating the specific observations that prove it.*
5. Can you conclude that your observations will be the same for all colored objects? Explain.

FIGURE 19–8.

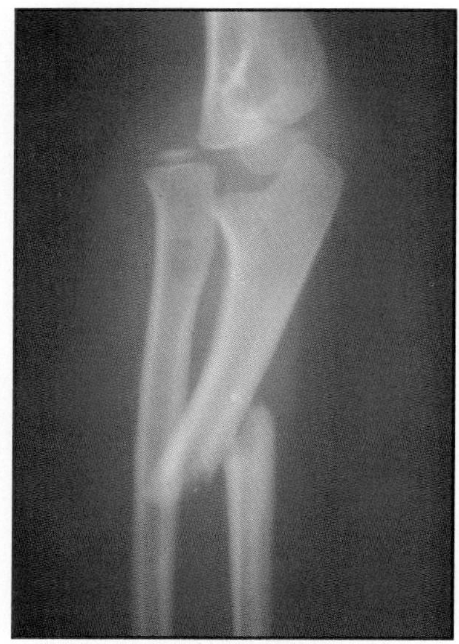

a

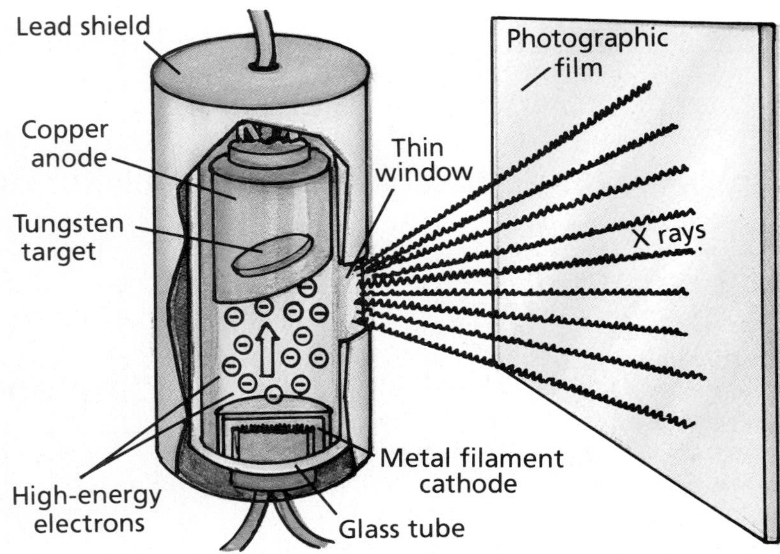

b

FIGURE 19–9. X rays are absorbed more by bone than by soft tissue (a). High-speed electrons striking the tungsten target causes its atoms to give off X rays (b).

Why can X rays be used to image bone inside the body?

Roentgen held his hand in front of the plate and saw an outline of the bones in his hand on the plate. Today doctors use sensitive photographic film rather than a fluorescent plate to detect X rays. Why do X rays pass through soft tissue more easily than through bones? All materials absorb X rays to some degree. The amount absorbed depends on the atomic number of the elements in the material. For example, bone contains a large amount of calcium. Calcium has a higher atomic number than most of the elements that make up softer tissue. Therefore, bone absorbs X rays better than soft tissue does. This allows X rays to be used to produce an image of bones within the body. X rays are also used in airports to detect metal weapons in unopened luggage.

X rays and gamma rays are high energy radiation that can harm cells. People who work with these forms of radiation must be protected against overexposure to the harmful rays. Lead is used as a shield because lead, with its large atomic number, absorbs both X rays and gamma rays more effectively than materials of lower atomic number.

Review

1. How can a rope be a model of an electromagnetic wave?
2. Why is FM radio often less noisy than AM radio?
3. Describe how microwaves cook food.

4. How could you detect ultraviolet radiation in a dark room?
★ 5. How do X-ray photographs aid physicians and dentists in their work?

LIGHT AND COLOR

GOALS

1. You will learn the difference between opaque, transparent, and translucent objects.
2. You will understand the basics of color vision.
3. You will understand how color addition and subtraction work.

Light is the only visible part of the electromagnetic spectrum. Our eyes are sensitive to a range of wavelengths, which we see as different colors. White light is a mixture of these colors. The colors of the objects we see depend on the color of the light that falls on them and on how they reflect that light into our eyes.

19:7 Light and Matter

Look around the room on a sunny day. You see objects because they reflect light. Some objects reflect more light than others. Dark rough objects reflect little light. Light-colored or white objects reflect much more light. They are more visible in dimly lighted rooms.

How did the light get into your room? It entered through the windows not the walls. Glass is transparent. A **transparent** material passes, or transmits light. A wall absorbs light. **Opaque** materials absorb all light. Materials that transmit light, but do not allow you to see clearly through them are called **translucent** materials. Whether an object is transparent, translucent, or opaque depends on the material, its thickness, and whether its surfaces are rough or smooth.

How are transparent, translucent, and opaque materials different?

19:8 Colors

How do we see colors?

As you have seen, light waves have wavelengths between 0.4 and 0.7 micrometers. The eye is sensitive to electromagnetic radiation with wavelengths between these two values. When light strikes the rear surface, or retina, of the eye, it causes chemical reactions. In the retina are a large number of nerve ends contained in cells. The nerves go from the retina directly to the brain. The chemical reactions stimulate the nerves, and the brain responds in a way that we call vision.

Certain parts of the retina, called cone cells, contain chemicals that react only when struck by certain wavelengths of light. Our brain responds to these signals in a way that we call color vision.

FIGURE 19–10. The transparent and translucent glass window ornament contrasts with the opaque window frame.

CAREER

Commercial Artist

One reason Naomi enjoys her job as a commercial artist is because there are so many different ways to be involved in illustration and design. Some people are hired to help promote, sell, or display products as well as events such as concerts. Others, such as Naomi, work for major advertising companies.

A few commercial artists begin their careers straight out of high school, but many, like Naomi, go on to art school or college to learn more about the technical aspects of lighting, color, and perspective. Understanding light and color mixing, as well as being creative, helps to improve her drawings, exhibits, and displays.

Many commercial artists work as freelancers. Naomi likes freelancing because it allows her to work for a variety of companies, use a variety of skills, and set her own schedule.

For career information write
The American Institute of Visual Arts
1059 Third Avenue
New York, NY 10021

Name the primary light colors.

The colors blue, green, and red are known as the primary light colors. Any color can be produced by mixing the correct amounts of light of these three colors. When all three are mixed in equal amounts, we see white light.

The three colors do not have to come from exactly the same location. A color television screen is covered with small spots of substances that give off blue, green, or red light. The spots are lighted in various amounts to produce the color picture on the screen, Figure 19–12a. The dots are so small that you need a magnifying glass to see them. The eye does not see the separately colored spots, but instead the color they produce together.

What is a filter?

One way of producing colored light is to use a filter. A filter is a transparent material that absorbs some col-

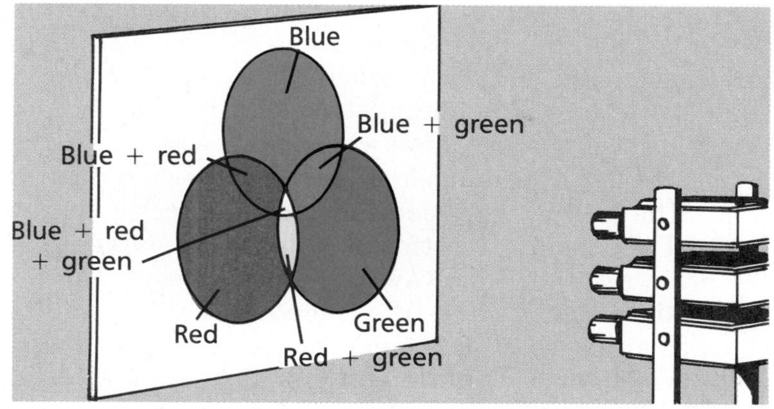

FIGURE 19–11. The three primary light colors mix to produce white light.

a

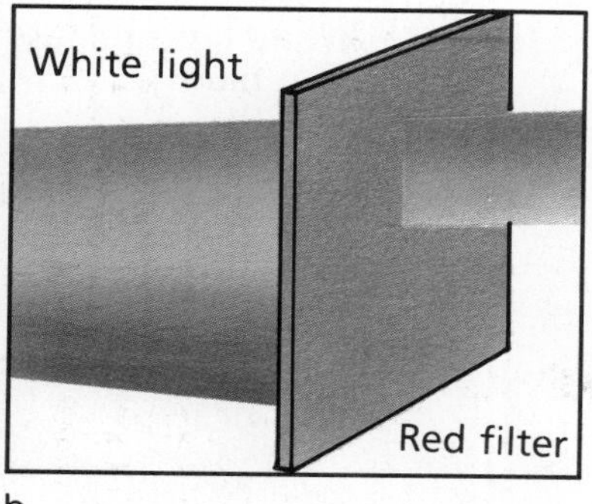

b

FIGURE 19–12. A TV picture tube can produce many colors using dots or stripes that flow red, green, or blue (a). A red filter absorbs all the colors outside the red area of the spectrum (b).

ors and allows others to pass through. The color of the filter is shown by the color of light it transmits, Figure 19–12b. The colors that do not pass through the filter are absorbed. Filters are used in theaters to light the stage with the color the director desires. Large screen televisions also use filtered red, green, and blue light to project the image on a screen.

F.Y.I. Sir Isaac Newton demonstrated that white light was a mixture of all the visible wavelengths.

Suppose white light shines on an apple and a grapefruit. Why is the apple red? Why is the grapefruit yellow? The light reaching our eyes was reflected off these objects. When struck by white light, the molecules of the grapefruit skin reflect green and red, but absorb blue. The light from the grapefruit stimulates the red and green cones of the eye. Your brain interprets the result as yellow. The molecules of an apple are different. They reflect mostly red light, absorbing blue and green.

Why does an apple appear red?

19:9 Pigment Colors

There is a great variety of color among the things you see. The color of an object often depends on the dye or pigment it contains. A dye is a material that dissolves in a liquid to form a colored solution. The dye molecule absorbs some colors of light and transmits others. Food coloring is a dye. The water can be evaporated, but the dye molecules themselves still interact with light. Clothing and many other things you use have been colored by dyes.

What is a dye?

A **pigment** is a colored material that absorbs certain colors and transmits or reflects others. A pigment particle is larger than a molecule and can be seen with a microscope. Often a pigment is a finely ground chemical such as titanium(IV) oxide (white), chromium(III) oxide (green), or cadmium sulfide (yellow). Pigments form suspensions rather than solutions. The color of paint is due to the pigments it contains.

How is a pigment different from a dye?

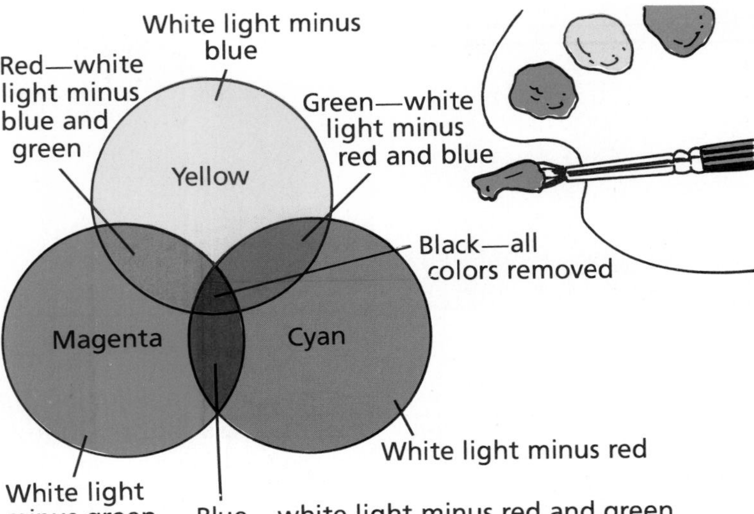

FIGURE 19–13. The basic pigment colors are mixtures of the primary light colors.

What are the primary pigment colors?

An artist needs to know about color and pigments when mixing paints. Only three primary pigments are needed to mix any color. The three primary pigment colors are magenta, yellow, and cyan, Figure 19–13. When we see magenta, the red and blue cones are stimulated. Cyan stimulates the blue and green cones. Yellow causes the red and green cones to respond.

Magenta paint reflects red and blue light and absorbs green. Yellow reflects red and green and absorbs blue. If magenta and yellow are mixed the result is red. Why? The magenta and yellow mixture absorbs the blue and green light, reflecting only red.

What are the differences between the additive colors and the subtractive colors?

What if all three primary pigment colors are mixed? Cyan absorbs red, magenta absorbs green, and yellow absorbs blue. Because the primary light colors, red, green, and blue, are all absorbed, no light is reflected. The result is black. Thus, these three pure pigments are called subtractive colors because they absorb all light and produce black when mixed. The primary light colors are additive colors because they combine to produce white light.

Review

6. What are the three primary light colors?
7. How does a color television screen produce a picture of a red apple on a white cloth?
8. How does a pigment differ from a dye?

FIGURE 19–14. When color photographs are printed, four plates must be used. One prints the yellow parts (a). A second plate prints the magenta (b). A third plate prints the cyan (c). A fourth plate prints the black. When all four are printed over one another, a color picture is the result (d).

9. Why does a mixture of the three primary pigment colors produce black?

★ **10.** A green filter is placed in front of a lamp. The light is projected on a screen. What color is the screen? Why?

WAVE PROPERTIES OF LIGHT

GOALS

1. You will learn how light is refracted.
2. You will understand how refraction depends on wavelength.
3. You will learn how white light is separated by interference.

Have you ever tried to dive for a coin you have seen on the bottom of a swimming pool? If you aimed for the spot where the coin seemed to be, you probably missed the coin. The light ray that was reflected from the coin was bent when it reached the surface of the water and entered the air. This bending of light is one of a number of ways light behaves when it passes from one type of material to another.

INVESTIGATION 19–2

The Spectrum of Light

Problem: How does a spectroscope separate light into its spectrum?

Materials 

diffraction grating
cardboard tube
aluminum foil
tape
knife
light sources: incandescent, fluorescent, flame tests

Procedure

1. Put together the parts of the diffraction grating spectroscope, as illustrated in Figure 19–15.
2. Cover one end of the tube with aluminum foil containing a slit about 1 mm wide cut with a knife.
3. Mount a 1-cm square piece of plastic diffraction grating on the opposite end. The lines in the grating must be parallel to the slit. To determine the direction of the lines, look at the light. The lines are perpendicular to the spreading of the spectrum that you see.
4. Observe white light from a lamp through the spectroscope. **CAUTION:** *You should never look directly at the sun.* Record your observations.
5. Observe light from a fluorescent lamp. Record your observations.
6. Observe other light sources such as street lamps, neon signs, or light from flame tests through your spectroscope. Record your observations.

FIGURE 19–15.

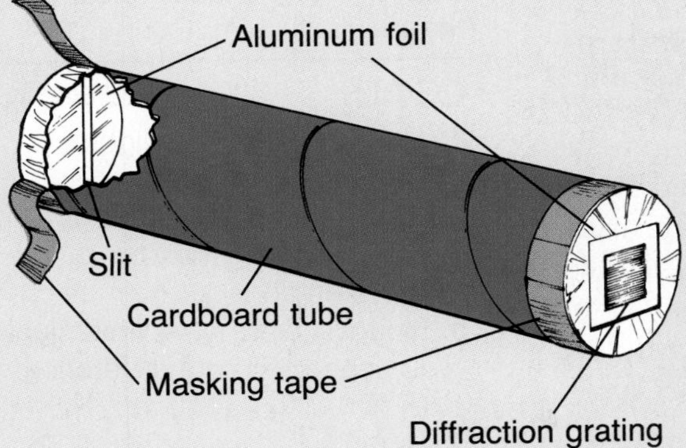

Data and Observations

Light source	What is seen through the spectroscope

Analysis

1. What colors are visible in the spectrum of an incandescent lamp?
2. Which two colors are at opposite ends of the spectrum?
3. Which color is diffracted through the largest angle by the grating?
4. In what way is the fluorescent lamp spectrum different from the incandescent light spectrum?

Conclusions and Applications

5. How does a spectroscope split light into its spectrum?
6. How can the spectroscope be used to analyze light?

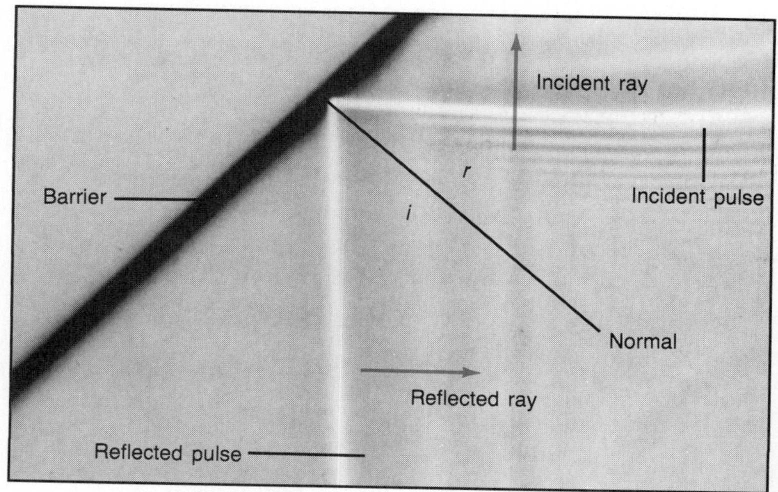

FIGURE 19–16. Water waves are reflected when they strike a barrier. When waves reflect, the angle of incidence equals the angle of reflection.

19:10 Reflection

How does reflection occur?

What is the angle of incidence? of reflection?

We have seen that both sound waves and light waves can be reflected off objects. Because we cannot see the wave crests of either of these waves, we will use water waves as a model. **Reflection** occurs when a wave strikes an object and bounces off. The waves that strike an object are called incident waves. The waves that bounce off are called reflected waves.

The angle between a wave striking a wall and a line drawn perpendicular to the wall is called the angle of incidence. It is shown as angle i in Figure 19–16. A line perpendicular to a surface is called a normal. The angle between the reflected wave and the normal is called the angle of reflection. On Figure 19–16 it is labeled angle r. When the waves are reflected from a surface, the angle of incidence always equals the angle of reflection.

19:11 Refraction

What is refraction?

How does refraction of waves occur?

Refraction is the bending of waves. Water waves can again be used to show how refraction occurs. When water waves move from deep to shallow water their velocity decreases. The frequency of the waves does not change. Thus, the wavelength becomes shorter.

When water waves move into shallow water at an angle, the waves are bent, or refracted, as in Figure 19–17a. Refraction always bends the waves toward the direction of slower wave velocity, as is explained by a model shown in Figure 19–17b. As the wheels roll across a tabletop, one wheel reaches a soft velvet cloth

F.Y.I. A light ray passing from one medium to another in a path normal to the surface is not refracted.

a

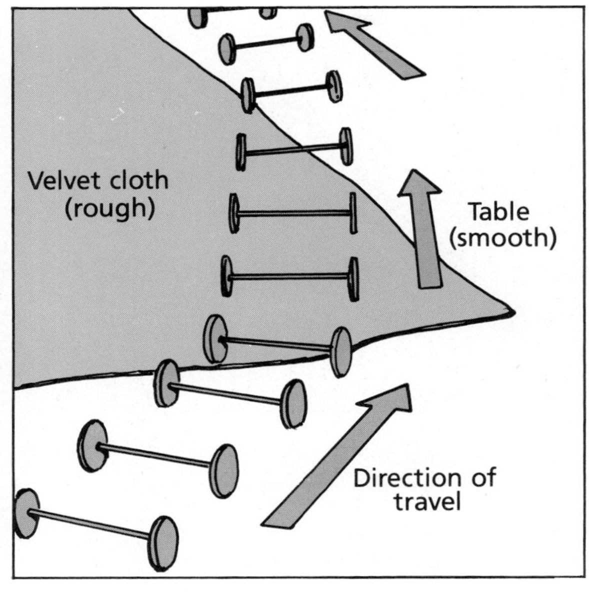

b

FIGURE 19–17. Water waves are refracted as they pass from deep to shallow water at an angle. The direction of the wheels change as they roll at an angle onto the rough surface of the cloth.

and is slowed down by friction. The other wheel continues at its original velocity. The change in velocity of the wheel on the cloth causes the change in direction. The wheels turn toward the soft cloth, the area in which velocity is decreased.

The speed of light may change as it passes from one transparent substance to another. For example, the speed of light in air is 300 000 km/s, but in glass it is only 197 000 km/s. If light passes at an angle from air into glass, its velocity decreases, and it is refracted. The amount of refraction depends on the type of material.

PROBLEM SOLVING

Air Waves

Coleman knows that the length of television antennas is proportional to the length of the electromagnetic wave carrying the television signal from the station's transmitter. He is switching from Channel 2 to Channel 7, and is trying to decide whether to shorten or lengthen the antenna. How can he solve his problem?

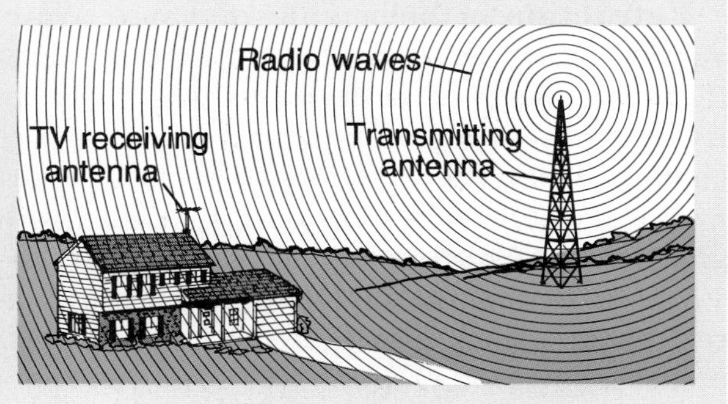

a

b

FIGURE 19–18. A prism has a triangular shape (a). When white light passes through the prism, different colors are refracted different amounts to form a spectrum (b). Violet light is refracted the most and red light the least.

The amount that light is refracted depends on the wavelength of light as well as the material. This property of matter was first used by Isaac Newton to separate white light into its spectrum of colors.

What determines how much a wave will be refracted?

A prism is made of transparent material with two plane faces at an angle to each other. From a side view, a prism has the shape of a triangle, Figure 19–18a. The path of light changes when it goes through a prism. The light is refracted twice, once as it enters and again as it leaves.

How does a glass prism produce a spectrum? Remember that white light is a mixture of all colors of light. When light passes through the prism, shorter wavelengths are refracted more than longer wavelengths. Violet light is bent more than red light. The different bending angles in glass separate the colors into a spectrum. Rain droplets in the atmosphere act as prisms to cause rainbows.

How does a prism produce a spectrum?

19:12 Diffraction and Interference

When sunlight comes into a room through a window, the edges of the window frame seem to cast sharp shadows. In 1649, however, the Italian scientist Francesco Grimaldi noticed that on the edge of the shadow were several bright and dark bands of light. Light was being bent around the edge of the window frame blocking its path. This behavior of waves is called **diffraction.**

F.Y.I. Thomas Young is said to have learned to read by the age of two, and to have read through the entire Bible by the age of six.

Diffraction occurs either when waves pass through an opening or around an object that blocks their path. The effects of diffraction are visible mainly when the size of the opening or the blocking object is close to the wavelength of the wave.

What causes diffraction?

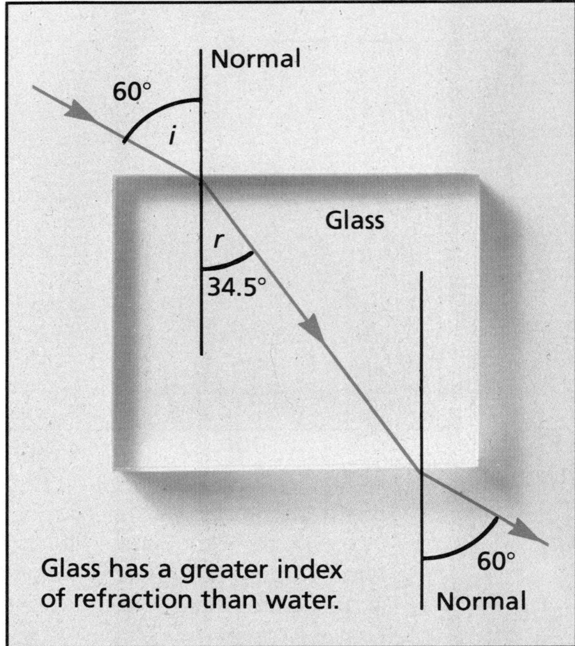

a

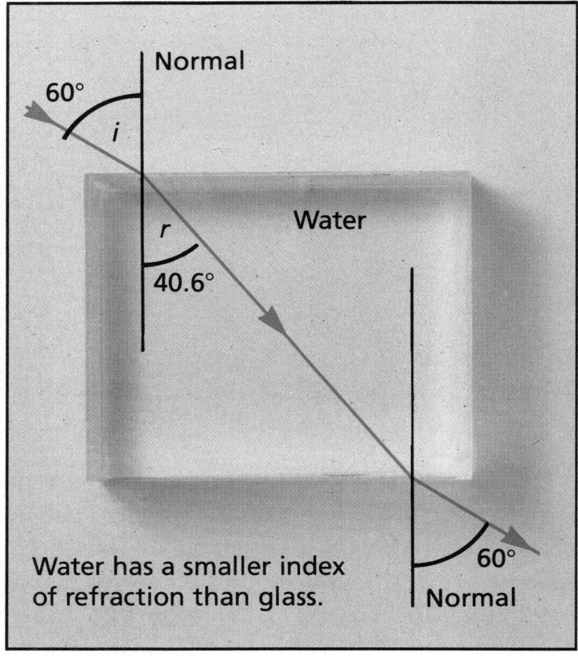

b

FIGURE 19–19. The light ray passing from air into glass (a) is refracted more toward the normal, than the ray passing from air into water (b).

When sound waves pass through the door of a room, they are moving through an opening about the size of a wavelength. The waves are diffracted by the door. If you walk by a room where music is being played, you will be able to hear the music long before you are directly in front of the door. If you listen carefully, however, you will discover that high-pitched sounds do not go around corners as well as low pitched sounds. The shorter the wavelength, the smaller the amount of diffraction.

As you have learned when studying sound, when two waves come together, or interfere, they can form regions

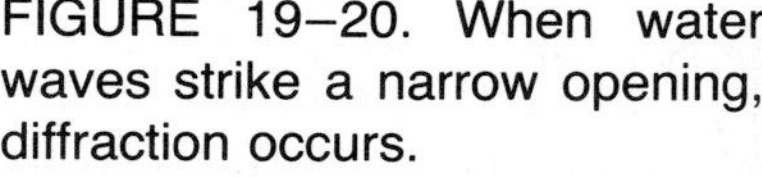

FIGURE 19–20. When water waves strike a narrow opening, diffraction occurs.

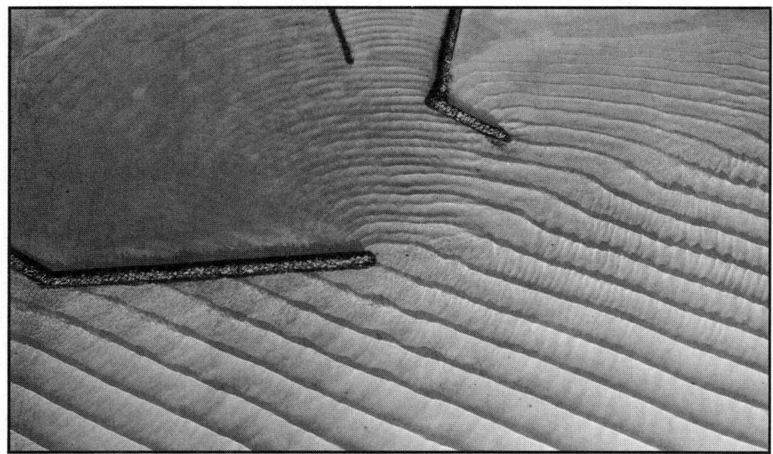

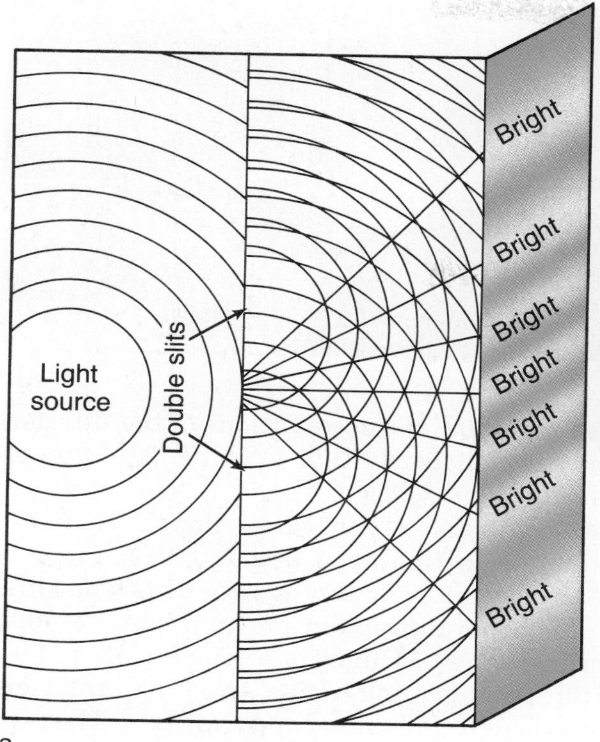

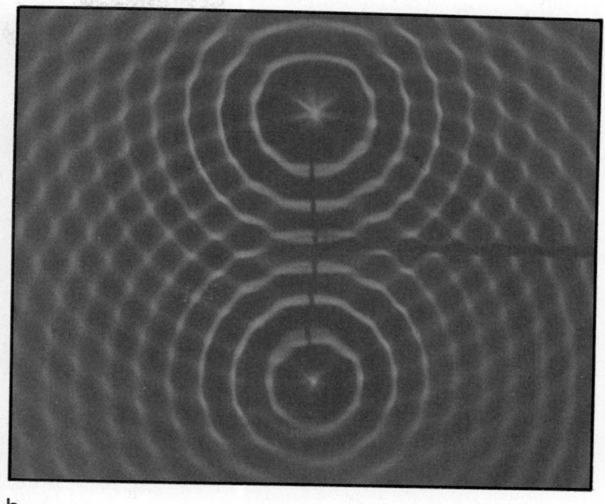

FIGURE 19–21. After passing through the double slits, the light waves reinforce to produce light and dark areas (a). Wave interference can be demonstrated with water waves (b).

of large amplitude and regions of small amplitude. In 1801 Thomas Young, an English scientist, showed that light can show interference effects. He first passed light through a narrow slit. That light was then passed through a pair of closely-spaced slits. The two slits acted like two separate sources of light of the same wavelength. The light from these slits fell on a screen. Look at Figure 19–21a. Young observed a series of dark bands where a crest from one wave crossed a trough from the other, and light bands where two crests or two

What is interference?

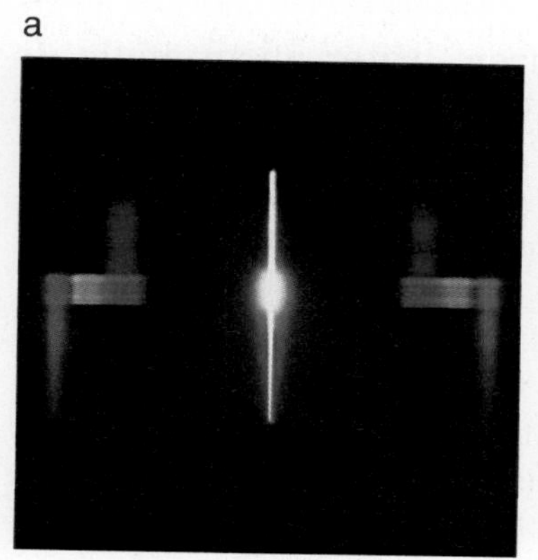

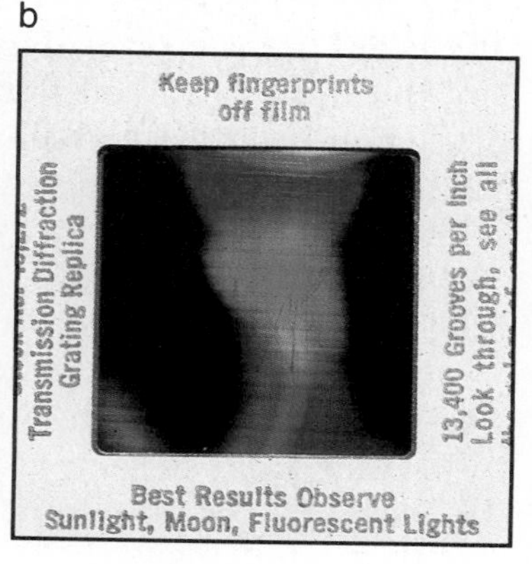

FIGURE 19–22. A spectrum is formed as light from a narrow source passes through a diffraction grating (a). A diffraction grating allows light to pass through many parallel slits to form a spectrum (b).

FIGURE 19–23. The laser shines through the "back" of a compact disk. The grooves in the disk act as a diffraction grating, producing a spectrum.

troughs added together. His observations of the interference patterns showed clearly that light had the characteristics of a wave.

Interference can also occur when there are many sources of light. A **diffraction grating** is a piece of glass or plastic containing many parallel lines or slits, Figure 19–22b. Some diffraction gratings have 10 000 slits per centimeter. When light of a single color passes through a diffraction grating onto a screen, an interference pattern of bright and dark bands appears. The separation between the bands depends on the color and is greatest for red light. White light forms rainbow-like colored spectra. Thus, diffraction gratings can be used in the same way prisms are used to separate white light into colors.

A phonograph record or compact disk has closely spaced grooves that can act like a diffraction grating. Look at the reflection of a distant lamp in a record. Note the separation of colors.

Review

11. Light moves into glass from water at an angle. Is the light refracted toward or away from the normal when it enters the glass?

12. Light moves from water into air. Is the light refracted toward or away from the normal when it enters the air?

13. The corner of a fish tank can serve as a water-filled prism. Would the red or violet light be bent more?

14. If you view white light in a diffraction grating, which light is seen at a larger angle, red or violet?

★ **15.** Is orange or blue light refracted more by glass? Support your answer.

Chapter 19 Review

SUMMARY

1. The transfer of energy by electromagnetic waves is called radiation. 19:1
2. Microwaves, having wavelengths shorter than radio waves, are used in communications and to cook food. 19:2
3. Infrared radiation is used to warm and dry materials. 19:3
4. Optics is the study of light and its uses. 19:4
5. Ultraviolet radiation can damage living cells. 19:5
6. X rays and gamma rays are electromagnetic waves with the shortest wavelengths, less than 0.1 micrometer. 19:6
7. Material that passes light is transparent, while material that blocks light is opaque. 19:7
8. The colors blue, green, and red are the primary light, or additive colors. 19:8
9. The three primary pigment, or subtractive colors, are magenta, yellow, and cyan. 19:9
10. Reflection occurs when a wave bounces off an object. 19:10
11. Refraction is the bending of waves toward the direction of slower wave velocity. 19:11
12. Diffraction is the bending of light around the edge of the object blocking its path. 19:12

VOCABULARY

a. diffraction
b. diffraction grating
c. electromagnetic spectrum
d. gamma rays
e. infrared radiation
f. light
g. microwaves
h. modulated
i. opaque
j. optics
k. pigment
l. radiation
m. radio waves
n. reflection
o. refraction
p. translucent
q. transparent
r. ultraviolet radiation
s. visible radiation
t. X rays

Matching

Match each description with the correct vocabulary word from the list above. Some words will not be used.

1. radiation with wavelengths just longer than light
2. radiation with wavelengths slightly shorter than radio waves
3. the bending of waves around barriers
4. material that absorbs, reflects, or transmits certain colors
5. material that blocks all light
6. the bending of a wave because of change in velocity
7. can be used to separate white light into its component colors
8. radiation used to picture the bones in the body
9. to change radio waves so they can be used for communication
10. arrangement of electromagnetic waves by wavelengths

Chapter 19 Review

MAIN IDEAS

A. Reviewing Concepts

Complete each of the following sentences with the correct word or phrase.

1. A glass prism ________ light rays.
2. A(n) ________ is a transparent material that absorbs some colors and allows others to pass through.
3. The color of a paint is due to the ________ it contains.
4. A diffraction grating has many parallel ____ through which light passes.
5. ________ lamps are used to kill germs.

Choose the word or phrase that correctly completes each of the following sentences.

6. The radiation that can be detected with a fluorescent substance is *(radio, microwave, infrared, ultraviolet).*
7. Shortwave radio broadcasts can be received at long distances because the waves are reflected by *(receivers, lightning, ionosphere, water).*
8. The following waves are part of the electromagnetic spectrum; *(rope waves, sound waves, water waves, microwaves).*
9. When a wave strikes an object and bounces off of it we have *(refraction, reflection, interference, diffraction)* of the wave.
10. The spreading of waves after passing through a narrow opening is called *(refraction, reflection, interference, diffraction).*

Determine whether each of the following sentences is true or false. If it is false, change the underlined word to make the sentence true.

11. <u>Refraction</u> can occur when the speed of a light beam is decreased.
12. A glass prism can produce a spectrum by <u>interference.</u>
13. All colors of light <u>have</u> the same wavelength and frequency.
14. Mixing equal amounts of red, blue, and green light produces <u>white</u> light.
15. Pigments are <u>additive</u> colors.

B. Understanding Concepts

Answer the following questions using complete sentences when possible.

16. Which has a shorter wavelength, the radiation from TV Channel 2 or Channel 6?
17. Explain why shortwave radio stations can transmit over long distances.
18. Describe the two main types of uses for microwaves.
19. How does bone compare with softer tissue in the amount of X rays it absorbs? How do aluminum and lead compare?
20. If you grind up a leaf in alcohol you obtain a solution of chlorophyll that looks green. What part of the spectrum is absorbed by the chlorophyll?
21. In Young's interference experiment, he observed light and dark bands of light. How were these interference bands produced?
22. Does a leaf appear green because of refraction, diffraction, or reflection?
23. Light refracted out of a diamond is split into colors. What does this tell you about the indeces of refraction of red and violet light in diamond?
24. Suppose you mix equal amounts of red, blue, and yellow crayons. Do you get black?
25. If you look directly at an asphalt highway it looks black. If, however, you look at it at an angle, it looks shiny. Is this because it refracts, diffracts, or reflects light?

C. Applying Concepts

Answer the following questions using complete sentences when possible.

26. Radio waves enter a long, narrow region, such as a tunnel. Radiation with wavelengths much longer than the width of the tunnel will be absorbed more than radiation with smaller wavelengths. Given that fact, would you expect AM or FM car radios to fade-out more when traveling through tunnels? Why?

27. The velocity of light in warm air is greater than that in cold air. The air just above a highway is warmer than the air a little higher. Will the light moving parallel to the highway be bent up or down?

28. In general, the longer the wavelength of electromagnetic radiation, the larger the detector must be. Would you therefore expect the eyes of small insects to be sensitive to infrared or ultraviolet waves?

29. The length of an antenna designed to pick up TV broadcasts depends on the wavelength of the radiation. If you saw a very short antenna, would it be designed to detect a high or low channel number?

30. Calculate the frequency of a microwave with a wavelength of 3 cm.

PROJECTS

1. Make a chart showing the frequencies and wavelengths of several AM radio stations in your region. Arrange the stations by their frequency.

2. Make a chart showing, for each type of electromagnetic radiation, the name, frequency and wavelength region, sources and uses of the radiation.

3. Investigate the different types of mirages to learn how they are produced. Relate what you learn to the refractive index of air.

4. Experiment with the color response of a variety of photocopy machines. Try copying a collection of different colors with machines of different types. Report your results.

SKILL REVIEW

1. On what basis do scientists draw conclusions?

2. What should you do before you draw any definite conclusions from the Skill activity?

3. In Investigation 19–2, what could you conclude about white light?

4. When making a flowchart, what is the shape of the decision making block?

5. In Table 19–1, what kind of radiation does a klystron tube produce?

READINGS

1. Birren, Faber. *Color: A Survey in Words and Pictures*. Secaucus, NJ: Citadel Press, 1984.

2. Hill, Julie, and Julian Hill. *Looking at Light and Color*. North Pomfret, VT: David and Charles, 1986.

3. "The Light Fantastic," *Science 84*. May, 1984, pp. 50–57.

4. *Sight, Light & Color*. New York, NY: Arco, 1984.

MIRRORS AND REFLECTION
LENSES AND REFRACTION
SPECIAL APPLICATIONS OF LIGHT

Mirrors and Lenses

Optics is one of the most useful fields of all the physical sciences. Eyeglasses have improved the vision of millions of people. Much of the progress in biology and medicine has occurred because of the development of the microscope. Today's research on optical fibers will surely lead to quieter, more secure telephone systems and to cable television systems with an almost unlimited number of channels.

MIRRORS AND REFLECTION

Have you ever looked at yourself in a spoon? Try it! If you look at the back of the spoon, your face appears smaller and rightside up. When you look into the bowl side your face is again smaller, but upside down. Now try looking from the bowl side and moving your finger toward the spoon. As your finger gets closer, the image gets bigger. Then, suddenly, it appears to fill the bowl, then ends up enlarged and rightside up. Why is this?

GOALS

1. You will understand how a mirror forms an image.
2. You will learn the types of images formed by curved mirrors.

20:1 Reflection in Plane Mirrors

Have you ever seen your reflection in a pond? In a window? Then you know that almost any smooth surface can act as a mirror. A mirror reflects light to form an image. It is usually made of a sheet of glass with an aluminum coating on the back surface. A mirror that is flat is called a **plane mirror.**

How does a mirror produce an image?

When you stand in front of a plane mirror, you see a reflection of yourself. Some of the light that falls on your face is reflected onto the mirror. That light is reflected by the mirror, and some of it reaches your eyes. You see the reflected light as if it were coming from behind the mirror. The reflection you see is called an image. The image is the same size as your face and is right side up.

F.Y.I. "A plausible impossibility is always preferable to an unconvincing possibility."
Aristotle

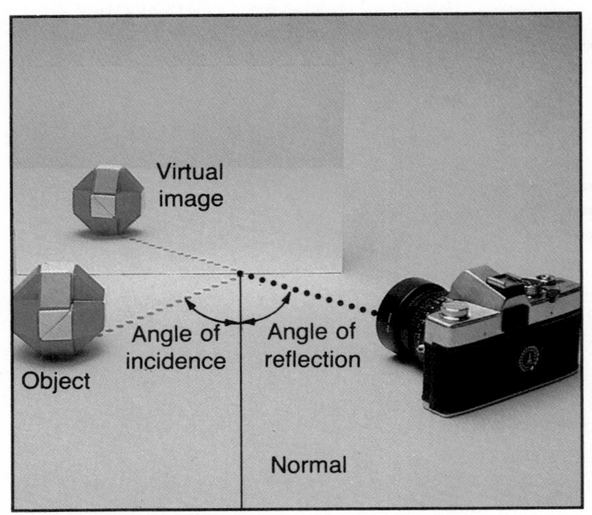

a

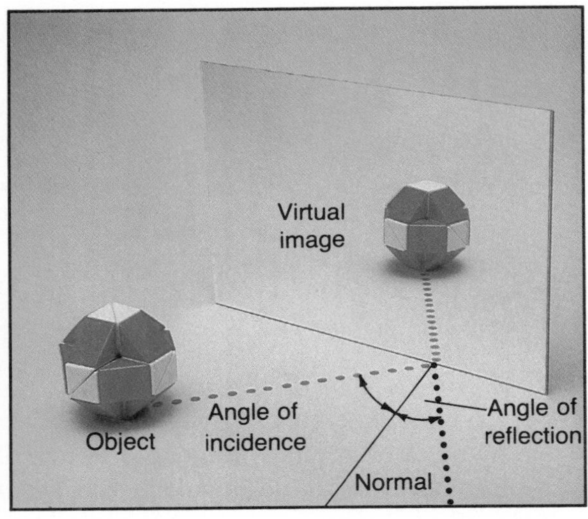

b

FIGURE 20–1. The red dots show the path of a ray of light from the object. Upon striking a plane mirror, the ray reflects toward the camera (a). To the camera, the ray appears as if it were coming from a virtual image behind the mirror (b).

What is a virtual image?

What kind of image is produced by a plane mirror?

However, its right and left sides are reversed. That is, if you touch your right ear, the image will be seen touching its left ear.

To study reflection we will use a ray model of light. A ray is a line in the direction of motion of the light. All objects emitting or reflecting light send countless rays streaming in all directions. The angle of reflection equals the angle of incidence for both waves and rays. Figure 20–1 shows how an image is produced by a plane mirror. Two rays that leave the object are shown. To the eye they seem to come from behind the mirror. The image is the same distance behind the mirror as the object is in front of it. Of course, there is really nothing behind the mirror, the image only appears to be there. It is called a **virtual image.** If you put a piece of paper at the location of the image, nothing would appear.

20:2 Curved Mirrors

A mirror curved like the inside of the bowl of a spoon is called a **concave mirror.** Concave mirrors can be used as shaving or make-up mirrors.

Figure 20–2 shows how a concave mirror reflects a beam of parallel light rays. A straight line through the center of a mirror or lens is called the **optical axis.** Light rays striking a concave mirror parallel to its optical axis are all reflected toward one point in front of the mirror. This common point is called the **focal point** of the mirror. If rays leave a lamp at the focal point of the mirror, the mirror will reflect them back in a parallel beam. Thus, concave mirrors are used as reflectors

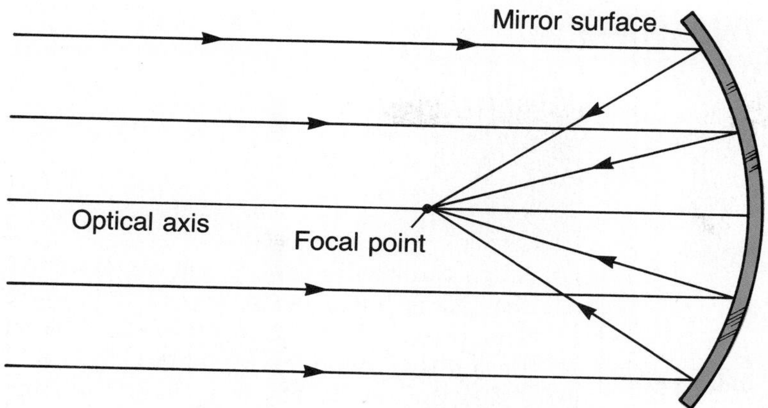

FIGURE 20–2. A concave mirror reflects parallel light rays to a point, called the focal point.

in flashlights and automobile headlights. The distance from the center of the mirror to the focal point is the **focal length** of the mirror. To find the focal point, let sunlight fall on the mirror. The sun's light is a parallel beam. Hold a piece of tissue paper in front of the mirror. Move it back and forth until the image of the sun is as small as possible. This is the focal point.

What is the focal point?

Suppose we follow two rays reflected from the same point on an object. The object is put beyond the focal point, Figure 20–3. A ray parallel to the optical axis is reflected through the focal point. A ray that goes through the focal point on its way to the mirror is reflected parallel to the optical axis. The two rays meet at the location of the image. Follow similar rays from a second point on the object. As shown in Figure 20–3, the image formed by an object beyond the focal point is larger and upside down. The rays actually meet at a point in space, so the image is a **real image.** If you put a piece of paper there, you could see the image on it.

FIGURE 20–3. A concave mirror can form a real image because it can focus rays.

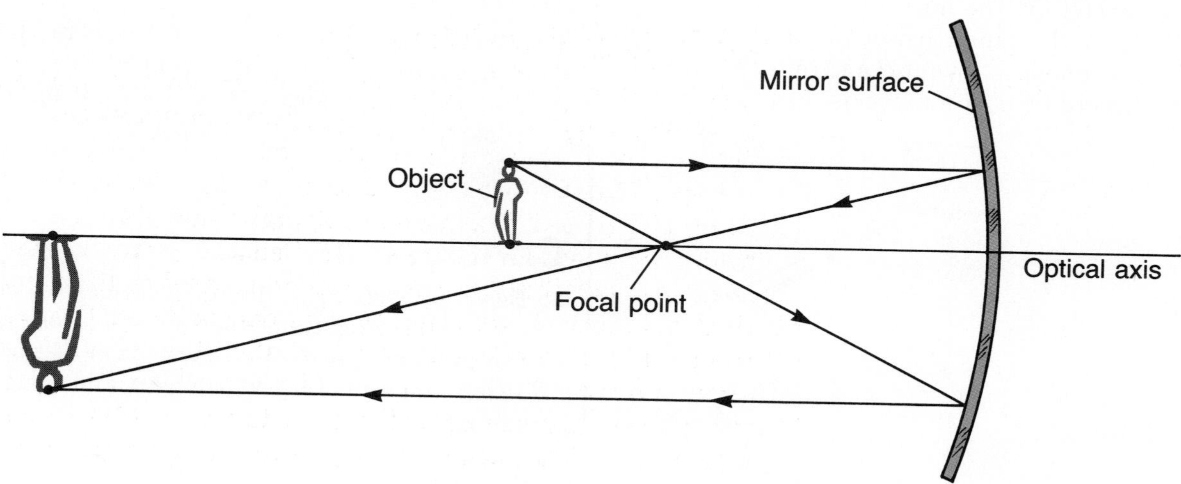

INVESTIGATION 20–1

Concave Mirrors

Problem: What kind of image is formed by a concave mirror?

Materials

concave mirror
candle
white index card
meter stick
matches
support for index card

Procedure

1. Anchor the candle on the table. Measure its height.
2. Place the candle 2 m in front of the mirror. Light the candle and darken the room.
3. Hold the index card slightly off center from the optical axis to allow light rays to reach the mirror and be reflected.
4. Move the index card until the image of the candle appears on it.
5. Record your observations on the Data Table. Include the distances of the candle and the index card from the mirror and the image height and orientation (upright or inverted).
6. Move the candle closer to the mirror. Repeat Steps 4 and 5.
7. Move the candle closer to the mirror until the candle and its image are the same distance from the mirror.
8. Move the candle closer to the mirror until the image is about 2 m from the mirror. Record your observations.

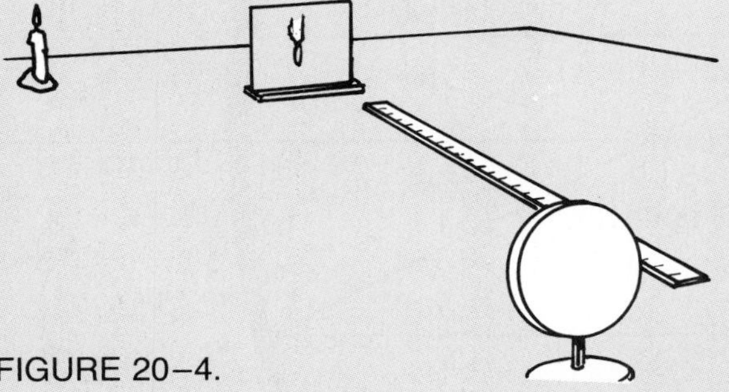

FIGURE 20–4.

9. Move the candle toward the mirror until the image blurs and begins to turn over. This point is the focal point of the mirror. Record this value.
10. Place the candle 10 cm from the mirror. Look in the mirror and describe what you see.

Data and Observations

Height of candle ______ Focal length ______

Step	Image height	Distance from mirror		Upright/ inverted
		Candle	Image	
5				
6				
7				
8				
9				

Analysis

1. How does the image size compare to the candle size in Steps 4, 6, 7, and 8?
2. Does the image appear to be in front of, or in back of the mirror in Step 10?

Conclusions

3. Based on your data and observations, write a conclusion for this experiment answering the Problem questions. Discuss how the position and size of both the object and image are related.

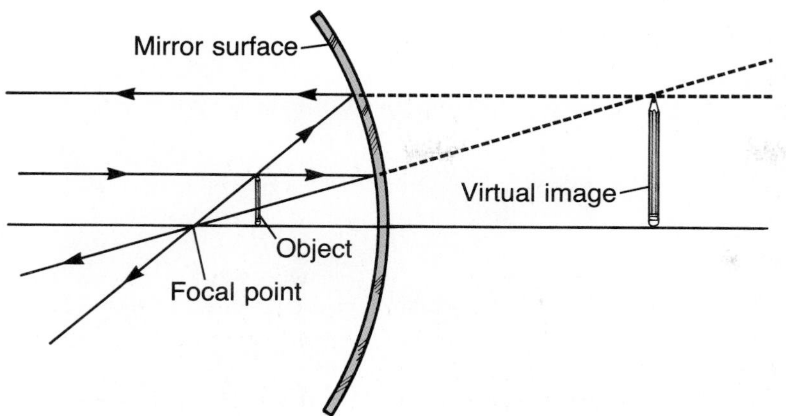

FIGURE 20–5. Objects placed between the focal point and the surface of a concave mirror form enlarged virtual images (a). For this reason, concave mirrors are used in makeup mirrors (b).

Figure 20–5 shows the image formed when the object is between a concave mirror and the focal point. One ray leaves the object parallel to the optical axis, and is reflected through the focal point. The second ray is the ray that would have come through the focal point. It is reflected parallel to the axis. These two rays are diverging. They never meet. They do, however, appear to have come from a point behind the mirror, a point on the image. The image is a virtual image and would not appear on a piece of paper. When you use a makeup or shaving mirror, you hold the mirror so that your face is between the mirror and the focal point. The image is enlarged, upright, and behind the mirror.

Describe the difference between a concave and a convex mirror.

What kind of images are formed by a convex mirror?

A mirror that is curved like the back of a spoon is a **convex mirror.** Figure 20–6 shows rays reflected by a convex mirror. The rays always spread out. The image is always a virtual image, located behind the mirror. It is upright and smaller than the object. Convex mirrors are used as security mirrors in stores or as side mirrors on cars and trucks. They allow you to see a wider view than you could in a plane mirror.

FIGURE 20–6. Convex mirrors always form smaller, virtual images (a). For this reason they are often used as wide angle mirrors for safety and security (b).

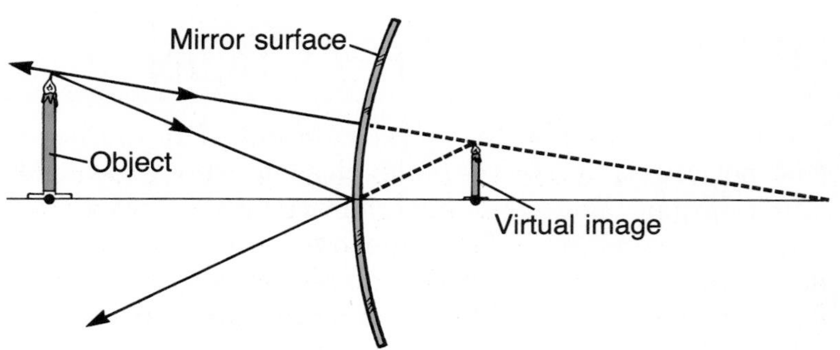

CAREER

Photographer

Obtaining clear, detailed images that do not distort an object's perspective is one of Mindy Fair's goals. She specializes in engineering photography. Some photographers specialize in scientific or medical photography. They also can create illusion and optical effects for cartoons and movies, or be a photojournalist for television.

According to Mindy, a good background in optics is important in photography. A photographer must be able to select the correct lens and lighting to capture an image.

For career information, write
Professional Photographers of America, Inc.
1090 Executive Way
Des Plaines, IL 60018

---

1. Describe the image formed by a plane mirror.
2. Describe the image formed by a convex mirror.
3. Describe the image formed by a concave mirror when the object is between the focal point and the mirror.
4. If you move an object that is beyond the focal point away from a concave mirror, does the image become larger or smaller? Hint: When the object is very far away, the rays are almost parallel and the image is at the focal point.
5. ★ You have been appointed photographer for your yearbook. First you will take a picture of the whole class, then a close-up shot of each student. To focus on one student, should you move the lens closer to the film or farther away? Why?

LENSES AND REFRACTION

GOALS

1. You will distinguish between concave and convex lenses.
2. You will learn how lenses produce real and virtual images.
3. You will understand how lenses are used in optical instruments.

Have you ever used a magnifying glass? If you have, you noticed that objects held close to the glass look much larger. You may have noticed that objects far away look smaller and upside down. You might also have used it as a "burning glass" to concentrate the sun's rays. Both alone and in combination, lenses have many everyday uses.

20:3 Lenses

A lens is a curved transparent object made of glass or plastic. There are two kinds of lenses: convex and concave. A **convex lens,** Figure 20–7a, is thicker in the middle than at the edges. A magnifying glass is an example of a convex lens. A **concave lens,** Figure 20–7b, is thinner in the middle than at the edges. Both kinds of lenses bend light by refraction.

A convex lens refracts light rays toward each other. Beams of parallel light rays are brought together at the focal point. Sunlight falling on a convex lens will be concentrated at the focal point.

Light is refracted both as it enters the lens and as it leaves it. The refractive index of a material is the ratio of the speed of light in a vacuum to the speed of light in that material. The larger the refractive index, the slower the light travels, and the more it is bent. The light is bent through an angle that depends on the material used to make the lens and its shape. A thick convex lens will bend the light more than a thin flat one, Figure 20–8. A convex lens can form a real image because it can focus light.

With a convex lens, the size of the image depends on the distance between the object and the lens. If the object is more than twice the focal length away from the lens, then the image is smaller than the object and inverted, Figure 20–9a. The image formed on film by the convex lens of a camera is usually smaller than the object is and inverted. The distance between the lens and

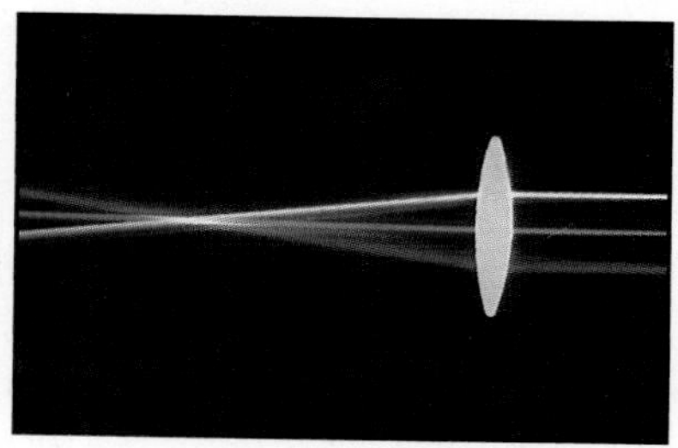

a

b

FIGURE 20–7. Light is refracted as it passes through a lens. In a convex lens (a), the rays converge. In a concave lens (b), the rays diverge.

How does a lens produce an image?

Name the two kinds of lenses and tell how they differ from each other.

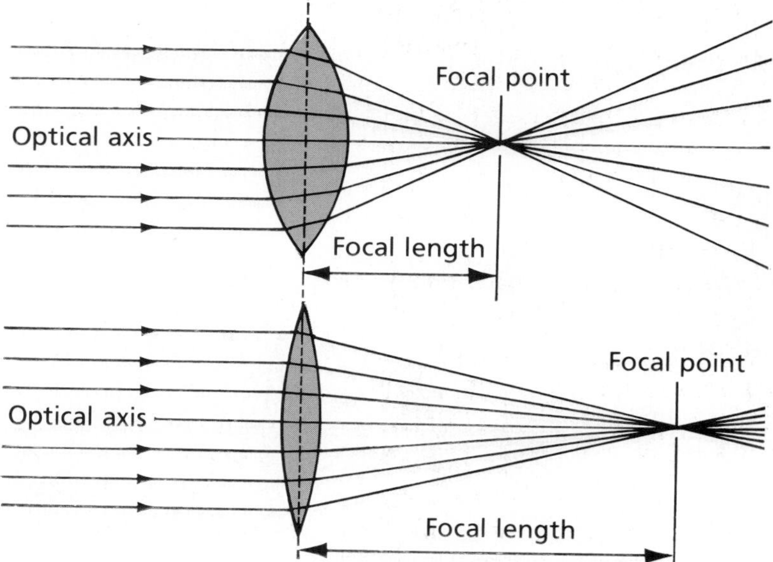

FIGURE 20–8. A convex lens that is more curved has a shorter focal length than one that is less curved.

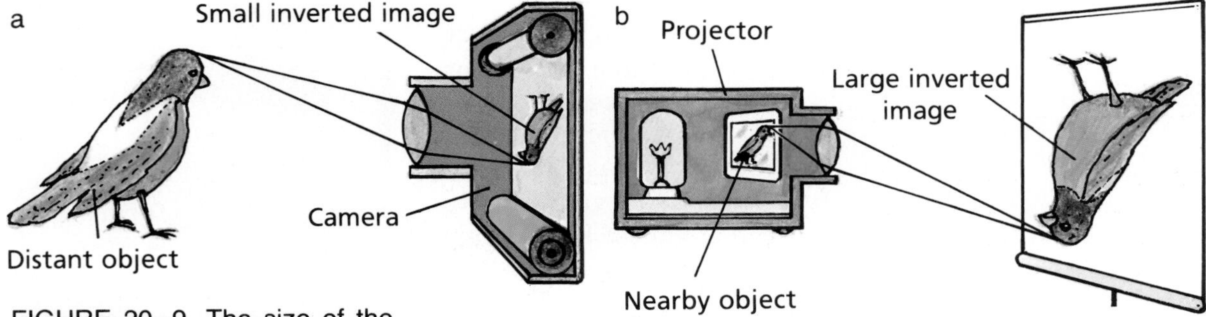

FIGURE 20–9. The size of the inverted real image formed by a convex lens depends on the distance between the object and the lens. You can see why slides must be placed upside-down in a projector.

image depends on the focal length of the lens, and the distance from the lens to the object. In a camera, the distance of the lens to the film can be adjusted to take pictures of objects at different distances. In the eye, the shape of the lens is changed.

If the object is between one and two focal lengths from the lens, then the image is larger than the object and inverted. In an overhead projector the object is close to the lens, Figure 20–9b. The enlarged image is projected on a screen a large distance from the lens.

The image formed when the object is between the lens and the focal point is shown in Figure 20–10. The refracted rays never meet, so the image is virtual. It is enlarged and upright. A convex lens can be used as a magnifying glass in this way.

A concave lens bends light rays away from each other. Concave lenses cannot form real images because they cannot focus light. When you look through a concave lens, you see a virtual image. The image is virtual, smaller, and upright. Concave lenses are seldom used alone. In cameras and eyeglasses they are used in combination with convex lenses to create a longer focal length.

F.Y.I. The refractive index of a material is the ratio of the speed of light in a vacuum to the speed of light in that material. The larger the refractive index, the slower the light travels, and the more it is bent.

Why do concave lenses form only virtual images?

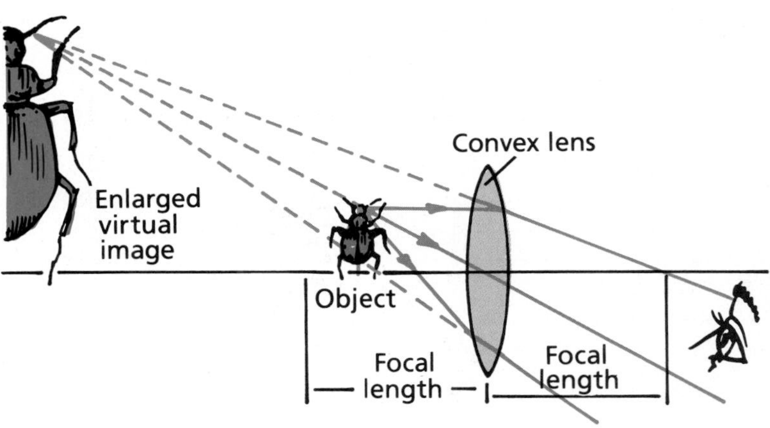

FIGURE 20–10. When you use a magnifying glass, the light striking your eye seems to come from a much larger object, an enlarged image.

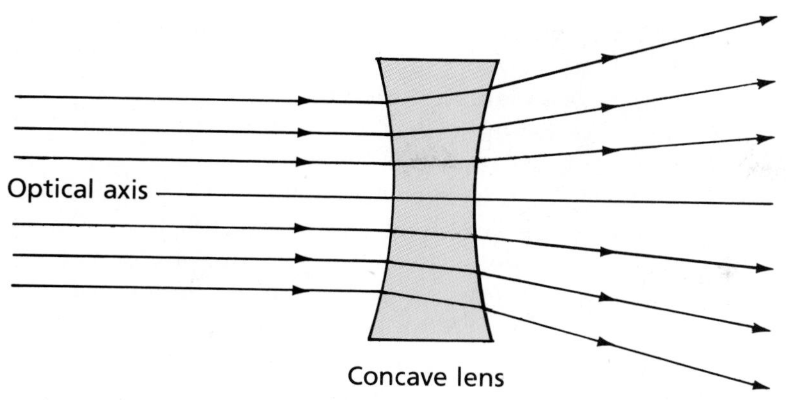

FIGURE 20–11. A concave lens bends light rays away from each other.

20:4 Lenses and Vision

How does the eye form images?

The human eye is filled with a liquid that is mostly water. Light enters through a transparent membrane called the cornea. It is refracted at this curved surface. It passes through a convex lens and forms an inverted image on the back surface of the eye, the retina. Nerves lead from the retina to the visual area of the brain.

The eye can focus on objects farther away than about 25 cm. The lens is made of a flexible transparent material, and muscles control its curvature. To focus an image of a nearby object, the focal length must be made smaller. The muscles tighten, causing the lens to become more convex. To focus images of distant objects, a longer focal length is needed. The muscles relax, allowing the lens to be less convex.

FIGURE 20–12. The diagrams show how lenses help correct nearsightedness (a) and farsightedness (b).

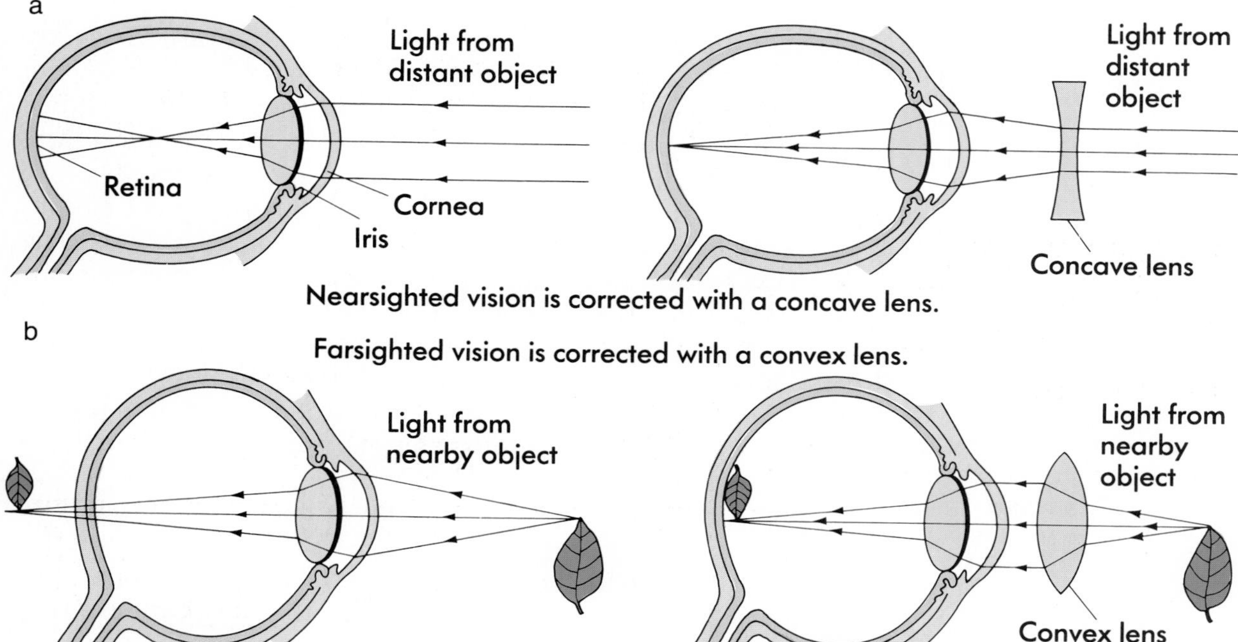

BIOGRAPHY

George R. Carruthers

1939–

George Carruthers is the senior astrophysicist at the Naval Research Lab in Washington, D.C. One of his projects was to design and build a camera/spectrograph for use in the Apollo 16 lunar mission. He has been awarded many prizes for his work, including the Warner Prize of the American Astronomical Society.

Many people have vision problems that make objects either far away or close up look fuzzy. People who see objects far away clearly, but find objects close to their eyes fuzzy, are farsighted. Either the cornea is too flat or the eyeball is too short. The lens cannot be made convex enough to focus images of nearby objects on the retina. To correct the problem, the farsighted person uses a convex lens to help the eye focus images of nearby objects, Figure 20–12b. As people become older, they often become farsighted. The lens of the eye becomes less flexible and tends to lose its ability to focus images of nearby objects.

What kind of lens is used to correct nearsighted vision?

People who see close-up objects clearly but cannot focus distant objects are nearsighted. Either the cornea bulges too much or the eyeball is too long. Even when relaxed, the lens is too convex to focus images of distant objects on the retina. Concave lenses help the eye produce sharp images of distant objects, Figure 20–12a.

Vision problems can be corrected by wearing contact lenses that fit directly on the cornea. They are small disks of plastic shaped into convex or concave lenses that bend light correctly to form sharp images.

20:5 Telescopes and Microscopes

About the year 1600, lens makers in Holland learned that two lenses could be used together to give an enlarged view of distant objects. In 1610, Galileo first used such a telescope to see that the planet Jupiter had four objects circling it.

Telescopes are used to view objects that are far away. For example, astronomers use telescopes to study the stars. Terrestrial telescopes can be used to watch whales or spot birds. Two small telescopes, called binoculars, give a close-up view at concerts or sporting events.

What is the difference between a refracting telescope and a reflecting telescope?

A **refracting telescope,** Figure 20–13a, has two convex lenses, the eyepiece lens and the objective lens. The eyepiece lens has a short focal length. The objective lens has a long focal length. Two lenses are used in binoculars and most terrestrial telescopes. The larger the diameter of a telescope, the brighter the view appears. Very large refracting telescopes are difficult to make because the heavy glass lenses sag under their own weight.

F.Y.I. Another disadvantage of a large lens is that the edges act like a prism and separate light into its colors. As a result, the image in a large refracting telescope can show false colors.

What is the advantage of a reflecting telescope?

A concave mirror and a convex eyepiece lens can also be used to make a telescope. The mirror reflects light, so this instrument is called a **reflecting telescope,** Figure 20–13b. Mirrors can be made thin and can be easily

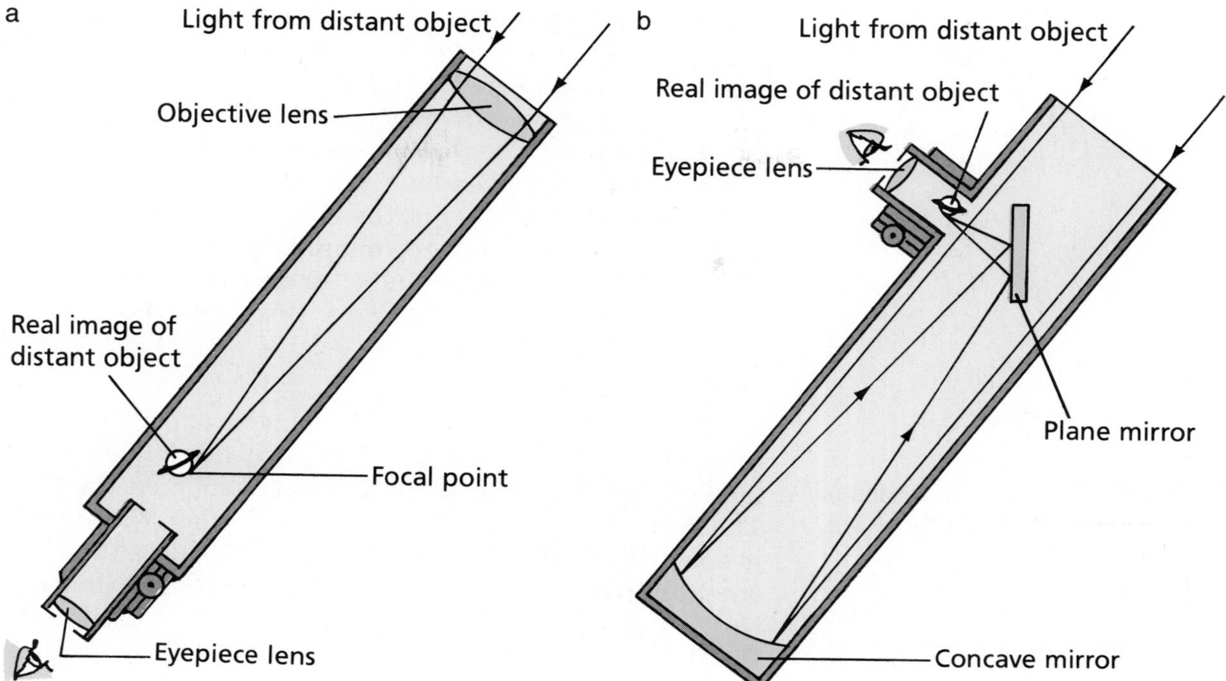

supported, so most large telescopes are reflectors. The largest reflecting telescope, with a 6-m diameter mirror, is in Zelenchukskaya, Soviet Union. The Multiple Mirror Telescope on Mount Hopkins, Arizona, has six mirrors, each 1.8 m in diameter. Special electronic devices are used to combine the images from the six mirors into one. As a result, it can gather as much light as a 4.5 meter mirror, but it costs much less to build.

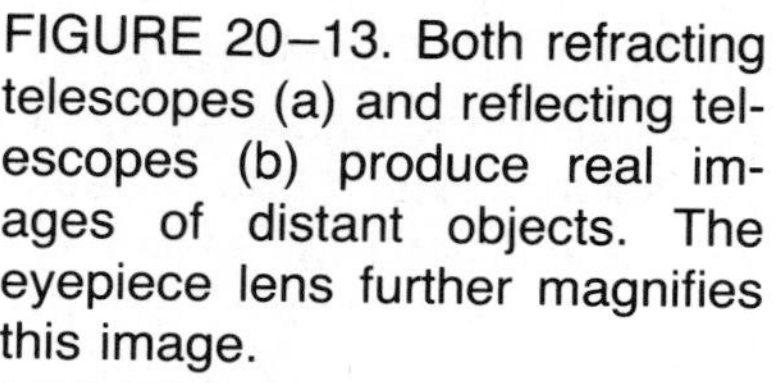
FIGURE 20–13. Both refracting telescopes (a) and reflecting telescopes (b) produce real images of distant objects. The eyepiece lens further magnifies this image.

FIGURE 20–14. Very large reflecting telescopes use a mirror to gather and focus light.

In a microscope, what does the eyepiece magnify?

A **microscope** uses two convex lenses to make magnified images of very small objects. The specimen, or object to be viewed, is placed on a slide. The slide is placed on a flat part of the microscope called a stage. Light rays are directed up through a hole in the stage and through the specimen. A convex lens, the objective lens, produces a magnified real image of the specimen. A second convex lens, the eyepiece lens, magnifies this image again. The total magnification can be 300x or more.

20:6 Cameras

What kind of image is formed on the film by the lens of a camera?

A camera forms an image on photographic film. The image is focused on the film by one or more lenses. The lens refracts lights and forms a real image on the film. The light passes through the lens only when the shutter is open. Many shutters expose the film for less than one one-hundredth of a second. A shorter exposure time can be used to "freeze" motion. A longer time is used when the light is dim. The amount of light reaching the film is also controlled by changing the size of the lens opening, or the aperture. In dim light a large aperture is

FIGURE 20–15. A compound microscope (a) produces a real image much larger than the object. A stereo microscope (b) gives a 3-dimensional view of an object.

a

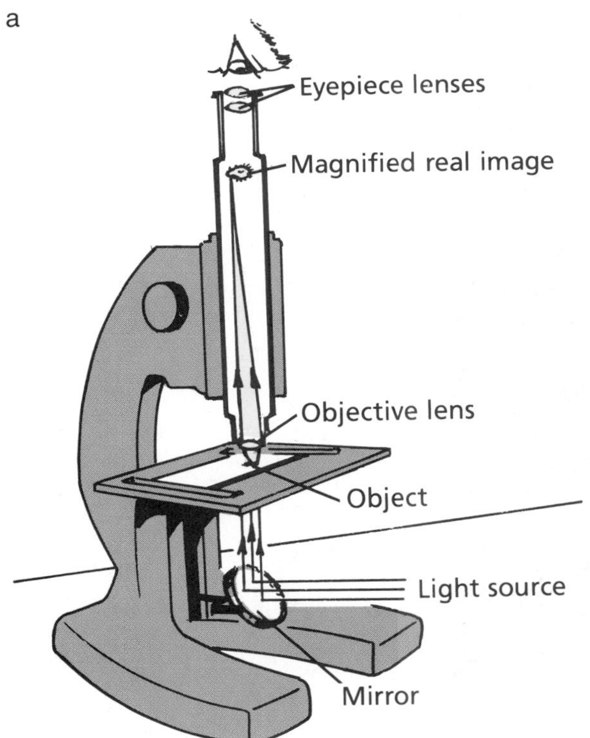

b

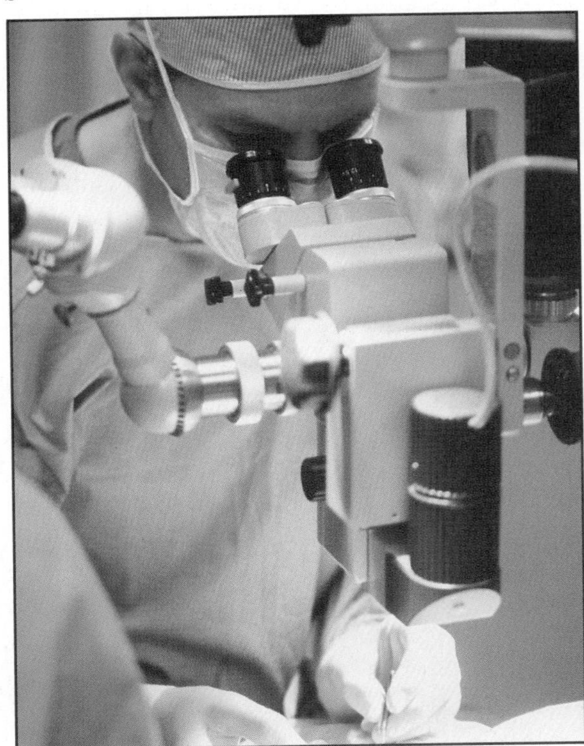

FIGURE 20–16. The photographs here are taken from the same position, using different lenses. Recall that the image of an object becomes larger with an increased focal length.

used to let in more light. Expensive cameras have large lenses so that photographs can be made in dim light with fast shutter speeds. The lens of a camera collects light and focuses it on the film. The lens can be replaced by a tiny pinhole that allows only single rays from each point on the object to pass through. The film must be exposed for a long time because little light passes through the pinhole.

How is the size of the image affected by the focal length of a lens?

Complex cameras, such as single lens reflex cameras (SLRs), have removable lenses. Lenses with different focal lengths can be attached as needed. Suppose you are photographing a friend standing two meters away. A lens with a short focal length will have to be placed close to the film. The image of your friend will be small, but a great deal of the surroundings will be included in the photograph. For this reason, lenses with short focal lengths are called **wide-angle lenses.** When you use a lens with a long focal length it will have to be put farther from the film. The image will be enlarged and your friend will appear closer than he or she actually is. These lenses are called **telephoto lenses.** In some lenses, called zoom lenses, the focal length can be adjusted. Zoom lenses and telephoto lenses are really combinations of lenses. The photographer can change the focal length continuously from wide-angle to telephoto. Many lens systems are now designed by computers. The three photographs in Figure 20–16 were taken from the same position with lenses of increasing focal length.

SKILL

Making Scale Drawings

Problem: How do you make drawings to scale?

Background

In general, drawings and diagrams are used visually to represent ideas to make them more understandable. A scale drawing is used to represent accurately something that is too large or small, or otherwise difficult to show full-sized. In a scale drawing the parts of the subject pictured are in exactly the same proportion to each other as they are in the original. Maps are probably the most familiar examples of scale drawings. By knowing the scale of the map, you can find the distance between two points without actually having to be there. Many of the illustrations in this chapter are drawn to scale, for example, Figures 20–3 and 20–5a.

Materials

textbook
sharpened pencil
paper

Procedure

1. Make a scale diagram of the figure on this page that is one-third the original size.
2. Make a scale diagram of the same figure that is two times the size of the original.
3. A convex mirror has a focal length of 1 m. The object, 50 cm tall, is on the optical axis, three focal lengths from a convex mirror. Construct a scale diagram and determine how large the image is and how far it is from the mirror.

Analysis and Conclusions

1. How long are the sides of the reduced drawing?
2. How long are the sides of the enlarged drawing?
3. In Procedure Step 3, what is the height of the image and how far is it from the mirror?
4. How do you make scale drawings?

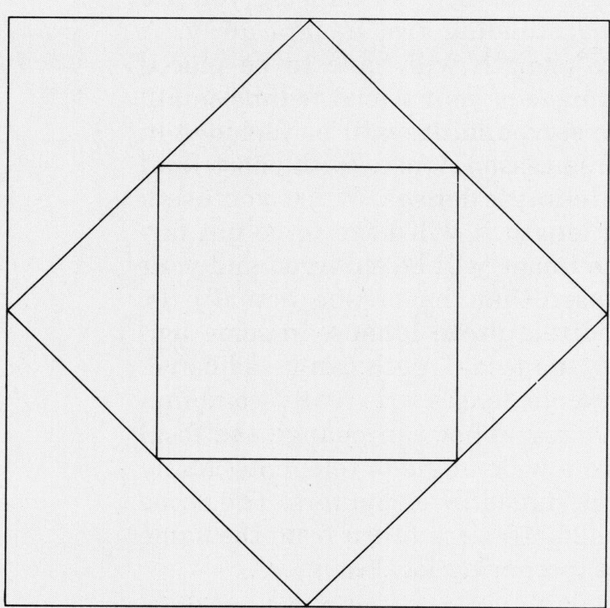

Review

6. How do the shapes of convex lenses and concave lenses differ?
7. Where do you place an object to form a virtual image using a convex lens?
8. Suppose you are a farsighted person without glasses reading a book. Are you likely to hold it close or far from your eyes? Explain.
9. What kind of lens would a photographer use to take a picture of several astronauts working together inside a spacecraft? Explain.
10. ★ Would you use a pinhole camera to take a picture at a baseball game? Explain.

SPECIAL APPLICATIONS OF LIGHT

GOALS

1. You will learn the nature and some uses of polarized light.
2. You will learn how a laser produces coherent light.
3. You will understand how light travels through optical fibers.

The laser is one of the most spectacular inventions of the past 25 years. Perhaps you have seen the pencil-thin beams cross the sky in a laser light show. Or you might have noticed the spiderweb-like pattern of laser beams in an automated supermarket checkout cash register. Lasers are another optical tool that will be important in the years to come.

20:7 Polarized Light

What is polarized light?

How does a polarizing filter affect light?

Light is a transverse wave, like a wave on a rope. You can form a wave on a rope by moving the rope up and down, or by moving it side to side, or in any plane in between. The waves in light can also vibrate in any plane. Most light consists of waves vibrating in many planes. **Polarized light,** however, consists of waves vibrating only in one plane. A filter can polarize light. The filter has long, thin molecules that are all lined up in parallel rows. Light vibrating parallel to the molecules is absorbed, while light vibrating at right angles to the rows passes through. Polarizing sunglasses contain such filters.

Polarizing sunglasses are useful because light coming from the sky is polarized as it is scattered by the atmosphere. The filters in the sunglasses are rotated so they absorb this polarized light, reducing the glare. Similar

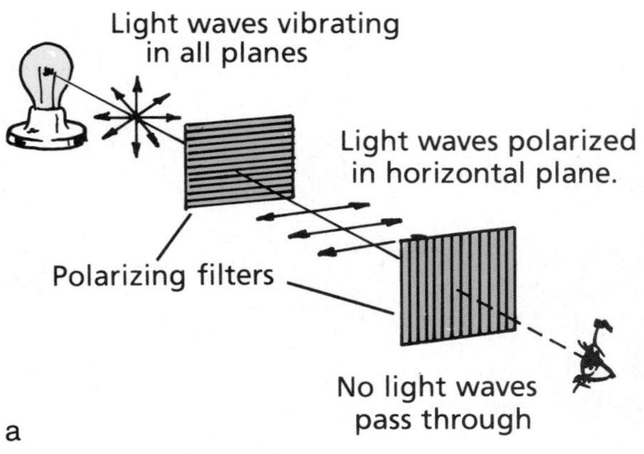

FIGURE 20–17. Light waves vibrating in one plane can pass through a polarizing filter (a). Polarizing filters are used in photography to reduce glare (b).

filters are used in cameras to make the sky appear darker. Light reflected at an angle from shiny surfaces is also polarized. Sunglasses reduce the glare of light reflected off the road or windows of other cars.

20:8 Lasers

What are the characteristics of laser light?

A **laser** is a light source that produces a bright narrow beam of light. Light produced by a laser is all of one color or wavelength. Laser light is also coherent. In **coherent light,** the crests and troughs of the light waves are all lined up together. A laser pulse may be many millions of wavelengths in length. In these ways, laser light is different from other light sources. Light from the sun or from lamps is a mixture of waves with different wavelengths and directions. In addition, the crests and troughs are not in step.

F.Y.I The wave train of a laser pulse may be many millions of wavelengths in length.

PROBLEM SOLVING

Mirror Mirror on the Wall

Terry was tired of never being able to see herself from head to toe when she dressed for school or for a date. No matter how she twisted and turned or moved closer to or farther away from the mirror, she could never see all of herself at one time. Now Terry's family was moving to a new apartment. She knew there would not be wall space for a full length mirror. However, her mother told her that if she could figure out something smaller that would serve the purpose, she could have it. Terry needed to find the shortest mirror that would let her see a full view of herself. After studying the problem, she decided that she first needed a sketch of herself, the mirror, and her image.

How did Terry solve her problem, and what did she tell her mother?

Lasers are made with different kinds of crystals, liquids, and gases. One kind of laser, the helium-neon laser, uses a hollow glass tube with mirrors at two ends. One mirror is totally reflecting while the other allows some light to escape. The tube is filled with a mixture of helium and neon at low pressure. An electrical spark is sent through the gases, turning them into a plasma. The electrical energy is changed into energy stored in the neon atoms, which is then released as red light. The light is reflected back and forth between the two mirrors. This light causes other atoms to release their energy as light. The intensity of the light increases, and all the waves have their crests and troughs aligned. The coherent waves leave the partially reflecting mirror at one end of the tube as a narrow beam of red laser light. Some lasers produce blue, green, or yellow light or infrared radiation. Note that lasers are not energy sources. Lasers merely convert one form of energy into light energy. Even though the laser beam is extremely bright, lasers are very inefficient. Most lasers convert less than 1% of their energy source into light energy.

FIGURE 20–18. Lasers are used to cut and weld metal and to cut paper and fabric.

Lasers made of small crystals of alloys of gallium, aluminum, and arsenic are becoming important. They change electrical energy directly into light energy. Opposite faces of the crystal are polished to form the two mirrors. Crystal lasers produce very tiny beams of light or infrared radiation.

List three uses for lasers.

Lasers have an increasing number of uses. The straight narrow beam is used by surveyors as a guide to build tunnels, roads, and bridges. Beams of intense laser light can be used to cut and weld pieces of metal. Lasers can be used in delicate surgery, such as welding a retina to the back surface of the eye. They are used to produce spectacular light shows and in supermarkets to read bar codes on food products. Crystal lasers are used in compact disk players and to transmit messages over optical fibers.

20:9 Optical Fibers

What is meant by total internal reflection?

When light passes out of glass into air, it is refracted away from the normal. If the angle of the ray inside the glass is large enough, the light ray is refracted so much that it can no longer leave the glass, but is completely reflected back into the glass. The ray has undergone **total internal reflection.** A diamond's sparkle is a result of total internal reflection.

FIGURE 20–19. If a light ray traveling from glass to air strikes the surface at too great an angle, it will be refracted so much that it cannot leave the glass. This phenomenon is called total internal reflection.

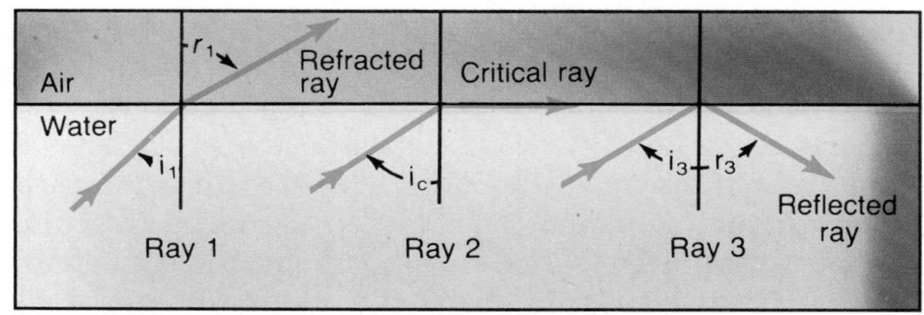

F.Y.I. If the ocean were as transparent as the glass in optical fibers, we could see to the bottom of its deepest parts.

Total internal reflection "pipes" light from one end of an optical fiber to the other. An **optical fiber** is a thin strand of glass covered by a second layer of glass. Often a protective plastic tube covers the fiber. The inner core has a higher index of refraction than the outer layer. It is said to be more optically dense. Light enters one end of the fiber. When light rays strike the surface between the inner glass core and the outer layer of glass, they undergo total internal reflection. The angle at which the rays are refracted is so great, more than 90°, that they are completely reflected back from the surface. They are trapped in the inner core of the fiber. The rays make many such reflections before leaving the other end. The fiber carries the light from one end to the other with no light escaping. Further, optical fibers are very transparent, so no light is absorbed.

Describe a fiberscope and tell how it is used.

Optical fibers have many practical uses. Bundles of optical fibers form a fiberscope. Each fiber carries one section of the image. Fiberscopes are used to see into places that are difficult to view, such as the inside of a nuclear reactor chamber or the combustion chamber of a jet engine. In one form of fiberscope used in medicine, one bundle carries light into the inside of a patient's stomach. The other bundle carries the image out to the doctor. This use of optical fibers enables a doctor to check internal body parts and functions without using X rays or surgery.

FIGURE 20–20. Optical fibers exhibit total internal reflection along the surface between the glass core and the outer layer of glass.

Optical fibers are being used to replace metal wires in communication systems. Crystal lasers are used as light sources because they have very narrow light beams. Electrical telephone signals modulate the brightness of the light. The light can be detected after traveling through up to 14 kilometers of glass fiber. The detector changes the light back into an electrical signal. Each fiber can carry as many telephone calls as 10 000 wires. Optical fiber telephone cables only 1 centimeter in diameter contain 144 fibers surrounded by a protective covering.

Optical fibers have several advantages over metal wires. The fibers take up less space and are less expensive. Signals cannot leak from one fiber into another, causing "cross talk." They are not affected by electrical interference and are difficult to tap. In addition to telephone signals, optical fibers can carry computer and television signals.

What advantages do optical fibers have over metal wires for communication?

Review

11. How does polarized light differ from normal light?
12. List three practical uses of polarizers and polarized light.
13. Why does light not leak out the sides of an optical fiber?
14. How does laser light differ from sunlight?
15. ★ Could you make a model of an optical fiber by filling a glass tube with water? The water plays the role of the core and the tube the outer layer. Explain.

TECHNOLOGY: APPLICATIONS

Liquid Crystal Displays

The numbers and letters on digital watches and calculators are usually dark numbers on a light background. The display is called a liquid crystal display, or LCD. The LCD is used because it uses an extremely small amount of electrical energy.

An LCD contains many long thin molecules in a liquid placed between two sheets of glass. Normally the molecules lie parallel to the glass, but when an electrical voltage is applied, they rotate until they are at right angles to the glass. Because of the shape of the molecules, they affect the passage of polarized light.

The display consists of a polarizing filter on the top, a layer of liquid crystal material, and a reflecting rear surface. Light passes through the filter and is polarized. If no electrical signal is applied to the display, the light is reflected by the rear surface back through the filter. The display appears light. When an electrical signal is applied to the liquid crystal material, the liquid crystal changes the direction of polarization of the light. The reflected light is now absorbed by the polarizing filter, and the display looks dark.

Engineers are developing ways of creating images using LCDs. LCDs are now used in portable computers and small television screens. They may soon be used in large, thin color television screens that can be hung on the wall like a painting.

INVESTIGATION 20–2

Convex Lenses

Problem: What kinds of images are formed by convex lenses?

Materials

convex lens on a stand
stiff white cardboard
meter stick
candle or lamp with clear glass bulb

Procedure

1. Place the lens on the table with a clear view of a bright, lighted distant object.
2. Put the screen behind the lens and move it until an image of the distant object is seen on the screen. The distance between the lens and the screen is the focal length of the lens. Record the focal length.
3. Put the lighted candle or lamp (the object) more than twice the focal length from the lens on the side opposite the screen.
4. Move the screen until a clear image appears. Measure the distance of the lamp and the image from the lens.
5. Repeat Steps 3 and 4 with the object exactly twice the focal length from the lens.
6. Repeat Steps 3 and 4 with the object between one and two focal lengths from the lens.
7. Hold the lens less than one focal length from the object. Try to find an image on the screen.
8. Look through the lens at the object and describe what you see.

Data and Observations

Focal length of lens F = ________________ cm

Position of Object	Position of Image	Type of Image	Image/Object Size	Direction of Image
Large Distance	at F			
Beyond 2 F				
2 F				
Between 2 F and F				
Less than F				

Analysis

1. How does the size of the image compare to the size of the object as you bring the object closer to the lens?
2. How does the distance of the image from the lens change as you bring the object closer?
3. Where does the image appear to be when the object is closer than one focal length?

Conclusions and Applications

4. Summarize your observations as to how the position and size of the object and image are related to each other.
5. If you are given a lens with a focal length of 15 cm and asked to produce an enlarged image, where will you put the object?

Chapter 20 Review

SUMMARY

1. Mirrors reflect light and can form an image. 20:1
2. An image that can be projected on a piece of paper is a real image. One that cannot be so projected is a virtual image. 20:1, 20:2
3. Lenses that are thicker in the middle than at the edges are convex; those that are thinner in the middle are concave. 20:3
4. In the human eye, light is refracted in the cornea and in the lens to form an image on the retina. 20:4
5. Telescopes, used to view objects that are far away, consist of an eyepiece lens and either an objective lens or a mirror. 20:5
6. A microscope uses two convex lenses to make a magnified image of very small objects. 20:5
7. A camera uses one or more lenses to focus an image on film. The focal length of the lens controls the size of the image. 20:6
8. Polarized light, waves vibrating only in one plane, comes from the sky, from reflections, and from light passing through polarizing filters. 20:7
9. Lasers produce a bright, narrow, coherent beam of light, all of one color or wavelength. 20:8
10. Optical fibers use total internal reflection to pipe light from one end of the thin thread of glass to the other. 20:9

VOCABULARY

a. coherent light
b. concave lens
c. concave mirror
d. convex lens
e. convex mirror
f. focal length
g. focal point
h. laser
i. microscope
j. optical axis
k. optical fiber
l. polarized light
m. plane mirror
n. real image
o. reflecting telescope
p. refracting telescope
q. telephoto lens
r. total internal reflection
s. virtual image
t. wide-angle lens

Matching

Match each description with the correct vocabulary word from the list above. Some words will not be used.

1. a mirror shaped like the bottom of a spoon
2. a lens that is thicker at the edges than in the center
3. a mirror that is flat
4. a magnifying glass is an example of this lens
5. an image that can be projected on a screen
6. a straight line through the center of the lens
7. distance from the center of a mirror to the focal point
8. light that vibrates only in one plane
9. occurs when rays in glass hit the surface at too large an angle
10. light that has all the crests and troughs lined up

Chapter 20 Review

MAIN IDEAS

A. Reviewing Concepts

Choose the word or phrase that correctly completes each of the following sentences.

1. An image is produced inside the eye by a *(concave mirror, convex lens, prism, concave lens).*
2. Farsightedness may be corrected with a *(concave mirror, convex lens, prism, concave lens).*
3. A refracting telescope focuses an image by means of a *(convex mirror, convex lens, concave mirror, prism).*
4. Microscopes produce magnified images by focusing light with *(lenses, mirrors, specimens, stages).*
5. Compared to ordinary light, laser light *(travels faster, is all one color, has many wavelengths, spreads into many directions).*

Complete each of the following sentences with the correct word or phrase.

6. The ____________ of the eye control the shape of the lens.
7. A(n) ____________ mirror is used in a reflecting telescope to gather the light.
8. A(n) ____________ camera takes a picture without a lens.
9. The light in an optical fiber undergoes ____________.
10. A(n) ____________ lens for a camera has a short focal length.

Determine whether each of the following sentences is true or false. If it is false, change the underlined word to make the sentence true.

11. A <u>convex</u> lens is thicker in the center.
12. A virtual image <u>cannot</u> be projected on a screen.
13. A camera forms a <u>virtual</u> image on the film.
14. A telephoto lens has a <u>long</u> focal length.
15. An optical fiber is made of <u>copper</u>.

B. Understanding Concepts

Answer the following questions using complete sentences when possible.

16. If you place a candle 35 cm from a plane mirror, where will the image be located?
17. Describe the image you would have if you placed an object 6 cm away from a convex mirror with a 12 cm focal length.
18. Describe the image you would have if you placed an object 8 cm away from a concave mirror with a 12 cm focal length.
19. What advantages do optical fibers have over metal wires in communication systems?
20. Suppose you first look at your teacher, then move your eyes to this book. Describe the change in the lens in your eye.
21. You have a single-lens reflex camera with a zoom lens that has focal lengths between 70 and 210 mm. You want to take a picture of a skydiver high in the sky. Which focal length should you choose?
22. Why are polarized sunglasses especially good for automobile drivers?
23. Suppose you have two glasses with indexes of refraction 1.48 and 1.52. Which should you use for the core of an optical fiber and which for the outer layer? Explain your answer.
24. Describe the light emitted by a laser.
25. Why do lasers make good light sources for optical fibers?

C. Applying Concepts

Answer the following questions using complete sentences when possible.

26. If you stand 40 cm from a mirror, your image appears 40 cm behind the mirror, or 80 cm away. If you now hold a second mirror 20 cm behind your head, you can see the back of your head in the two mirrors. If your head is 25 cm from front to back, how far from your eyes is the image of the back of your head?

27. Explain the difference between farsighted and nearsighted vision. How are these problems corrected with lenses?

28. Explain how a microscope produces an enlarged image of a specimen.

29. Some zoom lenses have focal lengths between 35 and 150 mm. Which of these two extremes would give the widest-angle view, which the most telephoto?

30. Plastic can be used as an optical fiber even though it absorbs more light than glass. In which applications of optical fibers could you use plastic? In which would you need glass?

PROJECTS

1. Prepare a report on the use of optical fibers for communications. List their advantages and disadvantages.
2. Do research on the uses of lasers in surgery. In what types of surgery are they most advantageous?
3. Learn about the space telescope. Why do astronomers want a telescope in space? Does it already exist? What do astronomers hope to learn using it?
4. Take a series of pictures using different apertures and shutter speeds. Prepare a poster exhibit of your pictures to show the effects of the different setting on the images produced.
5. Obtain a book on color photography and find out how color film works.

SKILL REVIEW

1. What is the purpose of making scale drawings?
2. Why is it important for scale drawings to be accurate?
3. If an object 7.5 m high were pictured at a scale of 1 m = 5 cm, how high would the picture of the object be?
4. What is the chemical formula for aluminum carbonate?
5. Why should you always study your science assignment with a pencil and paper handy?

READINGS

1. Berry, Richard. *Build Your Own Telescope.* New York: Scribner, 1985.
2. Jeffries, David. *Lasers.* New York: Franklin Watts, 1986.
3. Meredith, D. "How New 'Eyes' Track the Mysterious Origin of Cosmic Rays." *Popular Science.* March, 1986, pp. 68–71.
4. Riley, Peter. *Looking at Microscopes.* North Pomfret, VT: David and Charles, 1985.

SCIENCE AND SOCIETY

ELECTROMAGNETIC WAVES—BOON OR BANE?

X rays are used for medical diagnosis. Ultraviolet radiation contributes to making vitamin D. Visible light allows us to see. Infrared photographs allow us to identify warm objects and "see" them at night. Microwaves are used for telephone communications and cooking. Radio waves are used to broadcast information.

Background

The energy transmitted by electromagnetic waves can be explained in terms of bundles of energy, called *photons*. The higher the frequency of the wave, the greater the energy of the photon.

The frequency of gamma radiation and X rays is so great that the energy in one of their photons is great enough to strip an electron from an atom. When an electron is removed from an atom, an *ion* results. For this reason gamma radiation and X rays are known as *ionizing radiation*.

If an atom is ionized in the part of a cell responsible for reproduction, the cell may lose the ability to control its reproduction. When this happens, cancer can result. However, not only can ionizing radiation cause cancer, but it can also be used to treat it. Thus, while ionizing radiation can cause harm, it can also be used for positive purposes.

The same is true for nonionizing electromagnetic radiation. The type of electromagnetic waves with the frequencies just lower than X rays is ultraviolet. As in the case of ionizing radiation, the danger comes from overexposure. Overexposure to ultraviolet radiation can cause skin cancer.

Even overexposure to visible light can be harmful. Looking directly into the concentrated light of a laser beam can cause damage to your retina.

Infrared radiation can cause burns if it is too intense. Hot stove burners give off infrared radiation, which you can't see. But what happens if your finger gets too close?

Too many radio waves give another sort of problem—interference of radio stations. This is why radio and television broadcasting frequencies are regulated by the Federal Communications Commission.

Formerly used only for long distance communications, microwaves are now present in many homes in microwave ovens. Since microwaves can cook your fingers as well as a potato, these ovens must allow minimal leakage to the outside. Consumers Union reported in 1985 that none of the ovens they tested leaked more than half the legal allowance. Yet studies of tumors in rats have caused the safety of microwave exposure to remain an open question. There will undoubtedly be more research to investigate the safety of microwaves.

The same is true for the lowest frequency electromagnetic waves—those radiated from electric power lines. Because the electric current we use in our homes oscillates at a frequency of 60 Hz, electric power lines radiate electromagnetic waves of this frequency.

FIGURE 1. High voltage lines marching across the countryside are a common sight.

Many scientists won't live near an overhead power line or sleep under an electric blanket. They think that the body's own chemistry makes it susceptible to electromagnetic radiation.

A great deal of discussion has been caused by the following observations: a) a connection between cancer in children and how far they live from electric power lines; b) greater frequency of leukemia and brain tumors in people whose jobs expose them to large electric currents; c) increased reproduction of cancer cells when exposed to electromagnetic fields like those from power lines. The studies used to establish these connections are similar to those used to establish the link between smoking and lung cancer. However, the link between electromagnetic fields and cancer is not as clear as that for smoking and lung cancer.

Developing a Viewpoint

It is recognized that more research is needed on the effects of electromagnetic fields around power lines on humans. Read as many references as you can and come prepared to answer the following questions in a class discussion:

How much research and evidence would be needed to convince you that microwaves or radiation from electric power lines causes cancer? If you were convinced that microwaves or radiation from electric power lines causes cancer, what would you recommend?

Suppose that in the future, materials could be developed that are superconducting at room temperatures. What suggestions could you then think of to help lessen the effects of electromagnetic fields on humans?

Suggested Readings

Edwards, Diane D. "ELF: The Current Controversy." *Science News, 131*(7), 107, February 14, 1987.

Foster, Kenneth R. and Arthur W. Guy. "The Microwave Problem." *Scientific American 255*(3), 32-39, September 14, 1986; *Scientific American 255*(6) December 4, 1986.

"Is Radiation for Microwave Ovens Hazardous?" *Consumer Reports,50*(11), 647, November, 1985.

Kolbert, Elizabeth. "Study Cites Incidence of Cancer Near Power Lines." *The New York Times, CXXXVVI*(No. 47,195), July 9, 1986.

Richards, Bill. "New Study Strengthens Suspected Links Between Electromagnetism and Cancer." *The Wall Street Journal, CCX*(12), 31, July 16, 1987.

Wellborn, Stanley N. "An Electrifying New Hazard." *U.S. News and World Report, 102*(12), 72, March 30, 1987.

UNIT 7

Every minute of every day the sun provides Earth with a huge source of natural energy. The problem is to harness it to meet our needs. Unfortunately, however, we still lack the technology that would allow us to collect and concentrate solar energy to drive turbines or operate industrial equipment.

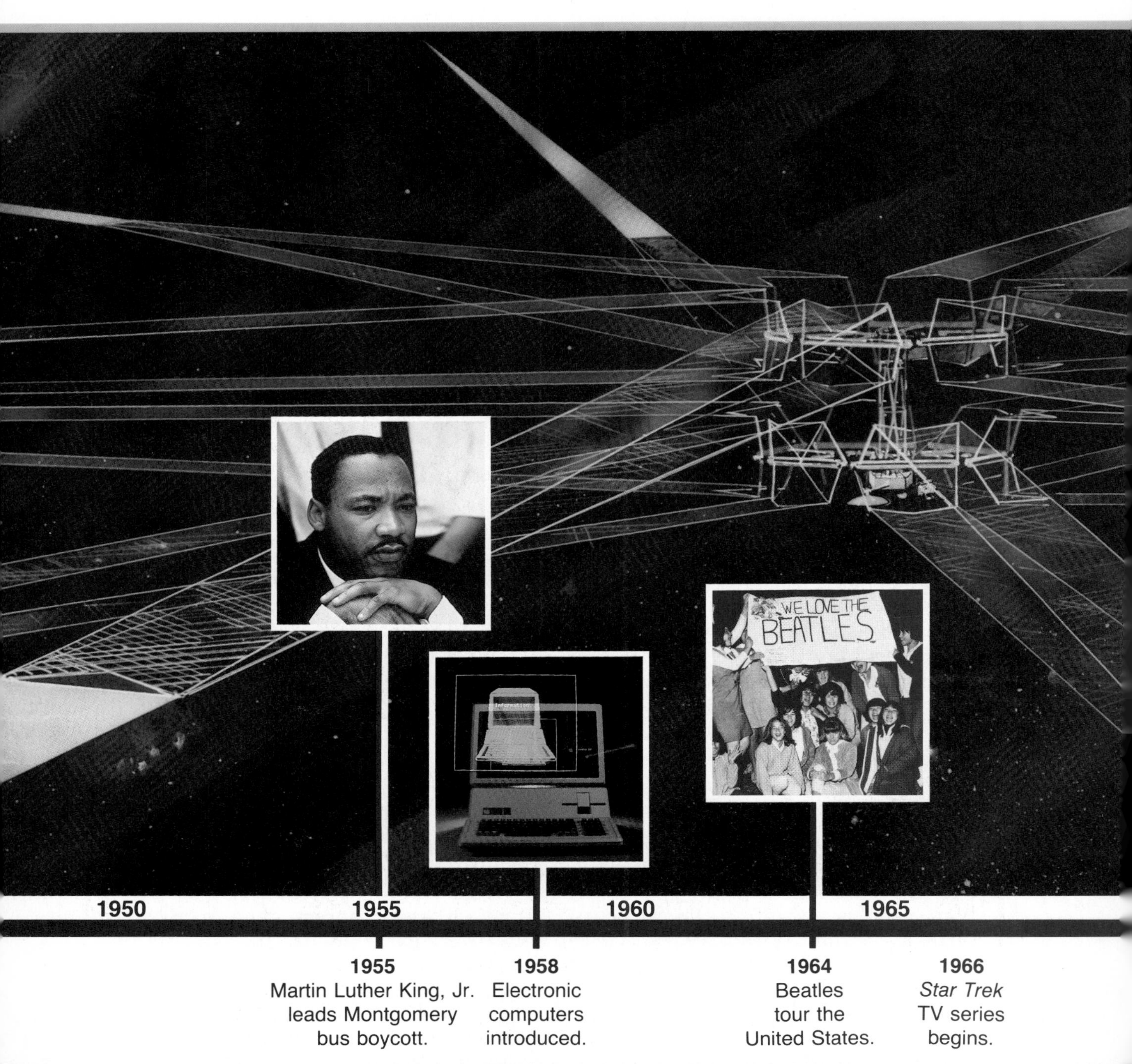

1955 Martin Luther King, Jr. leads Montgomery bus boycott.

1958 Electronic computers introduced.

1964 Beatles tour the United States.

1966 *Star Trek* TV series begins.

ENERGY RESOURCES

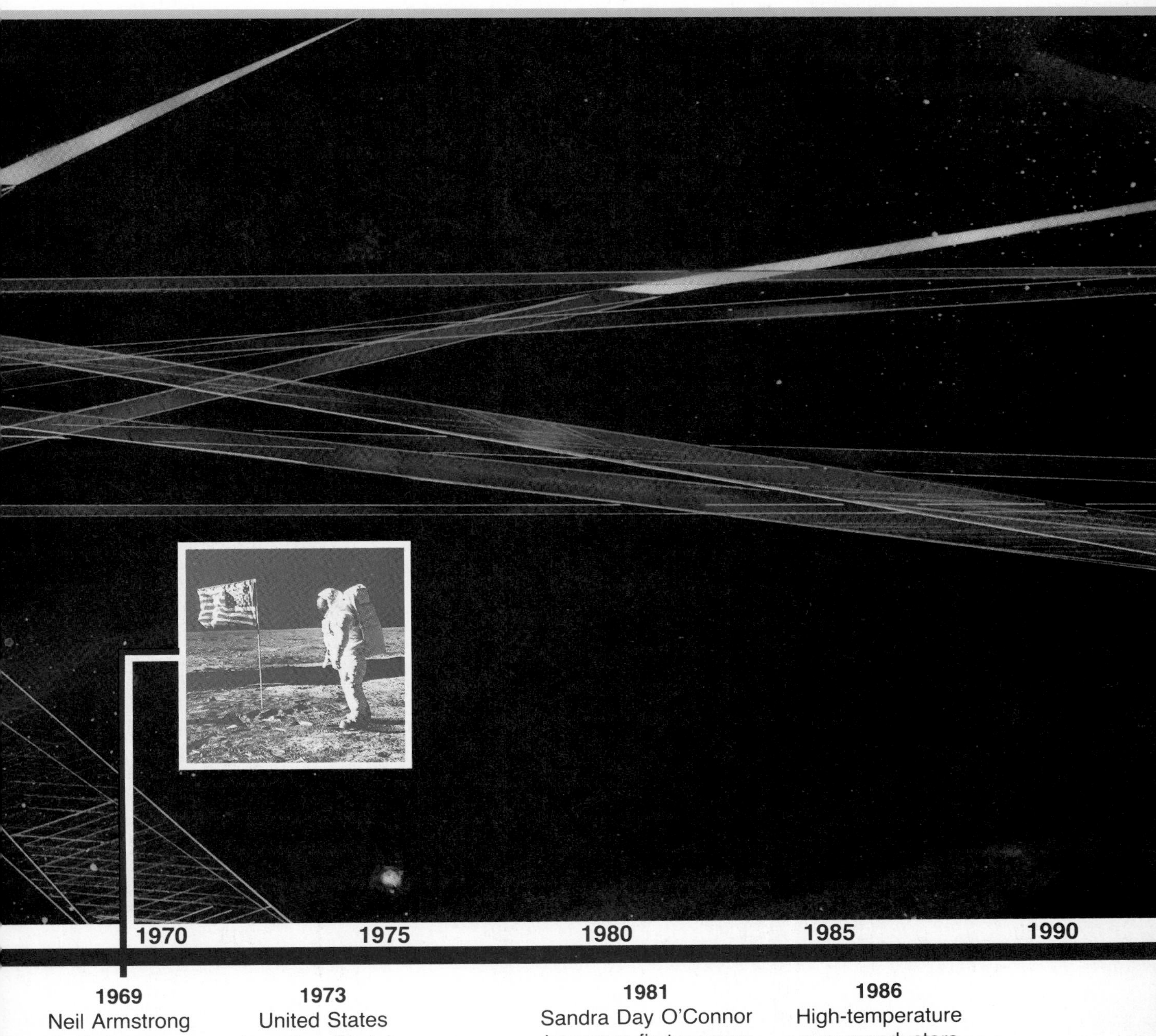

1969
Neil Armstrong is first person on moon.

1973
United States launches Skylab.

1981
Sandra Day O'Connor becomes first woman Supreme Court Justice.

1986
High-temperature superconductors discovered.

STATIC ELECTRICITY
CURRENT ELECTRICITY
ELECTRICAL CIRCUITS
ELECTRICAL ENERGY AND POWER

Chapter 21

Electricity

Have you ever experienced a shock as you touched a metal doorknob after walking across a carpet? If so, you have sensed electricity directly and perhaps painfully. The effects of electricity appear in many forms. A streak of lightning in the sky, a glowing wire inside a light bulb, and the heating of an electric stove are examples of the effects of electricity. In this chapter, we will begin to study this very useful form of energy.

STATIC ELECTRICITY

The ancient Greeks knew that if they rubbed an amber rod with a piece of cloth, the rod would attract dust or pieces of leaves. Benjamin Franklin's famous kite experiment showed that lightning was an extremely powerful form of the same electricity that resulted from rubbing cloth on amber.

GOALS

1. You will learn the nature of static electricity.
2. You will learn the difference between conductors and insulators.
3. You will learn how an electroscope can be used to detect static electrical charges.

21:1 Electric Charge

You can repeat the experiments that the ancient Greeks did by rubbing a plastic comb or ruler with a piece of fur or cloth. Then hold the plastic and cloth close together. If the cloth is "fuzzy" you will notice that the fuzz is attracted to the plastic. If you rub another piece of plastic with the cloth, you will find that the two pieces of plastic repel each other. Rubbing can produce forces that both attract and repel objects. What causes these forces?

Rubbing different materials together can give them electric charges. Where do the charges come from? Remember that all matter is made of atoms that contain charged particles. Atoms contain protons that have a positive charge and electrons with a negative charge.

F.Y.I. Amber is petrified tree resin, which the Greeks called *elektron.* Our word electricity comes from this Greek source.

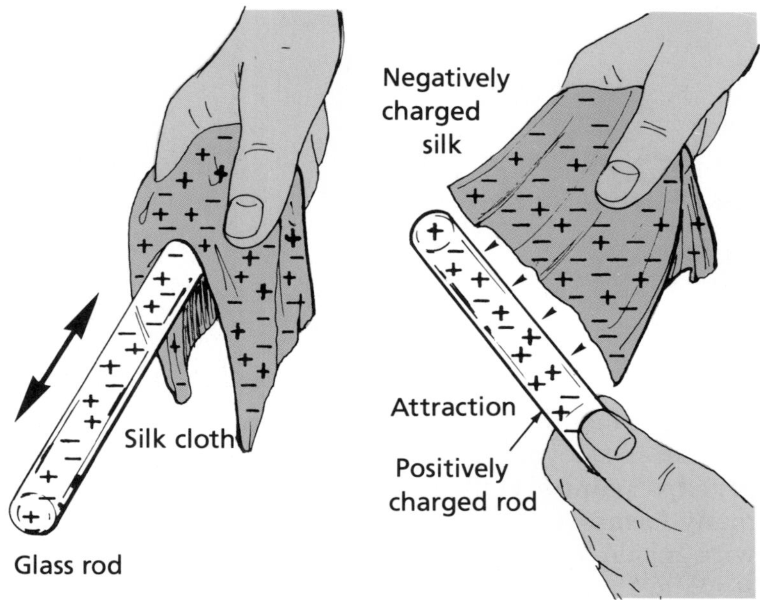

FIGURE 21–1. When glass is rubbed with silk, electrons from the glass move to the silk, leaving the rod positively charged. The silk becomes negatively charged.

The electrons can move through matter. When two objects are rubbed together, electrons can move from one object to the other. The object that gains extra electrons is negatively charged. The one that loses electrons is positively charged. Rubbing plastic with cloth causes the plastic to gain electrons from the cloth, becoming negatively charged. The cloth becomes positively charged.

How do objects get a static charge?

If a glass rod is rubbed with a silk cloth, the glass becomes positively charged. Electrons move from the glass to the silk, giving the silk a negative charge. An object that has an **electric charge** either has too many or too few electrons.

Two objects that are charged negatively repel each other. The same is true of two positively charged bodies. A negatively charged object, however, attracts a positively charged article. That is, like charges repel; unlike charges attract. Two charged glass rods repel each other, but a charged glass rod attracts the charged silk or a charged plastic ruler.

What is static electricity?

Positive or negative charges on an object are called static electricity. **Static electricity** is electric charge built up in one place. If you rub only one end of a plastic comb, only that end becomes charged. The electric charge stays in place. You may see examples of static electricity when you take clothes out of a dryer. For example, a wool sock or sweater may stick to clothes made of cotton. They became charged by rubbing against one another in the dryer.

FIGURE 21–2. Clothing often gains a static charge in a clothes dryer.

INVESTIGATION 21–1
Electrostatics

Problem: What are the forces on electrically charged objects?

Materials

two ebonite or hard rubber rods or hard rubber comb
fur
glass rod
silk or plastic wrap
ring stand
utility clamp
pith ball
thread

Procedure

A. Ebonite Rod

1. With the thread, suspend one ebonite rod from the clamp so it can swing freely.
2. Rub one end of the suspended rod with fur.
3. Charge one end of the second ebonite rod by rubbing it with fur. Bring it near the charged end of the suspended rod. Record your observations.
4. Charge a glass rod by rubbing it with silk or plastic wrap. Bring it near the charged end of the suspended rod. Record your observations.

FIGURE 21–3.

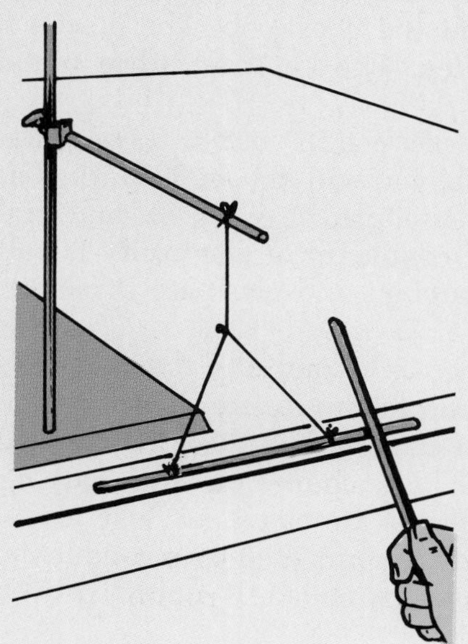

B. Pith Ball

5. Suspend the pith ball from the clamp.
6. Charge the ebonite rod with fur and touch the pith ball. Record your observations.
7. Charge the glass rod with silk. Bring it near the pith ball. Record your observations.
8. Recharge the ebonite rod and bring it near the pith ball. Record your observations.

Data and Observations

Step	Observations
3	
4	

Analysis and Conclusions

1. Explain your observations using the second charged ebonite rod.
2. Explain your observations when using the glass rod.
3. Suppose you had a second glass rod that you suspended and charged. If you brought the ebonite rod nearby, would the glass rod turn toward or away from the ebonite rod? Why?
4. If you now brought the other glass rod near the suspended glass rod, what would happen? Why?
5. Explain you observations in Step 6.
6. Explain your observations in Step 7.
7. Explain your observations in Step 8.
8. Assume that the fur gives the ebonite rod a negative charge. Explain Step 8 in terms of positive and negative charge.
9. What forces do electrically charged objects exert on each other?
10. How could you tell whether a charged object had a positive or negative charge?

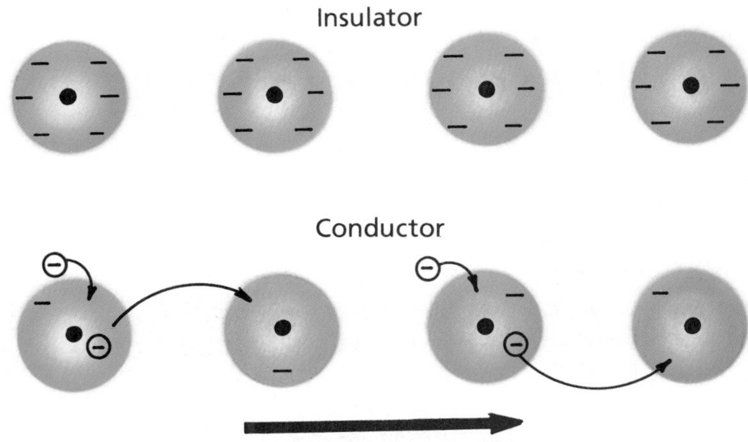

FIGURE 21–4. Metals are good conductors because the electrons in the outer energy levels of their atoms are loosely held and are free to move from atom to atom.

21:2 Conductors and Insulators

What is a static discharge?

When you walk across a thick carpet, you may pick up a negative electric charge on your shoes. If you bring your hand near a metal doorknob, you see and feel an electric spark. The spark is caused by electrons moving between your hand and the doorknob. The spark is a static discharge, a transfer of static electricity. The extra electrons on your body moved to the doorknob.

What is conduction?

Your body got a negative charge when you rubbed your feet against the carpet. How did the charge move through your body into your hand? The movement of electrons through a material is called conduction. Electrons can move through a material that is a **conductor.** Thus your body is a conductor. If you hold a key in your hand while you touch the doorknob, you will see a spark between the key and the doorknob. The electrons will move through the key. The key and other metals are also conductors.

What is an insulator?

If you hold a piece of wood in your hand and touch the wood to the doorknob, you will not see a spark. The electrons do not move through the wood. A material, like wood, that is a poor conductor of electricity is called an **insulator.** Plastic, rubber, and glass are three other examples of insulators.

If you rub your feet on carpet and touch a water faucet, a spark will jump to the faucet. Metal water pipes go into Earth. The electrons flow through the pipes into the ground, to Earth. The charge on your body becomes zero. Grounding allows an object to lose its charge. When a charged body is connected by a conductor to the ground, it is said to be grounded. If a positively charged body is touched to the water pipe, electrons will flow from Earth to the body, making the charge on it zero. Think of Earth as a large reservoir of electrons. The electrons can either flow into a positively charged body or out of a negatively charged body.

Many houses are protected by lightning rods. A lightning rod is a metal rod placed at the highest point of a house and is connected by a metal wire to the ground. In a thunderstorm, the static discharge between a charged cloud and Earth will strike the lightning rod. The electrical charge will safely pass through the wire to the ground.

FIGURE 21–5. An electroscope is used to detect electric charge by changes in the position of its leaves.

21:3 The Electroscope

Electric charges can be detected by the forces between charged bodies. An **electroscope** is a device that detects electric charges. A simple electroscope, Figure 21–5, contains two light metal leaves that are free to swing apart. In an uncharged electroscope, the leaves hang straight down. When the electroscope is charged, both leaves are given the same charge. They repel each other and spread apart. An electroscope can be charged by touching it with a negatively charged plastic comb. Electrons from the charged comb move to the metal knob of the electroscope, down the metal rod, and onto the leaves by conduction. Both leaves gain a negative charge and spread apart because like charges repel each other.

What is grounding?

Why do the leaves of an electroscope spread apart when it is touched by a charged object?

If the knob of an electroscope is touched with a positively-charged glass rod, the electroscope takes on a positive charge. The metal rod and knob conduct electrons out of the electroscope to the glass rod. The loss of electrons results in the leaves becoming positively charged. The leaves repel each other and spread apart.

How can you tell if an object has a positive or a negative charge? If you rub a piece of plastic with a cloth, it will become negatively charged. If you touch the electroscope with the plastic, the electroscope will also have a negative charge; the leaves will spread apart. If a negatively charged object is then brought near the knob of the electroscope, the leaves will move farther apart. The negative charge on the object repels the electrons in the knob, pushing down more electrons onto the leaves. The negative charge on the leaves increases as does their repulsion. However, if a positively charged rod is brought near the knob of a negatively charged electroscope, the opposite effect is seen. The leaves move closer together. The positively charged rod attracts electrons from the leaves to the knob. The charge on the two leaves decreases, and there is less repulsion between them.

Review

1. If you rub a balloon with a wool cloth, the balloon becomes negatively charged. Explain what gives the balloon its charge.
2. Would the charged balloon attract or repel a glass rod rubbed with silk? Explain your answer.
3. What is the difference between an electrical conductor and an insulator?
4. What materials in your classroom are conductors? Insulators?
5. ★ Can you use an electroscope to find out which charge, negative or positive, an object has?

TECHNOLOGY: ADVANCES

Superconductivity

About one-tenth of the electrical energy generated in the United States is lost as thermal energy when the electricity is carried from a power plant to the user. If the resistance of the wires delivering the electricity could be made zero, all the electrical energy could be put to use.

In 1911, the Dutch physicist Heike Kamerlingh-Onnes found that many metals lose all resistance when they are cooled to temperatures near absolute zero. They are then called superconductors. In the next 70 years many superconductors were developed, but none worked at temperatures higher than 23 K. Unfortunately, the energy needed to keep them that cold is often greater than the energy saved by their lack of resistance.

In 1986 the physicists Bednorz and Mueller, working in Switzerland, discovered a new type of superconductor. The superconductor is a ceramic, a brittle, glass-like material that is an insulator at room temperature. At temperatures below about 95 K (–168°C) the samples lose all their resistance. Many scientists are now trying to make flexible wires out of the ceramic. Others are searching for similar materials that might become superconductors at room temperature.

Room temperature superconductors not only would eliminate energy lost when electricity is sent long distances, but also would make possible small, very efficient motors and generators. They might lead to high-speed trains that do not roll on wheels, but are suspended by magnets.

CURRENT ELECTRICITY

GOALS

1. You will learn what an electric current is.
2. You will learn about electric potential difference.
3. You will understand the relationship between resistance, current, and potential difference in a conductor.

In the eighteenth century Benjamin Franklin and others knew that the powerful effects of static electricity soon died away. They could not be sustained. In 1800 Alessandro Volta (1745–1827), a professor in Italy, discovered that two different metals and a conducting liquid could also produce electrical effects. The sparks were weak, but they lasted a long time. He found that the two metals had to be connected by a continuous conductor to produce the effects. He proposed that the electrical effects were caused by a moving electric fluid, later called electric current.

21:4 An Electric Current

What is an electric current?

A flow of electrons or other charged particles through a conductor is an **electric current.** The discharge of a charged object such as an electroscope is an example of a current flow, but it lasts only a fraction of a second. A continuing flow of current is needed for practical uses of electricity, such as lighting a lamp.

Current flows when an electroscope is discharged because a force is exerted on the electrons. The force ends when the electroscope no longer has excess electrons. A continuing current requires a lasting force. One source of constant electric current is a **battery.** A battery acts like a "pump" that forces electrons through a conductor. Batteries are used to light flashlights, operate portable tape players, start cars, and for many other purposes.

What is a wet cell?

The simplest batteries consist of one cell. Often batteries contain several cells. A wet cell contains two different metals in a solution containing an electrolyte. When electrolytes dissolve in water, ions are released. Motion of the ions allows the solution to conduct electricity.

The wet cell in Figure 21–6 contains a strip of zinc in a zinc chloride solution and a strip of copper in a copper(II) chloride solution. The solutions are separated by a porous cup. The cup keeps the solutions separated but allows the movement of ions between them. When the zinc and copper strips are connected by a wire, a chemical reaction begins. The zinc chloride solution contains zinc ions and chloride ions. Zinc atoms from the strip of zinc enter the solution, releasing two electrons and becoming zinc ions.

FIGURE 21–6. In this type of wet cell, electrons move from the zinc metal to the copper metal through the wire.

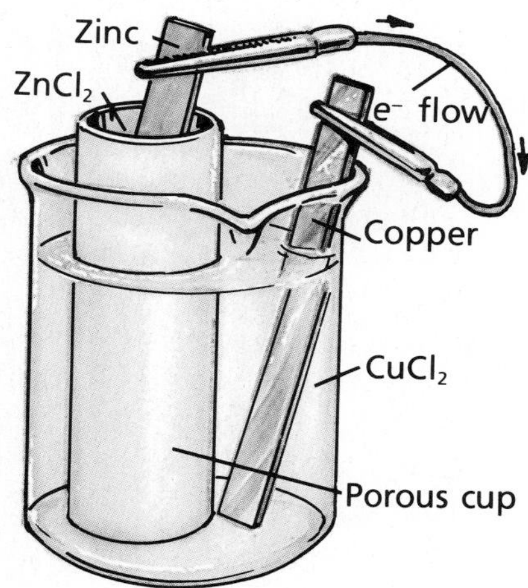

F.Y.I. Every ion is either positively or negatively charged. Review electrolytes, Chapter 15.

$$Zn(cr) \rightarrow Zn^{2+}(aq) + 2e^-$$

The two electrons left by each departing zinc atom move through the wire to the copper, creating an electric current in the wire. As a result, the copper strip becomes negatively charged. The positive copper ions in the copper(II) chloride solution are attracted to the charged copper strip. When the copper ions come in contact with the strip, they gain electrons, becoming copper atoms that remain on the strip.

$$Cu^{2+}(aq) + 2e^- \longrightarrow Cu(cr)$$

F.Y.I. A wet cell is sometimes called a voltaic cell, after Alessandro Volta.

Ions move through the solution in the wet cell while electrons flow through the wire connected to the cell. The flow of electrons through the wire is a current. If the wire is removed from the zinc or copper, the electric current stops. An electric current differs from static electricity. A static electric charge is an excess or shortage of electrons in one place. An electric current is a movement of electrons from one place to another.

A common form of a wet cell is in the storage battery in a car. The battery contains lead and lead dioxide (lead(IV) oxide) plates in a sulfuric acid solution. Lead loses electrons as it reacts with the sulfuric acid. Lead dioxide gains electrons and changes to lead(II) sulfate.

How does a dry cell produce a current?

$$Pb^0 \rightarrow Pb^{2+} + 2e^-$$
$$Pb^{4+} + 2e^- \rightarrow Pb^{2+}$$

The movement of electrons through a conductor from the lead to the lead dioxide plates forms a current.

A dry cell works in much the same way as a wet cell. One kind of dry cell contains a carbon rod set in the middle of a zinc can, Figure 21–7b. A moist paste fills the can. Chemicals in the paste react with the zinc and

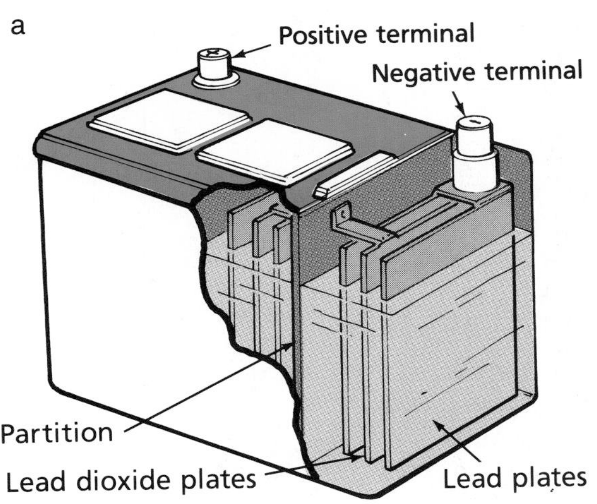

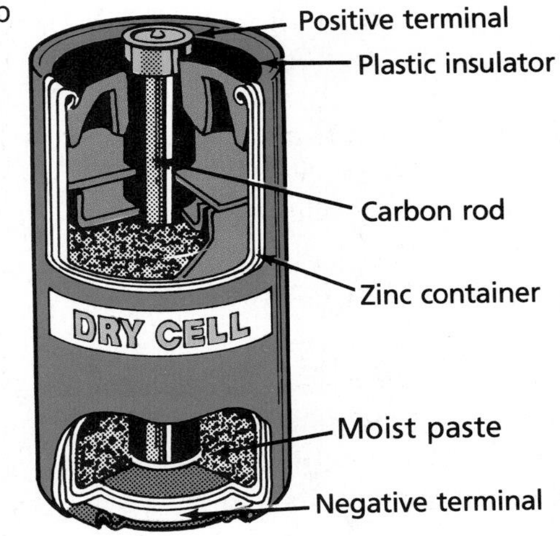

FIGURE 21–7. A storage battery (a) consists of a series of cells separated by partitions. A dry cell (b) is actually filled with a moist paste containing ions. The paste allows the movement of electrons.

release electrons. These electrons flow through a conductor such as a flashlight bulb connected to the dry cell. The current flows from the zinc can, through the bulb, and back to the carbon rod. Other chemicals in the paste react with the electrons in the rod.

Electric current is the movement of charge. The rate of flow of charged particles is measured in **amperes** (A). One ampere of current flows when one coulomb of charge moves through a conductor in one second. One **coulomb** is the charge on 6.24 billion billion electrons.

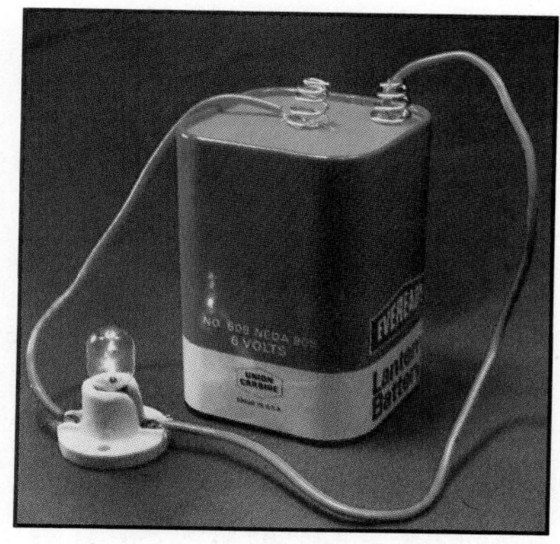

FIGURE 21–8. A potential difference exists between the two terminals of the battery. Electrons flowing through this potential difference do work by heating the filament of the bulb.

What is a coulomb?

21:5 Electric Potential

When a conductor is connected to a battery, current always flows in one direction. The flow of electrons in one direction is direct current. The terminal the electrons leave is called the negative terminal. Electrons flow through the conductor to the positive terminal. The "push" of the battery causes the electrons that leave the negative terminal to have a greater potential energy than those that return at the positive terminal.

The total amount of potential energy difference depends on the number of electrons leaving the battery. The potential energy difference per unit charge is called the electric potential. It does not depend on the number of electrons leaving. The unit of electric potential is the **volt** (V). The volt is one joule of potential energy per coulomb of charge. Just as only energy differences can be measured, only electrical potential differences are important. The difference in potential between electrons in one place and electrons in another place is called **potential difference.** Potential difference is also called voltage.

A single zinc-carbon dry cell has a potential difference of 1.5 V between the negative and positive terminals. Cells can be connected to produce a larger voltage. For example, many portable radios are powered by a 9-V battery that contains six dry cells, each having a 1.5-V potential difference. A lead-lead dioxide wet cell in a storage battery has a potential difference of 2 volts. An automobile storage battery has six wet cells and a 12-volt potential difference.

21.6 Resistance and Ohm's Law

Electric current flows through some conductors more easily than through others. A wire that is a good conductor is said to have low resistance. **Resistance** is a

What is resistance?

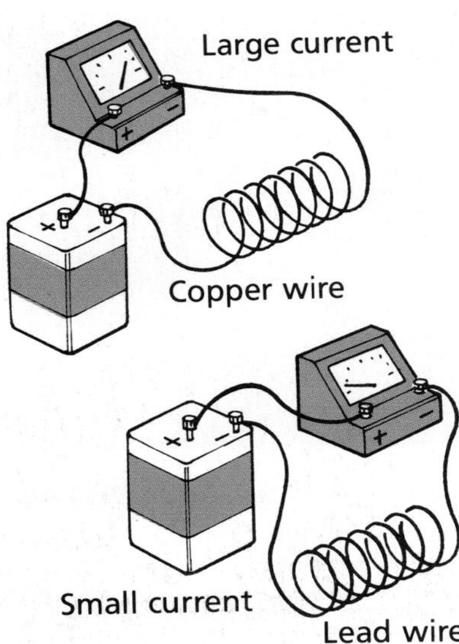

FIGURE 21–9. Resistance varies greatly with the type of conductor. A lead wire of the same diameter and length as copper wire, has about 13 times the resistance of the copper.

measure of how difficult it is to move electrons through a conductor. Resistance is measured in **ohms.** A 100-watt light bulb has a resistance of about 140 ohms. Electrical wires in a home may have as little as 0.004 ohm of resistance for each meter of length.

The resistance depends on the length and thickness of the conductor. It also depends on the type of material. For wires of equal length and thickness, the resistance of silver is less than copper. Aluminum has a resistance greater than copper but less than iron.

Devices called resistors are often used to control the flow of current. Carbon resistors, used in radios, televisions, and computers, are small cylinders less than one centimeter long. The amount of resistance depends on the length, thickness, and composition of the carbon core of the resistor.

When you connect a conductor to a battery, current flows because the battery gives a "push" to the electrons. The greater the potential difference of the battery, the greater the current flow. If the voltage doubles, the current also doubles. The resistance of the conductor provides an opposing force like friction on the electrons. For a fixed voltage, the larger the resistance, the smaller the current flow. If the resistance is doubled, only half as much current flows.

CAREER

Electrician

Maria Diaz has always found the study of electricity to be interesting. She liked learning about currents, circuitry, and power as a student. Now she enjoys working as an electrician.

Maria is involved in consulting, planning and directing the construction of new buildings and houses. Homeowners rely on her expertise to help modernize old wiring, install new switches, or add fixtures such as ceiling fans.

After Maria graduated from a technical school, she worked as an apprentice electrician. "I really enjoyed being out on the construction sites after being in the classroom," Maria says. "It was a great learning experience for me."

Most electricians specialize in one area, such as generation, transmission, or use of electric power. Some electricians work indoors all the time, others work outside, and some alternate. An electrician does much more than just cut and splice wires.

Electricians must have a thorough understanding of static and current electricity. They must also be constantly aware of safety factors involved with electricity.

For career information, write
Accreditation Board of Engineering and Technology
345 E. 47th Street
New York, NY 10017

Potential difference, current, and resistance in a conductor are related by Ohm's law. **Ohm's law** states that *current is equal to the potential difference divided by the resistance.*

$$\text{current(amperes)} = \frac{\text{voltage(volts)}}{\text{resistance(ohms)}}$$

$$I = \frac{V}{R}$$

The symbol for current is I, for voltage is V, and for resistance is R. The ohm is symbolized by the greek letter omega, Ω.

EXAMPLE Calculating Current

What current flows through a conductor having a resistance of 84 ohms connected across a 12-volt battery?

Given: resistance $R = 84\ \Omega$ voltage $V = 12\ \text{V}$

Unknown: current (I)

Basic Equation: $I = \frac{V}{R}$

Solution: $I = \frac{V}{R}$

$$= \frac{12\ \text{V}}{84\ \Omega} = 0.14\ \text{A}$$

EXAMPLE Calculating Resistance

A current of 5.0 A flows through a toaster connected to a 110-V source. What is the resistance of the toaster?

Given: current $I = 5.0\ \text{A}$ voltage $V = 110\ \text{V}$

Unknown: resistance (R)

Basic Equation: $I = \frac{V}{R}$

Solution: $I = \frac{V}{R}$ so $R = \frac{V}{I}$

$$= \frac{110\ \text{V}}{5.0\ \text{A}} = 22\ \Omega$$

PRACTICE PROBLEMS

1. Find the current through a 25-ohm resistor connected to a 12-volt battery.
2. What would be the current in Problem 1 if a 6.0-volt battery were used?
3. A light bulb with a resistance of 180 ohms is connected across a source having a 120-volt potential difference. What current flows?

BIOGRAPHY

Meredith Gourdine

1929–

Dr. Gourdine is both an engineer and an entrepreneur. Born in New York City, he was educated at Cornell and Cal Tech. He won a silver medal at the 1952 Helsinki Olympics in the broad jump. He now has his own corporation. One of the many inventions that has been produced by Dr. Gourdine's company is an electrostatic precipitator that reduces pollution and solid waste in smoke.

F.Y.I. Ohm's law is named after George Ohm (1789–1854). Ohm worked on electrical conduction, but when the Berlin Academy of Science refused to publish his work, he retired from scientific life in discouragement.

SKILL

Understanding Statistics

Problem: How do you interpret statistics correctly?

Procedure

1. Determine the purpose of the statistics. Reread the introduction, table headings, graph titles and scales, and captions of any illustrations.
2. Decide whether the statistics prove or disprove the hypothesis. Reread the hypothesis and determine the dependent and independent variables. Did the research actually test these variables? Were there adequate trials, subjects, and controls for the data to be meaningful? For example, a test of pain relievers on six patients for 4 hours is not a thorough test. Generally, if the test conditions are adequate, the hypothesis is considered proven if at least 90% of the results support the hypothesis.
3. Examine the scales of graphs carefully. Does a graph of the statistics use scales that are reasonable for the type of data plotted? Refer to Figure 21–10a and b. Both of these graphs show the amount of electric energy used in a home in the midwest for one year. Why does the amount of energy used seem to be so much lower and more consistent in Figure 21–10a? Figure 21–10b. gives a more realistic presentation of energy consumption. Note how the scales for kilowatt hours used has changed.

Questions

1. Refer to Figure 21–10c. This graph was used in an advertisement for orange juice. The manufacturers of orange juice C used the graph to show that their product contained twice as much vitamin C as any other leading orange juice. The recommended daily allowance of vitamin C is about 55 mg. Why do you think this graph may be misleading?
2. A report claimed that recent research proved that a new alloy was more weather resistant than one currently used to manufacture car body frames. List three questions to ask when evaluating this report.
3. Why is it important to know the number of subjects tested when evaluating statistics?

Data and Observations

FIGURE 21–10.

a

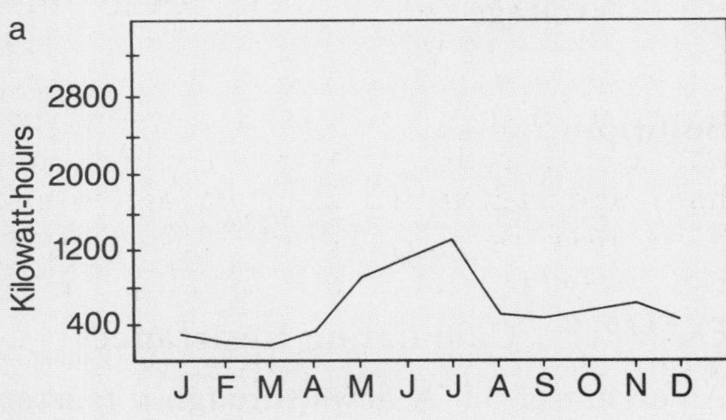

b

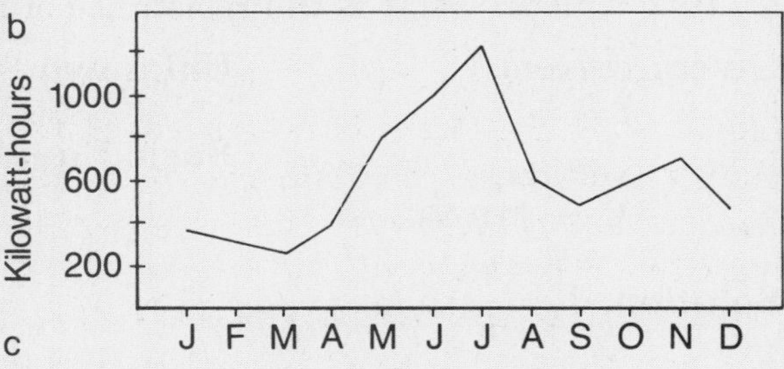

c

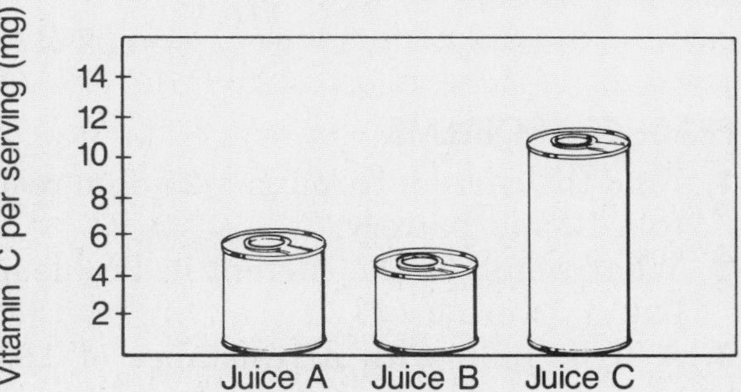

Review

6. Why does the electric current produced by a wet cell stop when the wire is removed? Explain in terms of the chemical reactions in the cell.
7. How is a current different from static electricity?
8. What is potential difference?
9. Find the potential difference across a 15-ohm resistor that has a 2.0-A current flowing through it.

★ 10. You have two pieces of wire, each 1.6 mm in diameter and 10 m long. One, made of copper, has a resistance of 0.080 ohms. The other, made of nichrome, has a resistance of 4.8 ohms. You want each to have a 3.0-A current flow. What would be the voltage of the source you would need for each wire?

ELECTRICAL CIRCUITS

GOALS

1. You will understand the nature and use of a series circuit.
2. You will understand the construction and use of a parallel circuit.
3. You will learn why fuses or circuit breakers are used.

Electricity is very useful because it carries energy efficiently. In your home, electricity may heat water, air, and food. It runs motors and enables lamps to produce light and radios and tape players to emit sound. All these uses require energy. The energy is carried by means of electrical current from a power plant far away.

21:7 Series Circuits

What is a circuit?

The path formed by electric conductors is called a circuit. A circuit consists of a battery or other source of potential difference, wires to carry the current, and a lamp or other device that uses the electrical energy. A circuit must be a complete path that allows current to flow from the battery, to the lamp, out of the lamp, and back to the battery.

Describe a series circuit.

One form of circuit is a **series circuit,** Figure 21–11a. The series circuit has only one path for current so the current is the same through every part. However, the potential difference across each part may not be the same. If a series circuit is broken any place, the current in all parts is stopped. Some Christmas tree lights are wired in a series circuit. If one bulb burns out, no current can flow through that bulb. As a result, no current flows through any bulb.

A switch is a device used to stop current flow in a conductor. When a switch is open, no current flows.

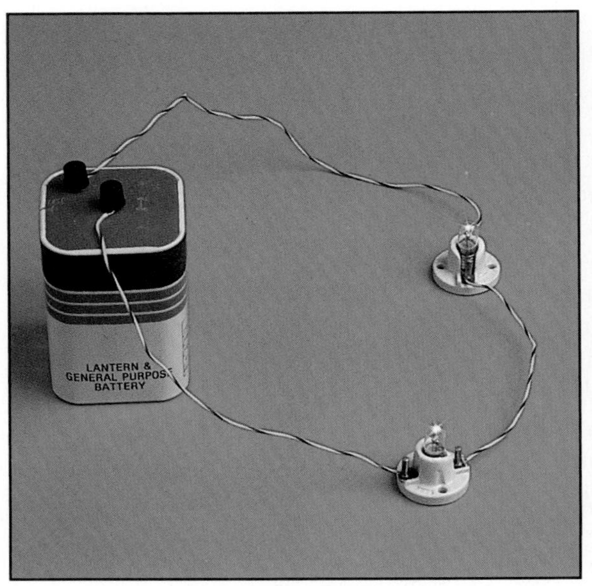

a

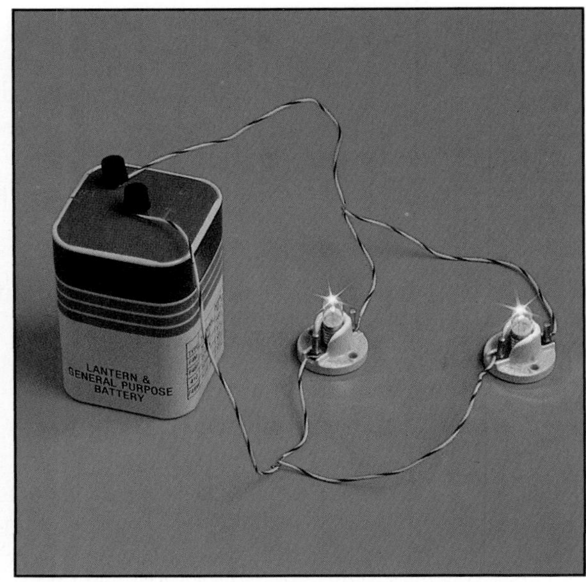

b

FIGURE 21–11. In a series circuit (a), there is a single pathway for current. A parallel circuit (b) allows several pathways. If one bulb burns out, current can still flow through other bulbs.

How do a series circuit and a parallel circuit differ?

21:8 Parallel Circuits

The other type of circuit is the parallel circuit, Figure 21–11b. In a **parallel circuit,** there are two or more separate branches for current to flow. If a switch in one branch of the circuit is opened, current still flows through the other branch. Suppose lights for a Christmas tree are wired in parallel. If any bulb burns out, the others continue to shine. In a parallel circuit, current that flows through an electrical device does not flow through other branches of the circuit. The potential difference, however, is the same across each branch.

Electricians and electronics technicians use symbols to show different parts of a circuit. Some common symbols for the parts of electrical circuits are shown in Figure 21–12b.

FIGURE 21–12. The circuit diagram (a) shows two light bulbs wired in parallel with a resistor, a switch, and a battery in series. Some common symbols used in drawing circuit diagrams are shown (b).

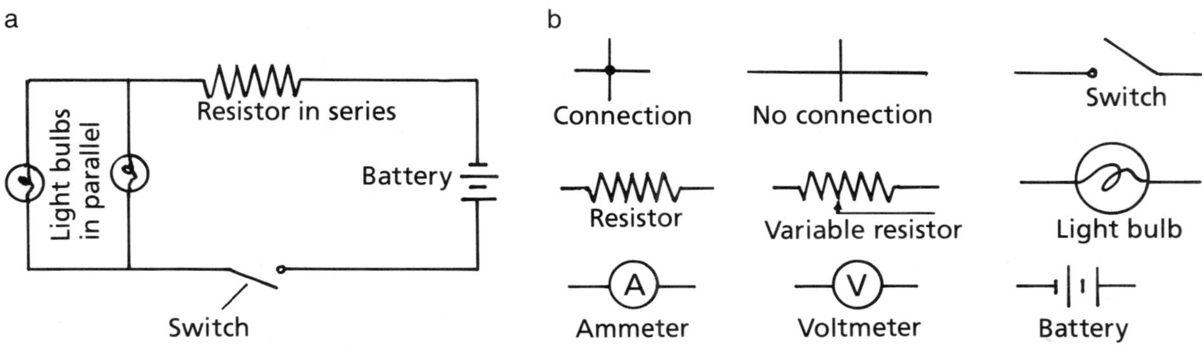

INVESTIGATION 21–2

Electric Circuits

Problem: How do electric circuits differ?

Materials

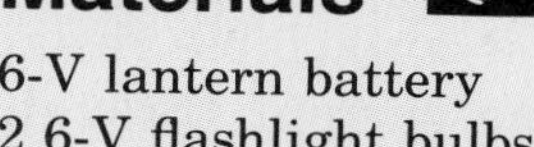

6-V lantern battery
2 6-V flashlight bulbs with sockets
ammeter
insulated hookup wire

Procedure

1. Connect one bulb with the battery and ammeter as shown in Figure 21–13a. Record the ammeter reading and your observations.

FIGURE 21–13.

a

b

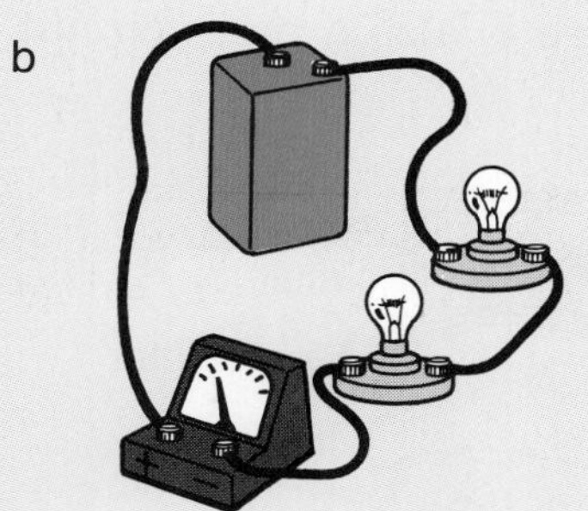

c

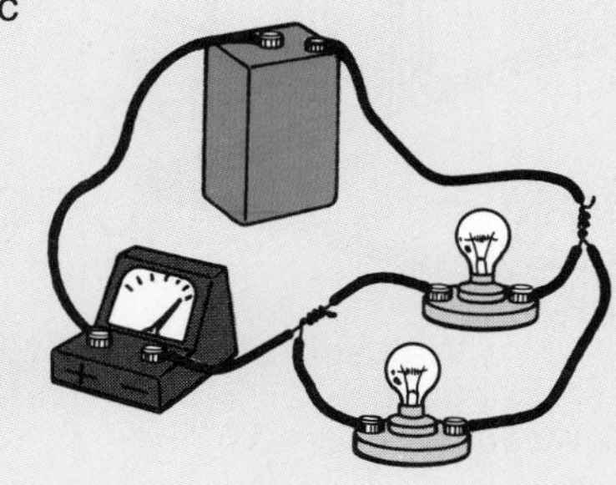

2. Place the second bulb in the circuit as shown in Figure 21–13b. Again record the ammeter reading and your observations.
3. Unscrew one of the bulbs from its socket. **CAUTION:** *The bulb may be hot.* Record ammeter readings and observations.
4. Change the circuit to that of Figure 21–13c. Record the ammeter reading and your observations.
5. Unscrew one of the bulbs from its socket. **CAUTION:** *The bulb may be hot.* Record ammeter reading and observations.

Data and Observations

Step	Current	Observations
1		
2		
3		
4		
5		

Analysis and Conclusions

1. Describe the flow of current in Step 2.
2. Explain what happened in Step 3.
3. Describe the flow of current in Step 4.
4. Explain what happened in Step 5.
5. In which circuits were the bulbs brightest? Dimmest?
6. Use Ohm's law together with the voltage of the battery and your current readings to calculate the resistance of the circuits in Steps 1, 2, and 4.
7. In which step(s) is the combination of bulbs in a series circuit? A parallel circuit?
8. How do series and parallel circuits differ?

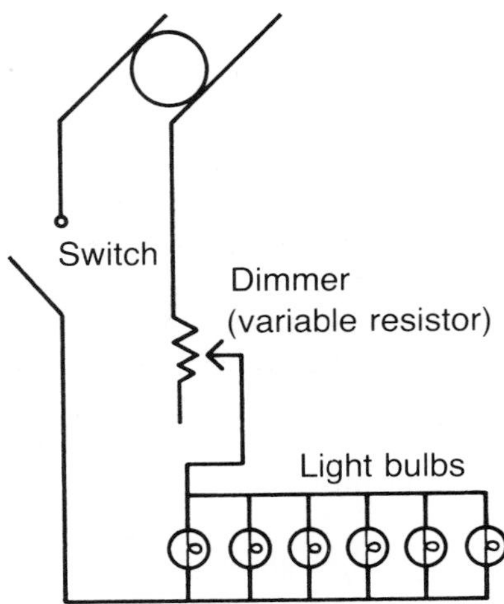

FIGURE 21–14. The 6-bulb parallel circuit is connected to the main circuit through a variable resistor. As the resistance is varied from high to low, the bulbs go from dim to bright.

21:9 A Complex Circuit

Complex circuits are made up of both series and parallel circuits. Consider, for example, a dining room lamp having six bulbs controlled by a dimmer switch, Figure 21–14. The six bulbs are connected in parallel. The voltage across all bulbs is the same. Separate currents flow through each bulb. If one bulb burns out, the others still light. The six bulbs are connected in a series circuit with a dimmer switch. The dimmer is a variable resistor. When the resistance is high, the current through the lamps is made smaller. The bulbs give off less light. When the resistance is low, more current flows and the bulbs shine brightly.

The electric wiring in a house is a set of simple circuits that are connected. Electrical current comes into the house through overhead or underground wires. At the entrance panel, the wires branch into several parallel circuits. Figure 21–15 shows a map of the electrical system for a house. Some of the parallel circuits go to wall sockets. The voltage across each socket is the same. When you plug a lamp into the socket, current flows through the house wires to the socket, through the cord and lamp, and back through the wires. If you plug a television into another socket on the same circuit, the television and lamp are in parallel. Some lights are connected directly to the entrance panel through a switch.

The entrance panel contains a fuse or circuit breaker in series with each circuit. There is also a main circuit

FIGURE 21–15. The diagram of the wiring of a house shows that there may be several circuits serving one room.

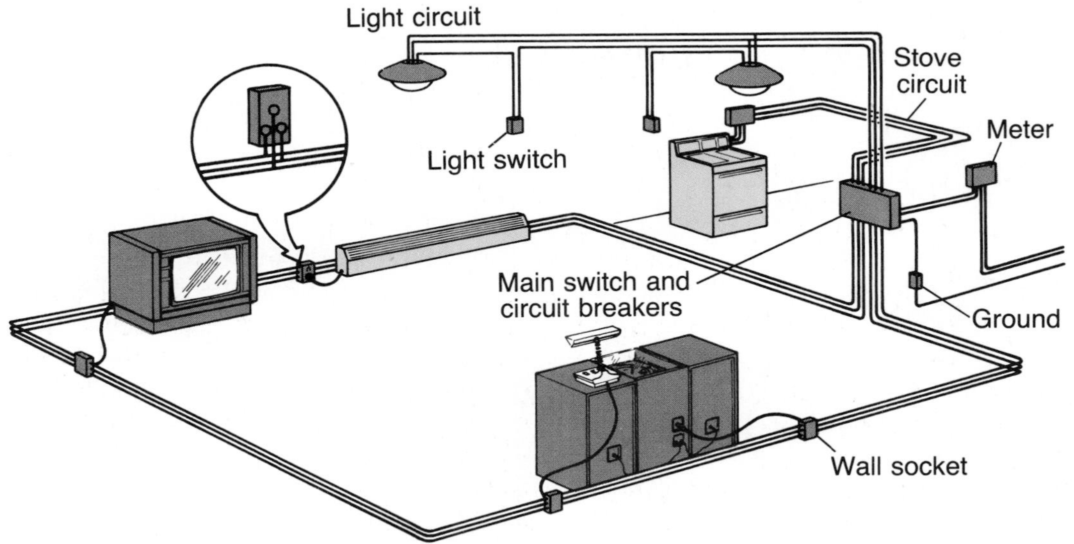

breaker connected in series with all the circuits. The main breaker allows the current to the whole house to be turned on and off. In addition, there is a meter to measure electrical energy usage.

When current flows through the house wiring, some of the electrical energy is converted to thermal energy and heats the wire. If there is too much current in a circuit, the wire can become hot enough to start a fire. Fuses and circuit breakers open the circuit when the current is larger than a specific value, usually 15 amperes for normal house wiring. They stop the flow of current before the wires get too hot. A fuse contains a small piece of metal that melts and breaks the circuit. A circuit breaker has a strip of metal that bends when it heats, allowing a spring to open a switch. Thus, fuses and circuit breakers help prevent electrical fires.

F.Y.I. Too many devices (too little resistance) connected to a circuit, or direct contact between the two conductors in a parallel circuit (a short circuit), will cause fuses or circuit breakers to open a circuit.

Review

11. Draw a series circuit containing a battery, switch, and two light bulbs.

12. Draw a parallel circuit having two light bulbs, two switches, and a battery. Have each light controlled by its own switch.

13. Suppose you have a circuit with a battery and three bulbs connected in parallel. Suppose you first remove bulb 1 from its socket. Do bulbs 2 and 3 still light?

14. Now bulb 1 in Question 13 is put back and bulb 2 is removed. Which bulb(s) is/are lit now?

★ **15.** Why are parallel circuits used in house wiring instead of series circuits?

ELECTRICAL ENERGY AND POWER

GOALS

1. You will learn to calculate electrical power knowing the current and voltage.
2. You will learn to find the electrical energy used in kilowatt hours.

Electrical current carries energy to your home from a distant generating plant. The energy used in your home is measured by an electric energy meter. The electric company charges people for the energy they use based on meter readings. Just as in the case of all other forms of energy, power is the rate at which energy is converted from one form to another. In this section, you will learn how to calculate electrical power and energy.

FIGURE 21–16. Energy usage depends on the power rating of a device and the time it is left on. The toaster uses energy at a much higher rate than the radio. However, the radio may be left on all day while the toaster is used for only a few minutes.

21:10 Electric Power

F.Y.I. Review power and energy in Chapter 5.

What is electric power?

Electrical devices convert electrical energy into other forms. Appliances, such as fans, blenders, and vacuum cleaners do work. They convert electrical energy into mechanical energy. Lamps convert electrical energy into light and thermal energy. **Electrical power** is the rate at which a device converts electrical energy into another form of energy. Power is measured in watts. Lamps are usually between 40 watts and 150 watts. A toaster or hair dryer may use energy at the rate of 1000 watts.

The power consumed by a device can be found by multiplying the current flow by the potential difference. One ampere of current flowing across a potential difference of one volt has a power of one watt.

$$\textit{power} = \textit{voltage} \times \textit{current}$$
$$P = V \times I$$

FIGURE 21–17. The bulb has a much higher resistance than the heater. Thus, the heater uses energy at a greater rate because it allows more current to flow.

EXAMPLE Calculating Power

The current flowing through a lamp is 2.5 A. The lamp is connected to a battery having a potential difference of 12 V. What is the power delivered to the lamp?

Given: current $I = 2.5$ A; voltage $V = 12$ V

Unknown: power (P)

Basic Equation: $P = V \times I$

Solution: $P = V \times I$
$= 12 \text{ V} \times 2.5 \text{ A} = 30 \text{ W}$

PRACTICE PROBLEMS

4. A source of 120 volts delivers a current of 1.25 A to light an electric bulb. How much power is delivered?

Table 21–1

Typical Energy Used by Some Home Appliances			
Appliance	**Power usage (watts)**	**Time of usage (hours/day)**	**Energy usage (kWh/day)**
Hair dryer, blower	1000	0.25	0.25
Microwave oven	1450	0.5	0.73
Radio/record player	109	2.5	0.27
Range (oven)	2600	1	2.60
Refrigerator/freezer (15 cu ft frostless)	615	24	14.76
Television (color)	200	3.25	0.65
Electric toothbrush	7	0.08	0.0006
100-watt light bulb	100	6	0.60
40-watt fluorescent light bulb	40	1	0.04

5. A hair dryer uses 1500 watts of power. If it is connected to a source of 120 V, what current flows through the dryer?

21:11 Calculating Electric Energy

The amount of energy used by a device depends on the power delivered and the length of time it is used.

What factors affect the amount of power used by an appliance?

$$\textit{energy} = \textit{power} \times \textit{time}$$
$$E = P \times t$$

Thus, a 100 W lamp that is operated for 10 seconds uses 1000 joules of energy. The joule is obviously a tiny unit of energy, so electrical energy is measured using a larger unit, the **kilowatt-hour.** One kilowatt-hour, kWh, is 1000 watts of power used for one hour (3600 seconds) of time. A typical home uses about 500 kWh of electrical energy each month. To calculate the energy a device uses, multiply its power in kilowatts by the time in hours that it is on.

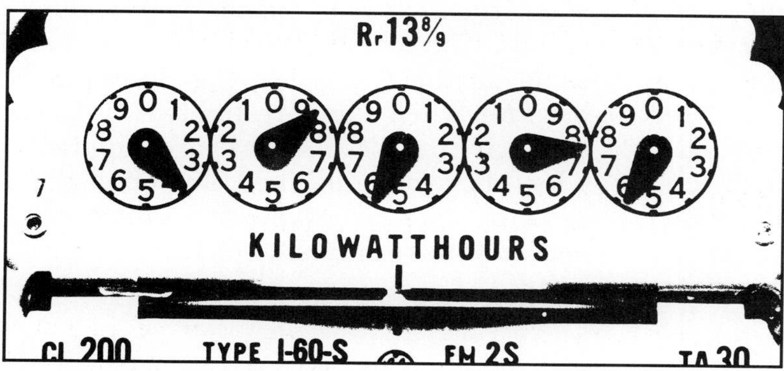

FIGURE 21–18. The dials on an electric meter show the quantity of energy used in a house.

EXAMPLE **Calculating Electrical Energy**

A lamp uses 150 W of electrical power. If it is on for 4 hours, how many kilowatt hours of energy is converted into light and thermal energy.

Given: power
$P = 150$ W
time
$t = 4$ hours

Unknown: energy (E)

Basic Equation: $E = P \times t$

Solution: Convert to kilowatts: $P = 150 \text{ W}/(1000 \text{ W/kW}) = 0.15 \text{ kW}$

$$E = P \times t = (0.15 \text{ kW})(4.0 \text{ h}) = 0.60 \text{ kWh}$$

PRACTICE PROBLEM

6. A self-cleaning stove uses 5400 W when cleaning the oven. If it takes 1.5 hours to clean, how many kilowatt hours of electricity are used?

Review

16. Find the power produced by a 1.8-A current at 120 V.
17. Find the energy used if the power above is produced for 8.5 h.
18. Find the number of joules in a kilowatt hour.
19. A current of 11 A at 240 V flows for 3.5 h. Calculate the power used in kW and energy used in kWh.
★ **20.** A refrigerator uses 88 kWh of energy per month. Find the cost/month if electricity is $0.098/kWh?

PROBLEM SOLVING

Lights Out

JoAnn is working on a laboratory activity using a battery, two bulbs, and a switch. She makes different circuits. The first has a single bulb lighted by the battery when the switch is closed. The bulb goes out when the switch is opened. The second has a single bulb lighted by the battery when the switch is open. The bulb goes out when the switch is closed. The third has the two bulbs lighted when the switch is closed; when the switch is opened both bulbs go out. The fourth circuit operates the same as the third, but the bulbs are brighter when they are lighted. In the fifth circuit, both bulbs are lighted when the switch is closed, and one bulb remains lighted when the switch is opened. Draw diagrams of the five circuits.

Chapter 21 Review

SUMMARY

1. Like charges repel, unlike charges attract. 21:1
2. Electrons can move easily through a conductor. 21:2
3. An electroscope is used to detect electric charges. 21:3
4. Wet and dry cells provide continuing electric currents. 21:4
5. The work done by electric currents depends on the charge moved and the electric potential difference, or voltage through which it is raised. 21:5
6. Resistance is a measure of how difficult it is to move electrons through a conductor. 21:6
7. Ohm's law states that 1 *voltage* = *resistance* × *current.* 21:6
8. Electric circuits can be series or parallel. 21:7, 21:8
9. Electrical circuits in houses are combinations of series and parallel circuits. 21:9
10. Electricial power is the energy converted into another form per second. 21:10
11. Electrical power equals current times potential difference. 21:10
12. Electrical energy is measured in kilowatt-hours (kWh). 21:11

VOCABULARY

a. ampere
b. battery
c. conductor
d. coulomb
e. electric charge
f. electric current
g. electrical power
h. electroscope
i. insulator
j. kilowatt-hour
k. ohm
l. Ohm's law
m. parallel circuit
n. potential difference
o. resistance
p. series circuit
q. static electricity
r. volt

Matching

Match each description with the correct vocabulary word from the list above. Some words will not be used.

1. what a body with either too few or too many electrons has
2. an object that opposes the flow of electrons through it
3. what you would use to get a continuing electric current
4. a device that detects static electrical charge
5. the quantity that determines the "push" given to current
6. the ratio of potential difference to current
7. the unit used to measure electrical energy
8. a circuit in which two bulbs can be controlled separately
9. unit of resistance
10. the product of current and potential difference across a device

Chapter 21 Review

MAIN IDEAS

A. Reviewing Concepts

Choose the word or phrase that correctly completes each of the following sentences.

1. A circuit breaker is used to open circuits when there is *(too much, too little, normal, no)* current in the circuit.
2. Copper, aluminum, silver, and iron are *(conductors, insulators, potential differences, wet cells).*
3. When a wet cell is used in a circuit, current flows through *(the wire, the solution, both wire and solution, neither wire nor solution).*
4. Potential difference is measured in *(volts, ohms, amperes, coulombs).*
5. Electric charge is measured in *(volts, ohms, amperes, coulombs).*

Complete each of the following sentences with the correct word or phrase.

6. A poor conductor has ____________ resistance.
7. A(n) ____________ is used to detect static electrical charge.
8. A circuit consisting of only one path for current to flow is a ____________ circuit.
9. An object becomes positively charged when it ____________ electrons.
10. A glass rod becomes ____________ charged when you rub it with silk.

Determine whether each of the following sentences is true or false. If it is false, change the underlined word to make the sentence true.

11. Like charges attract each other.
12. Objects build up a static charge when protons are lost due to friction.
13. A circuit is a complete path for current to flow.
14. The power consumed by a device depends on the potential difference applied and the current that flows.
15. When a fuse opens a circuit, more current flows.

B. Understanding Concepts

Answer the following questions using complete sentences when possible.

16. Suppose you rub one end of a plastic rod with fur. Would the other end become charged?
17. Would the charged plastic rod attract or repel a glass rod rubbed with silk? Explain your answer.
18. You first charge an electroscope negatively by touching it with a charged plastic rod. What would you see if you brought a charged glass rod close to the knob?
19. What current flows through a conductor having a resistance of 15 ohms connected across a 6-volt battery?
20. A current of 0.15 A flows through a portable radio that uses a 9-V battery. What is the resistance of the radio?
21. Draw a series circuit having two light bulbs, one switch, and a battery.
22. The current flowing through a lamp is 0.5 A. The lamp is connected to a battery having a potential difference of 3.0 V. What is the power delivered to the lamp?
23. A television uses 250 W of electrical power. If it is on for 6 hours, how many kilowatt hours of energy are used?
24. If electricity costs $0.12/kWh, how much would it cost to run the television of Problem 23?
25. Why are fuses or circuit breakers put in series with a lighting circuit in a house?

C. Applying Concepts

Answer the following questions using complete sentences when possible.

26. If you comb your hair on a dry day, your hair flies apart and is attracted to the comb. Explain.

27. You first charge an electroscope with negative charge. You then charge a glass rod and touch it to the knob. The leaves fall half way down. You charge and touch it again and the leaves fall all the way down. The next time you charge and touch the rod the leaves swing apart. Explain.

28. Draw a circuit containing a battery, switch, and two light bulbs. The bulbs are connected in parallel, but both are turned off and on by the single switch.

29. Suppose you are using your 1500-W hair dryer and your mother turns on a electric fry pan that uses 1200 W. Both are on the same circuit fused for 15 A. What happens? Explain.

30. An electric clock uses 2 W of power. In a town with 25 000 homes, each home has, on the average, one clock. The clocks run 24 hours a day. Find the energy used by the clocks in one year.

SKILL REVIEW

1. The Food and Drug Administration, FDA, requires that new drugs be thoroughly tested before approving them for use. Why would the FDA probably refuse to approve the general use of a drug even if the research results showed that it was effective in 99.99% of all laboratory animals tested?

2. A group of researchers claimed that their data proved that vitamin A was a cure for the common cold. They had tested several thousand people with colds and after administering low dosages of vitamin A for ten days 70% of the subjects reported complete relief of symptoms. Would you agree that these scientists have found a cure for the common cold? Explain your answer.

3. How can reading the introduction of a research report help you to understand the statistics reported?

4. In Figure 21–4, does the upper or lower row of particles represent metals? How can you tell?

5. What is the purpose of an indicator in an acid-base reaction?

PROJECTS

1. Do library research on the nature of lightning.

2. Obtain an automobile fuse box from a junkyard. Use the box and fuses to prepare an exhibit that explains how fuses protect circuits.

3. Make an inventory of electrical appliances in your home. Record the power each uses and the number of hours each is used in a day. Calculate the energy the appliances use in one month. In what ways could you reduce the use of electricity in your home?

READINGS

1. Brandt, Keith. *Electricity*. Mahwah, NJ: Troll Associates, 1985.

2. Gutnik, Martin J. *Electricity From Faraday to Solar Generators*. New York: Franklin Watts, 1986.

3. Loper, Orla E., and Edgar Tedsen. *Direct Current Fundamentals*. Albany, NY: Delmar, 1986.

MAGNETIC FIELDS AND FORCES
PRODUCTION OF ELECTRIC CURRENTS
ELECTRONICS

Chapter 22

Electricity and Magnetism

It is impossible to study electricity without studying magnetism; the two cannot be separated. Magnets have been known for two thousand years. Only in the nineteenth century, however, were the effects of electricity and magnetism on each other discovered. Those discoveries led to all the other devices that make electricity so useful to us today.

MAGNETIC FIELDS AND FORCES

GOALS

1. You will learn the basic properties of magnets.
2. You will be introduced to the magnetic field.
3. You will learn the effect of a magnetic field on a current-carrying wire.

As early as the sixth century B.C., the attraction of the natural mineral, lodestone, for iron was well known. When the stone was floated on wood in water, it always pointed in the same direction, and by the Middle Ages the magnetic compass was in use in Europe for navigation. In 1600 William Gilbert, an English physician, wrote a book describing the effects of lodestone. However, it was not until around 1820 that the connection between electricity and magnets was explored.

22:1 Magnets

How can you identify a magnet?

Lodestone is a black oxide of iron, called magnetite, Fe_2O_3. A **magnet** is any object that can exert force on another magnet. At the time of William Gilbert, it was known that small pieces of iron would stick to a magnet, mainly at two regions called the poles. The **magnetic poles,** usually at opposite ends of the magnet, are the location of the strongest magnetic forces.

F.Y.I. There is a Greek legend that describes how an island made of lodestone pulled the nails out of a ship, causing it to sink.

If iron is held near a magnet, it too can attract small iron pieces, becoming a magnet itself. When the iron is removed, however, it loses its magnetic qualities. Alloys of iron, such as some steels, can also be made into magnets, but they keep their magnetic properties for a long

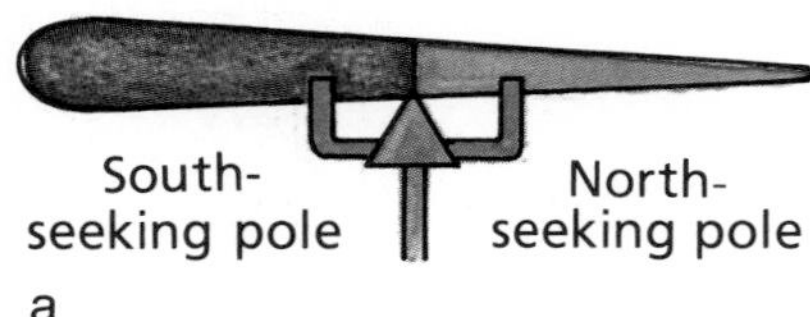

a

b

FIGURE 22–1. The needle of a compass (a) is a magnet on a pivot. Earth's magnetic field exerts a force on a compass needle, causing it to point toward magnetic north (b).

time. They are called **permanent magnets.** Materials that include nickel, cobalt, samarium, or aluminum can also be made into permanent magnets.

If a magnet is floated on a cork in water or balanced on a sharp point, one end points north, the other south. Such a device is called a **compass.** Another magnet brought near it will cause the compass to turn. Thus, magnets exert forces on one another. Gilbert knew that because of the way it affected a compass, Earth must be a giant magnet. The magnetic pole of a compass that points north is called the north-seeking pole, or simply the north pole. The other is called the south pole. Like poles repel each other; unlike poles attract.

22:2 Magnetic Fields

What is a magnetic field?

Magnets exert forces on other magnets, even though they are far apart. For example, a compass anywhere near Earth points north and south. The forces on the compass are caused by Earth's magnetic field. A **magnetic field** is the region around a magnet where the magnetic forces act.

Suppose you put a permanent magnet under a glass plate and sprinkle iron filings on the plate. Each filing turns in the direction of the magnetic force. The force on each filing is caused by the magnetic field at the location of the filing. The iron filings make a picture of the magnetic field, Figure 22–2. You can use iron filings to see that the field of the horseshoe magnet between the poles is stronger than the field of a bar magnet.

List three examples of fields.

Force fields other than magnetic fields also exist. An electric field is created by every electric charge. Earth, as well as every other body with mass, has a gravitational field around it. An object near Earth feels the force the field exerts on it. That field accelerates the object toward Earth.

Describe an electromagnet?

In 1820, the Danish scientist Hans Christian Oersted (1777–1851) found that an electric current could also cause a compass to turn. An electric charge moving in a wire causes a magnetic effect. That effect can be made even stronger by winding the wire into a coil. A coil of wire with current flowing through it is an **electromagnet.** One end of the coil becomes the north pole, the other end the south pole. The more turns of wire in the coil and the larger the current, the stronger the electromagnet. Putting a piece of iron, called the **core,** in the center of the coil also makes it a stronger electromagnet. If you reverse the current direction, the north and

FIGURE 22–2. The illustrations show field lines for repulsion of like poles (a) and unlike poles (b).

a

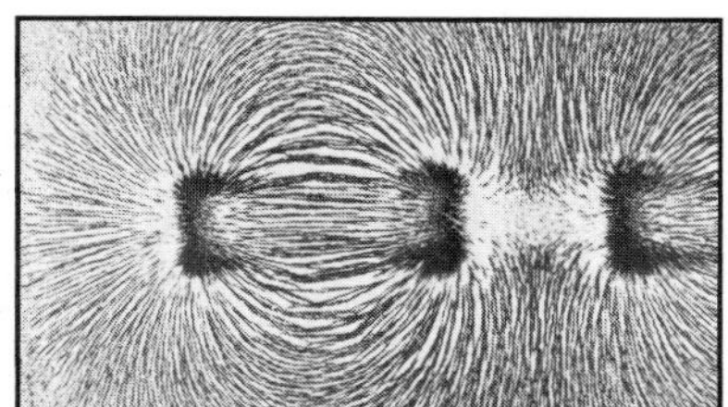

b

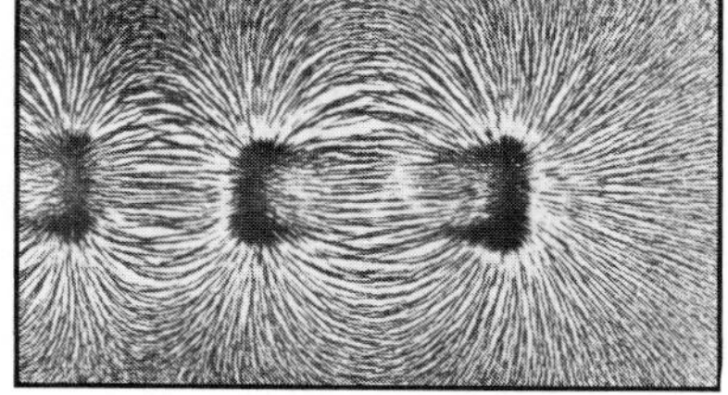

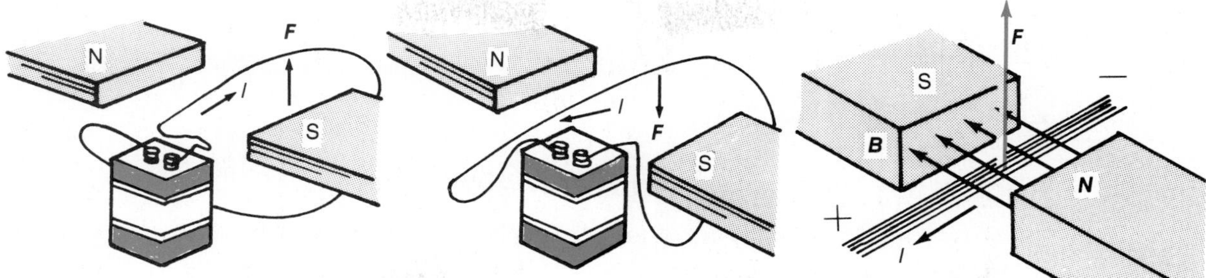

FIGURE 22–3. The diagram shows how the direction of the current, the magnetic field, and the force on the wire are related.

south poles exchange places. When the electric current stops, the magnetic effect also stops. Electromagnets are very widely used today in doorbells, automobiles, stereo loudspeakers, tape recorders, and television sets.

22:3 Effect of Magnetic Fields on Electric Charges

You know that magnetic fields exert forces on other magnets. You have also seen that moving electric charges cause magnetic fields. Therefore, if charges move in a wire, a magnetic field will exert a force on the wire, Figure 22–3.

F.Y.I. The frequency of the sound waves is the same as the frequency with which the current changes direction.

The force on a wire in a magnetic field is used in loudspeakers. A loudspeaker consists of a coil of thin wire between the poles of a magnet. The coil is attached to a cone-shaped piece of stiff paper. When current flows through the coil, the magnetic field exerts a force on it. The force moves the coil and the attached paper cone forward or backward, depending on the direction of the current. If the current changes direction rapidly, the cone vibrates back and forth, generating sound waves in the air. Thus, loudspeakers convert changing electric currents into sound.

How does a magnetic field affect a current-carrying wire?

How can a magnetic field and an electric current be used to produce sound?

a

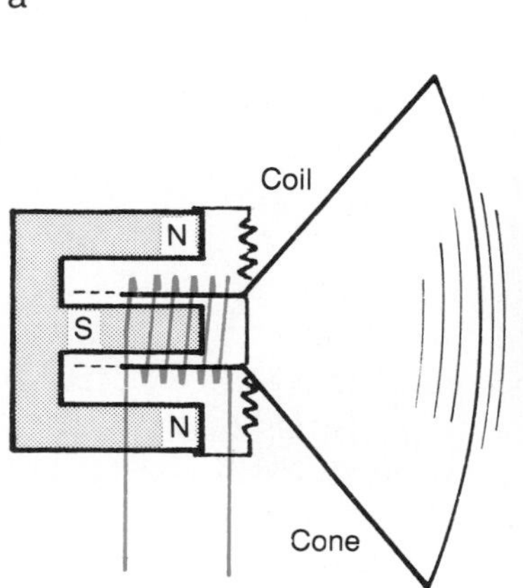

b

FIGURE 22–4. A schematic diagram (a) can be used to represent a loudspeaker (b).

INVESTIGATION 22–1

Electromagnets

Problem: What is the magnetic field of an electromagnet?

Materials 

lantern battery, 6 V
compass
insulated bell wire, 3 m long
several large nails

Procedure

1. Connect one end of the wire to the battery. Arrange the wire so it runs vertically past the edge of the table, Figure 22–5a.
2. Move the compass near the wire and then around the wire. Note the direction of the needle.
3. Connect the other end of the wire to the battery. Again move the compass around the wire and note the direction of the needle. Immediately disconnect one end of the wire from the battery. **CAUTION:** *If wire becomes very hot, disconnect it and wait for it to cool before continuing.*
4. Wind the disconnected wire into a 15 to 20 turn coil about 5 cm in diameter. The compass should be able to pass through the coil, Figure 22–5b.
5. Move the compass around and through the coil. Record the position of the needle.
6. Connect the ends of the wire to the dry cell. Again move the compass around and through the coil. Disconnect the wire from the battery. Record your observations of the compass needle.
7. Reverse the connections of the wire to the battery terminals. Repeat Step 6.
8. Hold the compass near one end of the coil. Insert the nails into the coil. Describe the effect on the compass. Disconnect the wire from the battery.

Observations

Record your observations for Steps 2 through 8.

Analysis and Conclusions

1. Does a wire carrying an electric current generate a magnetic field? Give a reason for your answer.
2. What is the direction of the magnetic field around a straight wire?
3. What is the direction of the magnetic field in the coil?
4. How does reversing the direction of current flow through the coil affect the magnetic field?
5. What is the effect on the magnetic field of putting the iron nails into the coil?

a

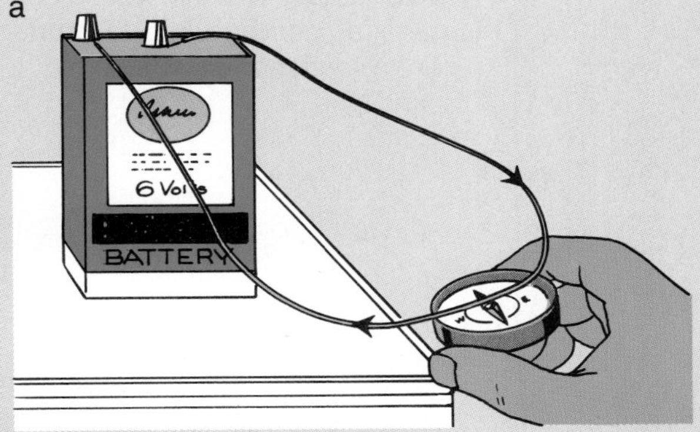

b

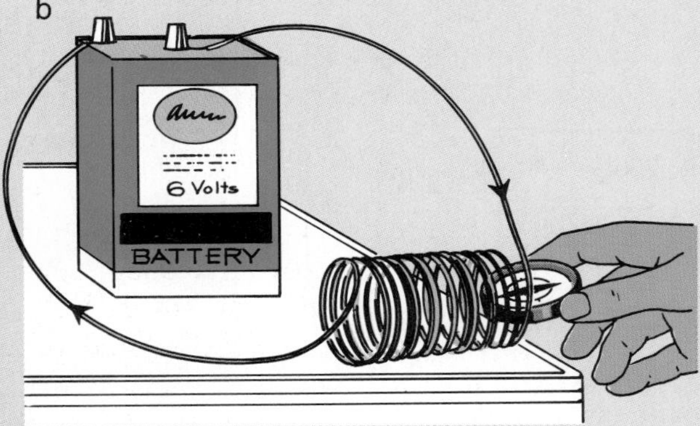

FIGURE 22–5.

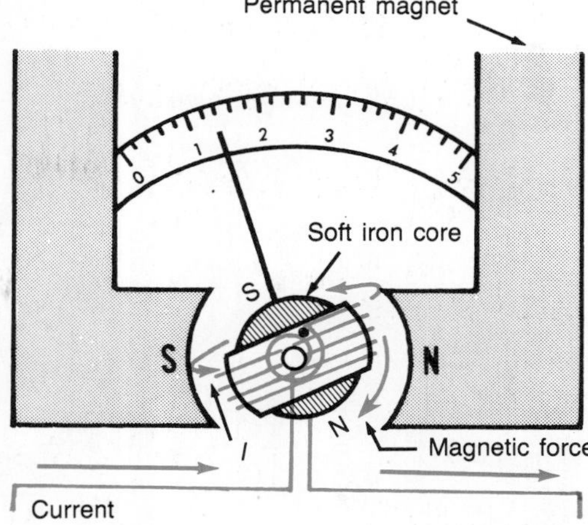

FIGURE 22–6. In a meter, as more current flows, the coil rotates farther between the poles of the magnet.

22:4 Meters

What makes an electric meter operate?

The force exerted by a magnetic field on a wire is employed in electric meters. The coil in a meter is mounted so it can rotate between the poles of a magnet, Figure 22–6. A needle is attached to the coil. When current flows through the coil, the force on the wire causes the coil to rotate. The stronger the current, the larger the resulting force. The coil rotates farther against the force of a spring. The needle attached to the coil points to a scale calibrated in electrical units.

Distinguish between an ammeter and a voltmeter.

An **ammeter** measures current. A **voltmeter** is used to measure potential difference. Both meters use the same design, but they differ in an important way. An ammeter is always connected in series in a circuit so that all the current in the circuit flows through the meter. It must have a low resistance so that it does not have a large potential difference across it. A voltmeter is always connected in parallel with the potential difference to be measured. A resistor is placed in series with the meter coil, giving the voltmeter a high resistance. The current that flows through the meter is proportional to the potential difference across it. As the voltage increases, the current in the coil increases.

22:5 Motors

List the parts of an electric motor.

A magnet and a coil with an iron core are also used in electric motors. The coil is placed between the poles of a magnet and is free to rotate. Current flowing through the coil in the magnetic field produces a force that causes the coil to rotate. It rotates until its north pole is closest to the south pole of the magnet. If the current always flowed in the same direction, the coil

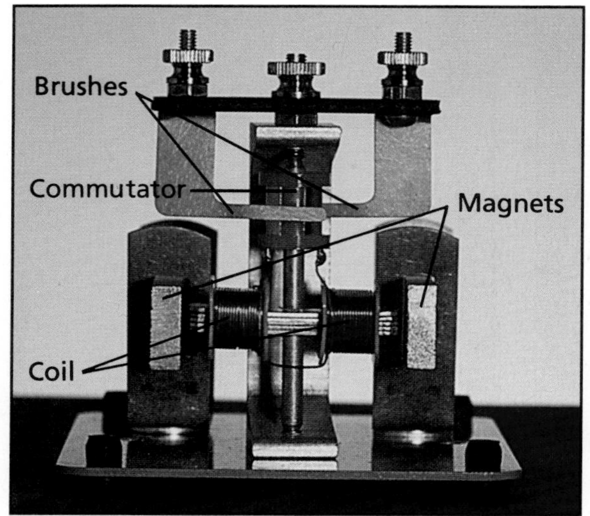

a

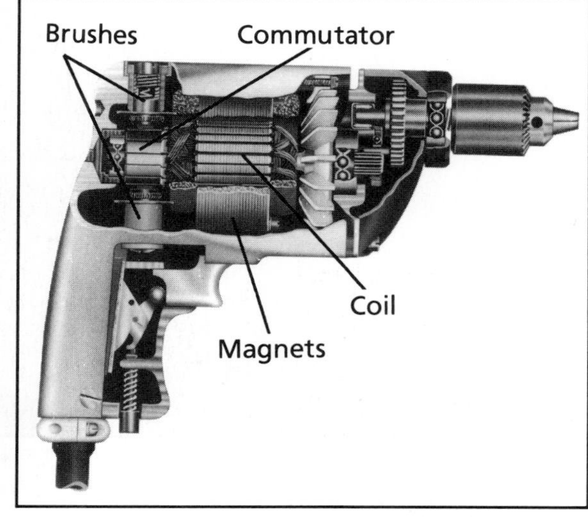

b

FIGURE 22–7. The basic parts of an electric motor are shown on the simple model (a). The motor in the electric drill (b) has the same basic parts.

would not continue to rotate. However, a motor that runs on direct current has a commutator. The **commutator** is a reversing switch that rotates with the coil and reverses the direction of the current every half turn of the coil. This reversal causes the force on the coil to reverse. The coil moves around another half turn. The commutator reverses the current direction again, and the coil rotates another half turn. Current flows to the commutator through electrical contacts made of carbon, called brushes. The brushes continuously touch the commutator as it turns. The coil is attached to a shaft that rotates. The rotation is smooth because of the rotational inertia of the coil.

TECHNOLOGY: APPLICATIONS

"Perpetual Motion" Toys

Have you seen "perpetual motion" toys for sale? You can often find them in museum stores. One such toy is a pendulum that swings "forever."

The pendulum bob contains a magnet, and there is a coil in the base of the toy. The moving magnet causes a tiny current in the coil. A transistor amplifier detects this current and acts as a switch. It controls the larger current from the battery. The battery current creates a magnetic field around a second coil, pushing the pendulum away. The current stops quickly. When the pendulum swings back down, the process is repeated.

The toy only looks like it is in perpetual motion, but the energy comes from the battery. The toy is an interesting demonstration of an electrical generator, amplifier, and motor all in one. Besides, it is fun to watch the motion of the pendulum.

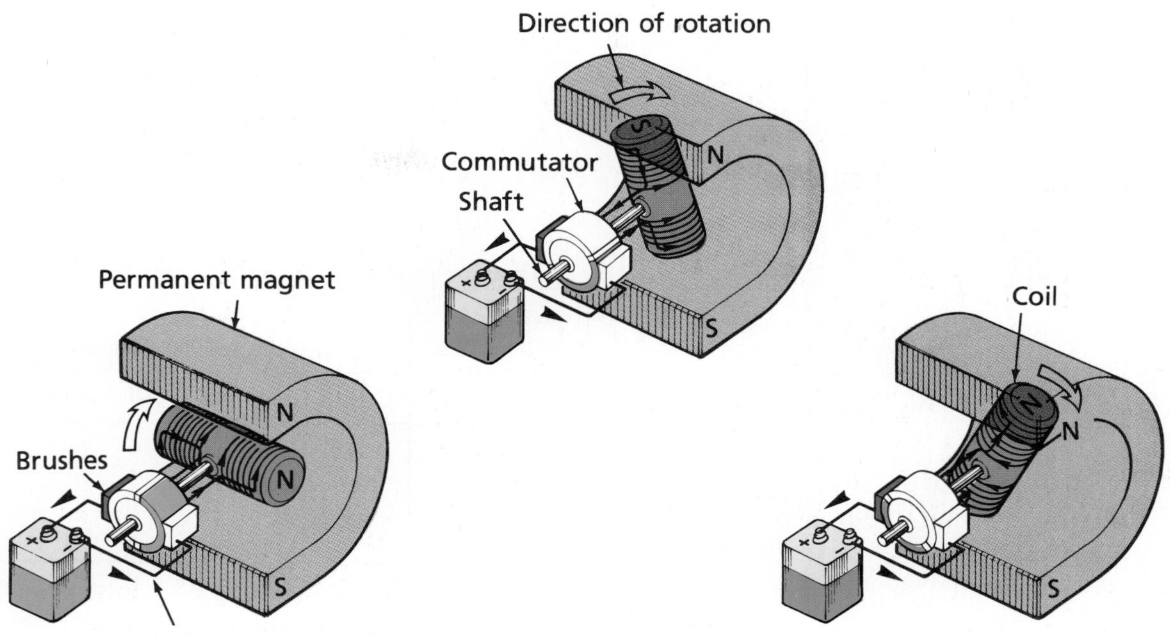

FIGURE 22–8. As the coil of a motor turns, the commutator switches the direction of current flowing in the coil. This reverses the magnetic poles of the coil, and the coil continues to rotate.

A motor converts electrical energy into mechanical energy that is used to do work. For example, in an electric drill, the shaft of the motor is attached to a drill bit. Some motors may appear more complex than the simple motor we have discussed. The main difference, however, is that they contain several coils attached to the shaft instead of just one. More coils give the motor greater power and smoother rotation.

What is the function of a motor?

Review

1. If you passed a horseshoe magnet over a pile of coins, only the nickels would be attracted. Why?
2. What is the function of a commutator in an electric motor?
3. Suppose you set up a circuit in which a battery causes a bulb to light. Explain how you would connect a voltmeter to find the potential difference across the bulb.
4. How would you measure the current flowing through the bulb of question 3?
5. ★ Suppose you made a model of Earth's magnetic field by putting a bar magnet inside a globe. Which magnetic pole would you put at the north end of Earth? Explain your answer.

INVESTIGATION 22–2

Generating Current

Problem: How can you generate an electric current?

Materials

galvanometer
insulated bell wire, 3 m long
bar magnet

Procedure

1. Wind the wire into a 20-turn coil, 5 cm in diameter. Connect the wire to the galvanometer. The galvanometer can show both the strength and direction of current flow.
2. Move the magnet, N-pole first, into the coil.
3. Hold the magnet motionless in the coil.
4. Pull the magnet out of the coil, north pole first.
5. Move the magnet into the same end of the coil, but this time south pole first.
6. Move the magnet into the opposite end of the coil, south pole first.
7. Move the magnet slowly back and forth in the coil.
8. Move the magnet back and forth in the coil, but much faster than in step 7.
9. Change the number of turns in the coil. Repeat Steps 7 and 8.

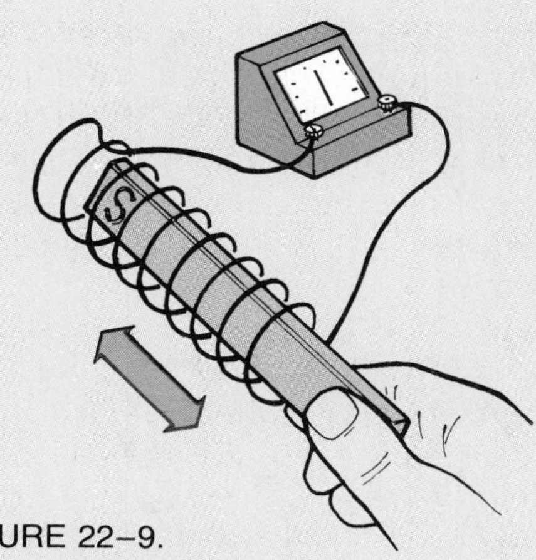

FIGURE 22–9.

Observations

Step	Needle displacement	
	Strength	Direction
2		
3		
4		

Analysis and Conclusions

1. How does the galvanometer indicate the direction and strength of current flowing in the coil?
2. How does the direction of the current depend on whether the magnet is moving in or out of the coil?
3. How does the direction of the current depend on the direction of the magnetic field?
4. How does the direction of the current depend on the end of the coil into which the magnet moves?
5. How does the current depend on the speed of the change of the magnet?
6. How does the current depend on the number of turns in the coil?
7. What kind of current is generated when the magnet does not move in the coil?
8. How can you generate current with a coil and a magnet?

PRODUCTION OF ELECTRIC CURRENTS

Michael Faraday was a talented British scientist who believed that connections must exist among natural phenomena. He knew that electric currents caused magnetic fields. He searched for electric currents produced by magnetic fields for years before he found that it took a change in a magnetic field to produce electrical effects. His discovery resulted in the development of generators that convert mechanical energy efficiently into electrical energy. The electric age was born.

GOALS

1. You will learn how a generator produces electric current.
2. You will understand the difference between alternating current and direct current.
3. You will learn how a transformer changes the voltage of alternating current.

22:6 Generators

Current flowing through a coil produces a magnetic field. A magnetic field produces a current in a coil only if the coil moves or the magnetic field changes. In a loudspeaker, electric current generates sound. The loudspeaker can also convert sound into electric current. Sound waves striking the cone cause it to vibrate. The cone's vibration moves the coil back and forth in the magnetic field. This causes forces on electrons in the wire, resulting in a varying current in the coil. A device that changes sound into electrical signals is a microphone. Thus, a microphone and a loudspeaker are very similar.

When will a magnetic field produce a current in a coil?

CAREER

Microwave Communications Engineer

Lamon Grier, Jr. is a supervisory electronics engineer for the academy of the Federal Aviation Administration (FAA). Mr. Grier manages the Communications Equipment Unit training programs.

Mr. Grier chose this career because he has always had an interest in electronics, engineering, physics, and computer science. In addition, Mr. Grier says, "You always need the ability to deal with people and people problems."

A modern aircraft relies on sensitive electronic equipment to keep track of flight conditions and provide information for navigation. Technicians on the ground must constantly test and repair this equipment to ensure that it is functioning properly.

For more information, write
Federal Aviation Administration
800 Independence Avenue, S.W.
Washington, DC 20591

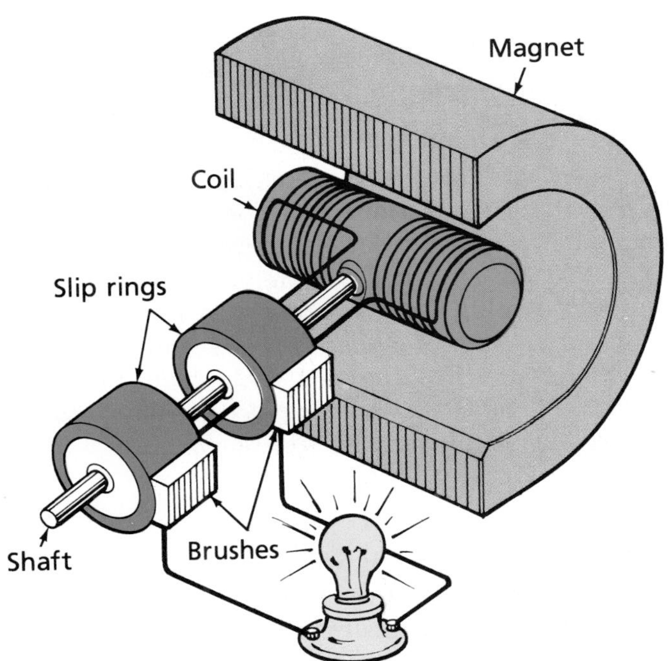

FIGURE 22–10. The generator shown here produces alternating current as the coil rotates in the magnetic field. The shaft must be connected to a source of mechanical energy to turn the coil.

What does a generator do?

List three forms of potential energy that are used to produce electrical energy.

FIGURE 22–11. In power generating plants, huge generators are turned by steam or water power.

Remember that a motor contains a coil that rotates in the field of a magnet. Putting a current through the coil makes it rotate. Suppose you rotate the coil rather than supplying a current. The motion of the coil in the magnetic field creates a force on electrons in the wire, producing an electric current. Mechanical energy is thus converted into electrical energy. A device that produces current by turning a coil of wire in a magnetic field is called a **generator,** Figure 22–10.

Small generators are used on bicycles to power head- and taillights. An automobile uses a generator, usually called an alternator, to power the electrical system while the car is running and to recharge the battery. The energy that turns the alternator comes from the car engine. The electrical energy for our cities is produced by extremely large generators. Some generators are turned by the energy of falling water that was stored behind dams. Most generators, however, are turned by steam turbine engines. The steam is generated by burning coal, oil, or natural gas, or in nuclear reactors. In each case the stored, or potential energy, in the fuel is converted into thermal energy in the steam. The steam's thermal energy is converted into kinetic energy of the rotating engine and generator and finally into electrical energy.

22:7 Direct and Alternating Current

In the last chapter we considered current that always flowed in the same direction. Current that does not periodically change direction is called **direct current (DC).** Current that changes or alternates in direction is called **alternating current (AC).**

Power companies in North America distribute alternating current that reverses direction 120 times a second. Two reversals make one cycle. The alternating current has a frequency of 60 hertz. Alternating current can produce thermal energy, light, and mechanical energy just as direct current can.

22:8 Transformers

An electric **transformer** is a device that increases or decreases the voltage of alternating current. High-voltage transmission lines carry electric current at voltages as high as 500 000 volts. Transformers are used to reduce the voltage to 120 V or 240 V so it can be used in homes. A transformer that operates a toy train reduces the 120 V to voltages between 5 V and 30 V.

A transformer has two coils of insulated wire wound around the same iron core. One coil is the primary (input) coil, and the other is the secondary (output) coil. When the primary coil is connected to an alternating current, a magnetic field is created. The magnetic field changes in strength and direction because it is created

BIOGRAPHY

Adriana Ocampo
1955–

Adriana Ocampo works on Project Galileo, a study of Jupiter, for the Jet Propulsion Lab. The Galileo spacecraft will carry her Near-Infrared Mapping Spectrometer (NIM), a remote sensing device used to study the atmosphere and surface chemistry of Jupiter and its satellites.

Both a geologist and a planetary scientist, Ocampo is involved in the analysis of photographs by computers, and in computer modeling of geologic events.

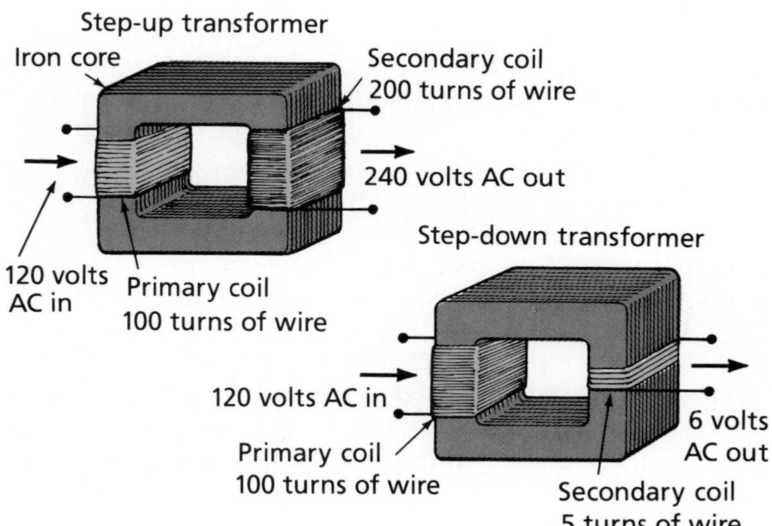

FIGURE 22–12. A step-up transformer has more turns in the secondary coil than in the primary. A step-down transformer has more turns in the primary than in the secondary.

Compare a step-up and a step-down transformer.

by an alternating current. The varying magnetic field exerts a force on the electrons in the secondary coil. Recall that when a magnetic field around a wire changes, a current flows in the wire. As a result, an alternating current is created in the secondary coil.

The voltage produced in the secondary coil depends on the relative number of turns of wire in the primary and secondary coils. If the number of turns is greater in the secondary coil than in the primary, the transformer increases the voltage. This kind of transformer is called a step-up transformer. If the number of turns in the secondary coil is less than in the primary coil, it is a step-down transformer. In a step-down transformer, the output voltage is less than the input voltage. A transformer in a neon sign steps up line voltage from 120 V to 20 000 V or more. The step-down transformer that operates a doorbell reduces the 120 volts to 24 V.

F.Y.I. The frequency of alternating current is specified the same way as the frequency of sound and light waves. One cycle per second is the same as one hertz.

How does a transformer illustrate the law of conservation of energy?

A transformer is like a lever. A lever can increase the force, but output work cannot be greater than input work. A transformer can similarly increase the voltage, but the output energy can never be more than the input energy. A transformer does not create energy.

Review

6. How does a generator produce electric current?
7. What energy source supplies the electrical energy produced by the bicycle generator?
8. How are the operation of a microphone and a generator alike?
9. Why does a transformer require varying current in order to operate?
★ **10.** Suppose you find an old doorbell transformer. It has two coils, one with a large number of turns, the other with only a small number. Which coil would be connected to the doorbell that uses 24 V?

ELECTRONICS

GOALS

1. You will learn about diodes and transistors.
2. You will understand what an integrated circuit is.
3. You will learn about computers.

You find electronics used often in your everyday life: radio, television, tape players, public address systems, motion pictures with sound, calculators, computers, and digital watches. All of these complex devices are really applications of the electricity and magnetism you have studied.

22:9 Diodes and Transistors

Electric circuits in most buildings carry alternating current, but some devices, such as stereos and computers, operate only on direct current. A **rectifier** is a device that conducts current in only one direction. When a rectifier is connected to a source of alternating current, direct current flows in the circuit because current can flow through the rectifier in only one direction.

What is a rectifier? How does it change AC into DC current?

Rectifiers are usually made of semiconductors, such as silicon and germanium. Semiconductors have resistance between that of insulators and conductors. When a voltage is placed across the semiconductor, only a small amount of current will flow. Pure silicon has a resistance a million times that of copper. The resistance of silicon can be reduced by adding tiny amounts of impurities, such as arsenic. Adding impurities to semiconductors to change their resistance is called **doping.**

What is the purpose of doping?

Arsenic has five electrons in its outer energy level while silicon has only four. When silicon is doped with arsenic, the crystal receives electrons that are free to move. Electrons are negative particles, so a semiconductor doped with arsenic is an n-type (negative-type) semiconductor. When a voltage is applied across the silicon, electrons move through the crystal.

What is a semiconductor?

When silicon is doped with gallium, a p-type (positive-type) semiconductor is formed. Gallium has one fewer electron in its outer energy level than silicon. As a result, there is a "hole" or absence of an electron near each gallium atom. When a voltage is applied across the crystal an electron can move to fill the hole, creating a hole where the electron came from. The result is a current flow through the crystal.

FIGURE 22–13. Doping semiconductor elements with impurities allows the movement of charge through the crystal.

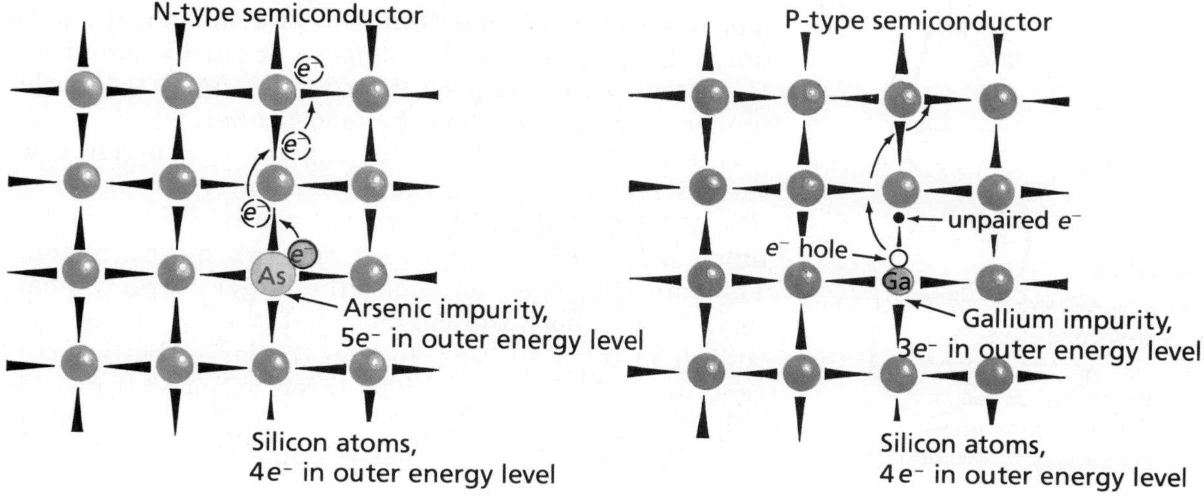

a

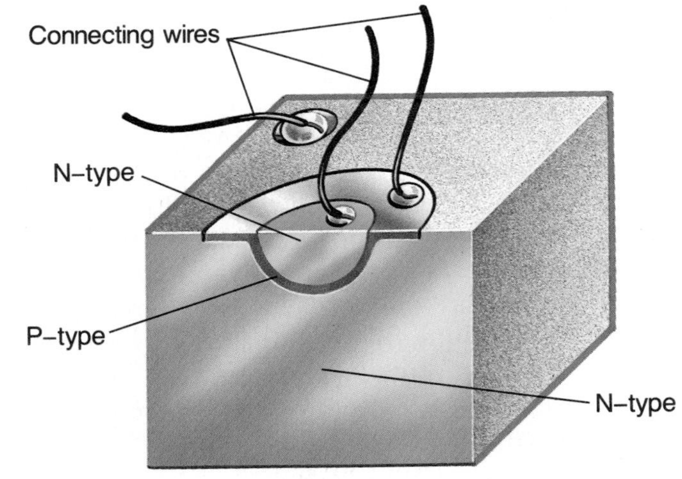

b

FIGURE 22–14. Transistors come in a variety of sizes (a). The diagram (b) shows how an npn transistor can be made by interlayering n and p types of materials.

A diode is made by doping one end of a piece of silicon with arsenic and the other end with gallium. One end is p-type, the other end is n-type. The result is a pn-diode. Current flows only from the n-type end to the p-type end, but not the other direction. The **diode** is a rectifier that converts alternating into direct current.

N-type silicon can be doped first with gallium to make a p-type layer, and then with arsenic to produce another n-type layer. The result is a "sandwich" of n-type silicon separated by a thin layer of p-type. Such a device is called an npn transistor. A **transistor** is a semiconductor used to amplify current. Wires connect the three transistor regions to electrical circuits, Figure 22–14b.

Signals in electronic devices are varying electric currents, like those produced by a microphone. The signal, a tiny varying current, must often be amplified, or made larger, to be used further. For example, in an electronic megaphone, the signal from the microphone might be only a few millionths of an ampere. It must be amplified to a tenth of an ampere in order to create the larger louder sound waves from the loudspeaker.

A transistor can amplify the signals. The current from the microphone flows through the center p-type region to one n-type region. This signal controls the flow of a much larger current between the two n-type regions. The transistor does not create the larger current; a battery must supply the current that the transistor controls. The small current changes the larger battery current in the transistor. Often three or more transistor amplifiers are needed in electronic devices such as the megaphone, stereos, tape players, and televisions.

FIGURE 22–15. A transistor acts as a kind of switch. It uses the weak input current to control the flow of a much larger current, but it does not create a current.

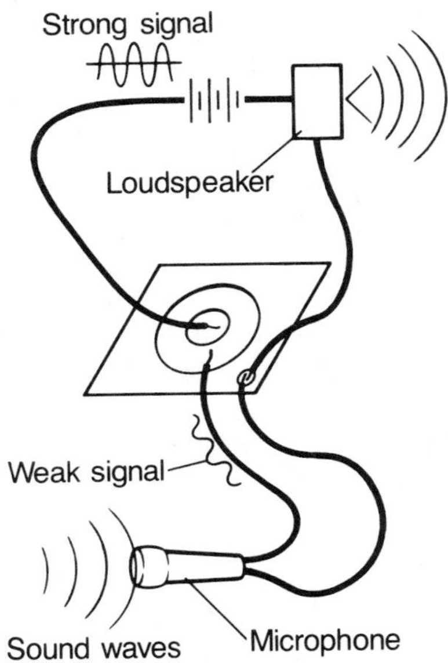

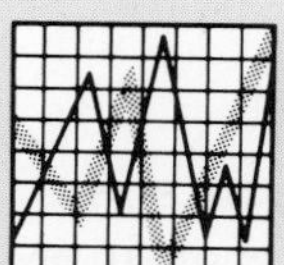

SKILL

Reading a Meter

Problem: How do you read electric meters?

Materials

text page

Background

Most electric meters have more than one range. Voltmeters typically have ranges of −1 to +3 volts, −5 to +15 volts, and −100 to +300 volts. The face of a voltmeter might look like Figure 22–16a. One scale is calibrated for the different ranges. The reading shown is 6.7 V. It could also be 135 V or 1.35 V if the negative lead were connected to a different terminal.

An ammeter often has ranges of −10 to +50 milliamperes (mA), −100 to +500 mA, and −1 to +5 A. Note that the units may be amps or milliamps. With the ammeter in 22–

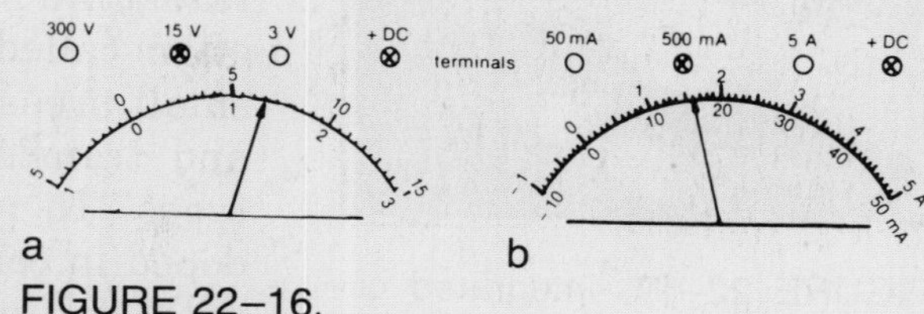

FIGURE 22–16.

16b connected as shown, the reading would be 160 mA. What would the readings be in the other two ranges?

Data and Observations

Record the correct reading for each meter. In each example, the X indicates the terminal being used.

Conclusions

1. How do you read electric meters?

1.

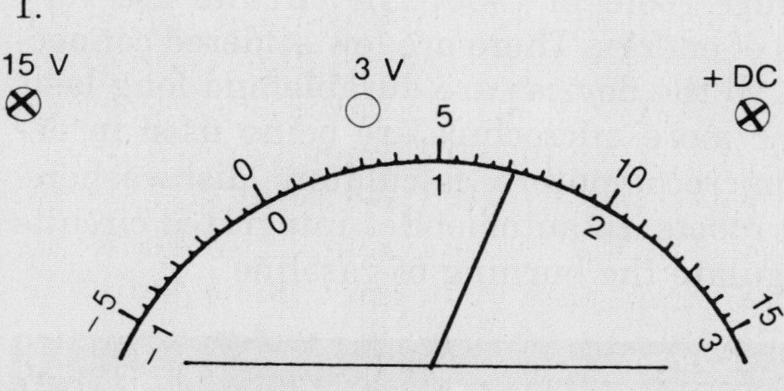

3.

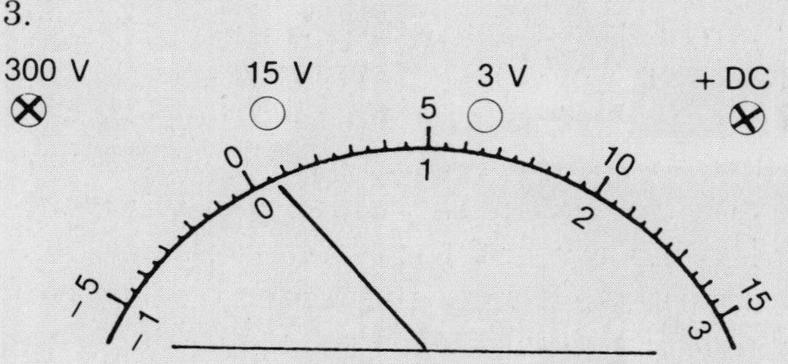

2.

4.

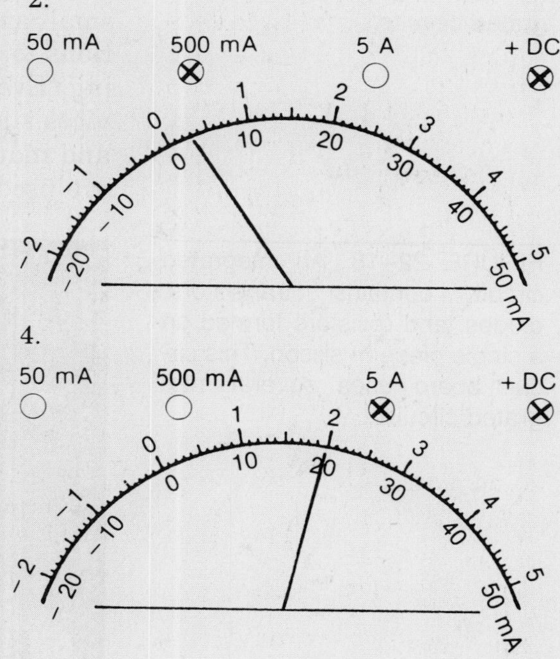

FIGURE 22–17. Integrated circuits make it possible to produce calculators in small sizes.

22:10 Integrated Circuits

Describe an integrated circuit.

Electronic circuits often use many transistors and other devices. These circuits can be combined, or integrated, into an integrated circuit, or IC. An **integrated circuit** is a circuit containing many resistors, diodes, and transistors, all on a single piece of silicon. The tiny, razor-thin slice of silicon, a few millimeters on a side, is often called a microchip. Resistors can be made from small areas of n-type or p-type semiconductors. Diodes and transistors require combinations of two or three types. To make the devices, the silicon chip must be doped in certain places with arsenic and in other places with gallium. Aluminum forms conductive paths between the devices on the chip. Under a microscope the features of a chip appear like the streets, parks, playgrounds, and buildings of a city seen from an airplane.

Tiny wires are connected to the aluminum, and the chip is sealed in a protective case made of plastic or ceramic. The wires from the chip are attached to pins that come out of the case. These pins allow the chip to be connected to electronic circuits.

List some advantages of integrated circuits.

The diodes, resistors, and transistors on an integrated circuit are connected as amplifiers and electronic switches. Integrated circuits allow very complicated circuits to be built in very small spaces. A hand-held calculator performs more functions faster than a computer that filled a huge room in 1950. The circuits use very small amounts of energy. There are few soldered connections to break, so the devices are durable and long lasting. Every year more microchips are being used in devices such as microcomputers, calculators, dishwashers, and industrial robots. In automobiles integrated circuits are used to regulate the burning of gasoline.

FIGURE 22–18. An integrated circuit contains transistors, diodes, and resistors formed on a single piece of silicon. This circuit board uses several integrated circuits.

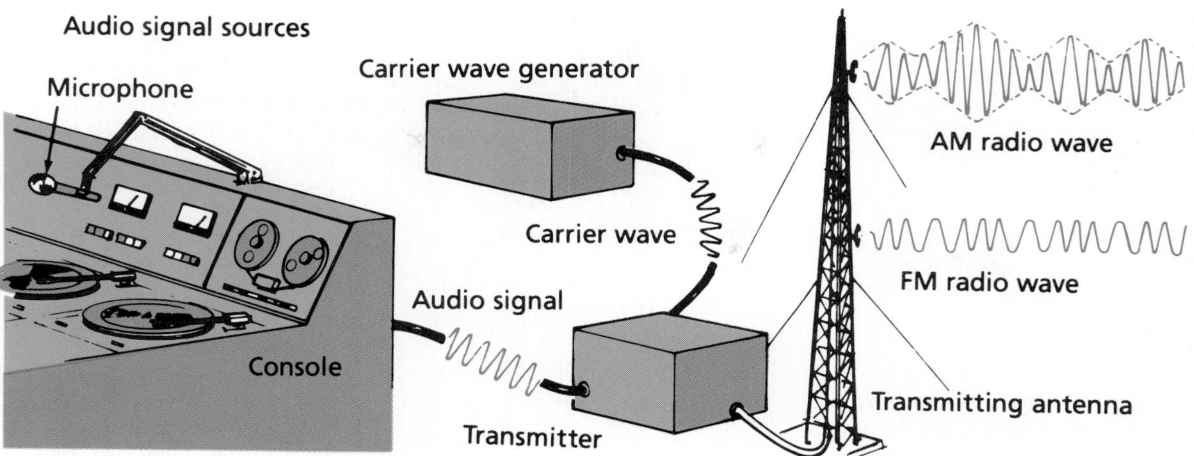

FIGURE 22–19. In radio broadcasting, an audio signal is used to vary a carrier wave.

22:11 Radio and Television Transmission

Suppose your favorite FM radio station broadcasts at 101.9 MHz. The broadcasting station has an oscillator that creates an alternating current with a frequency of 101.9 million cycles per second (101.9 MHz). This is called the carrier wave. The disk jockey talks into a microphone that changes the sound waves into electrical signals. The signal is amplified and sent into the modulator. The modulator varies, or modulates, the frequency of the carrier wave according to the signal from the microphone. The FM signal is further amplified and sent to the transmitting antenna. Many radio stations broadcast from 5000 to 50 000 watts of power.

How is an audio signal changed into a radio wave?

A radio receiver is used to tune and amplify the signal from a radio transmitter. Radio waves of all frequencies produce weak alternating currents in the antenna of the receiver. Tuning the receiver selects the frequency to be amplified. After amplification, the carrier wave is removed from the music or voice frequencies that were added in the modulator. After further amplification, a loudspeaker produces sound waves.

How does tuning affect a radio receiver?

Transmission of television programs is similar to radio transmission. The voice, or audio signal, is produced the same way an FM radio signal is. A television camera changes a light image into a varying electric current, called the video signal. Lenses in the camera focus an image of a scene on the surface of a light-sensitive tube. Light striking this tube produces a pattern of varying electric current that contains details of the scene. This video signal is amplified and used to modulate a carrier wave by amplitude modulation (AM). The

How is a television picture transmitted?

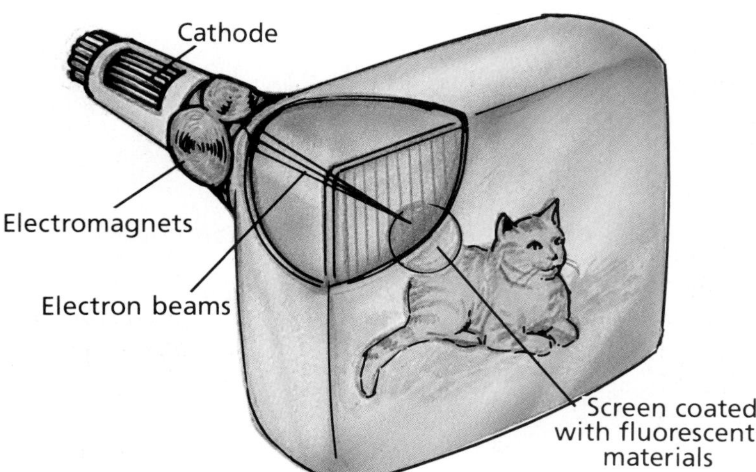

FIGURE 22–20. Shown here is a diagram of one kind of color CRT.

combined audio and video signals are sent to the station's transmitting antenna.

Tuning a television receiver allows only the selected carrier frequency to be amplified. The picture tube in a television is a form of a cathode-ray tube. A **cathode-ray tube (CRT)** is a device that uses electrons to produce images on a screen.

What is a CRT?

The CRT is a sealed glass tube from which all air has been removed. The electrons are emitted by a heated tungsten "cathode" at the rear of the CRT. They are accelerated and focused by electric fields into a narrow beam. The beam travels to the face of the tube that forms a screen. The inside of the screen is coated with fluorescent materials that glow when struck by electrons. The brightness of the glow is varied by changing the number of electrons in the beam. Electromagnets are placed around the neck of the CRT to change the direction of the beam. They cause the beam to move rapidly back and forth, up and down across the screen. Thus, the cathode-ray tube displays information in the form of a pattern of light, a picture of the scene viewed by the video camera.

How is the electron beam moved in a CRT?

What are three uses of a CRT?

22:12 Computers

A **computer** is a device that solves complex problems by breaking them down into many simple actions. The action may be the addition or subtraction of two numbers, or it may be a logical decision based on whether one number is larger or smaller than another number. An electronic computer uses electric devices to perform the arithmetic and logic actions.

The computer takes the logic or arithmetic actions following a set of instructions called a program. A **digital computer** stores numbers and instructions as a series of bits. Each bit has only two possible values, on and off. If a bit is on, the transistor switch closes an electric circuit, permitting current to flow. If the bit is off, the switch is opened, stopping the current flow.

A single bit can represent only two numbers, 0 and 1. A number system that has only two values is called a binary number system. Larger numbers are represented in a computer by using a series of bits. Eight bits, a byte, can represent 256 numbers, letters, or symbols.

Both the program and the data enter the computer through an input device. Data might be the mass and velocity of some object, a student's name, or a test score. Many computers have a keyboard like a typewriter for entering data. Each stroke of a key enters a symbol such as a letter, number, or plus sign.

The **program** consists of a series of instructions that are also entered through the keyboard. Even a simple problem like "add 7 to 8" may require several instructions. For this reason computer scientists have developed translators, or programming languages, that convert instructions that you can understand into logic and arithmetic instructions the computer can use.

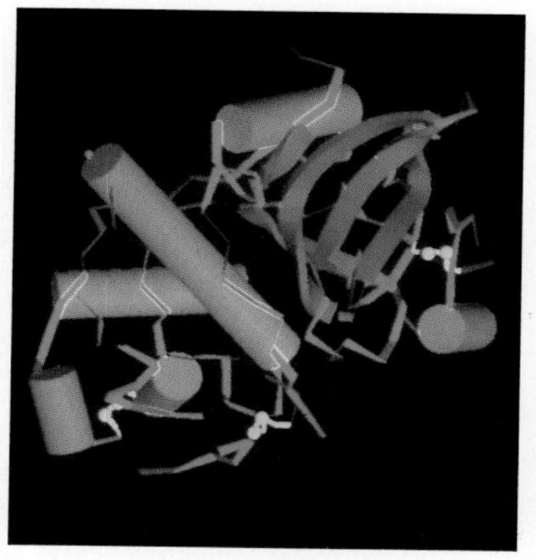

FIGURE 22–21. This CRT image of the structure of a protein molecule was generated by a computer using information about the molecule.

F.Y.I. The word "bit" is short for binary digit. A series of eight bits is usually called a byte. Sometimes four bits, or half a byte, is called a "nibble."

PROBLEM SOLVING

A Circuitous Path

Karen was using diodes in a circuit to convert alternating current into direct current. She found that with no diodes in the circuit, Circuit **A,** the current versus time graph looked like Graph **A.** With one diode in the circuit, she obtained a direct current that produced Graph **B.** After more experimenting, she found that by using four diodes to create an alternate path, she could produce Graph **C.** The circuit symbol for a diode is ▶|, with the arrow pointing in the direction the current can flow. Draw Circuit **B** and copy and add diodes to Circuit **C** to make circuits that produce Graphs **B** and **C.**

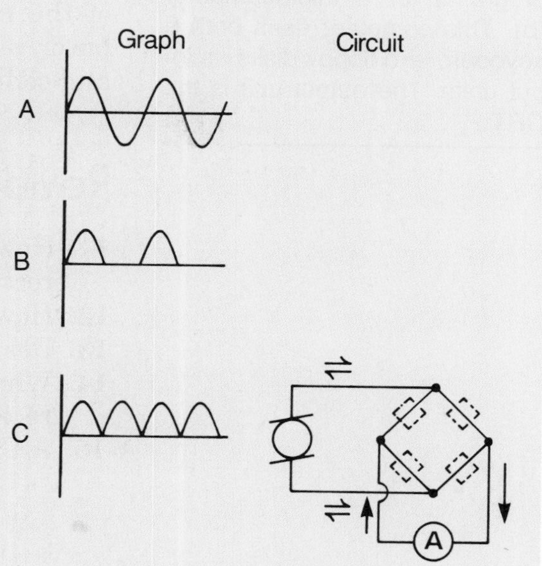

a

b

FIGURE 22–22. Millions of bits of information may be recorded on the magnetic coating of a floppy disk (a). A disk may store programs for a microcomputer (b). This computer uses both a keyboard and floppy disks as input units. The output unit is the CRT.

The "nerve center" of the computer is the microprocessor. The **microprocessor,** a single integrated circuit, contains the central processing unit, or CPU that acts on the instructions it receives. It has an arithmetic-logic unit, or ALU, to make the logical decisions and add or subtract two bytes. The microprocessor also contains a small amount of memory, called registers, that store the results of the instructions.

The data and instructions are stored in the memory of the computer. A single inexpensive integrated circuit can store over 256 000 bits. The computer can "write" to the memory, setting the bit either on or off. It can also "read" the memory, finding out whether the bit is on or off. Such memory is called read/write (R/W) memory. Because the computer can choose any bit to read or write, it is also called random access memory, or RAM. Another form of memory in a computer is permanent. The manufacturer sets each bit on or off. The computer can only read this memory, so it is called read-only memory (ROM). The translation instructions, often including BASIC, are stored in ROM.

Results of the computer's operations are displayed by the output device. The most common output device is a video display terminal that contains a cathode-ray tube.

When the computer is turned off, all information stored in the RAM is lost. Many uses of a computer, however, require storage of data and programs for use at a later time. Most microcomputers use a flexible plastic disk coated with magnetic iron oxide. This "floppy" disk stores data by arranging the north and south poles of the magnetic pieces in a certain pattern. The computer can later detect the magnetic pattern on the disk and convert it back to an electrical signal.

Review

11. How does a diode change alternating current to direct current?

12. How does doping affect a semiconductor?

13. Describe how transistors amplify weak signals.

14. What happens when you turn a radio or television receiver to a station?

★ **15.** A CRT uses an electron beam to make a light image.

a. How is the electron beam formed?

b. How does the electron beam produce light?

c. How is an image formed?

d. What signal determines the image?

Chapter 22 Review

SUMMARY

1. Like magnetic poles repel, unlike poles attract. 22:2
2. A moving charge creates a magnetic field. 22:2
3. Magnetic fields affect electric charges. 22:3
4. Ammeters and voltmeters use the force on a current-carrying wire in a magnetic field. 22:4
5. Motors convert electrical energy into mechanical energy. 22:5
6. Generators convert mechanical into electrical energy. 22:6
7. Alternating current changes or alternates in direction. 22:7
8. A transformer changes the voltage of alternating current. 22:8
9. Rectifying diodes change alternating to direct current. 22:9
10. Semiconductors are made by doping silicon with impurities. 22:9
11. Transistors are made from n-type and p-type semiconductors and can amplify weak signals. 22:9
12. An integrated circuit contains many resistors, diodes, and transistors all on a single piece of silicon. 22:10
13. A CRT converts an electric signal into a light image. 22:11
14. A computer uses electric circuits and currents to do calculations and make decisions. 22:12

VOCABULARY

a. alternating current
b. ammeter
c. cathode-ray tube
d. commutator
e. compass
f. computer
g. core
h. digital computer
i. diode
j. direct current
k. doping
l. electromagnet
m. generator
n. integrated circuit
o. magnet
p. magnetic field
q. magnetic poles
r. microprocessor
s. permanent magnet
t. program
u. rectifier
v. signal
w. transformer
x. transistor
y. voltmeter

Matching

Match each description with the correct vocabulary word from the list above. Some words will not be used.

1. a magnet that does not lose its strength
2. a coil of wire with a current flowing through it
3. the region around a magnet
4. a reversing switch in a DC motor
5. measuring device put in a circuit in parallel
6. produces an electric current by rotating a coil in an electric field
7. device that changes the voltage of alternating current
8. a semiconductor device that can amplify signals
9. adding impurities to silicon to control resistance
10. the set of instructions that tell a computer what to do

Chapter 22 Review

MAIN IDEAS

A. Reviewing Concepts

Choose the word or phrase that correctly completes each of the following sentences.

1. The amount of current flowing in a circuit may be measured with a(n) *(electroscope, ammeter, voltmeter, CRT).*
2. Magnets can be made of *(carbon, silicon, iron, gallium).*
3. Transistors are made of materials that are *(conductors, semiconductors, superconductors, insulators).*
4. Transistors are used in electronic equipment such as *(motors, transformers, rectifiers, amplifiers).*
5. Integrated circuits do not contain *(resistors, transformers, transistors, diodes).*

Complete each of the following sentences with the correct word or phrase.

6. To produce the 20 000 volts needed by a CRT, a television needs a(n) ____________ transformer.
7. North poles of magnets are attracted by ____________ poles.
8. The space around a magnet contains a(n) ________________ that exerts a force on other magnets.
9. Alternating current is current that ____________ direction.
10. Rectifiers are used in devices that need ________________ to operate.

Determine whether each of the following sentences is true or false. If it is false, change the underlined word to make the sentence true.

11. The north-seeking pole of a magnet attracts <u>north-seeking</u> poles.
12. Rectifiers are used to change <u>DC</u> to <u>AC</u>.
13. The primary coil of a <u>step-up</u> transformer has fewer turns than the secondary coil.
14. An electronic <u>digital</u> computer operates on binary numbers.
15. The <u>brightness</u> of a TV picture depends on the number of electrons striking the screen.

B. Understanding Concepts

Answer the following questions using complete sentences when possible.

16. Explain what makes the coil turn in a motor.
17. Describe the basic design of an ammeter or a voltmeter.
18. If you have a coil of wire and a horseshoe magnet, how could you create a current flow in the coil?
19. What device would you use to obtain direct current to power a tape player from the alternating current in your house?
20. What is the effect of tuning a radio dial to a particular station?
21. Why is it necessary to dope silicon to make diodes and transistors?
22. What forms of modulation are used in television broadcasting?
23. Explain what happens to the electrons in a CRT after they have been emitted by the filament.
24. If you buy a game program on a floppy disk and enter it into a computer, is it stored in RAM or ROM chips? Explain.
25. Which of the integrated circuits in a computer performs the computing functions?

C. Applying Concepts

Answer the following questions, using complete sentences when possible.

26. Given some wire and a battery, how could you magnetize a screwdriver?

27. Suppose you have a magnetized screwdriver and a mixture of screws made of aluminum, brass, and steel. How could you use the screwdriver to separate at least some of the screws?
28. Explain how a commutator works in an electric motor.
29. How would you connect an ammeter to find the current flowing when a motor is connected to a battery?
30. Compare an electric generator and a motor. How are they alike? How are they different?

SKILL REVIEW

1. Why is it necessary to check which terminals of a meter are connected into a circuit?
2. What would be the correct meter reading if the negative terminal in Example 1 on page 531 were connected to the 3-V terminal?
3. What would be the correct reading in Example 4 if the negative terminal were connected to the 5-A terminal?
4. What does Figure 22–13 tell you about a transistor?
5. A shipping clerk has 50 mailing cartons. Ten of the cartons are 1 m × 1 m × 0.5 m; 20 of the cartons are 0.5 m × 1 m × 2 m; 20 of the cartons are 20 cm × 50 cm × 30 cm. Assume that the boxes are stored individually and that the ceiling is 8 m high. What is the minimum amount of floor space required to warehouse these cartons?

PROJECTS

1. Take an old electric motor apart. Identify and make a diagram of the parts.
2. Visit an electric power plant to learn how electric current is generated.
3. Prepare a report on the advantages and possible problems involved with using extremely high voltage power lines to deliver electric energy from distant power plants.
4. Prepare a report on expert systems and artificial intelligence. Find out how computers are used in these fields.

READINGS

1. Becker, Robert O. and Gary Selder. *The Body Electric*. New York: Morrow, 1985.
2. Carter, Alden R. and Wayne J. Leblanc. *Supercomputers*. New York: Franklin Watts, 1985.
3. DeBruin, Jerry. *Young Scientists Explore: Electricity and Magnetism*. Carthage, IL: Good Apple, 1985.
4. Dobles, E. R. *Electricity and Magnetism*. New York: Methuen, 1984.

RADIOACTIVITY
RADIOACTIVE DECAY
DETECTING RADIOACTIVITY
NUCLEAR REACTIONS

Chapter 23

Radioactivity and Nuclear Reactions

A block of wood on the roof of a building has potential energy in many forms. If it is dropped off the roof, its gravitational potential energy is converted into kinetic energy. If it is burned, its chemical potential energy is converted to thermal energy and light. The nucleus of every atom in the wood has a large amount of potential energy. In this century, humans have learned to convert the potential energy of the nucleus to other forms. The uses that humankind makes of this tremendous energy will determine the future of Earth.

RADIOACTIVITY

GOALS

1. You will learn the meaning of radioactivity.
2. You will examine the structure of a radioactive nuclide.

Radioactivity was discovered by a French scientist, Henri Becquerel, in 1896. He left some uranium ore lying on a photographic plate in a dark desk drawer. When he developed the plate, Becquerel was surprised to find an outline of the uranium sample. Uranium had released invisible radiation that exposed the plate. He had discovered that uranium is a radioactive element.

23:1 Radioactive Elements

All elements are made of atoms. In the nucleus of an atom are the protons and neutrons. The strong nuclear force between the particles holds them together. However, the nuclei of some elements are not held together strongly enough. These nuclei are unstable. To be unstable means that a nucleus emits a particle or radiation. The particle or radiation is emitted with a large amount of kinetic energy. This process is called **radioactive decay.** The new nucleus that results from the decay may be unstable and decay again, or it may be stable.

What is radioactive decay?

F.Y.I. Nearly every element has one or more naturally occurring isotopes. Review isotopes, Chapter 10.

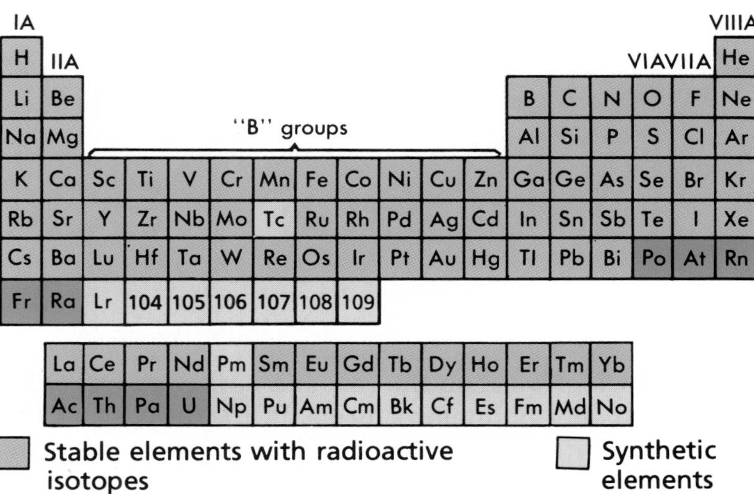

FIGURE 23–1. Although technicium, element 43, does not occur naturally on Earth, it has been detected in the spectrum of the sun and other stars.

F.Y.I. Einsteinium and nobelium are examples of synthetic elements.

Becquerel had made his discovery of radioactivity with uranium. In 1898, Marie and Pierre Curie discovered two new radioactive elements, polonium and radium, in uranium ore. Both polonium and radium are more radioactive than uranium. Since that time, many many more radioactive elements have been discovered. Recall that isotopes are atoms of the same element with different numbers of neutrons. All of the isotopes of elements with atomic numbers greater than that of bismuth are radioactive. However, some natural isotopes of lighter elements are also radioactive. For example, potassium, carbon, and oxygen all have naturally-occurring radioactive isotopes.

Synthetic elements are those that have been produced in the laboratory or in nuclear reactors. They do not occur naturally. Elements with atomic numbers between 93 and 109 are synthetic elements. All isotopes of the synthetic elements are radioactive.

FIGURE 23–2. The graph shows the numbers of protons and neutrons for isotopes of the first 35 elements on the periodic table.

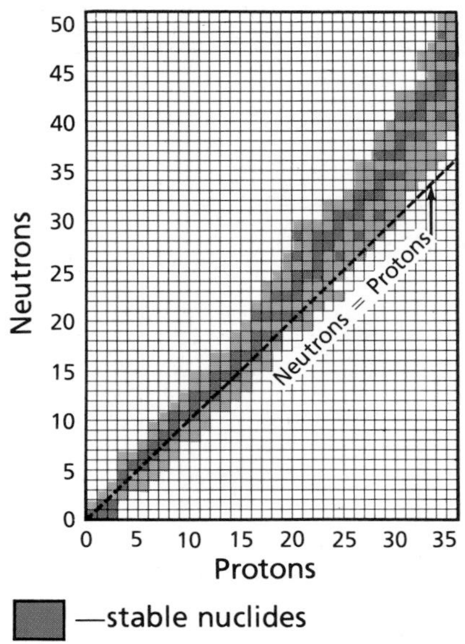

23:2 Nuclides

The study of radioactivity and nuclear reactions involves the study of the atomic nucleus. Thus, it is necessary to label different isotopes of the same element. A **nuclide** is the nucleus of an isotope that has a specific atomic number and atomic mass. The symbol used to show a particular nuclide includes the atomic number, mass number, and element symbol. The element carbon has several different nuclides. One carbon nuclide has the following symbol.

$$\begin{array}{l}\text{Mass number} \longrightarrow \\ \text{Atomic number} \longrightarrow \end{array} {}^{12}_{6}\text{C} \longrightarrow \text{Element name}$$

This nuclide is called carbon-12.

The stability of a nuclide depends upon the ratio of protons to neutrons in the nucleus. Look at the distribution of nuclides in Figure 23–2. The lighter nuclides that are stable have almost equal numbers of protons and neutrons. The stable nuclides of heavier elements have more neutrons than protons. Stable nuclides like carbon-12 do not decay. Carbon-12 has six protons and six neutrons.

CAREER

Nuclear Medicine Technician

Sarah Arrington was very young when they started up the nuclear plant near her home town. She was curious about why this form of energy production was so dangerous and why people didn't want the plant in their neighborhood. She was also confused by the fact that her uncle had been cured of cancer by undergoing something called nuclear radiation therapy. How could nuclear power both help and harm people?

Then one day she had to make a report for her 8th grade earth science class on radioisotopes. She began to research and found that radioisotopes are used in medicine to view the interior of the body to diagnose conditions such as ulcers, fractures, tumors, and malfunctioning organs. Once the problem is located, the physicians might then use the radiation therapy to attack the diseased cells without harming the healthy cells. She read about the benefits and dangers of nuclear radiation. This study answered some of her early childhood questions.

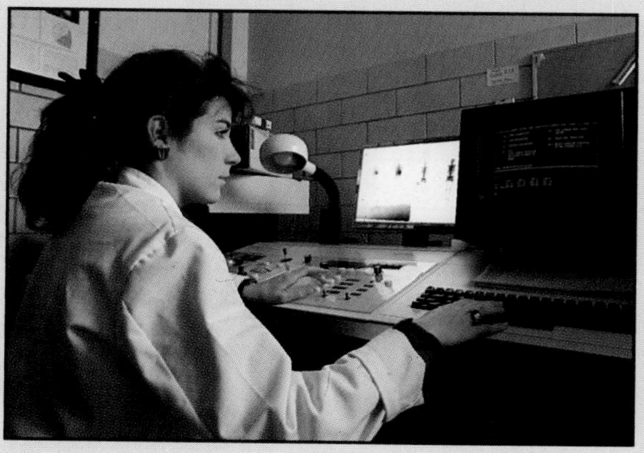

Sarah's knowledge of nuclear radiation helped her get a job as a nuclear medicine technician's assistant in a hospital soon after graduation from high school. After two years she became the head technician. Her main duties are to calculate and prepare correct dosages of radiation to give patients and to insure that radiation safety procedures are followed. The best part of her job is seeing sick patients recover and go home because of the radiation therapy she gives them.

For more career information, write
Society of Nuclear Medicine
136 Madison Avenue
New York, NY 10016

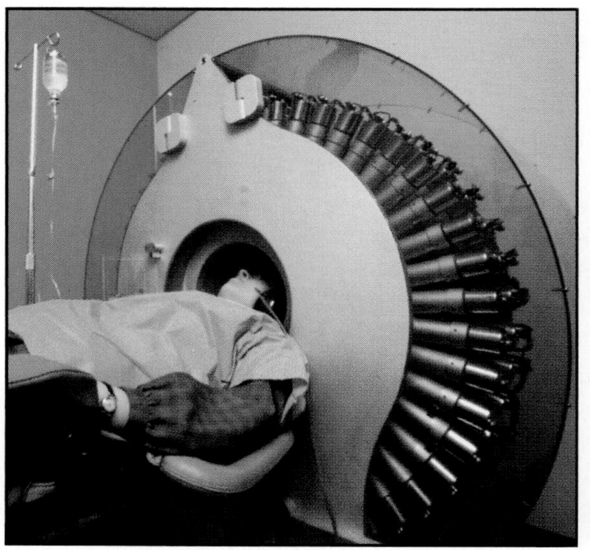

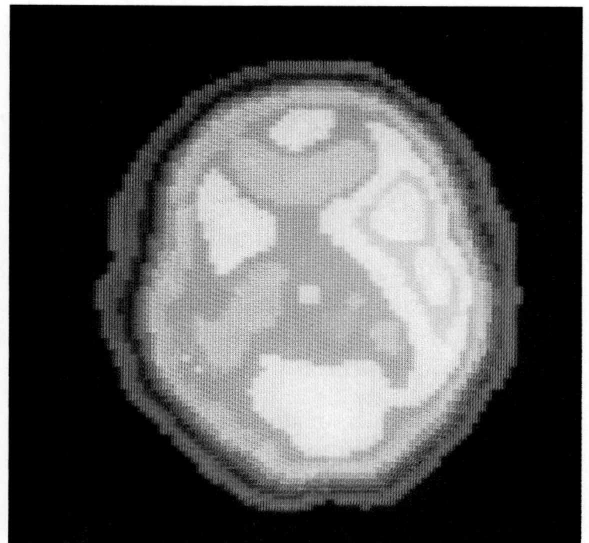

FIGURE 23–3. Radioactive elements are used as tracers in modern diagnostic procedures such as PET scans.

Describe two uses of radioactive nuclides.

If there are too many or too few neutrons compared with the number of protons in a atom, that nuclide may be radioactive. Carbon-14 has six protons and eight neutrons and is radioactive. Many of the common elements have radioactive nuclides.

Radioactive nuclides have many practical uses. They are used to trace a substance through a living system. For instance, radioactive phosphorus-32 placed in the soil around a plant will be absorbed into the plant. The movement of the phosphorus-32 through the plant can be followed with a Geiger counter, an instrument used to detect radiation. By tracking the movement of the element, scientists may learn how it is used in the plant.

Some radioactive nuclides, such as cobalt-60, emit high energy radiation that can be used to kill cancer cells. Radioactive nuclides are also used to detect tumors and other diseases in organs. Organs containing

Table 23–1

Radioactive Nuclides of Some Elements

Element	Nuclide	Atomic mass number	Protons	Neutrons
hydrogen	$^{3}_{1}H$	3	1	2
helium	$^{5}_{2}He$	5	2	3
lithium	$^{8}_{3}Li$	8	3	5
carbon	$^{14}_{6}C$	14	6	8
nitrogen	$^{16}_{7}N$	16	7	9
potassium	$^{40}_{19}K$	40	19	21

tumors use more of some substances than do normal tissue. A small amount of that substance, including a radioactive nuclide, can be injected into the blood, which carries it to the organ. Radiation emitted by the diseased organ can be compared with that emitted by a healthy organ.

TECHNOLOGY: APPLICATIONS

Supernova 1987A

In October 1604, astronomers in Italy, China, and Korea saw a new star in the sky. By November it was brighter than Venus, the brightest object in the heavens. It slowly grew dimmer, and Johannes Kepler recorded its brightness for a year. The object was called a "nova," which means new star in Latin. Objects that become as bright as the one Kepler saw are now called supernovas. Modern astronomers have proposed that these objects are not new stars, but old stars that have reached the end of their normal lives and have exploded.

Since 1604, no supernova has been seen that was close enough for astronomers to identify the star that had exploded. On February 23, 1987, astronomers in Chile noticed a bright spot of light in the fuzzy patch of light called the Large Magellenic Cloud, or LMC. The LMC is not actually a cloud, but is a nearby galaxy containing billions of stars. The LMC is far enough away that light takes 160 000 years to reach us. Training their telescopes on the LMC, the astronomers saw that one star was now brighter than all the other stars in the LMC put together.

Astronomers have now learned that the star that exploded was a blue giant, originally 100 000 times brighter than our sun, and 20 times its mass. While a star lives, fusion creates an outward force that is balanced by the inward force of gravity. As a star ages, hydrogen is converted to helium, carbon, oxygen, silicon, and finally iron. No further fusion is possible. At some point, the amount of iron in the center of the supernova became so large that fusion could no longer balance gravity. The core of the star collapsed. An object, once the size of the planet Mars, was squeezed into a ball only 70 kilometers in diameter. The nuclei of the atoms now were touching, and the repulsive force created a giant explosion. The explosion created a flash of ultraviolet light that has reached us 160 000 years later. It also formed a wave of matter that is spreading through the LMC. This matter will soon be part of other stars, and perhaps, even present or future planets.

Physicists in Ohio and Japan studying the particles that make up matter recorded a burst of neutrinos at the same time the explosion was seen. Neutrinos are uncharged, massless particles, produced when the core collapsed. They travel at the speed of light. Neutrinos from outside our own galaxy have never before been detected. This observation has added to knowledge about the supernova explosion.

As a result of seeing the death of this distant giant star, physicists and astronomers have gained greater understanding of how stars live and die.

Review

1. What is a synthetic element?
2. Which elements in the periodic table are synthetic?
3. How is a stable nucleus different from an unstable one?
4. In what ways are two isotopes the same? How are they different?
5. ★ What is the ratio of protons to neutrons in cobalt-60?

RADIOACTIVE DECAY

GOALS

1. You will study the particles that make up nuclear radiation.
2. You will learn how half-life is used by scientists.

Scientists who explored the particles emitted by radioactive elements found that some were charged positively, others negatively. Some were not charged at all. They named the particles after the first three letters in the Greek alphabet, alpha, beta, and gamma. Years later the true nature of these particles was discovered.

23:3 Nuclear Radiation

List the characteristics of alpha particles and beta particles.

There are three kinds of nuclear radiation that may be released from an unstable nucleus. They are alpha particles, beta particles, and gamma rays. An **alpha particle** is a helium nucleus with two protons and two neutrons.

$$^{4}_{2}\mathrm{He}$$

It has a positive charge because it has no electrons. An alpha particle does not have much power to penetrate matter. It can be stopped by a thin sheet of paper or after traveling through a few centimeters of air.

F.Y.I. Cosmic rays formerly were considered a special form of electromagnetic radiation. They are now known to be mostly high energy particles.

Beta particles are negatively-charged electrons.

$$^{0}_{-1}e$$

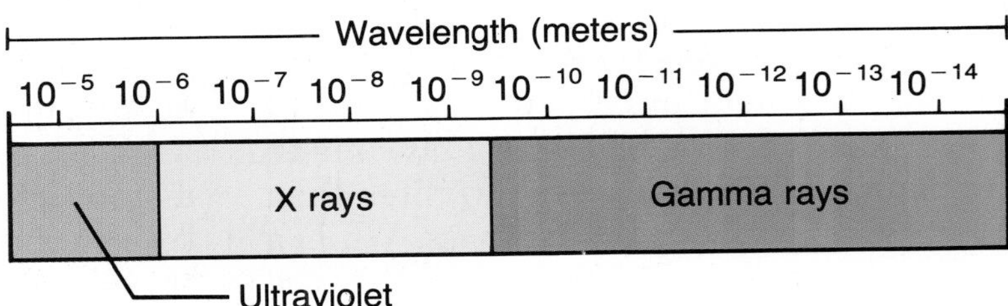

FIGURE 23–4. Gamma rays are part of the short-wavelength end of the electromagnetic spectrum.

Beta particles usually travel faster and farther than alpha particles. The penetrating power of beta particles is about 100 times greater than that of alpha particles. However, beta particles can be stopped by a sheet of aluminum one centimeter thick.

Gamma rays are not charged particles. They are electromagnetic waves of very short wavelength and high frequency. Like all electromagnetic waves, they travel at the speed of light. Gamma rays are more penetrating than either alpha or beta radiation. It takes dense materials, such as lead or concrete, to stop gamma rays.

BIOGRAPHY

Irene Joliot-Curie
1897–1956

Profoundly influenced by her mother, Nobel prize-winning physicist Marie Curie, Irene Joliet-Curie assisted her at the Radium Institute in Paris.

In 1921 Irene began her own research. By 1926 she and her husband were working on experiments with alpha particles. Together they won the Nobel prize in 1935 for the discovery of artificial radiation.

23:4 Decay and Half-Life

As a radioactive atom releases radiation from its nucleus, it decays to form an atom of another element. Uranium-238 decays through a series of nuclear changes to form stable lead-206.

Nuclear changes are completely different from chemical and physical changes. Chemical reactions involve changes in bonds formed by electrons. Nuclear reactions involve changes in the nucleus of an atom. The electrons in the electron cloud are not involved in nuclear reactions. In addition, a change in temperature or pressure does not affect a nuclear reaction.

What happens to radioactive atoms that have decayed? When the number of protons changes, the atom changes into an atom of another element. The decay of uranium-238 continues until lead-206 is formed. Notice that each step in the decay occurs at a different rate, which is expressed as the half-life.

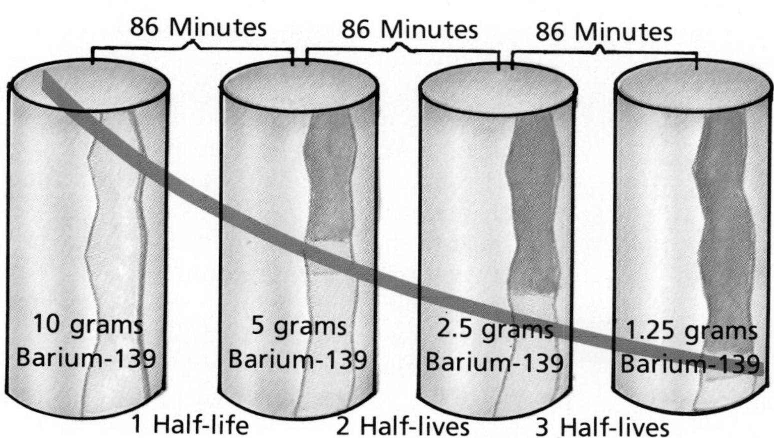

FIGURE 23–5. The mass of a radioactive barium nuclide is reduced by half during each half-life. The decayed mass eventually becomes a stable nuclide.

INVESTIGATION 23–1

Half-Life Simulation

Problem: How can coin-tossing simulate radioactive decay?

Materials

100 pennies
container with cover

Procedure

1. Place the 100 coins in the container and cover it. Shake vigorously for several seconds.
2. Gently pour the coins onto a desktop. Separate into piles with heads up and tails up.
3. Count the coins with heads up and record the number in the data table.
4. Put only the coins with heads up back into the container. Shake the container.
5. Repeat Steps 2, 3, and 4 until no more coins remain.

Data and Observations

Shake Number	Number of Heads

Analysis

1. Plot a graph of the shake number on the horizontal axis versus the number of heads remaining on the vertical axis.

FIGURE 23–6.

2. If you did this experiment with an extremely large number of coins, exactly half of the coins would be heads up each toss. Plot these idealized results on your graph.
3. Work with other members of your class to calculate the class number of heads remaining for each shake number. Plot a graph of these numbers in the same way you plotted your own results.
4. Plot the predicted class results on the same graph.

Conclusions

5. How many atoms are represented by the coins?
6. Are the represented atoms stable or are they unstable?
7. How many shakes represent one half-life?
8. Are there still unstable atoms after one half-life? After two or more half-lives?
9. Is a radioactive sample safe once it is one half-life old?
10. Compare the number of heads actually remaining to the idealized numbers on your graph. Were your results usually higher, usually lower, or about evenly divided between higher and lower?
11. Were the results obtained by adding the data from the entire class closer to the idealized numbers or farther away?

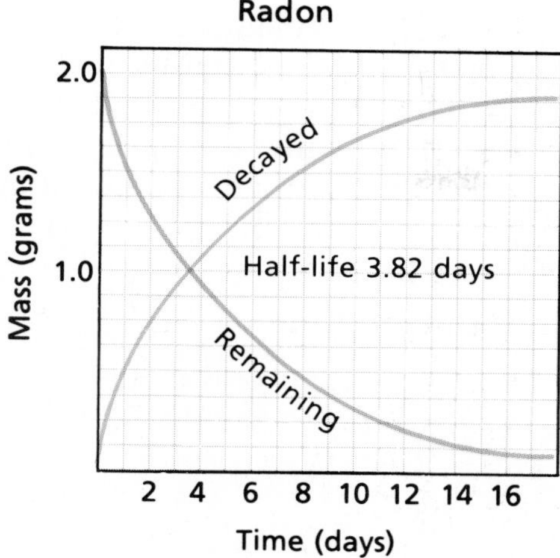

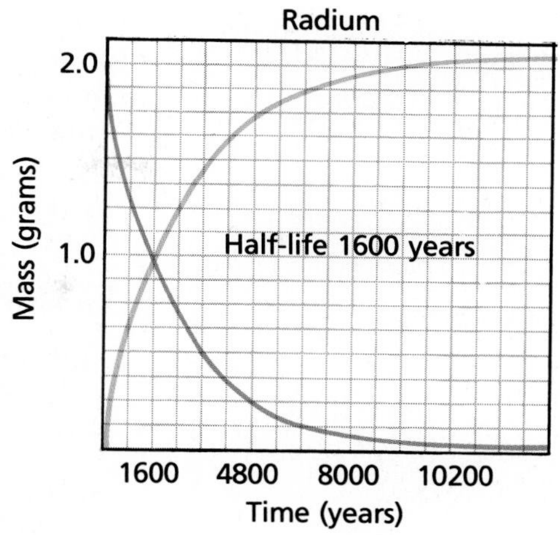

FIGURE 23–7. The shorter half-life of radon means it is less stable than radium.

Half-life is the time it takes for half of a sample of radioactive material to decay to form another nuclide. A half-life may be a fraction of a second or thousands of years. For example, barium-139 has a half-life of 86 minutes. Suppose you have ten grams of pure barium-139. After 86 minutes, half of the atoms would have experienced beta decay to form lanthanum-139. You would have 5 grams of barium-139 remaining. After another 86 minutes, one half of the remaining barium-139 atoms would have decayed to form lanthanum-139. You would then have 2.5 grams of barium-139 and 7.5 grams of lanthanum-139.

The half-life of some radioactive nuclides makes them useful in determining the age of very old objects such as rocks and fossils. For example, carbon-14, with a half-life of 5730 years, is used to determine the age of some fossils. Carbon-14 is formed in the atmosphere and becomes part of CO_2. While an animal or plant is alive, it respires CO_2 and thus, maintains a constant level of carbon-14. When the animal or plant dies, it no longer brings in new CO_2, and the carbon-14 level decreases

F.Y.I. Other dating methods with longer half-lives such as K $\rightarrow$ Ar and U $\rightarrow$ Th, are employed to find the age of objects such as rocks, not suitable for carbon-14 dating.

Table 23–2

Half-Life of Some Radioactive Elements

Element	Half-life
polonium-214	0.001 second
radon-222	3.82 days
radium-226	1600 years
uranium-238	4 500 000 000 years

over time. In carbon dating, the amount of carbon-14 in a small sample of material is calculated by measuring the beta radiation it emits. Carbon-14 dating is only usable on objects that were once living. Furthermore, very old objects may have too little carbon-14 remaining to be detected.

EXAMPLE **Half-Life Calculation**

Radium-226 has a half-life of 1600 years. How much of a 40-gram sample of this nuclide should be left after 4800 years?

Solution:

a. Divide the age by the half-life. This answer is the number of half-lives.

$$\frac{4800 \text{ y}}{1600 \text{ y/half-life}} = 3 \text{ half-lives}$$

b. Reduce the mass by half 3 times.

$$\tfrac{1}{2} \times 40 \text{ g} = 20 \text{ g}$$

$$\tfrac{1}{2} \times 20 \text{ g} = 10 \text{ g}$$

$$\tfrac{1}{2} \times 10\text{g} = 5 \text{ g}$$

Thus, 5 g of radium-226 are left and 35 g have decayed to another nuclide.

PRACTICE PROBLEM

1. How much of a 100.0 gram sample of radon-222 would be left after 7.64 days?

Review

6. What do the 4 and 2 stand for in the symbol of the alpha particle ${}^{4}_{2}He$?

7. Compare the penetrating power of gamma rays, alpha particles, and beta particles.

8. Why does the decay process for uranium stop at lead-206?

9. How much of a 10.0 g sample of barium-139 is left after 4 hours and 18 min?

★ **10.** Wood from a modern campfire has 20 mg of carbon-14. An equal-sized sample of a fossil campfire is found with 5 mg of carbon-14. How old is the fossil campfire?

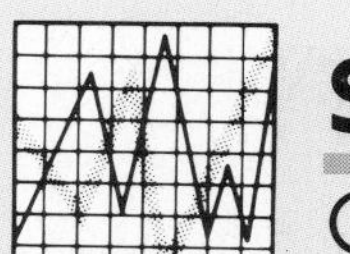

SKILL
Carbon-14 Dating

Problem: How do scientists use carbon-14 dating?

Materials

paper and pencil

Procedure

1. To find the age of a specimen, multiply the number of half-lives by the half-life for C-14, 5370 years. The result is the age of the specimen. Example: the ratio of C-14 to C-12 indicates two half-lives; 2 × 5370 years = 10 740 years.
2. To find the number of half-lives, divide the half-life of the specimen by the half-life of C-14. Example: age = 10 740 years, half-life = 5370 years, thus, $\frac{10\ 740\ \text{y}}{5370\ \text{y/half-life}}$ = 2 half-lives.

Data and Observations

Number of Half-lives	Age of Specimen
1	5370
2	10 740

Questions

1. Copy the table in your notebook. Complete the table by determining the number of half-lives or age of specimen.
2. An archeologist predicted that the age of recently discovered animal remains was approximately 35 000 years. How can the accuracy of this prediction be tested?
3. Refer to Figure 23–8. Determine how much of the C-14 has decayed to complete statements a., b., and c. in the figure.

FIGURE 23–8.

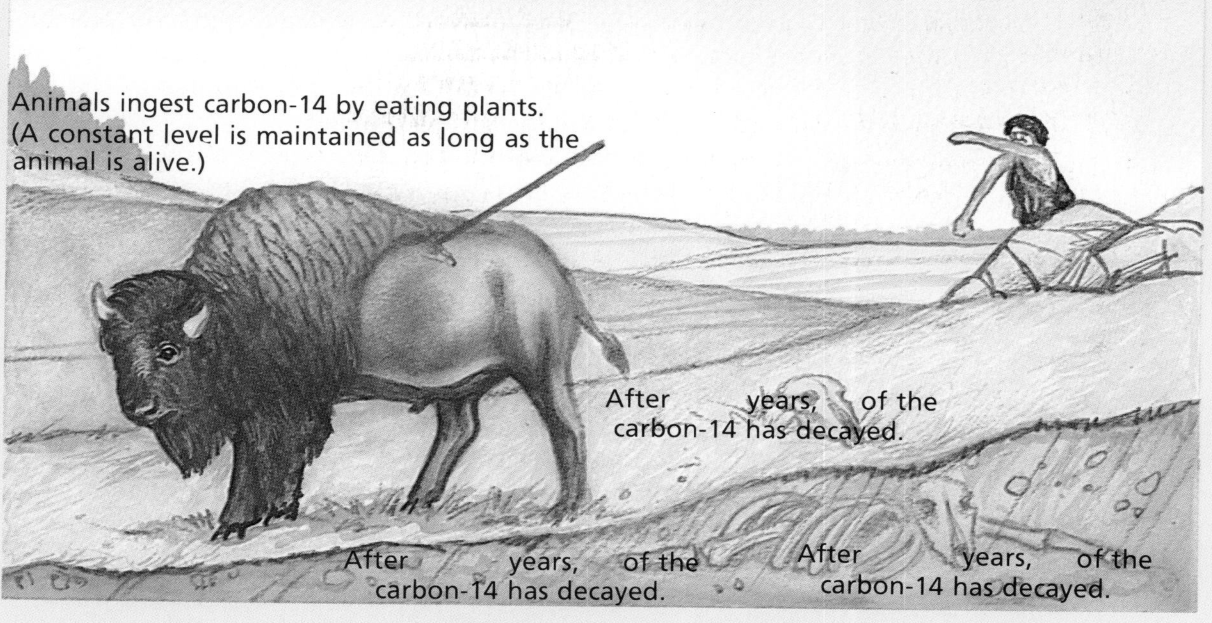

DETECTING RADIOACTIVITY

GOALS

1. You will examine several radiation detectors.
2. You will learn how a Geiger counter works.

Alpha, beta, and gamma radiation cannot be seen, heard, tasted, smelled, or felt. However, it is possible to detect its presence. One way to detect radioactivity is with an electroscope.

23:5 Radiation Detectors

F.Y.I. The thick layer forming a nuclear emulsion sometimes is called a "frozen cloud chamber." The emulsion is a colloid rather than a gas or liquid.

Radiation produces ions when it passes through matter. These ions will discharge a charged electroscope. As the charge is lost, the leaves of the electroscope drop. The greater the radioactivity, the more rapid the discharge.

Radiation can be detected with a cloud chamber. A **cloud chamber** detects charged nuclear particles because they leave cloud tracks. A cloud track is a line of condensed water vapor formed along a particle's path. It is similar to the vapor trail of a high-flying jet.

One kind of cloud chamber contains air supersaturated with water vapor. The supersaturated vapor is unstable and will condense easily. When a charged particle passes through the chamber, it produces a trail of ions. Tiny drops of water condense around ions, making a cloud track. A beta particle forms a long thin track. The track of an alpha particle is shorter and fatter.

FIGURE 23–9. A radioactive source will discharge an electroscope.

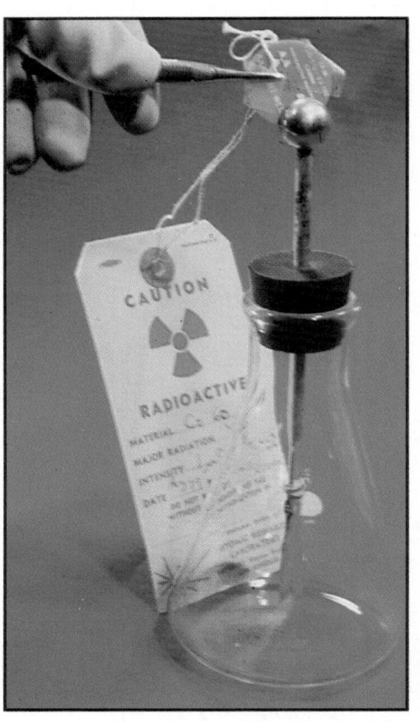

A **bubble chamber** is filled with a superheated liquid. A superheated liquid is hot enough to boil, but remains in the liquid state. A charged particle passing through the chamber produces ions. The liquid boils at the location of the ions. The lines of bubbles in the liquid are used to track the particle.

Charged particles can be detected by a nuclear emulsion. A **nuclear emulsion** is a thick layer of the coating used on photographic film and print paper. The emulsion contains grains of silver bromide, AgBr. Charged particles cause a chemical reaction in the silver bromide grains in the emulsion. The effect is like the exposure of film to light when a picture is made. When the emulsion is developed, the path of the nuclear particle appears as a dark track. Nuclear particles travel relatively short distances because the emulsion is very dense. Nuclear tracks are a few millimeters or less in length. Because they are so short, the tracks are studied with a microscope.

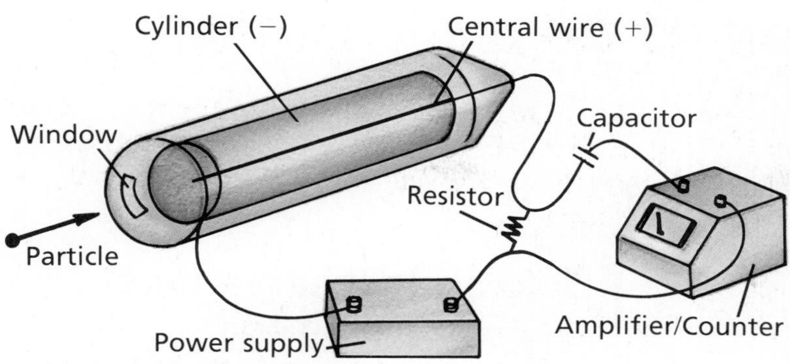

a

b

FIGURE 23–10. A radioactive source will cause the gas in a Geiger-Müller tube to ionize (a). A Geiger counter is used to find the intensity of radiation (b).

How does a Geiger counter detect radiation?

23:6 Radiation Counters

A **Geiger counter** detects radiation by means of the formation of an electric current. The current is formed in a Geiger-Müller tube. The tube contains a gas such as argon or helium at reduced pressure. Inside the tube is a copper cylinder, Figure 23–10a. A fine tungsten wire runs down the center of the copper cylinder. The wire and the metal cylinder are connected to an electric circuit. A thin window at the end of the tube allows radiation to enter.

When radiation passes through the gas in the tube, ions are produced. For example, when a beta particle enters through the window, it frees a few electrons from the gas atoms. The atoms become positively-charged ions. These positive ions are attracted to the negative wall of the cylinder (cathode). The free electrons are attracted to the positive wire in the center of the tube (anode). The flow of electrons to the wire produces a surge of current that is amplified and fed into recording or counting devices. A small lamp or speaker may be used as a counting device.

Review

11. Why is it necessary that the water vapor in a cloud chamber be supersaturated?

12. Name three ways radiation can be detected.

13. What are the advantages of using a Geiger counter for detecting radiation compared to an electroscope?

14. Explain how an electroscope is used to detect nuclear radiation.

★ **15.** How does a Geiger counter work?

INVESTIGATION 23–2

Radiation Protection

Problem: How can you protect yourself from radiation?

Materials

paper and pencil

Background

The amount of radiation absorbed by the body is measured in rem (Roentgen-equivalent-man) units. Present government regulations state that workers should receive no more than 100 mrem (milli-rem) each month. Geiger counters usually record radioactivity in mrem/h (milli-rem per hour).

Procedure

1. Jack, who works with radioactive isotopes in a hospital, is planning to handle a shipment due next week. He is told that the isotope will be in a jar. At the surface of the jar, a Geiger counter records 600 mrem/h activity. Record in Data Table 1 the amount of radiation Jack would receive from the jar after 1 minute, 2 minutes, and so on up to 10 minutes.
2. Jack is told that the Geiger counter records 400 mrem/h when it is 20 mm from the jar, 100 mrem/h when it is 60 mm from the jar, and 25 mrem/h when it is 140 mm away. Record in Data Table 2 the amount of radiation Jack would receive if he were each of these distances away from the jar for a total of 1 minute, 10 minutes, and 1 hour.
3. Jack knows that he can shield the isotope by surrounding it with lead. He knows that 10 mm of lead reduces the Geiger counter reading to one half its original amount. Each additional 10 mm will reduce the reading by another factor of 2. Fill in Data Table 3, showing the reading on the counter when it is 60 mm from the jar for each amount of lead.

Data and Observations

Data Table 1

Time (min)	Amount of Radiation
1	
2	
3	

Data Table 2

Distance (mm)	Amount of Radiation		
	1 min	10 min	1 hour
20			
60			
140			

Data Table 3

Pb Thickness (mm)	Geiger Counter Reading (mrem/h)
10	
20	
30	

Analysis and Conclusions

1. How many minutes could Jack hold the jar each month without receiving an overdose of radiation?
2. How many hours could Jack be 140 mm away from the jar in each month?
3. How many hours could Jack be 60 mm away from the jar each month if the entire 60 mm were filled with lead?
4. Summarize your conclusions by listing three methods of protecting a person against radioactivity.

NUCLEAR REACTIONS

GOALS

1. You will understand the process of nuclear fission.
2. You will learn what is involved in a thermonuclear reaction.

Radioactive decay releases some energy, but a great deal more energy can be released if the nucleus undergoes greater changes. One such change involves the splitting of the nucleus into two pieces. Another is to join two smaller nuclei together into one. The first such reaction is called fission, the second fusion.

23:7 Fission

What changes occur during nuclear fission?

Some radioactive nuclei undergo a reaction that is more violent than emitting an alpha or beta particle or a gamma ray. They split into two new nuclei. This reaction is called **nuclear fission.** Fission means to divide. Elements having atomic numbers greater than 90 can undergo fission. Uranium is one such element. In nuclear fission, the nucleus of an atom breaks up into two roughly equal pieces.

While some nuclei undergo fission spontaneously, others only split when struck by another particle. When uranium-235 is bombarded with a beam of slowly moving neutrons, its nucleus may split into two pieces and also emit one or more neutrons. In one reaction, barium-144 and krypton-90 are formed and two neutrons are released.

$$^{235}_{92}\text{U} + ^{1}_{0}n \rightarrow ^{144}_{56}\text{Ba} + ^{90}_{36}\text{Kr} + 2^{1}_{0}n$$

The mass of the ^{144}Ba, ^{90}Kr, and 2n is slightly less than that of the original ^{235}U + 1n. This missing mass has been converted into kinetic energy of the fission particles. A large amount of energy is released in nuclear fission.

Uranium-235 can also divide to produce other products. Note that in each case different numbers of extra neutrons are produced.

$$^{235}_{92}\text{U} + ^{1}_{0}n \rightarrow ^{90}_{37}\text{Rb} + ^{144}_{55}\text{Cs} + 2^{1}_{0}n$$

$$^{235}_{92}\text{U} + ^{1}_{0}n \rightarrow ^{87}_{35}\text{Br} + ^{146}_{57}\text{La} + 3^{1}_{0}n$$

$$^{235}_{92}\text{U} + ^{1}_{0}n \rightarrow ^{72}_{30}\text{Zn} + ^{160}_{62}\text{Sm} + 4^{1}_{0}n$$

Fission of uranium atoms may result in a chain reaction. A nuclear chain reaction is a rapid series of nuclear fissions. Even a small sample of uranium contains billions of atoms. When one uranium-235 nucleus is split by a neutron, it may release two neutrons. The two neutrons may cause two more uranium nuclei to split.

F.Y.I. The relationship between mass and energy is expressed in Einstein's famous equation, $E = m \times c^2$, where c equals the speed of light, 3×10^8 m/s.

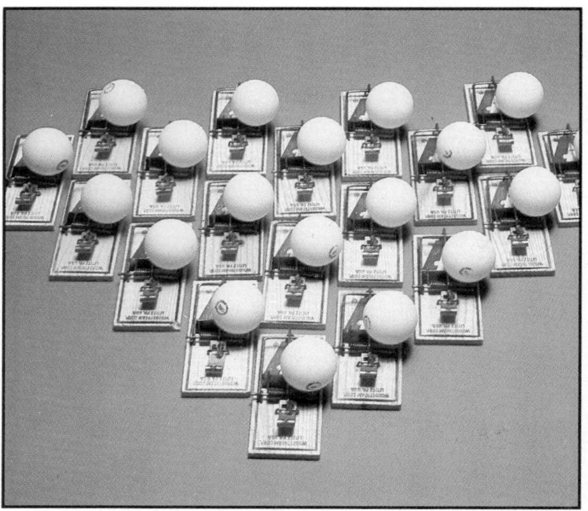

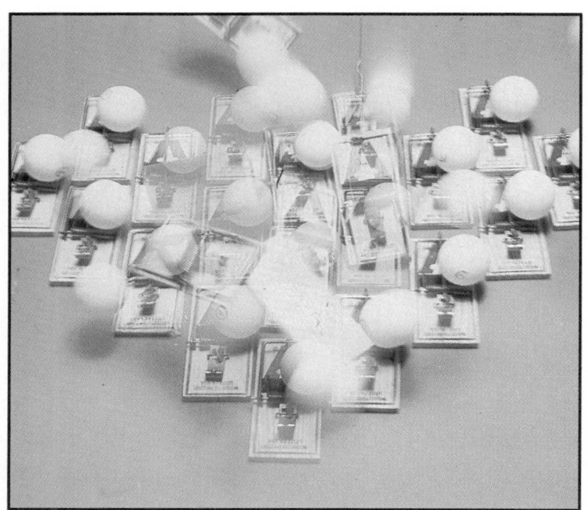

FIGURE 23–11. Mousetraps and table tennis balls can be used as a model to show what occurs during a chain reaction.

Each fission produces two more neutrons. These neutrons may be captured by four more nuclei causing them to split. The fission of nuclei and release of neutrons becomes a chain reaction. In a chain reaction, billions of fission reactions may occur each second.

23:8 Fusion

What changes occur during nuclear fusion?

Another important reaction that certain light elements can undergo is fusion. Nuclear fusion is the opposite of nuclear fission. **Fusion** occurs when two low mass nuclei are joined together to form one nucleus. Elements with small masses combine to form elements with larger masses. An element such as hydrogen can undergo fusion. Hydrogen has the smallest mass of all the elements.

FIGURE 23–12. Fusion reactions occur in the sun and other stars. Tremendous temperatures are needed for nuclei to fuse.

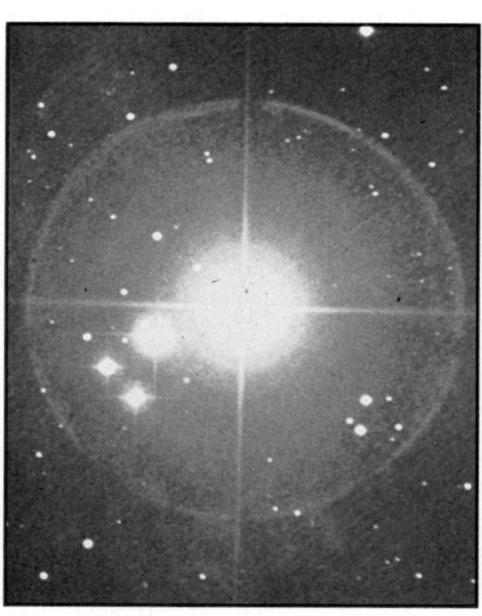

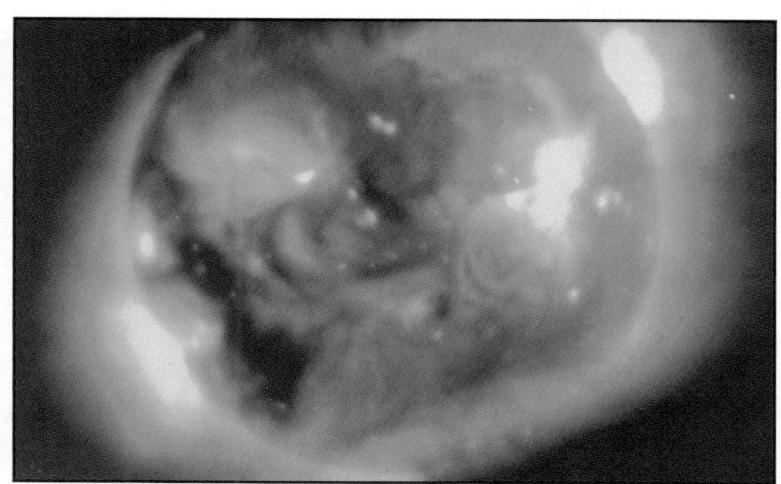

For nuclear fusion to occur, temperatures well over a million degrees Celsius must be reached. Nuclear fusion is called a **thermonuclear reaction.** *Thermo* refers to heat. At the tremendous temperatures of thermonuclear reactions, neutral atoms no longer exist. The atoms lose their electrons, ionize, and become plasma. Plasma is the state of matter consisting of nuclei, or positive ions, and free electrons. The nuclei have enough kinetic energy to overcome forces of repulsion between them.

Where does nuclear fusion occur naturally?

The temperature conditions needed for fusion to occur exist in the sun and stars. The sun has an internal temperature of about 20 000 000°C. In the sun, four hydrogen nuclei are fused into one helium nucleus in a series of reactions. Thus, the sun is constantly converting hydrogen to helium. Each helium atom that is formed has a mass almost one percent less than the mass of the four hydrogen atoms. This one percent mass loss is converted to energy. A tremendous amount of energy is released by the conversion of mass into energy. Much of it is converted into electromagnetic radiation by the atoms at the surface of the sun.

Light and other forms of electromagnetic energy from nuclear fusion travel 150 million kilometers from the sun to Earth. The energy that reaches Earth is only a tiny fraction of the total energy released by the sun. The rest spreads out into space.

How is nuclear fusion useful to scientists?

The fusion process gives scientists information about the history and composition of our sun and other stars. A prism or diffraction grating produces a spectrum from the light given off by the sun. Because each element has its own special spectrum, analysis of this spectrum shows the chemical composition of the sun. From the chemical composition of a star, it is possible to get some indication of its age. A star that is composed of mostly hydrogen is a young star. As a star gets older, its hydro-

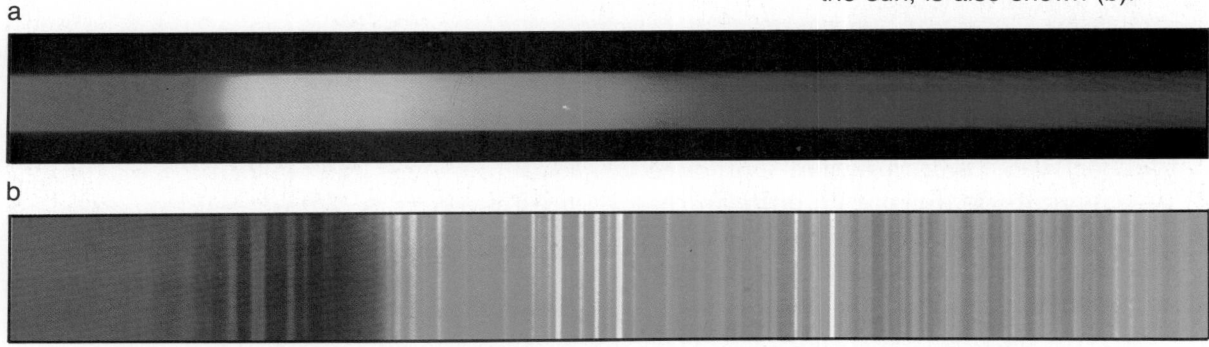

FIGURE 23–13. The continuous spectrum of the sun (a) can be used to determine its composition. The spectrum of hydrogen, the most abundant element on the sun, is also shown (b).

gen is converted into helium. The sun is a middle-aged star, and contains mostly hydrogen, with a little helium. Through nuclear reactions, more helium will be produced. Since there is so much hydrogen, the sun is expected to keep burning for another five billion years.

The production of heavier elements such as carbon, oxygen, silicon, and iron occurs in the later stages of a star's life. Very heavy elements, heavier than iron, are produced only when a very old star explodes. The sun and its whole solar system contain elements produced in stars that have been born, lived, and exploded in death, even before the sun was born!

Review

16. In what way are neutrons produced in the fission of uranium?

17. What is a chain reaction? Describe one example.

18. How are hydrogen nuclei changed in a nuclear fusion reaction?

19. What evidence shows that nuclear fusion reactions occur in the sun and stars?

★ **20.** Why is the amount of helium in the sun increasing?

PROBLEM SOLVING

A Problem From the Past

Your social studies class is studying about the above-ground tests of nuclear weapons in the 1940s and 1950s. You learn that the radioactive isotope strontium-90 was produced and are concerned about what effects of the test might still remain. You decide to research strontium-90 to find the type of radioactive contamination produced and its half-life. Prepare a bulletin that will alert any particular group of people that might need to be aware of ^{90}Sr contamination.

Chapter 23 Review

SUMMARY

1. While many radioactive nuclides occur in nature, others are made in the laboratory. 23:1, 23:2
2. Alpha and beta particles and gamma rays are released by nuclei of radioactive elements. 23:3
3. An alpha particle is a positively charged helium nucleus containing two protons and two neutrons. 23:3
4. A beta particle is a high-speed electron emitted from a nucleus. It has a negative charge. 23:3
5. Gamma rays are high-frequency electromagnetic radiation. 23:3
6. Half-life is a measure of the time required for a radioactive element to decay. 23:4
7. Radiation can be detected with an electroscope, Geiger counter, cloud chamber, bubble chamber, or nuclear emulsion. 23:5, 23:6
8. Nuclear fission is the splitting of heavier nuclei into two lighter nuclei with the emission of neutrons. 23:7
9. A fusion reaction combines two low-mass nuclei to form one heavier nucleus. 23:8

VOCABULARY

a. alpha particle
b. beta particle
c. bubble chamber
d. cloud chamber
e. fusion
f. gamma rays
g. Geiger counter
h. half-life
i. nuclear emulsion
j. nuclear fission
k. nuclide
l. radioactive decay
m. synthetic elements
n. thermonuclear reaction

Matching

Match each description with the correct vocabulary word from the list above. Some words will not be used.

1. a negatively charged particle emitted in radioactive decay
2. the nucleus of a specific isotope
3. reaction that combines two hydrogen atoms into a helium atom
4. a measure of the length of time a radioactive element exists before it decays
5. a detector of radiation that uses super-saturated vapor
6. the nuclear reaction in which a large nucleus splits into two smaller ones
7. a solid detector of radiation
8. elements not found in nature
9. a radiation counter
10. electromagnetic radiation emitted during radioactive decay

MAIN IDEAS

A. Reviewing Concepts

Choose the word or phrase that correctly completes each of the following sentences.

1. A nuclear chain reaction may be produced when a uranium-235 nucleus is split by a(n) ____________.
2. In the nuclear decay series, uranium finally becomes ____________.
3. A beta particle has a ____________ charge.
4. A(n) ____________ is an instrument that produces bursts of electric current when struck by nuclear radiation.
5. Silver bromide is a chemical in a(n) ____________ used to detect radioactivity.

Complete each of the following sentences with the correct word or phrase.

6. For low-mass elements, as the proton-neutron ratio approaches one, the stability of a nucleus *(remains the same, increases, decreases, does not exist).*
7. A helium nucleus is the same as a(n) *(alpha particle, neutron, beta particle, gamma ray).*
8. Electromagnetic radiation released in radioactive decay is *(alpha particles, neutrons, beta particles, gamma rays).*
9. In nuclear fusion, two or more nuclei *(unite, split, decay, break apart).*
10. A fast electron emitted by a nucleus is a(n) *(alpha particle, neutron, beta particle, gamma ray).*

Determine whether each of the following sentences is true or false. If it is false, change the underlined word to make the sentence true.

11. The change of uranium to lead is an example of <u>a fusion reaction</u>.
12. A beta particle <u>is neutral</u>.
13. Carbon-12 is a <u>stable</u> nuclide.
14. <u>Fusion</u> occurs in the sun and other stars.
15. <u>Fusion</u> is the splitting of the nucleus of an atom.

B. Understanding Concepts

Answer the following questions using complete sentences when possible.

16. Compare the number of protons and neutrons in a uranium nucleus.
17. Is the change of uranium to lead an example of fission, fusion, or radioactive decay?
18. Which radiation, alpha, beta, or gamma, would be attracted toward a positively charged plate?
19. What kind of material would you use to shield against possible particles from radioactive decay?
20. What are some common uses of radioactive isotopes?
21. Fluorine-18, with a half-life of 110 minutes, is used in some medical tracing applications. You are able to trace the fluorine until all but 1/8 of it has decayed. Approximately how long can you do the tracing?
22. What force holds protons and neutrons together in the nucleus?
23. Consider two fission reactions of uranium-235. One produces barium-144, krypton-90, and 2 extra neutrons. The other results in zinc-72, samarium-160, and 4 neutrons. Which would produce a faster chain reaction? Why?
24. The spectra of two stars are examined. One shows mostly hydrogen, while the second has lines produced by carbon and silicon. Which is older?
25. An old star, about to supernova, has a core of iron. In which state of matter would the iron be? Why?

C. Applying Concepts

Answer the following questions, using complete sentences when possible.

26. How can you tell if an element is stable or radioactive?

27. Which nuclide would you expect to be more stable, oxygen-16 or oxygen-18? Explain why.

28. The number of radioactive decays that occurs in a second is called the activity of a nuclide. The number of decays is proportional to the number of radioactive atoms. Compare the activity of radon-222 today, and one half-life (3.82 days) later.

29. Would you expect the mass of a helium nucleus to be smaller than, equal to, or larger than the sum of the masses of the two protons and two neutrons that make it up? Why?

30. Someone has said that we are made up of the dust of dead stars. What is meant by this statement?

PROJECTS

1. Find out how radiation is used to treat diseases. Make a report to your class.

2. Read a biography of Marie Curie that describes her discovery of radium.

3. Make a report on the radioactive isotopes released in the Chernobyl reactor accident. Look up their half-lives to determine how long they may remain dangerous.

SKILL REVIEW

1. An article in a local newspaper claimed that carbon-14 dating had been used to determine the age of some animal bones that were recently excavated. The article claimed that the bones were 70 000 years old. Why is this age questionable?

2. How can the age of a specimen be determined if the ratio of carbon-14 to carbon-12 is known?

3. The age of a specimen was found to be 39 200 years. How many half-lives of carbon-14 have elapsed since the specimen died?

4. Why is it especially important to include units when recording meter readings?

5. The explosion of the Hindenburg dirigible was due to a spark igniting the hydrogen gas, which combined with the oxygen in the air. This reaction produces water and a great deal of energy. Write a balanced equation for the reaction.

READINGS

◆ **1.** Hawkes, Nigel. *Nuclear Power.* New York: Franklin Watts, 1984.

▲ **2.** Heppenheimer, T. A. *The Man-Made Sun.* Boston: Little, 1984.

● **3.** Stranahan, Susan Q. "Three Mile Island." *Science Digest.* June, 1985, pp. 54–57, 82–83, 87.

ENERGY USE TODAY
RENEWABLE ENERGY SOURCES
NUCLEAR ENERGY

Chapter 24

Energy Alternatives

Each time you turn on a lamp or ride in a car, it is likely that you are using energy from the sun. The car's engine burns fuel, releasing energy that first came from the sun. The electric current lighting the lamp may have been generated by burning coal. The coal contains stored energy from the sun. Our world is rapidly using its stored energy resources. How can the sun's energy be trapped and used directly? Are there any other resources available?

ENERGY USE TODAY

GOALS

1. You will learn the uses and limitations of fossil fuels.
2. You will become aware of methods of energy conservation.
3. You will understand the need for alternative energy sources.

You have probably heard of the "Energy Crisis" of the 1970's. Everyone said that the United States was "running out" of energy. How can you run out of a quantity that cannot be created or destroyed? Actually, energy is not "used," it is just changed into less useful forms, such as thermal energy. Our world is rapidly using its energy resources. What are these resources, and how do we make use of them?

24:1 Fossil Fuels

Name three fossil fuels.

About 90% of the total United States energy needs are met by fossil fuels. Coal, crude oil, and natural gas are **fossil fuels.** These materials are called fossil fuels because they are the remains of plants and animals that lived a long time ago. The energy in fossil fuels originally came from the sun. Fossil fuels are the main fuels used for transportation and heat, and to generate electricity. When fossil fuels are burned, stored chemical energy is changed to thermal energy.

What is petroleum?

Crude oil is another name for **petroleum.** This thick black liquid is obtained from wells drilled deep into the ground. Much of our petroleum comes from wells in the

Table 24–1

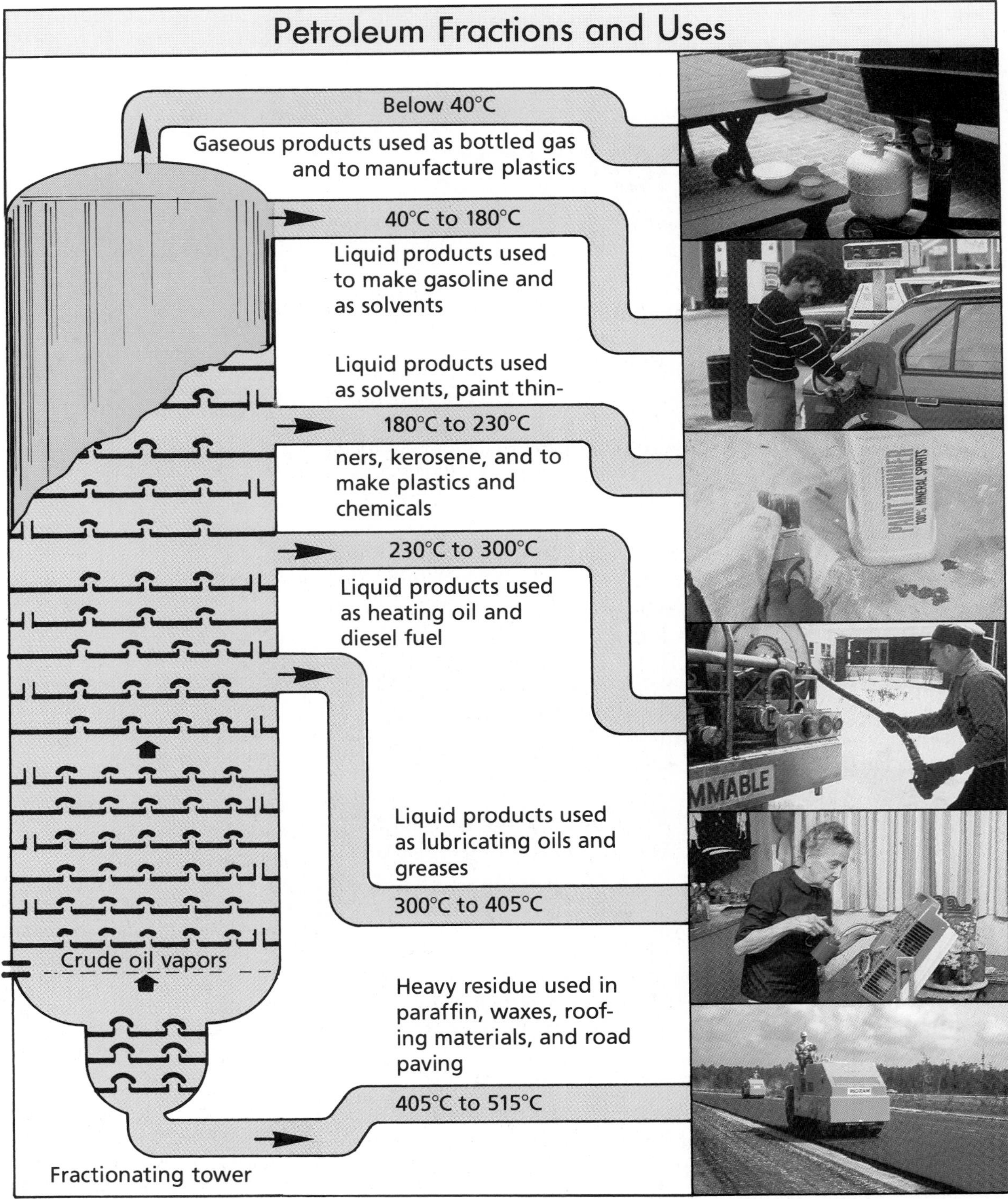
Petroleum Fractions and Uses
Below 40°C
Gaseous products used as bottled gas and to manufacture plastics
40°C to 180°C
Liquid products used to make gasoline and as solvents
Liquid products used as solvents, paint thin-
180°C to 230°C
ners, kerosene, and to make plastics and chemicals
230°C to 300°C
Liquid products used as heating oil and diesel fuel
Liquid products used as lubricating oils and greases
300°C to 405°C
Heavy residue used in paraffin, waxes, roof-ing materials, and road paving
405°C to 515°C
Crude oil vapors
Fractionating tower
PAINT THINNER
100% MINERAL SPIRITS
MMABLE

CAREER

Environmental Health Technician

Dan Clark could not understand why the new trash burning plant built in his hometown was considered cleaner and safer than the old landfill. All the smoke he saw and smelled seemed much worse than just piling the trash at a place he never went near.

One day when his class visited the plant, he learned that this method of getting rid of trash was much cheaper and better than the physical decaying of the trash at the landfill.

It was because of this initial visit that Dan decided to become an environmental health technician. He learned how to perform chemical analyses on samples of food, water, and air to make sure that legal standards of sanitation and purity were being followed. Dan now assists engineers and health agencies in promoting a healthy environment. He enjoys providing people a cleaner, and more healthful place to live.

For career information, write

National Health Council
70 W. 40th Street
New York, New York 10018

United States. A large supply also comes from other countries. Crude oil provides about 42% of all the energy used in the United States.

How is petroleum separated?

Petroleum is a mixture of hydrocarbons. The mixture is separated by a method called **fractional distillation.** Each of the hydrocarbons in the mixture has a different boiling point. The mixture is heated, and as the temperature increases, each fraction changes to a vapor and is collected separately, Table 24–1. Gasoline, heating fuel, diesel fuel, and other transportation fuels are major products produced from petroleum. Other products include solvents, lubricating oils and greases, and raw materials for making many plastics, paints, and synthetic fibers.

Write the equation for the burning of methane.

Natural gas is methane, CH_4. Almost all the natural gas burned in the United States is used for heating, cooking, and industrial processes. Like petroleum, natural gas is obtained from wells. It is transported through pipelines.

When natural gas or petroleum products are burned, the carbon and hydrogen in the fuel molecules combine with oxygen in the air. The substances produced are carbon dioxide and water. In addition, energy is released as thermal energy and light. The following equation shows how methane, a typical hydrocarbon, burns.

$$CH_4(g) + 2O_2(g) \longrightarrow CO_2(g) + 2H_2O(l) + \text{energy}$$
$$\text{methane} + \text{oxygen} \rightarrow \text{carbon dioxide} + \text{water} + \text{energy}$$

FIGURE 24–1. One advantage of natural gas is that it can be pumped through pipes to distant users.

BIOGRAPHY

Jose V. Martinez

1932–

Jose Martinez is the chief physicist for the Department of Energy, where he supervises atomic energy research. In 1986, he was named one of the five outstanding Hispanic employees in government service by the Office of Personnel Management. He has been president of the Society for the Advancement of Chicanos in Science, and has appeared on the program, 3-2-1 Contact, for public television.

Natural gas is a "clean fuel." This means it usually burns completely, producing little air pollution. Petroleum fuels, however, often do not burn completely, especially when used in engines. This results in air pollution. The incomplete burning gives off unburned fuel vapors and carbon monoxide. In addition, the high temperatures of burning cause some of the nitrogen in the air to combine with oxygen to produce oxides of nitrogen. These oxides are acidic anhydrides and become acids when combined with the moisture in the air.

About 93% of the world's fuel reserve is coal, the compressed remains of ancient plants. Although coal is mainly carbon, it often contains sulfur impurities. When coal burns, the sulfur reacts with oxygen to form sulfur oxides. These oxides also form acids when combined with the moisture in air. In addition, burning coal often produces smoke, small particles of unburned carbon. Coal is used mainly to generate electricity.

Why is coal an important energy resource?

24:2 Energy Conservation

Energy conservation is the wise and careful use of energy resources. To conserve energy means to use an energy resource more efficiently and not to waste it. Most of the energy we use ends up as low-temperature thermal energy that cannot be converted to any useful form. It is usually lost to the air. In addition, many of the energy resources we use are nonrenewable. A **nonrenewable resource** is one that cannot be replaced after it is used. Fossil fuels such as coal, oil, and natural gas are examples of nonrenewable resources.

How is a renewable resource different from a nonrenewable resource?

What kind of fuels are our main energy resources?

Fossil fuels will probably be our main source of energy for many years. For this reason, it is important to use them wisely. A major use of fossil fuels is to transport goods and people. One way to save energy is to make trucks and cars with engines that burn fuel more completely. Another is to reduce our use of inefficient forms of transportation. Using car pools and public transportation can make travel more efficient.

Energy used to warm and cool buildings can be saved by keeping them cooler in winter and warmer in summer. Insulating homes and other buildings saves energy by cutting down heat loss in winter and heat gain in summer. Many newer appliances such as late-model refrigerators and televisions use energy more efficiently than older ones.

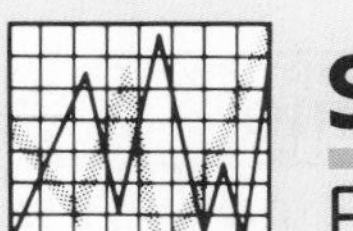

Skill

Evaluating Scientific Literature

Problem: How do you evaluate the reliability of scientific literature?

Background

Not all of the information that we read is presented honestly or accurately. In order to make informed decisions, you must be able to evaluate critically the information you read to make sure that the information is not only accurate, but that it is not biased or slanted to one particular view. Use the following guidelines to determine if the scientific information you read is reliable.

Procedure

1. Check the background of the author. Most articles written in journals or magazines give a brief biographical sketch of the author. If the person is writing about nuclear physics, is he or she a professional in that field, or is he or she trained in another unrelated field? See if the author has earned awards in that field, such as the Nobel Prize, or awards from any of the major scientific societies. Also check to see if the author has other related publications.
2. Check the source of the article. Has the article been written for a scientific journal like *Scientific American,* or has the article appeared in a popular magazine or local newspaper? If you are looking for specific information on a scientific topic, scientific journals will provide you with more current and complete information on that topic. Your teacher or a reference librarian can help you determine the credibility of your reference source.
3. Evaluate the emotional level of the information. Scientific information is generally written in a straightforward style. When you read an article, consider these questions: Is the information presented in such a way as to elicit emotions? Does the headline or title make you angry, sad, or happy?
4. Read the article for content presentation. Check to see that concepts are clearly explained and supported by research. Be wary if extensive conclusions are drawn from only one limited experiment. Also watch for overuse of such comments as "I think," or "In my opinion."
5. Determine whether the information has been taken out of context. Is the scientist writing the article or has someone reinterpreted the experimenter's comments? When a person is quoted, it is possible that only parts of the comments are reported. The information left out may change your own interpretation of the article significantly. Also, if the author is quoting another source, he or she may only select information from the source that supports his or her viewpoint.

Questions

1. Read the following headlines. Which one do you think would contain more reliable information?

   Strange Fish Kill Has Public Upset

   Scientists Investigate the Death of Fish in Plum River
2. Which of the following three periodicals would be the best source of information for the situations below?

   Sierra Club *Consumer Reports* *Science News*

   a. You want to know which detergent will clean your clothes the best.
   b. You want to know what new compounds are being used in making detergents.
   c. You want to know what effect phosphate detergents have on the environment.
3. Why is it important to know in what context a statement is made when you read information that quotes someone's remarks?

Table 24–2

Recommendations to Conserve Energy in the Home
Take short showers to use less hot water. Insulate the water heater if possible.
Use insulated draperies. Heat or cool only those areas of the house that are in use.
Set the thermostat at 20°C in winter and at 25°C in summer. Change to a thermostat controlled by a timer.
Use the dishwasher, washing machine, and clothes dryer only with full loads.
Use energy-efficient appliances. Air-dry dishes and clothes when possible.
Check the weather stripping and caulking around windows and doors.
Turn off all lights and appliances when they are not needed.
Close the damper on a fireplace when it is not in use. Find and seal air leaks.
Add insulation if necessary. A minimum of 15 cm is recommended above the ceiling.

F.Y.I. The energy content of various fuels and foods is surprisingly constant. Coal contains 29 MJ/kg; gasoline, 44 MJ/kg; wood, 14 MJ/kg; and butter, 10 MJ/kg. 1 megajoule (MJ) = 1 000 000 joules

Using other, or alternative, energy resources reduces our need for fossil fuels. These alternative resources include solar energy, nuclear energy, and energy from wind and water. The supply of fossil fuels will last longer if we develop and use other energy sources. However, until other sources of energy can be developed, our best resource is conservation.

24:3 The Need for Alternatives

What are the advantages of a fuel gas made of coal?

Using alternative fuels can help conserve nonrenewable resources such as oil and natural gas. Different kinds of fuels can be made from coal, plants, and other sources of hydrocarbons. For example, fuel gas can be

TECHNOLOGY: ADVANCES

Solar-Powered Automobiles

In the fall of 1987, 24 automobiles held the first transcontinental road race for solar-powered vehicles. The cars raced 3000 km from the north to the south coast of Australia. The winning car, Sunraycer, completed the course in five and a half days.

Computers were used to design Sunraycer's shape to reduce air resistance. The eight square meters of solar cells that power it are made of gallium-arsenide rather than silicon. Its electric motors, which use lightweight alloys containing neodymium, are 92% efficient. The Sunraycer can travel at a constant 110 km/h, although during the race its average speed was 67 km/h.

Will we see Sunraycers in use soon? The car has no energy storage, so it can run only when the sun is shining. In addition, although sunlight is free, the car cost well over three million dollars.

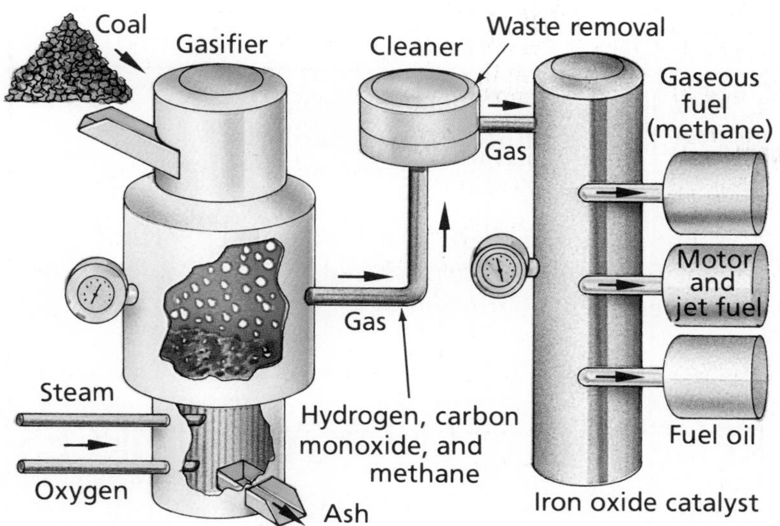

FIGURE 24–2. The process of gasification can make coal more practical by changing it to a gaseous fuel that can be sent through pipelines.

made from coal. The coal is heated to a high temperature under high pressure. Steam is then passed over the hot coal. Carbon in the coal combines with hydrogen in the steam to form hydrocarbons. This process is called coal gasification. Although coal is fairly plentiful, it contains impurities and, being a solid, cannot be sent easily through pipelines. Gasification produces a cleaner fuel that can be pumped through pipelines. One disadvantage of gasification is that a large part of the coal's energy is lost in the conversion process. In addition, the fuel gas produced is currently much more expensive than natural gas.

List four alternative fuels.

A large amount of petroleum is trapped in rocks called oil shale. Huge amounts of oil shale are found in Colorado, Utah, and Wyoming. About one-half barrel of oil can be removed from one metric ton of oil shale by heating the rock to about 500°C. At present, producing oil from shale is expensive. The process also produces air and water pollution. Mining the vast quantities of oil shale needed would also damage the environment.

Alcohols such as methanol and ethanol can be used as clean-burning fuel. Wood, wood wastes, woody crop residues, and garbage can be heated without oxygen to produce methanol. Corn and other grains, as well as many kinds of plant material, can be fermented and distilled to yield ethanol. Fermenting is a process carried out by yeast or bacteria that converts starch, sugar, or cellulose to ethanol. Ethanol is now being added to some kinds of gasoline to make them burn more efficiently.

Review

1. How is a fuel gas made from coal?
2. How is oil obtained from oil shale?
3. What are three energy resources other than fossil fuels?
4. What are fossil fuels? Why are they important?
5. ★ List four substances produced by burning fossil fuels that cause air pollution.

RENEWABLE ENERGY SOURCES

GOALS

1. You will learn some uses for and methods of storing solar energy.
2. You will discover several alternative sources of energy.

Only the sun provides new energy for Earth. Fossil fuels are the result of energy from the sun in earlier times. Some alternative, or renewable, energy sources use the energy coming from the sun now.

24:4 Solar Energy

List four uses for solar energy.

Solar energy is radiation from the sun. For centuries it has been used to dry foods and evaporate salt water to obtain salt. One way to collect solar energy is by allowing it to warm water. The hot water can be piped into a house to be used for washing or heating. Greenhouses sometimes use solar energy to warm the air while the transparent walls and roof reduce loss of thermal energy by convection.

Under the best conditions, about 1.2 kilowatts of solar radiation strike each square meter of Earth's surface. This amount of power can light twenty 60-watt lamps. Because the sun is not directly overhead, nor does it shine 24 hours a day, the average value in the United States is only 177 watts per square meter. Large curved mirrors are sometimes used to collect the sunlight from a large area and focus it onto a small region to produce high temperatures. Solar energy systems also must have a means of storing energy for times when there is no sunlight. One storage method is to warm water or rocks in a storage container. The stored energy may be used when the sun is not shining.

FIGURE 24–3. This billboard operates on electricity supplied by the photovoltaic cells on top.

Most space satellites are powered by batteries that are kept charged with electricity produced by solar energy. The electricity is generated by panels of many photovoltaic cells. Similar panels are used to supply electricity in remote places on Earth.

Photovoltaic cells are also known as solar cells. They consist of a layer of the semiconductor, silicon. The silicon is coated on the front with a thin, transparent conducting film. The back is coated with a thicker conducting aluminum layer. When light strikes the cell, electrons flow between the two conducting layers producing an electric current in an external circuit.

Photovoltaic cells are only 10 to 15% efficient in converting the energy of sunlight to electric energy. At present, the cost of generating electricity with photovoltaic cells is much greater than the cost of generating electricity by burning coal.

F.Y.I. Although the rate at which solar energy enters the atmosphere is 1300 W/m^2, the amount that falls on the level ground, averaged over day and night, varies from 324 W/m^2 in El Paso, Texas, in July, to 29 W/m^2 in Seattle, Washington, in December.

24:5 Hydroelectricity

Hydroelectricity is electric current produced by falling water. Usually the water is stored behind a dam on a river. This stored water has potential energy. The water is allowed to fall through a turbine where it spins the turbine blades. The potential energy of the water is transformed into the kinetic energy of the spinning turbine. Rotation of the turbine turns a generator that produces electrical energy.

The energy in hydroelectricity depends indirectly on the sun. Sunlight warms water in the sea and evaporates it into the air. This water vapor rises, cools, forms clouds, and falls back to Earth as rain or snow. Because it is higher, water in rain or snow in the mountains has

FIGURE 24–4. The potential energy of water stored behind the dam can be used to generate electricity by allowing the water to flow through turbines.

greater potential energy than water at sea level. Over time, most of this water will run downhill to the sea. Along the way, it may pass through a hydroelectric plant. About one-half of the hydroelectricity in the United States is produced in the western part of the country. Here there are many mountains as well as heavy rain and snowfall.

What are some advantages of hydroelectric energy?

An important characteristic of hydroelectricity is that it produces almost no pollution and is lower in cost than other forms of energy. Only about one-tenth of the world's hydroelectric potential has been developed. In the United States, however, nearly all good hydroelectric sites have been developed. One drawback to hydroelectricity is that building a dam or changing the flow of a stream can harm the environment.

24:6 Wind Energy

How can the energy of the wind be stored?

What are some disadvantages of wind energy?

During the early part of this century, more than six million windmills were used in the United States to pump water. These windmills were eventually replaced by pumps run by electricity. Today, the cost of generating electricity by fossil fuels has increased. There are problems with producing electricity by nuclear energy, Sections 24:9 and 24:10. Therefore, there is renewed interest in the use of wind energy.

FIGURE 24–5. For efficiency, wind turbines must be concentrated in areas where the wind is steady. Some people object to their appearance.

Wind can provide a clean and safe source of energy. There are several kinds of wind energy systems. One type of system uses large propeller blades mounted on towers. The blades are connected to an electric generator. This arrangement is called a wind turbine. As wind blows, the propeller spins and the generator produces electricity. The kinetic energy of the wind is changed to electric energy.

Energy must be stored, to be used when the wind is not blowing. One storage method is to charge batteries. The stored battery energy is used when there is no wind. Another possible storage method is to use the electric energy to pump water into a reservoir. The water could then be released through a turbine on calm days to generate electricity.

Objections to wind energy include the unsightly appearance of large numbers of wind turbines concentrated in a windy area. Noise pollution from the turbines could also be a problem. Large metal wind turbines can also interfere with television reception and microwave communications.

INVESTIGATION 24–1

Solar Energy

Problem: How can solar energy be used for heating?

Materials

500-mL flask and stopper
strip of lightweight black construction paper, 1 cm × 25 cm
large magnifying lens
2 clear soda bottles
2 shoe boxes
aluminum foil
2 thermometers
3 toy balloons
colored soda bottle
clear plastic wrap

Procedure

1. Attach one balloon to the neck of each soda bottle. Cover one of the clear bottles with aluminum foil.
2. Place the bottles in bright sunlight for 20 minutes. Predict the effect the light will have on the bottles. Record your observations in the Data Table.
3. Lay a thermometer in the bottom of each shoe box. Put the cover on one box. Cover the other box with clear plastic wrap and seal it with tape.
4. Place both boxes in bright sunlight or under a bright lamp for 10 minutes. Predict the effect of the light on the temperature in each box. Record the temperatures in the Data Table.
5. Suspend the strip of paper lengthwise in the flask. Hold it in place by inserting the stopper into the mouth of the flask.
6. Place the flask in sunlight. Use the magnifying lens to focus the sun's rays on the center of the strip. Observe the effect on the paper and record the time it takes for the paper to change.

FIGURE 24–6.

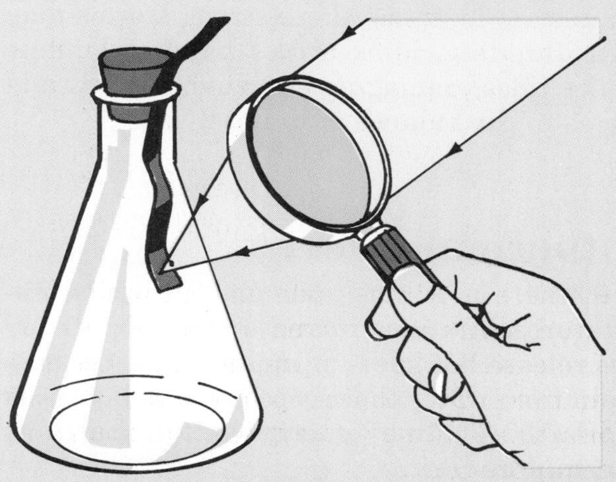

Data and Observations

Setup	Time	Observations
clear bottle	20 min	
bottle with aluminum	20 min	

Analysis and Conclusions

1. What evidence in this activity would support the idea that solar energy has a heating effect?
2. Write an explanation of your observations in Steps 1 and 2. Draw on your knowledge of gases.
3. Explain your observations in Steps 3 and 4. How was thermal energy transferred into the box?
4. How did the plastic wrap reduce the amount of energy leaving the box?
5. Review Section 20:3. What happened to the light that passed through the lens in Step 6?
6. How might you use mirrors to carry out Step 6?
7. What are some of the advantages of using lenses or mirrors in systems that collect solar energy?

FIGURE 24–7. Electricity is generated by turbines beneath this dam as the tides rise and fall.

The major disadvantage of wind energy is that it can be developed in only a few locations. The winds must be fairly steady. The average annual wind speed must be no lower than 15 kilometers to 20 kilometers per hour. Although its use is limited, wind energy could generate a large percentage of the needed electricity in suitable locations.

24:7 Tidal Energy

What forces produce tides?

Ocean tides are created by the gravitational forces between Earth, moon, and sun. Often tides can be used as a source of energy. As Earth rotates, the tides in a location change several times each day. When a tide rises and falls, water flows in and out of bays and river openings. If the entrance can be closed by a dam, the energy in the flowing water can be trapped to operate turbines. This form of energy is called **tidal energy.** As with hydroelectric energy, tidal energy uses water to do work as it moves from a higher to a lower level.

What is tidal energy?

There are about twenty-four sites suitable for tidal energy development. Two of these sites have been developed, one in France and the other in the Soviet Union. Possible tidal energy project locations in the United States are the Cook Inlet in Alaska and Passamaquoddy Bay in Maine. The largest tides, a change of about 15 meters, occurs in the Bay of Fundy, New Brunswick, Canada.

Tidal energy produces almost no air pollution. However, as with other forms of energy, there are problems with the development of tidal energy. Seawater may corrode the machinery used in the power plant. Many tidal energy sites are in areas where strong storms may cause damage. Building dams across bays and inlets may change the tides, damaging the environment and causing changes in the balance of living things.

24:8 Geothermal Energy

What is geothermal energy?

Inside Earth there is a huge amount of thermal energy. Temperatures in mines increase with depth. Active volcanoes release hot gases or molten lava. Geysers shoot out steam from water that seeps down to hot rocks deep within Earth. Thermal energy within Earth is called **geothermal energy.**

FIGURE 24–8. This plant generates electricity using geothermal energy from deep wells.

INVESTIGATION 24–2

Energy Uses

Problem: How much energy does my household use?

Materials

data on energy and gasoline use

energy conversion table

Procedure

1. Determine how much electricity, natural gas, coal, heating oil, propane, and so forth was used in your home for about a month.
2. Record the amount of gasoline used in your family automobile over at least one month.
3. Calculate or estimate the number of food calories used by your family in one month.
4. Estimate any other direct energy input (wood fuel, public transportation, and so forth) over the same amount of time.

Analysis

1. Calculate the energy from each source using the conversion values in the table.
2. Divide each value by the total number of days to find the average daily use. Then divide again by the number of people using the energy. This is your share.
3. Divide the total of column A by the total of Column C and multiply by 100% to find what percent your share represents.

Conclusions and Applications

4. The energy used to generate electricity is about 3 times the energy produced. Find the energy used to generate the electricity.
5. List the energy sources in order of use.
6. The average daily energy use per person for manufacturing is 400 MJ. Add this to your personal energy total.
7. The average energy use/person/day to heat and light schools, shopping malls, and so forth is 150 MJ. Add this amount to your personal daily total.
8. Average daily energy use for the United States is 1000 MJ/person/day; for the world, 200 MJ/person/day. Compare these figures with your daily use.

Data and Observations

Number of days ____________ Number of people ____________ Your Share ____________ %

Source	Amount	Conversion Factor	A. Amount in MJ	B. Amount per day	C. Amount person/day
Electricity	______ kWh	3.6 MJ/kWh			
Natural gas	______ ccf	100 MJ/ccf			
Fuel oil	______ gal	130 MJ/gal			
Gasoline	______ gal	133 MJ/gal			
Food energy	______ Cal	.0042 MJ/Cal			
Other	______				
Total					

Geothermal energy is obtained by drilling wells down into underground deposits of hot water. The best wells provide water ranging in temperature from 150°C to 350°C. The hot water is pumped out to the surface and used to generate electricity. However, if not properly handled, salts and hydrogen sulfide in water pumped up from within Earth can cause pollution. If the waste products from geothermal wells are put back into the ground in disposal wells, many pollution problems can be avoided. Geothermal energy plants have been in operation in Italy, California, and Iceland for many years without harming the environment.

Review

6. Describe three ways to collect solar energy.
7. Why do solar energy systems need a method for storing energy?
8. How does the production of hydroelectricity depend on the sun?
9. What are the major advantages of wind energy? The major disadvantages?
★ **10.** How can geothermal energy be obtained for generating electricity?

NUCLEAR ENERGY

GOALS

1. You will learn about the advantages and disadvantages of nuclear power.
2. You will learn some of the problems with and methods of nuclear waste disposal.
3. You will learn about thermonuclear reactions.

The most concentrated source of energy is in the nucleus of the atom. The example you are probably most familiar with is the energy in the nucleus of uranium atoms. This source is a nonrenewable fuel. The uranium was most likely created in a supernova explosion before the solar system was formed. Mankind has learned to release this energy rapidly to make weapons. Methods of producing electricity from the energy of the nucleus have also been developed. These methods may reduce our needs for fossil fuels. However, they also have serious problems that must be solved.

24:9 Nuclear Reactors

A **nuclear reactor** is a device for obtaining and using the energy from a controlled nuclear chain reaction. Controlled means the rate or speed of the nuclear reaction can be changed by the operator. The six main parts of a nuclear reactor are fuel, moderator, control rods, coolant, heat exchanger, and safety shields.

The fuel in a nuclear reactor is uranium oxide pellets. It is inserted into long rods. When the uranium nucleus fissions, energy and extra neutrons are released. These neutrons can cause other uranium nuclei to split.

The moderator is a material that slows the neutrons released during nuclear fission. To keep a chain reaction going, the speed of the neutrons must be reduced. The neutrons must be moving at a speed that allows them to be captured and produce fission of the other nuclei in the fuel. Most reactors in the United States use water as a moderator.

Control rods regulate the rate of fission in the fuel. They absorb any excess neutrons not required to keep the chain reaction going. Control rods contain boron or cadmium to absorb neutrons. By pushing the rods into the reactor or pulling them out, the fission rate is controlled. Pushing the rods all the way in stops the fission reaction.

The coolant removes thermal energy from the reactor. The energy from the nuclei undergoing fission heats the water in the reactor. The water is pumped from the reactor to a heat exchanger. Thus, the water acts as both a moderator and as a coolant.

In the heat exchanger, the coolant water flows around pipes containing more water. The heat from the coolant water changes the water in the pipes to steam. Steam carries the heat away from the reactor to a turbine. The coolant water and water that is changed to steam are in separate pipes. They do not mix.

FIGURE 24–9. A nuclear power plant generates electricity by using thermal energy from a fission reaction.

Describe the main parts of a nuclear reactor.

What is the function of the moderator in a fission reactor?

What is the function of the coolant in a fission reactor?

How is the water in the heat exchanger changed into steam?

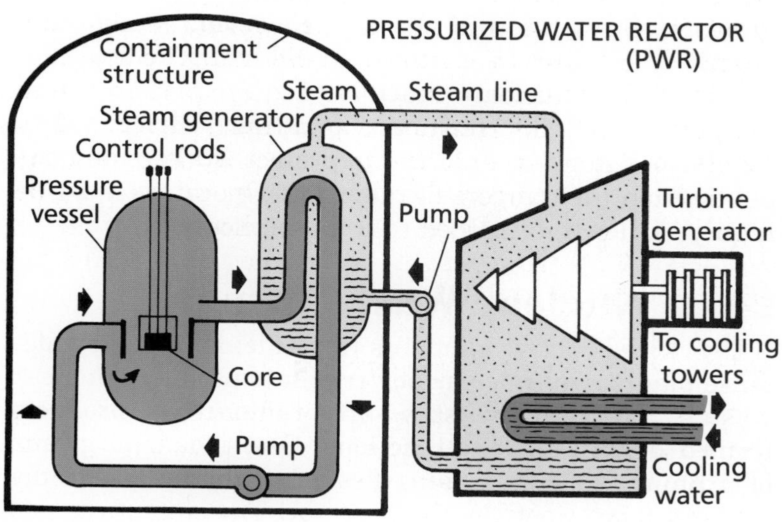

FIGURE 24–10. This diagram shows the operation of a water-cooled nuclear power plant. Notice that the coolant water and the water that produces the steam to turn the turbine are never mixed.

The steam produced by a nuclear reactor is used to do work. Steam is carried from the heat exchanger to turbines. A steam turbine is a machine with a central shaft connected to large blades. Steam under pressure passes over the blades, causing the shaft to rotate. Steam turbines are used to turn electric generators. A reactor generating one million watts of electric power uses about three grams of fuel per day.

F.Y.I. "The discovery of the nuclear chain reaction need not bring about the destruction of mankind any more than did the discovery of matches."
Albert Einstein

Safety shields are necessary to protect people from the nuclear radiation produced by a reactor. Nuclear radiation can produce burns, cancer, loss of hair, vomiting, and destruction of blood cells. An extremely large dose can cause death.

Generating electricity with nuclear energy has some advantages over using fossil fuels such as coal and oil. The burning of coal and oil can cause air pollution. Properly built nuclear reactors do not add pollutants to the air. Also, a greater amount of energy can be produced from smaller amounts of nuclear fuels, reducing pollution from transporting fuels.

Like other electric-generating plants, nuclear power plants require huge amounts of water to cool their steam turbines. If this hot water is dumped into rivers or oceans, thermal pollution may result. The higher temperature can have a harmful effect on fish. To protect the environment, the water must be cooled to near its original temperature before it is released. Large cooling towers are used for this purpose.

Accidental escape of radioactive material from a nuclear power plant is a hazard. The radiation could harm and kill plant and animal life. Overheating of the core containing the nuclear fuel could result in the release of radioactive wastes into the air. However, many safeguards are used to prevent overheating. Successful operation of nuclear reactors requires that these safeguards be in constant operation. Strict safety regulations must be enforced to protect workers and the public from the dangers of radiation. Operators must be highly skilled and trained to work carefully.

24:10 Nuclear Waste Disposal

What are nuclear wastes?

Use of radioactive elements in medicine, industry, defense plants, and nuclear power plants produces nuclear wastes. **Nuclear wastes** are radioactive products formed during nuclear reactions. One thousand grams of uranium-235 undergoing fission produces 999 grams of radioactive waste.

Several methods are used to dispose of nuclear wastes. Low-level radiation wastes are released into the air, water, or ground. The wastes are diluted as they spread into the environment. Radioactive wastes with short half-lives are stored in tanks and allowed to decay and then are released.

A third method of disposal is used for highly radioactive wastes with long half-lives. These wastes must be stored for tens, hundreds, thousands, or even millions of years before they become harmless. High-level radioactive wastes are now being stored temporarily in underground tanks and under water in special pools. Scientists are investigating different methods for long-term storage. One idea is to solidify the wastes in glass or ceramic capsules. The capsules would then be placed in metal containers and stored in deep underground caverns such as old salt mines.

FIGURE 24–11. One technique for storing nuclear wastes is to mix the material with molten glass and solidify it. These "capsules" are placed in metal containers and stored deep underground.

There are many possible problems with the safe storage of nuclear wastes. Underground storage tanks can corrode and leak if not properly maintained. Leakage of toxic, radioactive wastes can pollute underground water supplies. Another problem occurs during the transport of wastes from nuclear power plants to storage sites. A nuclear waste carrier involved in an accident might release deadly radioactive wastes into the environment. Many states and communities do not want to have disposal sites or even to have the wastes shipped through their areas. Nuclear energy requires a foolproof method of radioactive waste storage for many thousands of years. The disposal system must be protected from wars, terrorist acts, and natural disasters during this long period.

24:11 Thermonuclear Energy

The development of controlled nuclear fusion is being investigated by scientists and engineers in many countries. A nuclear fusion reaction requires a temperature of well over one million degrees Celsius. At this temperature, the nuclear fuel is in the plasma state. The plasma must be of extremely high density for the nuclei of the atoms to fuse. The plasma is so hot that it would vaporize any material container used to hold it.

What conditions are necessary for nuclear fusion?

One type of experimental fusion reactor uses a "magnetic bottle" to hold the plasma fuel. An electric current produces a magnetic field in a tube containing the fusion fuel. High-voltage alternating current heats the

F.Y.I. Heavy hydrogen refers to certain isotopes of hydrogen with heavier nuclei.

fuel to the required temperature. Magnetic fields squeeze the nuclei together inside the tube. The fields keep the plasma from the walls of the tube.

To make use of the energy of a thermonuclear reaction, scientists must discover how to maintain extremely high temperatures for several seconds. Further, they must learn how to trap the thermal energy produced by the fusion and convert it into electricity. The rewards may be worth the effort. Fusion of the nuclei in one gram of heavy hydrogen releases energy equivalent to that produced by burning over 8000 kilograms of coal. In addition, the problems of nuclear waste disposal would be eliminated. This is because there are no long-lived radioactive wastes from fusion.

Review

11. How is the fission rate of a nuclear reactor controlled?

12. Why are cooling towers needed in a nuclear power plant?

13. List three ways that water is used in a nuclear power plant.

14. What is the main problem with the disposal of nuclear wastes having long half-lives?

★ **15.** List two advantages of generating energy by nuclear fusion.

PROBLEM SOLVING

Not Too Cool

Lisa lives in an old house with very large windows. One window, facing south, has a black shade that can be pulled down to cover the window. One sunny day Lisa pulls the shade down to keep the bright sunshine out of the room. She soon notices that the room is getting very warm. She feels the shade and finds it hot to the touch.

Why is this happening, and how can Lisa keep the room cooler?

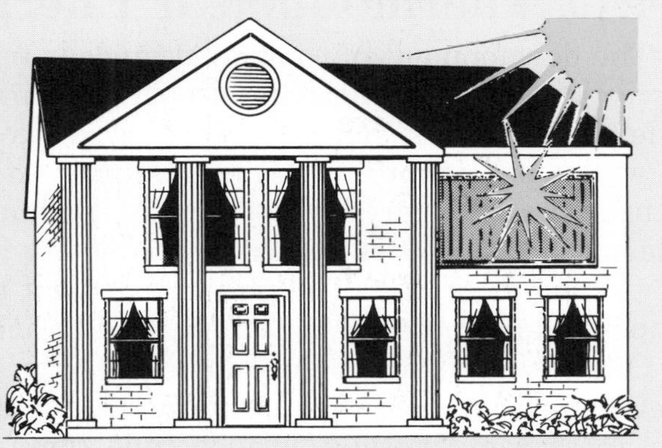

Chapter 24 Review

SUMMARY

1. About 90% of the energy used in the United States comes from the fossil fuels coal, crude oil, and natural gas. 24:1
2. If we conserve energy, our nonrenewable resources will last longer. 24:2
3. Alternative fuels can be produced from coal and organic matter. 24:3
4. Solar energy can be used to heat air and water and to generate electricity. 24:4
5. Falling water is used to generate hydroelectricity. 24:5
6. The energy in the wind and tides can be trapped and converted to electrical energy. 24:6, 24:7
7. Geothermal energy is obtained from underground deposits of hot water. 24:8
8. Controlled nuclear reactions produce thermal energy, which can be used to generate electricity. 24:9
9. Nuclear reactors produce radioactive wastes that pose problems in safe transport and disposal. 24:10
10. Thermonuclear energy may provide clean, inexpensive energy if the reacting plasma can be confined. 24:11

VOCABULARY

a. energy conservation
b. fossil fuels
c. fractional distillation
d. geothermal energy
e. hydroelectricity
f. nonrenewable resource
g. nuclear reactor
h. nuclear wastes
i. petroleum
j. photovoltaic cells
k. solar energy
l. tidal energy

Matching

Match each description with the correct vocabulary word from the list above. Some words will not be used.

1. a thick, black liquid that comes from the ground is
2. an energy source that cannot easily or quickly be replaced
3. a method of separating petroleum into a variety of fuels
4. an energy source that actually comes from the motion of the moon about the earth
5. a source of energy from falling water
6. an energy source from the thermal energy in rocks
7. device that is used to get energy from fission
8. energy sources that actually come from ancient solar energy
9. a source of energy that does not involve obtaining new energy sources
10. devices that convert solar energy into electrical energy

Chapter 24 Review

MAIN IDEAS

A. Reviewing Concepts

Choose the word or phrase that correctly completes each of the following sentences.

1. Hydrogen isotopes are raw materials for *(nuclear fission, transmutation, photovoltaic cells, nuclear fusion)*.
2. *(Coal, Oil, Uranium, Heavy hydrogen)* is a fuel for nuclear reactors.
3. As you go deeper into Earth, its temperature *(increases, remains the same, decreases, reaches absolute zero)*.
4. A moderator slows *(protons, electrons, neutrons, photons)* in a chain reaction.
5. Alcohol can be produced from *(grain, rock, uranium, heavy hydrogen)*.

Complete each of the following sentences with the correct word or phrase.

6. Natural gas is composed mostly of ______________.
7. In the gasification of coal, carbon combines with ______________ in steam.
8. Gasoline and fuel oil are distilled from ______________.
9. A(n) ______________ uses the kinetic energy of the moving air.
10. Thermonuclear reactions require high ______________.

Determine whether each of the following sentences is true or false. If it is false, change the underlined word to make the sentence true.

11. <u>Nitrogen oxides</u> cause air pollution.
12. A moderator <u>speeds up</u> a chain reaction.
13. <u>Geothermal energy</u> is produced by falling water.
14. A photovoltaic cell changes <u>solar</u> energy into electrical energy.
15. <u>Winds</u> are produced by the gravity of the sun and moon.

B. Understanding Concepts

Answer the following questions using complete sentences when possible.

16. What kind of materials are used to make photovoltaic cells?
17. What is the role of the cadmium rods in a nuclear reactor?
18. Describe two conversions of energy in a nuclear reactor.
19. Out of what material is coal made?
20. What kinds of fuel are obtained from
    a. fermenting grain?
    b. oil shale?
21. List five ways to save energy.
22. List the advantages and disadvantages of using coal, oil, and natural gas for fuel.
23. How is fractional distillation used to separate the hydrocarbons in petroleum?
24. What is energy conservation?
25. Explain how alcohol is obtained from plant material.

C. Applying Concepts

Answer the following questions, using complete sentences when possible.

26. List three problems in developing tidal energy.
27. What is a major problem in the development of thermonuclear energy plants?
28. A nuclear reactor has a device that can drop the control rods into the reactor in an emergency. Why?
29. In what ways are the production of hydroelectricity and tidal energy alike?
30. What are nuclear wastes? What methods are used for their disposal?

SKILL REVIEW

1. List two things you might want to check before even reading a scientific article.
2. Why should you evaluate the emotional tone of a scientific article?
3. What problem could quoting out of context cause?
4. Why is carbon-14 dating unsuitable for some specimens?
5. Element Q has five electrons in the third energy level. What is the name of this element?

PROJECTS

1. Read more about tidal power. Build a model of a tidal power system and demonstrate its operation.
2. Design and build a model solar heater.
3. Do library research to obtain information on the Three Mile Island and Chernobyl nuclear power plant accidents.
4. Make a study of energy conservation practices and solar power development in your local community.

READINGS

1. Arnold, Guy. *Coal.* New York: Franklin Watts, 1985.
2. Hawkes, Nigel. *Oil.* New York: Franklin Watts, 1985.
3. Johnson, Gary L. *Wind Energy Systems.* Englewood Cliffs, NJ: Prentice-Hall, 1985.
4. Petersen, David. *Solar Energy at Work.* Chicago, IL: Childrens Press, 1985.

SCIENCE AND SOCIETY

PLUTONIUM: WHAT SHOULD WE DO WITH IT?

Uranium and many of the products of nuclear fission are radioactive. Because the radiation from radioactive nuclei can be harmful, we need to shield ourselves from uranium and its radioactive fission products.

Nuclear reactors are designed to shield people from harmful radiation. But after three years, the uranium fuel in most American nuclear reactors has been used up so that it no longer can keep a chain reaction going. It must then be replaced. After uranium fuel has been removed from a reactor, it is called "spent fuel."

Background

The fuel put into a reactor consists of uranium oxide. Three percent of the uranium is uranium-235, the only naturally occurring isotope of uranium that fissions. Almost all the remaining 97% is uranium-238. While the fuel is in the reactor, two thirds of the uranium-235 fissions. An equal amount of uranium-238 is converted to radioactive plutonium-239.

Plutonium-239 is formed when the nuclei of uranium-238 absorb neutrons to become nuclei of uranium-239, which then decay to neptunium-239. The nuclei of neptunium-239 then decay to plutonium-239.

Plutonium-239 can fission when bombarded with neutrons. The spent fuel is then 95% uranium-238, 1% uranium-235, 1% plutonium-239, and 3% other fission products.

Of the original uranium oxide fuel, only 3% has been converted into unusable fission products, and this is the only fraction that can be considered waste. The remaining uranium and plutonium can be used to fuel another reactor. However, first they undergo chemical processing to separate them from the waste products.

Case Studies

1. The uranium-238 and plutonium-239 extracted from spent fuel were intended to be used to fuel special reactors called "breeder" reactors. They were called breeder reactors because they would produce more plutonium-239 from uranium-238.

2. A plant at West Valley, New York, extracted uranium and plutonium from about 650 tons of spent fuel between 1966 and 1972. The plant was then shut down. Two other plants never began operations.

3. Plutonium-239 can be used to build nuclear weapons as well as to fuel nuclear reactors. Thus, plutonium would be of interest to nations or terrorist groups wanting to build nuclear weapons.

4. Seeking to control the spread of nuclear weapons, President Carter in 1977 ordered that no plutonium be extracted from the spent fuel of American reactors.

What should we do with this plutonium? Those who oppose the spreading of nuclear weapons say that it should be buried along with the rest of the spent fuel from nuclear reactors. Other people point out that buried plutonium will remain a radiation and a security hazard for more than half a million years. This is because of Plutonium-239's long half-life.

FIGURE 1. Breeder reactors like the one in the illustration are used in Europe. There are none in the United States.

Inhaling a quarter of a milligram of plutonium is considered deadly. It must be handled by remote control. Radioactive waste is not considered to have reached a safe level until twenty half-lives have passed.

Rather than worry about buried plutonium for half a million years, some people feel that the best thing to do is to get rid of it by "burning" it in a breeder reactor, so that it could not be made directly into nuclear weapons. However, the current decline in the nuclear power industry has reduced demand for uranium. With lower demand and price of nuclear fuel, there is also lower motivation to build breeder reactors to make more nuclear fuel. Furthermore, the electricity from France's breeder reactors costs 2.2 times as much as electricity from its other reactors. The U.S. Department of Energy presently operates special reactors to make the plutonium used to make U.S. nuclear weapons, but many of these are now over forty years old and in need of repair or replacement.

In addition to giving us energy, nuclear reactors have also given us plutonium. As is the case with most science and society issues, there is no problem-free way to deal with it. But the longer we wait, the more problems arise.

Developing a Viewpoint

Share the information in this article with five adults, then ask them, "What do you think we should do with plutonium?" 1) Bury it; 2) Burn it (in breeder reactors); 3) No opinion. Report your findings to your class and compare them with the findings of your entire class as a whole. Discuss what you think would be the best answer.

Suggested Readings

William P. Bebbington. "The Reprocessing of Nuclear Fuels." *Scientific American, 235(12)*. 30–41, December 1976.

Bernard L. Cohen. "Plutonium—How Great is the Terrorist Threat?" *Nuclear Engineering*. February 1977.

Bernard L. Cohen. "The Disposal of Radioactive Wastes from Fission Reactors." *Scientific American 236(16)*. 21–31, June 1977.

Eliot Marshall. "End Game for the N Reactor?" *Science, 235*. 17, January 2, 1987.

Eliot Marshall. "Hanford's Radioactive Tumbleweed." *Science, 236*. 1616–1620, June 26, 1987.

William Sweet. "Despite Superphenix, Startup, Outlook for Breeders is Poor." *Phys. Today, 39*(9). 53–54, September 1986.

William Sweet. "Breeders and Reprocessing are Challenged in Germany, UK." *Phys. Today, 39*(10). 115–117, October, 1986.

The New York Times, p. A14, March 18, 1987.

APPENDIX A

SI Units of Measurement

Table A–1

SI Base Units					
Measurement	**Unit**	**Symbol**	**Measurement**	**Unit**	**Symbol**
length	meter	m	temperature	kelvin	K
mass	kilogram	kg	amount of substance	mole	mol
time	second	s	intensity of light	candela	cd
electric current	ampere	A			

Table A–2

Units Derived from SI Base Units			
Measurement	**Unit**	**Symbol**	**Expressed in Base Units**
energy	joule	J	$kg{\cdot}m^2/s^2$
force	newton	N	$kg{\cdot}m/s^2$
frequency	hertz	Hz	$1/s$
potential difference	volt	V	$kg{\cdot}m^2/A{\cdot}s^3$(W/A)
power	watt	W	$kg{\cdot}m^2/s^3$(J/s)
pressure	pascal	Pa	$kg/m{\cdot}s^2$($N{\cdot}m^2$)
quality of electric charge	coulomb	C	$A{\cdot}s$

Table A–3

Common SI Prefixes					
Prefix	**Symbol**	**Multiplier**	**Prefix**	**Symbol**	**Multiplier**
	Greater than 1			Less than 1	
mega-	M	1 000 000	*deci-*	d	.1
kilo-	k	1 000	*centi-*	c	.01
hecto-	h	100	*milli-*	m	.001
deka-	da	10	*micro-*	μ	.000 001

APPENDIX B

B:1 Safety in the Science Classroom

1. Always obtain your teacher's permission before beginning an investigation.
2. Study the procedure. If you have questions, ask your teacher. Be sure you understand any safety symbols shown on the page.
3. Use the safety equipment provided for you. Goggles and a safety apron should be worn when any investigation calls for using chemicals.
4. Always slant test tubes away from yourself and others when heating them.
5. Never eat or drink in the lab, and never use lab glassware as food or drink containers. Never inhale chemicals. Do not taste any substance or draw any material into a tube with your mouth.
6. If you spill any chemical, wash it off immediately with water. Report the spill immediately to your teacher.
7. Know the location and proper use of the fire extinguisher, safety shower, fire blanket, first aid kit, and fire alarm.
8. Keep all materials away from open flames. Tie back long hair and loose clothing.
9. If a fire should break out in the classroom, or if your clothing should catch fire, smother it with the fire blanket or a coat, or get under a safety shower. **NEVER RUN.**
10. Report any accident or injury, no matter how small, to your teacher.

Follow these procedures as you clean up your work area.

1. Turn off the water and gas. Disconnect electrical devices.
2. Return all materials to their proper places.
3. Dispose of chemicals and other materials as directed by your teacher. Place broken glass and solid substances in the proper containers. Never discard materials in the sink.
4. Clean your work area.
5. Wash your hands thoroughly after working in the laboratory.

Table B–1

FIRST AID	
Injury	**Safe response**
Burns	Apply cold water. Call your teacher immediately.
Cuts and bruises	Stop any bleeding by applying direct pressure. Cover cuts with a clean dressing. Apply cold compresses to bruises. Call your teacher immediately.
Fainting	Leave the person lying down. Loosen any tight clothing and keep crowds away. Call your teacher immediately.
Foreign matter in eye	Flush with plenty of water. Use eyewash bottle or fountain.
Poisoning	Note the suspected poisoning agent and call your teacher immediately.
Any spills on skin	Flush with large amounts of water or use safety shower. Call your teacher immediately.

SAFETY SYMBOLS

This textbook uses the safety symbols in Table B–2 below to alert you to possible laboratory dangers.

Table B–2

Safety Symbols	
DISPOSAL ALERT This symbol appears when care must be taken to dispose of materials properly.	**ANIMAL SAFETY** This symbol appears whenever live animals are studied and the safety of the animals and the students must be ensured.
BIOLOGICAL HAZARD This symbol appears when there is danger involving bacteria, fungi, or protists.	**RADIOACTIVE SAFETY** This symbol appears when radioactive materials are used.
OPEN FLAME ALERT This symbol appears when use of an open flame could cause a fire or an explosion.	**CLOTHING PROTECTION SAFETY** This symbol appears when substances used could stain or burn clothing.
THERMAL SAFETY This symbol appears as a reminder to use caution when handling hot objects.	**FIRE SAFETY** This symbol appears when care should be taken around open flames.
SHARP OBJECT SAFETY This symbol appears when a danger of cuts or punctures caused by the use of sharp objects exists.	**EXPLOSION SAFETY** This symbol appears when the misuse of chemicals could cause an explosion.
FUME SAFETY This symbol appears when chemicals or chemical reactions could cause dangerous fumes.	**EYE SAFETY** This symbol appears when a danger to the eyes exists. Safety goggles should be worn when this symbol appears.
ELECTRICAL SAFETY This symbol appears when care should be taken when using electrical equipment.	**POISON SAFETY** This symbol appears when poisonous substances are used.
PLANT SAFETY This symbol appears when poisonous plants or plants with thorns are handled.	**CHEMICAL SAFETY** This symbol appears when chemicals used can cause burns or are poisonous if absorbed through the skin.

B:2 Using the Balance

FIGURE 1.

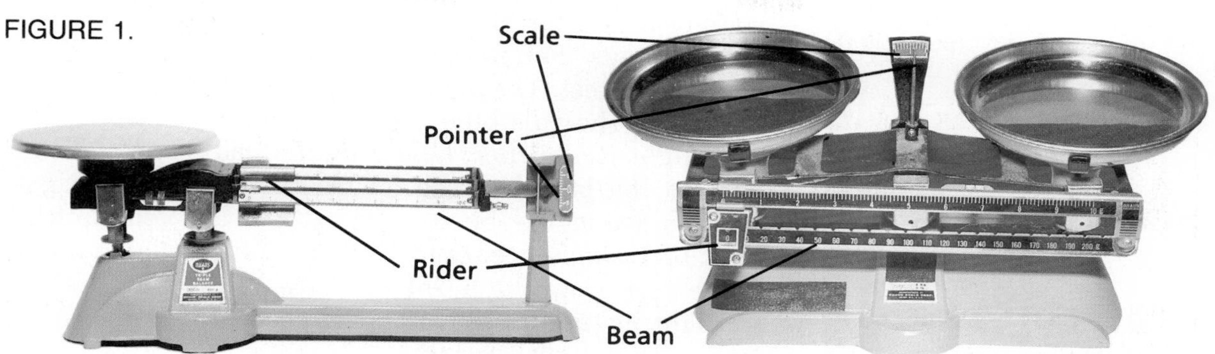

Although the balance you use may look somewhat different from the balances pictured here, all beam balances use similar steps to find an unknown mass.

1. Slide all the riders back to the zero point. Check to see that the pointer swings freely along the scale an equal distance above and below the zero point. Use the adjustment screw to obtain an equal swing if necessary
2. Never place chemicals directly on the balance pan. Any dry chemical that is to be massed should be placed on waxed paper or in a glass container.
3. Place the object to be massed on the pan. Move the riders along the beams beginning with the largest mass first. Make sure all riders are in a notch before reading. The pointer need not stop swinging if the swing is an equal distance above and below the zero point on the scale.
4. The mass of the object will be the sum of the masses indicated on the beams.

FIGURE 2.

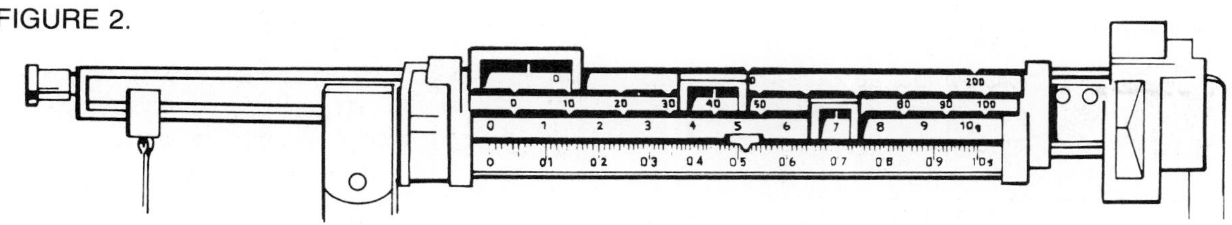

The mass of the object would be read as 47.52 grams.

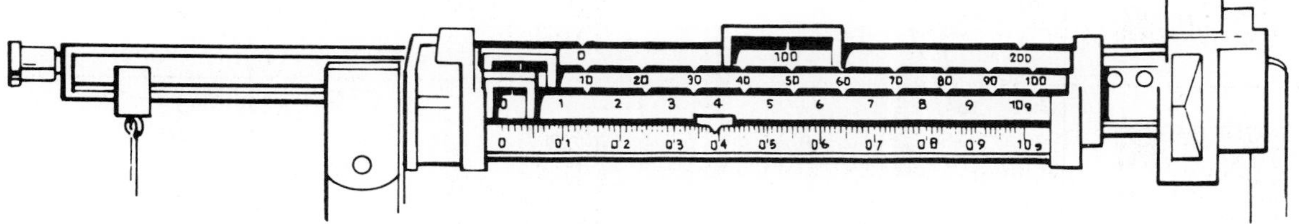

The mass of the object would be read as 100.39 grams.

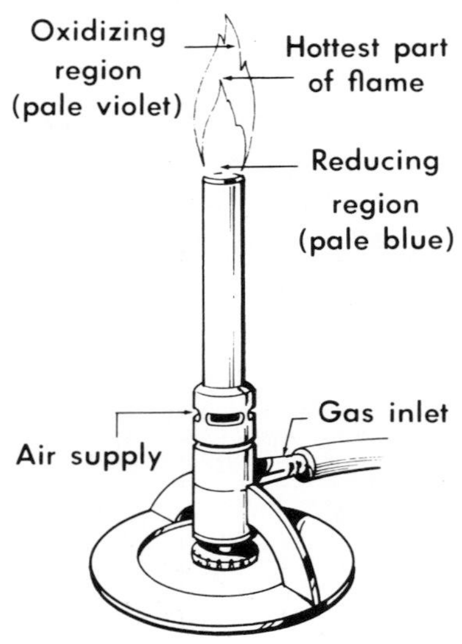

FIGURE 3.

B:3 Adjusting the Flame on a Laboratory Burner

Most laboratory burners have an inlet for gas and a vent or valve for the adjustment of air that is mixed with the gas. For maximum heat, the air-gas mixture must be correct. The object to be heated should be placed just above the pale blue part of the flame.

To light the burner, hold a lighted match or a striker next to the barrel of the burner and turn on the gas. After lighting the burner, adjust the air vent until a light blue cone appears in the center of the flame. If the flame rises from the burner or appears to "blow out" after lighting, reduce the supply of gas. If the flame is yellow, open the air regulator.

B:4 Filtering Techniques

It is often necessary to separate a precipitate from a liquid. A common process of separation is filtration. The solution is filtered through folded filter paper to catch any precipitate that has not settled to the bottom of the beaker. To avoid splashing, pour the liquid down a stirring rod. The solid should be rinsed several times with small amounts of distilled water to remove any solvent particles. This rinse water should also be decanted and filtered.

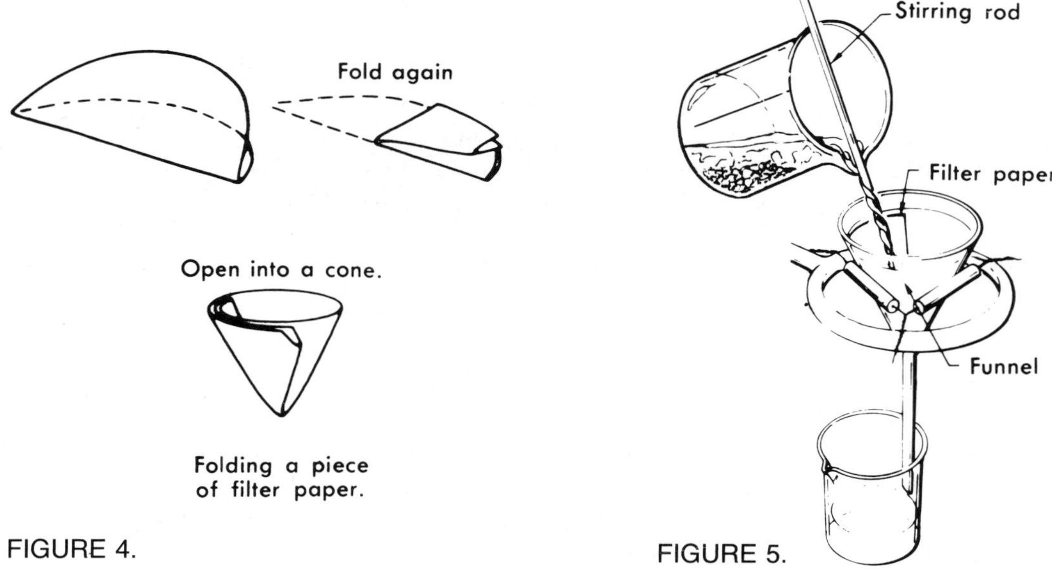

FIGURE 4.

FIGURE 5.

B:5 Working with Glass Tubing

When setting up apparatus for various activities, it is often necessary to use glass tubing. Figures 6 and 7 show the proper techniques to be used to fire polish glass tubing and insert it in a stopper. **CAUTION:** *Glass cools slowly. Do not touch glass that has been heated unless sufficient time has been allowed for cooling.*

FIGURE 6.

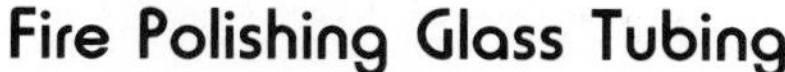

Fire Polishing Glass Tubing

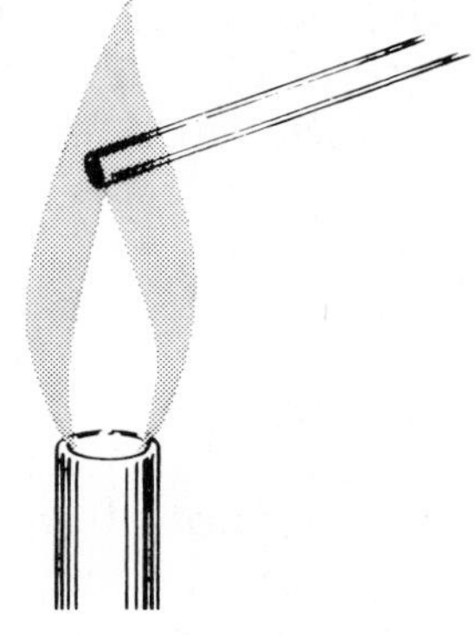

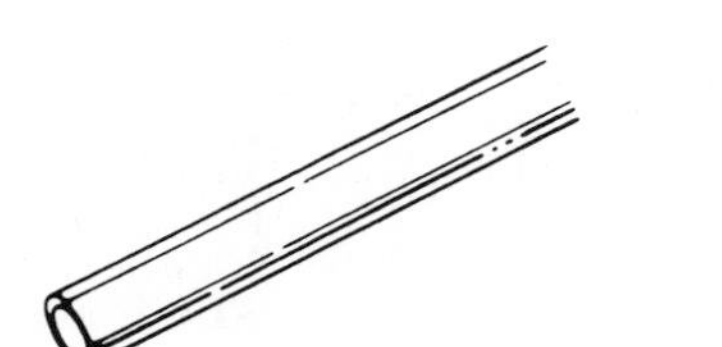

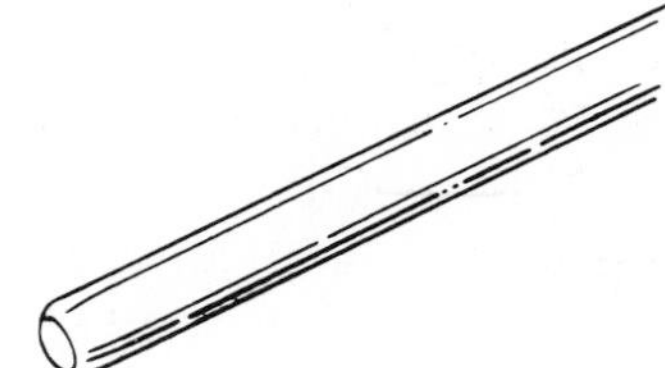

Rotate the tube in a laboratory burner flame until the edges are rounded. Do not hold in the flame too long or the end will close.

Inserting Glass Tubing into a Rubber Stopper

FIGURE 7.

Begin by lubricating the tip of the glass tubing with water, glycerol, or some other suitable substance your teacher provides. The glass tubing must be cool. Protect your hands with a cloth or paper towels. Never force the tubing into the stopper. Ease it in with a gentle twisting motion.

GLOSSARY

The glossary contains all of the major science terms of the text and their definitions. Below is a pronunciation key to help you use these terms. The word or term will be given in boldface type. Whenever necessary, the pronunciation will follow the term in parentheses.

a . . . **b**a**ck** (bak)
ay . . . **day** (day)
ah . . . f**a**ther (fahth ur)
ow . . . fl**ow**er (flow ur)
ar . . . **car** (car)
e . . . l**e**ss (les)
ee . . . l**ea**f (leef)
ih . . . tr**i**p (trihp)
i (i + con + e) . . . **i**dea (i dee uh), l**i**fe, (life)
oh . . . g**o** (goh)
aw . . . s**o**ft (sawft)
or . . . **or**bit (or but)
oy . . . c**oi**n (coyn)
oo . . . f**oo**t (foot)
ew . . . f**oo**d (fewd)
yoo . . . p**u**re (pyoor)
yew . . . f**ew** (fyew)
uh . . . comm**a** (cahm uh)
u (+con) . . . flow**er** (flow ur)
sh . . . **sh**elf (shelf)
ch . . . na**t**ure (nay chur)
g . . . **g**ift (gihft)
j . . . **g**em (jem)
ing . . . s**ing** (sing)
zh . . . vi**s**ion (vihzh un)
k . . . **c**ake (kayk)
s . . . **s**eed, **c**ent (seed, sent)
z . . . **z**one, rai**s**e (zohn, rayz)

A

absolute zero: zero on the Kelvin temperature scale; the coldest possible temperature

acceleration: the rate at which velocity changes

accuracy: how close your value is to the actual or accepted value

acid: a substance that dissolves in water to produce hydronium ions

acidic anhydride: a nonmetallic oxide that forms an acid when added to water

acoustics: the study of sound and its effect on people

actinoids: the fourteen elements that follow actinium on the periodic table; all but four are synthetic; all are radioactive

action-reaction pairs: two forces having equal strength but opposite directions

additive color: a primary light color, red, blue, or green; these three colors produce white light when added together

air resistance: the force of air against a moving object

alcohol: a hydrocarbon in which a hydrogen atom has been replaced by a hydroxyl, –OH group

alkali metals: the family of elements in Group 1 of the periodic table; the most reactive of all the metals

alkaline: having a pH above 7

alkaline earth metals: the family of elements in Group 2 of the periodic table; very reactive, thus not found free in nature

alkane series: saturated hydrocarbons where all the carbon atoms are joined by single covalent bonds

alkene series: the group of unsaturated hydrocarbons with one double bond

alkyne series: group of unsaturated hydrocarbons with one triple bond

allotropes (AL uh trohps)**:** different molecular forms of the same element

alloy: a material that contains more than one element and has metallic properties; for example, steel

alpha particle (α): a positively charged particle made up of two protons and two neutrons; a helium nucleus

alternating current (AC): a continuous back and forth movement of electrons in a circuit, changing direction of the current

amino acid: an organic compound that contains a carboxylic acid ($-COOH$) group and an amino ($-NH_2$) group in specific locations in its structure

ammeter: an instrument used to measure the amount of electric current in a circuit in amperes

amorphous (uh MOR fus) **substance:** a material such as glass or plastic that has no regular crystalline shape

ampere (AM pihr) **(A):** the rate of electron flow in a circuit

amplify: to increase the amplitude of a wave; increase the volume of sound or strength of an electric current

amplitude: the greatest distance the particles in a wave rise or fall from their rest position

amplitude modulation (AM): signal in which amplitude of carrier wave is varied

anesthetic: substance that produces sleep or numbness

angle of incidence: the angle made between a wave striking a barrier and the normal to the surface

angle of reflection: the angle between a reflected wave and the normal to the barrier from which it is reflected

anhydride (an HI dride): a compound formed from another by the removal of water

anhydrous: without water

anode (+): the positive electrode in an electrical circuit; gains electrons in a circuit

aqueous solution: solution with water as the solvent

Archimedes' principle: the buoyant force on an object submerged in a fluid is equal to the weight of the fluid displaced by that object

asbestos: mineral that readily separates into long flexible fibers, suitable for use as a noncombustible or nonconductor; dangerous to health (lungs)

atom: the smallest unit of an element that retains the properties of that element

atomic mass: mass of an atom compared to a standard mass, the carbon-12 atom

atomic mass unit (u): 1/12 the mass of the carbon-12 atom

atomic number (Z): the number of protons in the nucleus of an atom

average atomic mass: the average of the atomic masses of the naturally occurring isotopes that make up an element

average speed: the total distance an object travels divided by the total time it takes to travel the distance

axle: a shift on which a wheel turns

B

balanced chemical equation: an equation showing the same number of each kind of atom on reactant and product sides of the arrow

balanced forces: forces, acting on the same body, equal in size but opposite in direction

banked curve: a curve in which the outside edge is higher than the inside edge

barometer: an instrument used to measure air pressure

base: a substance that increases the hydroxide ion concentration when added to water

basic anhydride: a metallic oxide that forms a base when added to water

battery: two or more wet or dry cells that produce an electric current; forces electrons through a conductor

beats: variations between two tones of slightly different pitch that are sounded together

Bernoulli's principle: the pressure in a fluid is high where its velocity is low; the pressure is low where the velocity is high

beta particle (β): a negatively charged electron moving at high speed

binary (BI nuh ree) **compound:** a compound composed of only two elements

biochemistry: the study of the chemistry of living systems

bit: single on-off switch in a computer that acts with other bits to store information

block and tackle: an arrangement of several pulleys that allows a person to lift heavy machinery

boiling point: the temperature at which a substance changes rapidly from a liquid to a gas

bond: an attraction between atoms or ions that is the result of gaining, losing, or sharing electrons by atoms

Boyle's law: decreasing the volume of a gas will increase the pressure the gas exerts if the temperature remains constant

brine: a concentrated salt or ocean water solution

Brownian motion: the random motion of colloidal particles due to their bombardment by molecules of the solvent

brushes: contacts that supply current to the commutator

bubble chamber: chamber filled with a superheated liquid; a charged particle passes through the chamber producing ions; bubble formations track the particles

buoyant force: the upward force of a fluid on an object in it

buret: precision-made piece of glassware used to measure and deliver accurate volumes of solutions

byte: a group of adjacent binary digits; 8 bits

C

calorimeter (kal uh RIHM ut ur): an instrument used to measure changes in thermal energy

cancellation: process that occurs if a compression of one wave arrives at the same time as a rarefaction of another wave

carbohydrate: an organic molecule that has hydrogen and oxygen present in a ratio of two hydrogen atoms to one oxygen atom

carbonate: a compound containing the CO_3^{2-} ion

carboxylic acid: organic compound that contains the –COOH group

carburetor: an apparatus in which gasoline is broken into very fine droplets and mixed with air

catalyst: a substance that increases the rate of a chemical reaction without being permanently changed itself

cathode (–): the negative electrode in an electric circuit; releases electrons in a circuit

cathode-ray tube (CRT): a device that uses electrons to produce an image on a screen

Celsius (SEL see us) **(C):** the temperature scale on which 0° is the freezing point of water and 100° is the boiling point

centi- (c): 1/100 (one hundredth)

centripetal (sen TRIHP ut ul) **force:** a force on an object acting toward the center of a circular path

Charles' law: the volume of a gas increases as its temperature increases if the pressure remains constant

chemical activity: the ease with which an element reacts with other elements

chemical change: change in which a substance becomes another substance having different properties

chemical equation: a shorthand description of a chemical reaction; tells the reactants and products and their ratios

chemical formula: a group of chemical symbols that tells the atoms in a compound and their ratios

chemical property: characteristics of a substance that determine how a substance reacts to form other substances

chemically combined: two or more substances joined in such a way that they cannot be separated by physical means

circuit: a closed-loop path of conduction through which an electric current flows

circuit breaker: device that stops the flow of current before wires in a circuit get too hot; a strip of metal bends when heated and allows a spring to open a switch

cloud chamber: a device that detects nuclear particles through the formation of cloud tracks

coal gasification: process in which steam and hot coal produce hydrocarbons

coefficient: the number placed in front of a symbol or formula; used in balancing chemical equations

coherent light: light in which all the waves are vibrating in a single plane; kind of light produced by a laser; the crests and troughs of the light waves are all aligned

colloid: a mixture with particle size between that of solutions and suspensions

combustion: burning

commutator: switch on a motor running on direct current that causes the current in the coil to reverse every half turn

compass: a suspended magnet with one end pointing toward Earth's magnetic north pole

compound: a substance containing atoms of two or more elements chemically combined, always in the same ratio

compound machine: two or more simple machines working together

compression: the most dense concentration of wave particles in a compressional wave

compressional wave: a wave in which matter vibrates in the same direction as the wave moves

computer: a complex electronic device used to solve problems through mathematical operations

concave lens: a lens thinner in the middle than at the edges; refracts light rays away from each other

concave mirror: a mirror that is curved like the bowl of a spoon

concentrated: large amount of solute in solution compared with amount of solvent

concentration: the amount of solute per unit volume of solvent

conclusion: a judgment or decision based on interpreting observations

condensation: the change from the gaseous state to the liquid state

conduction: energy transferred through matter from particle to particle, most effective in solids; the movement of heat or electricity through a substance

conductor: material electrons can move through

cones: color receptors in the human eye; stimulated by red, blue, or green light waves

conservation of momentum: principle that states momentum cannot be created or destroyed

conserve: to keep the same

constant: a factor that does not change throughout an experiment

constant speed: no change in speed; acceleration is zero

control: group or activity that serves as standard of comparison for change in an experiment

control rods: part of a nuclear reactor; regulates the rate of fission in the nuclear fuel by absorbing neutrons

control unit: the part of the computer that regulates its operation

convection: the transfer of thermal energy by the actual movement of the warmed matter; occurs in liquids and gases

convex lens: a lens thicker in the middle than at the edges; refracts light rays toward each other

convex mirror: mirror that is curved like the back of a spoon

coolant: part of nuclear reactor; removes thermal energy from the reactor

core: a piece of iron in the center of a coil making a stronger electromagnet

corrosion: a destructive chemical change in a metal; rusting is an example

coulomb (KOO lahm) **(C):** unit of electric charge

covalent bond: bond between atoms produced by the sharing of electrons

central processing unit (CPU): "nerve center" of a computer; contains the control unit and the arithmetic/logic unit

crest: the high point of a wave

crude oil: another name for petroleum; thick, black liquid obtained from wells driven deep into the earth

crystal: a solid material having a regular repeating geometric form characteristic of a given compound or element

current: the movement of a charge; the flow of electrons in a conductor

cylinder: the piston chamber in an engine; where gasoline is drawn into on its way to the spark plugs

D

data: factual information gathered in an experiment or stored in a computer

deci- (d): 1/10 (one tenth)

decibel (dB): the unit to measure the volume or loudness of sound

decomposition reaction: a chemical change in which a substance breaks down or decomposes into other substances

density: the mass of a material divided by its volume; expressed in g/cm^3

dehydrate: remove water

dependent variable: the quantity that changes because of the variation in the independent variable

derived unit: unit formed by combining the base units; for example, meters cubed is a unit derived from cubing meters

deuterium (dew TIHR ee um)**:** the hydrogen isotope with one proton and one neutron in its nucleus

diatomic molecule: a particle made up of two covalently bonded atoms

diesel: engine that injects fuel directly into the cylinders, compresses the fuel-air mixture to temperature high enough to ignite the mixture

diffraction: the bending of waves as they pass through an opening or around the edge of an object

diffraction grating: a piece of transparent or reflecting material that contains many thousands of parallel lines per centimeter; used to produce a light spectrum by interference

digital computer: a device using numbers to solve mathematical problems; specifically, an electronic machine that uses stored instructions and information as a series of bits

dilute: little solute in solution compared with amount of solvent

diode: a rectifier that controls the direction of current; can convert alternating current to direct current

direct current (DC): flow of electrons in one direction through a conductor

discharge: loss of negative or positive electric charge

dissociation (dihs oh see AY shun)**:** the process in which an ionic compound breaks apart and forms ions when dissolved in water

distillation (dihs tuh LAY shun)**:** physical separation of the parts of a liquid through vaporization and condensation

doping: the process of adding impurities to semiconductors to change their resistance

Doppler effect: a change in wave frequency caused by the motion of the wave sound source or motion of the observer

double covalent bond: attraction between two atoms caused by sharing two pairs of electrons

double displacement reaction: the positive part of one compound unites with the negative part of another compound

dry cell: a device for producing a current with moist chemicals

dry ice: solid carbon dioxide

ductile: can be pulled into wires; property of metals

dye: a material that dissolves in a liquid to form a colored solution

E

efficiency (ih FIHSH un see)**:** the ratio of the work output of a machine to its work input

effort arm: the place on a lever where the effort force is applied

effort force: the force you apply to the machine

electric charge: having too many or too few electrons

electric current: the flow of electrons or other charged particles through a conductor

electrical power: the rate at which the energy of electric current is converted to other forms

electrolysis (ih lek TRAHL uh sus)**:** any chemical change produced by an electric current

electrolyte: substance that conducts electric current when in a water solution

electromagnet: a soft iron core surrounded by a wire coil through which an electric current is passed, thus magnetizing the core

electromagnetic spectrum: transverse energy waves, ranging from low frequency to very high frequency, that travel at the speed of light in a vacuum; includes radio, infrared, visible, ultraviolet, X rays, and gamma rays

electron: a negatively charged particle that moves around the nucleus of an atom; narrow rays of electrons create a picture on a TV screen

electron cloud: region around the nucleus occupied by electrons

electron cloud model: a model of an atom showing a cloud of negative charge surrounding the nucleus

electroscope (ih LEK truh skohp)**:** an instrument used for detecting positive and negative electrical charges

electrostatic: electrically charged particles

element: substance that cannot be broken down by physical or chemical means; composed of one kind of atom

endothermic (en duyh THUR mihk)**:** energy is taken in or absorbed

endpoint: the point at which the indicator changes color in a titration

energy conservation: the wise and careful use of energy resources

energy level: the specific amount of energy possessed by an electron or group of electrons in an atom

enzyme: a protein that speeds up a chemical reaction in living systems to keep reactions going at the rate needed for life

equation: a shorthand statement using chemical symbols of the changes that take place during a chemical reaction; a mathematical equality

escape velocity: the velocity required to free an object from the force of gravity acting on it

ester: an organic compound made from an alcohol and a carboxylic acid; has a characteristic odor or flavor

esterification: reaction in which an organic acid and an alcohol combine to produce an ester and water

evaporation (ih vap uh RAY shun)**:** change from the liquid to the gaseous state at the liquid surface

exercise: something performed or practiced in order to develop, improve, or display skills

exothermic (ek soh THUR mihk)**:** energy is released or given off

experiment: a process designed to yield observations under carefully controlled conditions; tests a hypothesis

F

family: a group of elements with common characteristics or properties

farsighted: can see objects far away clearly, but cannot focus objects close up

fat: a lipid; a compound composed of carbon, hydrogen, and oxygen; a nutrient

fatty acid: carboxylic acid having a long hydrocarbon chain

fermentation: process carried out by yeast or bacteria that converts starch, sugar, or cellulose to ethanol

fiberscope: a device containing parallel optical fibers, high intensity light source, and lenses; used to see into places that are difficult to view, such as the digestive tract

filter: a device used to separate parts of a mixture; a transparent material that separates colors of light

flame test: a procedure for identifying an element by heating it in a flame and observing the color given off

floppy disk: a device that stores data for a computer by arranging the north and south poles of iron oxide pieces on a disk in a certain pattern

fluids: name given to liquids and gases because they flow

fluorescent: emitting light only when exposed to radiation such as cathode rays, X rays, and ultraviolet rays

focal length: the distance from the center of the mirror to the focal point

focal point: the place that all light rays from a parabolic mirror or convex lens pass through

force: a push or pull one body exerts on another

formula: combination of chemical atomic symbols showing the atoms present in a compound and their ratio

formula mass: sum of the average atomic masses of the atoms or ions present in the formula of a compound

fossil fuels: fuels such as coal, natural gas, and petroleum that are formed from the remains of plants and animals that lived long ago

fractional distillation: a type of distillation in which compounds are separated because of differences in boiling points

freefall: unrestrained motion in a gravitational field

freezing: changing from liquid to solid

freezing point: temperature at which a liquid changes to a solid

Freon: the compound CCl_2F_2; substance used in refrigeration systems that is alternately evaporated and condensed

frequency: the number of waves that pass a point in a given unit of time

frequency-modulated (FM): signal in which frequency of carrier wave is varied

friction: a force that opposes motion between two surfaces that are touching each other

fuel injection: engine that does not use a carburetor, but sprays very fine droplets of fuel directly into the compressed air in the cylinders

fulcrum: (FUHL krum)**:** the point on which a lever rotates or pivots

fundamental frequency: the lowest frequency in a sound that contains more than one tone

fuse: a safety device that stops the flow of current before wires get too hot; contains a small piece of special metal that melts and breaks the circuit

fusion: the process of two low mass nuclei being joined to form one nucleus

G

galvanizing: coating iron or steel with zinc

galvanometer (gal vuh NAHM ut ur)**:** a device consisting of a coil of wire rotating between the poles of a magnet; used to detect small electric currents

gamma ray (γ): high-energy, high-frequency electromagnetic wave with a wavelength shorter than X rays; produced in the nucleus of radioactive atoms; very penetrating

gas: the state of matter that lacks definite shape or volume

Geiger counter: an instrument used to detect radioactivity through the formation of an electric current

generator: a machine that changes mechanical energy into electrical energy; a device that produces current by turning a coil of wire in a magnetic field

geothermal energy: heat from within the Earth

glass: a solidlike supercooled liquid that does not have a true crystalline structure

gravity: the mutual force of attraction that exists between all objects in the universe; force Earth exerts on all objects on or near it

ground: the connection of an object to Earth by an electrical conductor to allow electrons to move freely into and out of the object

group (family): a vertical column in the periodic table; elements within a group have similar chemical properties

H

half-life: the time required for one-half of the atoms in a radioactive substance to decay

halogen: means salt producer; combines with metals to form salts; member of the halogen family

halogen family: elements in Group 17 on the periodic table; reactive nonmetals, each with seven electrons in its outer energy level

harmony: the sound produced by a combination of tones whose frequencies are multiples of the fundamental and can be expressed in small whole number ratios

heat: energy transferred between objects because of a difference in temperature, from high temperature to low temperature

heat engine: a machine that converts thermal energy into mechanical energy, converts heat into work

heat exchanger: part of a nuclear reactor; coolant water changes water in pipes into steam, which carries heat away from the reactor to a turbine

heat of fusion: the energy necessary to change a solid to a liquid

heat of vaporization: the energy needed to change a liquid to a gas

heat mover: a machine that removes heat from an object at a low temperature and gives it to one at a high temperature

heat pump: a heat mover that can operate in two directions, removing thermal energy from outside air and delivering it to the inside or vice versa

hertz (Hz): the unit of wave frequency equivalent to 1 cycle per second

heterogeneous mixture: a mixture of two or more materials not evenly distributed throughout each other

homogeneous mixture: a mixture that is the same throughout; a solution

horizontal velocity: velocity parallel to Earth's surface

hydrate: a crystal that contains water molecules

hydrocarbon: a compound containing only carbon and hydrogen

hydroelectric power: electric power generated by moving water

hydroelectricity: electric current produced by falling water

hydronium (hi DROH nee um) **ion:** H_30^+; a positive ion containing a proton (hydrogen ion) bonded to a water molecule

hydroxide (hi DRAHK side) **ion:** OH^-; a negative ion containing one oxygen atom and one hydrogen atom

hypothesis (hi PAHTH uh sus)**:** the proposed answer to a question or tentative solution to a problem; an educated guess based on observation

I

image: the reproduction of an object formed with lenses or with mirrors

incident wave: a wave that strikes an object

inclined plane: a slanted surface used to raise objects; a simple machine

independent variable: the experimental factor that is changed by the experimenter

index of refraction: ratio of speed of light in a vacuum to its speed in a given substance

indicator: organic compound that changes color in an acid or a base

inertia (ihn UR sha)**:** the property of a body that resists any change in velocity

inference: is a judgment based on reasoning from evidence

infrared: invisible electromagnetic radiation with a longer wavelength than red light and next to red light in the electromagnetic spectrum; used to warm and dry objects

inhibitor: a substance that slows down a chemical reaction

insulation: a material used to slow the flow of heat or electricity

insulator (IHN suh layt ur)**:** a substance through which heat or electricity cannot flow readily

integrated circuit: a small electronic device that has many resistors, diodes, and transformers, all on a single piece of silicon

intensity: related to the amplitude of the sound wave; expressed using the decibel scale

interference: the ability of two or more waves to add together to form a new wave

internal combustion engine: an engine run by a fuel burned within the engine

International System of Units (SI): units and standards of measurement used by scientists all over the world

ion: a charged particle formed from an atom or atoms that have gained or lost one or more electrons

ionic bonding: a type of bonding in which ions are held together by the strong attraction of their opposite charges

ionization (i uh nuh ZAY shun)**:** process in which a molecular compound dissolves in water to form ions; process in which atoms lose or gain electrons

isomers: compounds having the same molecular formula but different structural formulas

isotopes (I suh tohps)**:** atoms of the same element with different numbers of neutrons

J

joule (J): a unit of work or energy; a newton meter

K

kelvin: SI unit of temperature; zero kelvin = absolute zero = − 273°C

kilo- (k): 1000

kilogram (kg): the SI base unit of mass; 1000 g

kilowatt: equals 1000 watts; watt is a very small unit of power

kilowatt-hour (kWh): a unit used to measure electrical energy; equal to 1000 watt-hours

kinetic (kuh NET ikh) **energy:** energy of motion

kinetic theory of matter: all matter is made up of tiny particles that are in constant motion; the motion and spacing of the particles determines the state of the matter

L

lanthanoids: the fourteen elements that follow lanthanum on the periodic table

laser: a device that produces a highly concentrated, powerful beam of coherent light that is all one frequency or color

law: a "rule of nature" that describes the behavior of matter and energy

law of conservation of energy: energy can change from one form to another, but can never be created or destroyed

law of conservation of mass: mass is neither gained nor lost in a chemical change

law of conservation of momentum: the total momentum of colliding bodies is not changed, providing there are no outside forces acting on the set of objects

lens: a curved, transparent object; usually made of glass or clear plastic

lever: a bar free to rotate around a point; a simple machine; consists of an effort arm, fulcrum, and resistance arm

light: the only visible part of the electromagnetic spectrum

lipids: a class of organic compounds commonly called fats and oils

liquid: the state of matter having a constant volume but no definite shape

liter (L): a unit of volume equivalent to 1000 cm^3 or 1000 mL; one cubic decimeter

litmus paper: an indicator that turns red in acid and blue in base

longitudinal wave: see compressional wave

loudness: describes a person's response to sound intensity; loud sounds produce a sound wave with a large amplitude

M

machine: a device that makes work easier by changing the speed, direction, or amount of a force

macromolecule: large molecule formed by covalent bonding

magnet: any object that has a magnetic field and is able to exert forces on other magnets

magnetic field: area of magnetic lines of force

magnetic poles: locations of the strongest magnetic force; usually at opposite ends of the magnet

magnetism: a property of matter in which there is an attraction due to unlike poles

magnification: the number of times an image is larger than the actual object

malleable: can be rolled into sheets; property of metals

mass: the amount of matter in an object; the measure of the inertia of a body

mass number: the sum of protons and neutrons in an atom

mechanical advantage *(MA)*: the amount by which the applied force is multiplied by a machine

mechanical energy: the kinetic energy and potential energy of lifting, bending, and stretching

melting: change from solid state to liquid state

melting point: the temperature at which a substance changes from a solid to a liquid

meniscus: the curved surface of a liquid

metallic bonding: the force holding metals together, characterized by the outer electrons of the atoms forming a common electron cloud distributed throughout the crystal

metalloid (MET ul oyd)**:** an element that has properties of both metals and nonmetals; B, Si, Ge, As, Sb, Te, Po, At

metallurgy: the process of mining and refining metals from their ores

metals: elements whose atoms generally have three or fewer electrons in their outer energy level; are shiny, conduct heat and electric current, tend to lose electrons in reactions

meter (m): the SI base unit of length; a device that measures and sometimes records

micro- (μ): 1/1 000 000 (one millionth)

microprocessor: a single integrated circuit that combines memory and controls circuits to regulate computer operations

microscope: magnifies extremely small objects; produces an image much larger than the object being magnified; uses two convex lenses

microwaves: very short wavelength radio waves; they send telephone messages, television programming, and computer information

milli- (m): 1/1000 (one thousandth)

mixture: two or more elements or compounds that are blended without combining chemically

model: a representation of an idea in order to make it more understandable; an idea, system, or mathematical expression that is similar to what someone is trying to explain

moderator: part of a nuclear reactor; material that slows the neutrons released during nuclear fission; most United States reactors use water

modulation: variation of either the amplitude or frequency of radio waves to make possible transmission for radio and television broadcasting

mole: the formula mass of a substance expressed in grams

molecular mass: the sum of the atomic masses of the atoms in a molecule

molecule: neutral particle formed by atoms bonded covalently; may be an element or a compound

molten: melted

momentum: the mass of an object multiplied by its velocity

monomer: one of the small molecules that combine to form polymers; usually has double or triple bonds that break easily allowing molecules to bond to each other

motion: change in position

motor: device that converts electrical energy into mechanical energy

musical scale: a series of notes that are related to one another by certain ratios of frequencies; most common has eight notes

N

n-type semiconductor: negative type semiconductor; has been doped with an element having more outer-level electrons than the semiconductor element

nearsighted: can see objects close up clearly, but cannot focus distant objects

net force: force that results from unbalanced forces acting on an object; changes the motion of an object

network crystal: a crystal formed by covalent bonds between atoms and becoming one large molecule; generally nonmetallic

neutral: neither acid nor base; pH of 7; not electrically charged

neutralization (new truh luh ZAY shun)**:** a chemical reaction in which equal numbers of hydronium ions (acid) and hydroxide ions (base) combine to form water and a salt

neutron: particle with no charge; 1800 times the mass of an electron; located in the nucleus of an atom

newton (N): the unit of force; force required to accelerate a 1-kg mass at the rate 1 m/s^2

Newton's first law of motion: an object remains in a state of rest unless an unbalanced force causes it to move, and an object continues in motion along a straight line unless a force stops it or causes the object to change direction

Newton's second law of motion: the acceleration of an object increases as the amount of net force applied from outside the object increases; for the same force, acceleration is inversely proportional to the mass of the body

Newton's third law of motion: when one force exerts a force on a second object, the second object exerts an equal and opposite force on the first object; forces always come in pairs

noble gas family: elements in Group 18 on the periodic table; all except helium have eight electrons in their outer energy level; member elements are stable and occur as single atoms in nature

noise: sounds produced by irregular vibrations; sound at the wrong time and place

noise pollution: annoying and unpleasant sound; sound that causes damage

nonelectrolyte: substance that does not conduct electricity when dissolved in water

nonmetal: an element with five or more electrons in the outer energy level; a poor conductor of heat and electricity; tends to gain electrons when it reacts with metals

nonrenewable resource: resource that cannot be replaced after it is used

normal: a line drawn perpendicular to a line or plane

north-seeking pole: the end of a magnet that always turns to point toward the north

nuclear chain reaction: a series of continuous rapid nuclear fissions, beginning with the splitting of a nucleus

nuclear decay series: the nuclear reactions through which a radioactive element breaks down to a stable element; in each reaction, a different radioactive isotope is formed

nuclear emulsion (ih MUL shun)**:** a photographic emulsion, containing silver bromide dissolved in a gelatinlike solid; used to detect nuclear particles

nuclear fission: a nuclear change in which a heavy nucleus is divided into two smaller, roughly equal nuclei

nuclear fuel: part of a nuclear reactor; uranium oxide pellets; when split, energy and extra neutrons are released

nuclear fusion: a nuclear change in which two or more small atomic nuclei unite to form a single heavier nucleus

nuclear reaction: change in the nucleus of an atom; temperature or pressure does not affect this

nuclear reactor: a device for producing energy from a nuclear fuel, such as uranium, through a controlled chain reaction

nuclear wastes: the radioactive products formed during nuclear reaction

nucleus: the central portion of an atom containing neutrons and protons

nuclide: the nucleus of an isotope that has a specific atomic number and atomic mass

observation: the act of taking notice and gathering data; process of gathering information using the senses

octave: series of eight notes in which the last note has a frequency two times as great as the first note

ohm (Ω): unit for measuring electric resistance

Ohm's law: current is equal to the potential difference divided by the resistance; voltage divided by resistance (ohms); $I = V/R$

opaque: material that absorbs light

optical axis: the line straight out from the center of a parabolic or curved mirror; straight line through the center of a lens or mirror

optical fiber: a thin strand of glass through which light passes, covered by a second layer of glass

optics: science devoted to the study of light and its uses

orbit: to travel in circles

ore: a mineral or other natural material from which one or more metals may be profitably obtained

organic chemistry: the study of carbon and its compounds

organic compounds: compounds that contain carbon, usually bonded to hydrogen

output device: displays computer's operations; commonly a video display terminal containing a cathode-ray tube; printer

output signal: electric current after it is amplified

overtone: a tone in a musical sound that has frequency higher than the tone with the lowest frequency; produces the quality of a sound

oxidation number: the combining capacity of an element

P

p-type semiconductor: positive type semiconductor; has been doped with an element having fewer outer-level electrons than the semiconductor element

parallel circuit: a circuit in which two or more conductors are connected across two common points in the circuit to provide separate conducting paths for the current

pascal: the SI unit of pressure; one newton per square meter

Pascal's principle: pressure applied to a fluid is transmitted unchanged throughout the fluid, the force is the same everywhere

peptide linkage: the $\text{—}\overset{\overset{\displaystyle O}{\|}}{C}\text{—}\underset{\underset{\displaystyle H}{|}}{N}\text{—}$ unit that forms between amino acids to make protein polymers

periodic: occurring at regular intervals

periodic table: an arrangement of the chemical elements in rows according to increasing atomic numbers, in vertical columns having similar properties

periods: the horizontal rows of the periodic table

permanent magnet: a substance that remains magnetized for a long time

petroleum: a liquid mixture of hydrocarbons that is obtained from wells drilled into Earth; crude oil

pH: a number that shows acidity; a measure of hydronium ion concentration in a solution

phenolphthalein (feen ul THAYL en)**:** an indicator that is colorless in an acidic solution and pink in a basic solution

photochemical smog: particles that form in the atmosphere as a result of the action of sunlight on airborne pollutants

photoconductor: a metal whose electrical conductivity is controlled by light

photodetector: a device used to measure light intensity

photoelectric cell (photocell): a device containing a photoelectric metal that produces an electrical current when struck by light

photon: a packet or bundle of radiant wave energy

photosensitive: changed by the action of light or other radiant energy

photosynthesis: process in which organisms use the sun's energy and chlorophyll to combine CO_2 and H_2O to produce glucose and oxygen

photovoltaic cell: device that converts energy from sunlight into electric current

physical change: a change in size, shape, color, or state; a change without a change in chemical composition

physical property: a characteristic of matter that may be observed without changing the chemical composition of the substance

physical science: the study of matter and energy

physics: the study of how matter and energy are related

pickling: process that removes oxides and other impurities from the surface of steel or other metals

pigment: a colored material that absorbs certain colors of light and reflects other colors

piston: a sliding piece moving inside the cylinder of an engine

pitch: the way a person hears the frequency of a sound; in general, the greater the frequency, the higher the pitch

plane mirror: a mirror with a flat surface

plasma: the high temperature state of matter in which atoms lose their electrons; high energy, electrically charged particles

polar molecule: a molecule that is positively charged at one end and negatively charged at the other end

polarized light: light in which all waves are vibrating in a single plane

pollution: unwanted or harmful matter or energy in the environment

polyatomic ion: a group of covalently bonded atoms that act together as one charged atom

polyester: a polymer made from ester molecules

polymer (PAHL uh mur)**:** a large molecule formed from many smaller units (monomers) bonded together

position: the location of a person or any object

potential (puh TEN chul) **difference:** the difference in electric potential between electrons in one place and electrons in another

potential energy: the energy due to position or condition

power: amount of work done per unit of time

precipitate: insoluble substance that crystallizes out of solution

preservative: an inhibitor; slows down decay by retarding the processes that cause the decay

pressure: amount of force per unit area

primary coil: part of a transformer; when connected to alternating current creates a magnetic field

primary light colors: red, blue, and green; when mixed together in equal amounts they produce white; can make any other color

primary pigment colors: magenta, yellow, cyan; mixed together produce black

prism: an object of transparent material with two straight faces at an angle to each other; refracts light twice; produces visible light spectrum

product: a substance formed as a result of a chemical change; substance to the right of a yield sign (→) in an equation

program: a set of instructions to a computer

projectile: an object such as a stone, ball, bullet, or rocket, which is thrown or shot

property: a feature of matter or the way it acts

protein: one of the major group of polymers formed from amino acids

proton: a positively charged particle in the nucleus of an atom

pulley: a form of a lever; a simple machine

Q

quality: a special characteristic of sound caused by overtones; enables you to tell the difference between sounds of the same pitch and volume

quarks: particles that make up protons and neutrons.

R

radiant energy: energy that can travel through space in the form of waves

radiation: transfer of energy that does not require matter; energy released from atoms and molecules as they undergo internal nuclear change; transfer of energy by electromagnetic waves

radiator: a device with a large surface area designed to warm the air

radioactive decay: process in which unstable nuclei emit a particle or radiation with a large amount of kinetic energy

radioactivity: the emitting of high energy radiation or particles from nuclei of radioactive atoms

radio waves: radiation having the lowest frequencies and the longest wavelengths; travel at the speed of light; used for communication

radius: the distance from the center to the edge of a circle

RAM: random access memory

rarefaction: the least dense concentration of wave particles in a compressional wave

rate: the ratio between two quantities

ratio: the relationship or quotient of two numbers

reactant: a substance that undergoes a chemical change; substance to the left of a yield sign (→) in an equation

reactive: property of elements and compounds by which they easily form other substances; reactive elements are not found free in nature

read/write memory: the computer can choose any bit to read or write; RAM

real image: an image that can be projected onto a screen; formed by a parabolic mirror or convex lens

rectifier (REK tuh fire): a device for changing alternating current to direct current

reflecting telescope: a telescope in which magnification is produced by a parabolic mirror; has a concave mirror and a convex eyepiece lens

reflection: bouncing of a wave or ray off a surface; change in direction

refracting telescope: a telescope in which magnification is produced by two convex lenses

refraction: bending of a wave or light ray, caused by a decrease in speed as it passes from one material into another

reinforcement: the coming together of the compressions or rarefactions of two or more waves

resistance: any opposition that slows down or prevents movement of electrons through a conductor opposition to the flow of electricity

resistance arm: the distance from the fulcrum to the resistance force in a lever

resistance force: the force exerted by the machine

resistors: devices used to control the flow of current

reverberation: a mixture of many different reflected sounds that combine and die away slowly

ring compound: organic compound in which carbon atoms are joined in the shape of a ring

ripple tank: a shallow, transparent, waterproof box containing a layer of water about 1 cm deep; used to study waves

ROM: computer can only read this memory; permanent memory

R-value: a measure of the resistance to heat flow

S

salt: compound containing a positive ion from a base and a negative ion from an acid

saponification: soap formation; involves heating an ester in a strong base to form soap and an alcohol

saturated: solution contains the maximum amount of solute for a given temperature; all carbon-to-carbon bonds in molecule are single bonds

saturated hydrocarbon: a hydrocarbon in which each carbon atom is bonded to four other atoms by single covalent bonds

scale: a series of notes that have certain frequencies

science: process for observing, studying, and attempting to explain our world

screw: an inclined plane wound around a cylinder; a simple machine

secondary coil: the output coil of a transformer

semiconductor: a material with a resistance between that of a conductor and an insulator; conducts electric current weakly

series circuit: an electric circuit in which the parts are connected so that the same current flows through all parts of the circuit

SI: abbreviation for International System of Units

signal: varying electric current; controls the flow of larger currents between the two ends of a transistor

significant digits: numbers that result from measurement

silica: silicon dioxide, one of the most common silicon compounds; ordinary sand

silicates: compounds containing silicon, oxygen, and at least one metallic ion; contain SiO_3^{2-}

silicones: compounds containing long chains of silicon and oxygen bonded to carbon compounds

simple machine: a device that makes work easier by changing the speed, direction, or amount of force; it consists of only one machine

single displacement reaction: one element displaces another from a compound

soap: the salt of a fatty acid; made by heating an ester with a strong base

solar cell: a device that is able to change solar energy directly into electricity

solar energy: energy or radiation from the sun

solar heating system: a system that uses the sun's energy for heating

solid: the state of matter having a definite volume and shape

solubility (sahl yuh BIHL ut ee)**:** the amount of a substance (solute) that will dissolve in a specific amount of another substance (solvent) at a given temperature

solute: the substance dissolved in a solvent

solution: a homogeneous mixture in which one substance (solute) is dissolved in another substance (solvent)

solvent: the substance in which a solute is dissolved

sound wave: a compressional wave produced by vibrations

south-seeking pole: the end of a magnet opposite the north-seeking pole

specific gravity: the ratio of the density of a substance to the density of water

specific heat: the amount of energy needed to raise the temperature of 1 kilogram of a substance 1 Celsius degree

speed: rate of change of the position of an object; rate of motion

stable: unreactive

standard: an exact quantity people agree to use for comparison

standard solution: solution whose concentration is known exactly

standing wave: a wave produced by continuous reflection and reinforcement

static discharge: loss of static electricity

static electricity: electricity produced by charged bodies; charge built up in one place

steel: iron alloyed with carbon and one or more other metals

step-down transformer: transformer in which the output voltage is less than the input voltage; secondary coil has fewer turns than the primary coil

step-up transformer: transformer in which the output voltage of the secondary coil is greater than the input voltage to the primary coil; secondary coil has more turns than the primary coil

stereo microscope: two microscopes, one for each eye; produces a three-dimensional image

strong acid: an acid that completely breaks up into ions when added to water

structural formula: a simple formula showing the symbols of atoms in a molecule of a compound and how they are bonded

sublimation (sub luh MAY shun)**:** the direct change of state from a solid to a gas or a gas to a solid

subscript: the small number that gives the ratio of how many atoms of each element combine in a compound

substance: an element or a compound; a homogeneous material with a definite composition

substituted hydrocarbon: an organic compound in which one or more hydrogens has been replaced with another kind of atom or group of atoms

subtractive color: one of the three pure pigment colors, magenta, yellow, cyan; these pigment colors produce black when mixed

supercooled liquid: a liquid cooled below its normal freezing point without having changed into a solid; appears to be solid but does not have a regular crystalline structure

supersaturated: solution contains more solute than would normally dissolve at a given temperature

suspension: heterogeneous mixture in which the particles are large enough to be seen; particles will eventually settle out

switch: device used to break current flow in a conductor; when open, no current flows

symbol: the shorthand way to write the name of an element

synthesis reaction: a chemical change in which two or more elements or compounds unite to form one compound

synthetic: not naturally occurring

synthetic elements: elements produced in the laboratory or in nuclear reactors

synthetic fuel: a fuel made from some other substance; not found in nature

T

tarnish: a form of corrosion

technologist: a specialist who uses technical methods and scientific knowledge to achieve practical purposes

technology (tek NAHL uh jee): the application of science for practical purposes

telephoto lens: camera lens; a lens with a long focal length; produces enlarged images

temperature: a measure of average kinetic energy of the particles of a material; usually measured with a thermometer

terminal velocity: the greatest velocity reached by a falling object

terrestrial: of or relating to Earth and its inhabitants

tetrahedron (te truh HEE drun): a solid with four triangular faces; four-sided shape of the molecule formed when a carbon atom shares electrons with four other atoms

theory (THEE uh ree): an explanation based on observations during repeated experiments

thermal energy: the total energy of all the particles in an object

thermal expansion: the increase in volume of matter as the temperature goes up

thermal pollution: problem caused when waste thermal energy raises the temperature of the environment

thermocouple: a device with two different metals twisted or bonded together, used to produce an electric current

thermography: technique that detects heat with a special photographic film

thermonuclear power: energy from controlled nuclear fusion

thermonuclear reaction: a nuclear fusion reaction; occurs at a temperature of millions of degrees

thermostat: a device that regulates cooling and heating systems

tidal power: the forces and energy generated by ocean tides

titration: process that makes use of a solution of known concentration to determine the concentration of another solution

tone quality: differences among sounds of the same pitch and loudness

total internal reflection: condition in which the light ray is refracted so much that it reflects back into the medium

transformer: a device that increases or decreases the voltage of alternating current

translucent: material that transmits light, but does not allow you to see clearly through it

transistor: a semiconductor used to amplify or switch electric current

transition elements: the elements in Groups 3 through 12 on the periodic table: usually have two electrons in the outer energy level; include some familiar metals

transparent: having the property of transmitting or passing light

transverse wave: wave in which matter vibrates at right angles to the direction in which the wave travels

triatomic (try uh TAHM ik): composed of three atoms

triple covalent bond: attraction between atoms caused by sharing three pairs of electrons

tritium (TRIHT ee um): the hydrogen isotope with two neutrons and one proton in its nucleus

trough: the valley of a wave

tuning: adjusting a radio or TV to receive the broadcast carrier frequency of the radio or TV station

turbine: a rotary engine, usually large, where steam or water powers the blades

Tyndall effect: the scattering of light by particles in heterogeneous mixtures so that a light beam is visible

U

ultrasonic (uhl truh SAHN ihk): sound waves with frequencies above 20 000 hertz

ultrasound: very high frequency and intensity, but no loudness

ultraviolet radiation: invisible radiation that has a shorter wavelength than light; next to violet light in the electromagnetic spectrum

unit: a quantity adopted for measurement, as grams or centimeters

unit cell: the simplest arrangement of particles in a crystal

unsaturated hydrocarbon: a hydrocarbon in which two or more carbon atoms are joined by double or triple bonds

unsaturated: solution can dissolve more solute; molecule contains carbon-to-carbon double or triple bonds

unstable: reactive; nucleus emits a particle or radiation

V

vaporization: the change from a liquid state to a gaseous state

variable: subject to change; a quantity that is changed in an experiment

velocity (vuh LAHS ut ee): the speed and direction of a moving object

velocity of sound: speed at which sound waves travel through a medium; it is faster through warm air than through cold and faster through liquids and solids than gases

vertical: extending up and down, or at right angles to the ground

vertical velocity: velocity in a vertical direction, up or down

vibration: rapid back and forth movement

virtual image: an image formed by a mirror or lens that cannot be projected onto a surface and from which light only appears to come

viscosity: the property of a liquid that describes how it pours

visible light spectrum: band of colors produced by a prism

visible radiation: light; electromagnetic radiation with wavelengths between 0.4 and 0.7 micrometers

vitamin: an organic compound used in small amounts by cells in many of the chemical changes that take place within the body

volt (V): the SI unit of electric potential

voltage: potential difference

voltmeter: an instrument used to measure the potential difference between two points in an electric circuit

volume: loudness of a sound; determined by the amplitude of the sound wave; the amount of space occupied by an object, measured in units of length cubed

W

watt (W): the SI unit of power; one watt is one joule of work per second

wave: rhythmic disturbance that carries energy; transfers energy from one place to another

wavelength: the distance between a point on one wave to the same identical point on the next wave

weak acid: one that exists as a mixture of molecules and ions in water solution; produces relatively few hydronium ions in water

weak forces: forces that result from the attraction between positively charged nuclei in one molecule and the electron clouds in other molecules

wedge: an inclined plane with either one or two sloping sides; a simple machine

weight: the force of gravity that Earth exerts on an object resting on its surface

weightless: object that is in freefall; lacking apparent gravitational pull

weightlessness: the condition of an object in freefall

wet cell: a device for producing electric current from two metals in a chemical solution

wheel and axle: a simple machine that is a variation of the lever; consists of a large wheel fixed to a smaller wheel that rotates together

wide-angle lens: camera lens; lens with a short focal length; includes wide area in a picture

wind power: source of energy using wind-blown propeller blades connected to generators to produce electricity

wind turbine: large propeller blades connected to electric generators to produce electricity

work: the transfer of energy as a result of motion of objects

work input: the effort force multiplied by the effort distance

work output: the resistance force multiplied by the resistance distance

X rays: invisible high energy electromagnetic radiation of great penetrating power; waves with the shortest wavelengths and the highest energy

INDEX

A

acceleration: of gravity, 82–85; of motion, **60–63, 79–85;** *illus.*, 60, 62, 80, 81, 82

accuracy, 26–27

acetic acid, 326, 390

acid, 387–390; etching with, 388; ions in, **387, 392–393;** organic, 390, **403–406;** and pH, 395–397; *inv.*, organic acid, 406; titration, 402; *tables,* 390, 394

acidic anhydride, 394

acoustics, 432

actinoids, 279

action-reaction pairs, 92–93; *illus.*, 92, 93

air, *inv.*, behavior of air, 190

air resistance, 82, 83; *illus.*, 83

alcohol, 323–324, 569; *table*, 324

Alexander, Benjamin, 319

alkali metals, 268–269; *table*, 269

alkaline earth metals, 269–273; *illus.*, 269, 271; *table*, 272

alkane series of hydrocarbons, 319; *table*, 319

allotrope, 297

alloys, 281–283, 295; shape-memory, 282; *inv.*, 298; *tables,* 281, 282

alpha particle, 546

alternating current (AC), 527

aluminum, 295; *illus.*, 295; *table*, 294

Alvarez, Luis W., 42

amides, 391

amines, 391

amino acid, 328–331

ammeter, 521

ammonia, 195, 196, 391

amorphous solid, 171

ampere, 501

amplitude, 416; *illus.*, 417

angle of incidence, 455; *illus.*, 455

angle of reflection, 455; *illus.*, 455

anhydride, 394

anhydrous compound, 248; *illus.*, 248

antimony, 299; *table*, 299

applied science, 16

aqueous solution, 344

Archimedes' principle, 179–180

argon, 293; *table*, 293

Arrhenius, Svante, 389

arsenic, 299, 529, 530; *illus.*, 299; *table*, 299

artist, 450

asbestos, 309–310; *illus.*, 309

astatine, 292; *table*, 291

atom, 215–222; isotopes of, 221–222; **models of, 216, 224; parts of, 217–218; structure of, 215–217;** *illus.*, 217, 218, 221; *inv.*, atomic models, 224

atomic clock, 38; *illus.*, 37

atomic mass, 220–221; average, 227; *illus.*, 221

atomic number, 218

average atomic mass, 227

average speed, 56

B

barium, 272

base, 390–391; ions in, 390, 392–393; organic, 391; and pH, 395–397; *inv.*, 402; *tables,* 391, 394

basic anhydride, 394

battery, 499–501; *illus.*, 499, 500, 501

Becquerel, Henri, 541

benzene, 323, 349

Bernoulli, Daniel, 182

Bernoulli's principle, 181–183

beryllium, 269–270; *illus.*, 269

beta particle, 546–547

bicycle, 155–156; *illus.*, 155

bimetallic strip, 173; *illus.*, 173

binary compound, 253

biochemistry, 328

biological molecules, 328–333

biophysicist, 108

bismuth, 299; *table*, 299

block and tackle, 150

body temperature, 37

Bohr, Niels, 216

boiling, 186

boiling point, 37, 38, **184,** 187

bond: chemical, 241, **242–254;** covalent, 244, **245,** 246–247; in crystals, **245–248;** ionic, **242–243,** 244, 247; metallic, **265,** 267; and oxidation number, **249–253;** *illus.*, 243, 245, 246, 247; *inv.*, 244

boron, 294–295; *table,* 294

Boyle, Robert, 176

Boyle's law, 176

brine, 291

bromine, 291–292; *illus.*, 290; *table*, 291

Brownian motion, 200

bubble chamber, 552

buoyant force, 179–180; *illus.*, 180

buret 400, *illus.*, 400

butane, 322; *table*, 322

C

cadmium 277–278; *illus.*, 277; *table*, 278

calcium, 270–271

calcium carbonate, 307; *illus.*, 305

calcium chloride, 243, 270

calculator, 109

calorie, 112

calorimeter, 114–115; *illus.*, 114

camera, 420, 476–477; *illus.*, 466

cancellation, 431

carbohydrate, 331–332

carbon, 304–307; isotopes of, 221–222; *illus.*, 305; *table*, 306

carbonate, 306–307

carbon dioxide, 240–241, 305–306; *illus.*, 240, 305

carbon-14 dating, 551

carbon group, 304–311; *table*, 306

carbon monoxide, 305–306

carbon tetrachloride, 323, 349

carboxylic acid, 326

careers: biophysicist, 108; carpenter, 41; chemical engineer, 270; chemistry teacher, 255; commercial artist, 450; cosmetologist, 292; dry cleaning operator, 350; electrician, 502; electron microscopist, 222; environmental health technician, 565; heating, ventilation, and air conditioning technician, 132; hydraulic engineer, 174; metallurgical engineer, 145; microwave communications engineer, 525; nuclear medicine technician, 543; nu-

tritionist, 334; photographer, 470; recording engineer, 426; research chemist, 395; science textbook editor, 196; sports medicine technician, 61; stunt car driver, 80; technical writer, 12; water treatment technician, 366
carpenter, 41
Carr, Emma, 251
Carruthers, George R., 474
catalyst, 375
cathode-ray tube (CRT), 534; *illus.*, 534
cause and effect, 131
Celsius scale, 37, 38
centi-, 29
centripetal force, 88; *inv.*, 94
ceramics, 307
cerium, 279
cesium, 231–232, 267, 268, 269; *illus.*, 231
Charles, Jacques-Alexandre, 176
Charles' law, 176–177
chemical activity, 231–232; *illus.*, 232
chemical change, 206–209; *illus.*, 205, 206, 208
chemical engineer, 270
chemical properties, 204–206; *illus.*, 205; *inv.*, 207
chemical reaction, 365–382; decomposition, **371;** displacement, **371,** 373, 374; endothermic, **381–382;** and energy, **381–382;** equation for, **365–369;** exothermic, **381;** synthesis, **370;** *inv.*, displacement reactions, 374; reactions that produce gases, 372
chemist, 395
chemistry teacher, 255
Chien-Shiung, Wu, 279
chlorine, 291; isotopes of, 222; *illus.*, 290; *table*, 291
chloroform, 323
chlorophyll, 270, 333; *illus.*, 271
circular motion, 87–88; *illus.*, 88
classifying, 312
cloud chamber, 552
coal, 566, 569
cobalt, 275; *illus.*, 274; *table*, 274
coefficient, 367
coherent light, 480
colloid, 198, 200; *illus.*, 200; *tables*, 198, 200
color, 449–452; *illus.*, 451, 452, 453
commercial artist, 450
commutator, 522; *illus.*, 523
compass, 518; *illus.*, 518
complex circuit, 508–509; *illus.*, 508
compound, 196, 239–241; binary, **253;** chemical changes in, 206, 208; covalent, 245; ionic, 243; organic, 317–333; *illus.*, 196; *table*, 240
compound machine, 155–158
compound microscope, *illus.*, 476
compressional wave, 420–421; *illus.*, 421; *inv.*, 440
computer, 534–536; digital, **535;** *illus.*, 536
concave lens, 471, 472, 474; *illus.*, 471, 473
concave mirror, 466–469; *illus.*, 467, 469; *inv.*, 468
concentration, 354–355
conclusion, 8–9, 17, 447
concrete, 248
condensation, 184, 187
conduction: of electricity, 496–497; in solutions, **351–352;** of thermal energy, **121–122;** *illus.*, electricity, 496; thermal, 122; *inv.*, 138
conservation: of energy, **104–106, 566–568;** of mass, **378–379;** of momentum, **95**
constant, 18, 20, 160
control, 17–18
convection, 122; *illus.*, 122; *inv.*, 138
convex lens, 471 472, 474, 476; *illus.*, 471, 472; *inv.*, 484
convex mirror, 469; *illus.*, 469
cooling tower, 136–137; *illus.*, 137
cool stove, 123
copper, 215, 275; *table*, 277
core, 519
Cori, Gerty, 401
corrosion, 205–206
cosmetologist, 292
cotton, 197
coulomb, 501
covalent bond, 245; in crystals, 247; *illus.*, 245, 247; *inv.*, 244
crest, 415
crocoite, *illus.*, 311
crystal, 171, 245–248; covalent bonding in, 247; hydrated, **248,** 252; ionic bonding in, 246–247; network, 247; weak forces in, 245–246; *illus.*, 245, 246, 247, 248; *inv.*, hydrated crystals, 252
Curie, Marie 542
Curie, Pierre, 542
current electricity, 499–503; *illus.*, 499; *inv.*, 524
cyclohexane, 323
cysteine, 329

Dalton, John, 216
deci-, 29
decibel, 424
decomposition reaction, 371
density: comparing, 36; determining, **33,** 35; *illus.*, 35; *table,* 33
dependent variable, 18
derived unit, 33
detergent, 405; *inv.*, 406
diagrams, interpreting, 423
diamond, 247, 305; *illus.*, 305
diesel engine, 133–134
diffraction, 457–458; *illus.*, 458
diffraction grating, 460; *illus.*, 459, 460
digital computer, 535
diode, 530
direct current (DC), 527
displacement reactions, 371, 373; *illus.*, 371; *inv.*, 374
dissociation, 350
distance, 55
distillation, 293
doping, 529–530
Doppler effect, 425
double displacement reaction, 373
dry cell, 500–501; *illus.*, 500
dry cleaning operator, 350
dry ice, 306
ductility, 265
duralumin, 295

E

Edison, Thomas, 14
efficiency, 156–157
effort arm, 148
effort force, 143, 144–145
Einstein, Albert, 42, 578
electric charge, 493–495, 496–498;

and magnetic fields, **519;** *illus.*, 494; *inv.*, 495
electric circuit, 505–509; complex, **508–509;** parallel, **506,** 508–509; series, **505,** 508–509; *illus.*, 505, 506, 508; *inv.*, 507
electric current, 499–503; alternating, **527;** calculating, **503;** direct, **527;** production of, **525–528;** *illus.*, 499; *inv.*, 524
electric energy, calculating, **511–512**
electrician, 502
electricity, 493–512; calculating usage of, **511–512;** conduction of, **496–497;** current, **499-503;** static, **493–495;** *illus.*, conduction, 496; current, 499, 500, 501, 502; static, 494; *inv.*, electrostatics, 495
electric meter, 521; *illus.*, 521; *inv.*, 531
electric motor, 521–523; *illus.*, 522, 523
electric potential, 501; *illus.*, 501
electric power, 509–510
electrolysis, 208, 209; *illus.*, 208
electrolyte, 351
electromagnet, 518–519; *inv.*, 520
electromagnetic spectrum, 441–442
electron, 217–220; and bonding, **242–245;** in metals, 230; in nonmetals, 230; *illus.*, 220
electron cloud, 218–220; *illus.*, 218, 219
electronics, 528–536
electron microscope, *illus.*, 15
electron microscopist, 222
electroscope, 497–498, 552; *illus.*, 497, 552
element, 195–196, 215–216; chemical activity of, 231–232; **groups of, 227;** metal, 230, 265–273; metalloid, 230; nonmetal, 230; **period of, 230–231; radioactive, 541–542;** symbols of, 215–216; **synthetic, 542; transition,** 231, **273–279;** *illus.*, 196; *table*, symbols, 216
emulsion, 200
endothermic reaction, 381–382
endpoint, 400
energy, 101–116, 563–580; alternative sources of, **568–580;** and chemical reactions, 381–382; conservation of, **104–106, 566–568;** electric, **511–512;** geothermal, **574,** 576; hydroelectric, 571–572; kinetic, **102;** mechanical, **103, 107;** nuclear, 576–580; potential, **102–103;** solar, **130,** 570–571; thermal, **108–116;** thermonuclear, **579–580;** tidal, **574;** wind, **572,** 574; and work, **103–104,** 107; *inv.*, solar energy, 573; thermal energy, 116; uses, 575; work, 107, *table*, petroleum, 564
energy level, 220; *illus.*, 220
energy resources: nonrenewable, **566;** renewable, **570–576**
engine, 132–135; *illus.*, 132, 133, 134
environmental health technician, 565
enzymes, 329, 375
equations, 41–43, 365–369; balancing, **367–369,** 376; mass relationships in, **380–381**
ester, 403–404; *table*, 403
esterification, 403
etching, 388
ethanol, 323, 349, 569
ethene, 320
ethyne, 320
evaporation, 185, 186–187
exothermic reaction, 381
experiment, 17–18; designing, 348; *illus.*, 18
eye, 449, 473–474

F

falling objects, 81–85
family, of elements, 227
Faraday, Michael, 525
farsightedness, 474; *illus.*, 473
fats, 332, 333
fiberglass, 124
fiber-reinforced plastics, 318
film, 443
Fischer, Emil, 375
fission, 555–556; *illus.*, 556
flame tests, 267–268; *inv.*, 266; *table*, 267
floppy disk, 536; *illus.*, 536
flow charts, 284
fluid, 179–183; and **convection, 122**
fluorine, 232, 290–291; *illus.*, 232; *table*, 291
fluorocarbon gases, 291
focal length, 467; *illus.*, 477
focal point, 466–467, 469
force: action-reaction, 92–93; buoyant, 179–180; calculating, 81; centripetal, 88, 94; **effort, 143,** 144–145; **measuring, 72,** 73; **and motion, 65–73,** 81; **net, 66,** 179; resistance, 143–144; weak, 245–246; *illus.*, 66, 67, 69, 70, 71, 180; *inv.*, centripetal, 94; measuring, 72
formaldehyde, 338–339
formic acid, 390
formula, 240; for organic compounds, **318–320;** structural, **319;** writing, **249–253,** 256; *table*, compounds, 240
formula mass, 380
fossil fuels, 563–566; *table*, 564
fractional distillation, 565
Franklin, Benjamin, 493
Franklin, Rosalind, 9
Frasch process, 301; *illus.*, 301
freefall, 90–91
freezing poing, 37, 38, **184**
Freon, 187–188
frequency, of wave, **416,** 418, **419**
friction, 69–70; *illus.*, 69
fuel: alternative, **568–580;** fossil, **563–566**
fulcrum, 148
fusion, 556–558; heat of, **185;** *illus.*, 556

G

galena, *illus.*, 311
Galilei, Galileo, 65, 82
gallium, 295, 529–530; *illus.*, 295
gamma rays, 446, 448, 547; *illus.*, 546
gas, 170, 175–177, 179–183; **condensation of, 184;** and heat, 174; natural, 565–566; **noble, 227,** 241, **293;** particles in, 171; pressure of, 175–177; volume of, 176–177; *illus.*, 170, 171, 175, 176, 177; *inv.*, air, 190; reactions that produce gas, 372
gasification, 569; *illus.*, 569
Gay-Lussac, Joseph, 176
Geiger counter, 544, **553;** *illus.*, 553
Geiger-Müller tube, 553; *illus.*, 553
generator, 525–526; *illus.*, 526
geothermal energy, 574, 576; *illus.*, 574

germanium, 226, 310; *table,* 306
Gilbert, William, 517, 518
glass, 308–309; *illus.*, 309
glucose, 331–332
glycine 329
gold, 275, 281; *illus.*, 275; *table*, 277
Gourdine, Meredith, 503
graphing, 43–45, 46; *illus.*, 44; *inv.*, 59
graphite, 304; *illus.*, 305
gravity: acceleration of, 85; and falling objects, 81–85; **force of, 70–71**
group: of elements, **227;** reactivity of, 241
gypsum, 250

H

half-life, 547–550; *illus.*, 547; *inv.*, 548; *table*, 549
halogen family, 227, 241, 290–292; *illus.*, 290; *table*, 291
harmony, 429
heat, 108–116, 121–138; of fusion, 185; specific, 112, 115; of vaporization, 186; and work, 111, 130–137; *inv.*, conduction and convection, 138; radiation, 127
heat engine, 132–135; *illus.*, 132, 133, 134
heating, ventilation, and air conditioning technician, 132
heating systems, 128–130; radiator, **128–129;** solar, **130;** *illus.*, 128, 129, 130
heat mover, 135
heat pump, 135, 187–188
heat transfer, 121–126; conduction, **121–122;** convection, **122;** radiation, **122–124;** *illus.*, 122, 123; *inv.*, 127, 138
helium, 227, 241, 293; *table*, 293
hertz, 416
heterogeneous mixture, 197; *illus.*, 197
homogeneous mixture, 198
horizontal velocity, 86–87
hydrate, 248, 250
hydrated crystals, 248; *inv.*, 252
hydraulic engineer, 174
hydrocarbon, 318–322; saturated, **319;** substituted, **323;** unsaturated, **320;** *table*, alkane series, 319
hydrochloric acid, 389–390
hydroelectricity, 571–572; *illus.*, 571
hydrogen, 215, 289–290; isotopes of, 221; *illus.*, 221
hydronium ion, 387, 392; *illus.*, 392
hydroxide ion, 390, 392; *illus.*, 392
hypothesis, 8, 17

I

image, 466–472; real, **467,** 471–472; virtual, **466,** 469; *illus.*, 466, 467, 469, 472; *inv.*, 468
inclined plane, 152–154; *illus.*, 152, 154; *inv.*, 153
independent variable, 18
indicator, 396–397; natural, 405; using, 398; *illus.*, 396, 397
inertia, 65; *illus.*, 65
inference, 6, 9
infrared radiation, 444–445
inhibitor, 377
insulation, 124–126, 496; *illus.*, 125, 126; *table*, 124
integrated circuit (IC), 532; *illus.*, 532
interference: light, 459–460; sound, **430–431;** *illus.*, 459
internal combustion engine, 133–134 *illus.*, 132, 133
international system of units, 26; *table*, prefixes, 26
Io, *illus.*, 300
iodine, 232, 293, 353; *illus.*, 290, 353; *table*, 291
iodoform, 323
ion: in acids and bases, **387,** 390, **392–393;** polyatomic, **253–254**
ionic bond, 242–243; in crystals, 246–247; *illus.*, 243, 247; *inv.*, 244
iridium, 281
iron, 274; *illus.*, 280; *table*, 274
isobutane, 322; *table*, 322
isomer, 322
isotope, 221–222; *illus.*, 221

J

Joliot-Curie, Irene, 547
Joule, James Prescott, 102, 105, 112, 113
joule (unit), 102

K

Kamerlingh-Onnes, Heike, 498
Kelvin scale, 38
Kepler, Johannes, 545
kilo-, 30
kilogram, 31
kilowatt, 158
kilowatt-hour, 511
kinetic energy, 102; *illus.*, 102, 105
kinetic theory of matter, 170–171
krypton, 293; *table*, 293

L

labeling, 39
laboratory safety, 39–41
lanthanoids, 278–279; *illus.*, 278
Large Magellenic Cloud (LMC), 545
laser, 479, **480–481;** *illus.*, 481
Lavoisier, Antoine, *illus.*, 367
Lavoisier, Marie-Anne, *illus.*, 367
law, 9–10; Boyle's, 176; Charles', 176–177; of conservation of energy, 105–106; of conservation of momentum, 95; of motion, 66–67, 79–81, 91–93; Ohm's, 503
lead, 310; *illus.*, 311; *table*, 306
length, 29–30
lens, 470–477; camera, 476–477; concave, **471,** 472, 474; convex, **471,** 472, 474, 476, 484; microscope, **476;** telephoto, **477;** telescope, **474–475;** and vision, 473–474; wide-angle, **477;** *illus.*, 471, 472, 473, 475; *inv.*, 484
lever, 148–149; *illus.*, 148, 149
Libby, Willard, 551
light, 445, **449–460;** coherent, **480;** and color, 449–452; diffraction of, 457–458; interference in, 459–460; of laser, **479, 480–481;** polarized, **479–480;** reflection of, 455, 465–469; refraction of, 455–457, 471–472; wave properties of, **453–460;** *illus.*, 466, 480; *inv.*, 454
lightning rod, 497
lime, 271
limestone, 270
lipid, 332
liquid, 170, 179–183; boiling point of, 184; evaporation of, 185; and heat, 173–174; supercooled, **308;** viscosity of, **171;** *illus.*, 170, 171
liquid crystal display (LCD), 483
liter, 32
lithium, 232, 269; *illu.*, 268

litmus paper, 396; *illus.*, 396
loudness, 422, 424

M

machine, 143–159; compound, **155–158;** efficiency of, **156–157;** mechanical advantage of, **144–146;** power of, **157–159;** simple, **143–154;** *inv.*, inclined plane, 153; pulleys, 147
macromolecule, 247
magnesium, 270; *illus.*, 271
magnet, 517–518; permanent, **518;** *illus.*, 518
magnetic field, 518–519; and electric charges, **519;** *illus.*, 519; *inv.*, 520
magnetic poles, 517; *illus.*, 518
magnifying glass, 472; *illus.*, 472
malleability, 265
Marcet, Jane, 369
Martinez, Jose V., 566
mass: atomic, 220–221; conservation of, 378–379; in equations, 380–381; formula, 380; measurement of, **31; molecular, 379**
Massey, Walter E., 104
mass number, 220–221
matter, 195–210; chemical changes in, **206–209;** chemical properties of, **204–206,** 207; classifying, 210; composition of, **195–200;** kinetic theory of, **170–171;** physical changes in, **204;** physical properties of **202–203;** states of, **169–170,** 172, **184–188;** *inv.*, change of state, 172; chemical properties, 207; mixtures, 201
Mayer, Julius Robert, 105
measurement, 25–38; of density, **33,** 35–37; of force, 72, **73;** of length, **29–30;** of mass, **31;** of speed, **56–57;** of temperature, **37–38, 112–114;** of time, **37;** uncertainty in, **26–28;** of volume, **32,** 34
mechanical advantage, 144–146; of inclined plane, 152; **of lever, 149;** of pulley, 147, 150; **of wheel and axle, 151–152**
mechanical energy, 103; *inv.*, 107
melting, 185–186; *illus.*, 185
melting point, 184, 187
Mendeleev, Dimitri, 225, 226
mercury, 278; *table*, 278
metal, 265–283; alkali, **268–269;** alkaline earth, **269–273;** alloy, **281;** chemical activity of, 232; electrons in, 230; ores, 280; properties of, **265;** transition, 231, 273–279; *inv.*, flame tests, 266; metals and alloys, 298; metals and nonmetals, 234; transition elements, 276; *tables*, alloys, 281, 282; flame tests, 267; oxidation numbers, 249; transition elements, 274, 277, 278
metallic bond, 265, 267
metalloid, 230, 294; *illus.*, 231
metallurgical engineer, 145
meter, 29; *illus.*, 29
methane, 320, 565–566; *illus.*, 320
methanol, 324, 569
Metric Conversion Act, 27
microprocessor, 536
microwave, 444; *illus.*, 444
microwave communications engineer, 525
milli-, 30
mimetite, *illus.*, 311
mirror, 465–469, 480; concave, **466–469;** convex, **469;** plane, **465–466;** *illus.*, 466, 467, 469, *inv.*, 468
misch metal, 279
mixture, 197–201; heterogeneous, **197;** homogeneous, **198;** separation of, 199; *illus.*, 197, 198, 200; *inv.*, 201; *tables*, 198, 200
model: of atom, 216; scientific, **10;** *illus.*, 10, 217, 218
model making, 325
modulated radio waves, 442; *illus.*, 442
mole, 400
molecular mass, 379
molecule, 245
Molina, Mario, 310
momentum, 91–96; conservation of, 95; *illus.*, 95
Morrison, Philip, 425
Moseley, Henry, 227
motion, 54–73, 79–96; accelerated, **60–63, 79–85;** circular, 87–88; energy of, **102;** of falling objects, **81–85;** and force, **65–73, 81;** laws of, **66–67, 79–81, 91–93;** and momentum, **91–96;** and speed, **56–58;** in a straight line, **55–63;** in two different directions, **86–91;** and weightlessness, **90–91;** *inv.*, centripetal force, 94; speed, 59; velocity, 84
motor, 521–523; *illus.*, 522, 523
music, 426–430, 434; *inv.*, 428
musical instruments, 429–430; *illus.*, 429, 430

N

natural gas, 565–566
Neal, Homer, 218
nearsightedness, 474; *illus.*, 473
neodymium, 279; *illus.*, 278
neon, 293; *table*, 293
net force, 66, 179
network crystal, 247
neutralization, 397, 399
neutron, 218
Newton, Isaac, 5, 66, **95**
newton (unit), **80**
Newton's laws of motion: first, **66–67,** 79; second, **79–81;** third, **91–93**
nickel, 275; *illus.*, 275; *table*, 274
nitric acid, 389
nitrogen, 296; *illus.*, 296; *table*, 299
nitrogen group, 296–299; *table*, 299
noble gas family, 227, 241, 293; *table*, 293
noise pollution, 433–434
nonelectrolyte, 352
nonmetal, 230, 232, **289–292;** *illus.*, 230; *inv.*, 234; *table*, oxidation numbers, 249
nonrenewable resources, 566
nuclear emulsion, 552
nuclear energy, 576–580
nuclear fission, 555–556; *illus.*, 556
nuclear fusion, 556–558; *illus.*, 556
nuclear medicine technician, 543
nuclear radiation, 546–547
nuclear reactions, 555–558
nuclear reactor, 576–578; *illus.*, 577
nuclear waste, 578–579
nucleus, 217
nuclide, 542–545; *illus.*, 547; *table*, 544
nutritionist, 334

O

observation, 6, **8,** 9, 17
Ocampo, Adriana, 529
octave, *illus.*, 427
Øersted, Hans Christian, 518
ohm (unit), **502**
Ohm's law, 503

oil, 563–565
oil shale, 569
opal, *illus.*, 307
opaque material, 449
optical axis, 466
optical fibers, 481–483; *illus.*, 482
optics, 445
organic acid, 390, 403–406; *inv.*, 406
organic bases, 391
organic chemistry, 317
organic compound, 317–333; formulas for, **318–320;** hydrocarbon, **318–322;** isomer, **322;** naming, 329; polymer, **326–328;** *inv.*, 321, 330
organic molecule, *inv.*, 321
oxidation number, 249–253; *tables*, 249, 251
oxygen, 299–300; *inv.*, 303; *table*, 302
oxygen group, 299–303; *inv.*, 303; *table*, 302

P

parallel circuit, 506, 508–509; *illus.*, 506
particle colliders, 90
Pascal, Blaise, 181
pascal (unit), **175**
Pascal's principle, 180–181
peptide linkage, 331
period, of elements, **230–231**
periodic table: structure of, **225–232;** *illus.*, 226, 227, 228–229, 230
permanent magnet, 518
perpetual motion toys, 522
petroleum, 563–565, 569; *table*, 564
PET scan, *illus.*, 544
pH, 395–397
phenolphthalein, 396
phosphate, 297
phosphorus, 296–297; *illus.*, 296, 297; *table*, 299
photoconductor, 301–302
photographer, 470
photographic film, 443
photosynthesis, 333
photovoltaic cells, 570–571; *illus.*, 570
physical change, 204
physical property, 202–203; *illus.*, 203
physical science, 16–17
pigment, 451–452; *illus.*, 452
pitch, 424–425; *inv.*, 428
plane mirror, 465–466; *illus.*, 466
plasma, 169
plastics, 318, 326–327
platinum, 281
Pockels, Agnes, 206
polarized light, 479–480; *illus.*, 480
polar molecule, 349–351; *illus.*, 351
pollution: noise, **433–434;** thermal, **136–137**
polonium, 542; *table*, 302
polyatomic ion, 253–254; *illus.*, 253; *table*, 254
polyester, 197
polymer, 326–328; *illus.*, 326; *table*, 328
position, 55
potassium, 269
potassium bromide, 351
potential difference, 501; *illus.*, 501
potential energy, 102–103; *illus.*, 103, 105
power, 157–159; electric, 509–510
precipitate, 367; identifying, 382; *illus.*, 373
preservative, 377; *illus.*, 377
pressure, 175–177
problem solving, 11–14; 1-Chinese puzzle, 19; 2-making an instrument to measure density of liquids, 45; 3-gravity problem, 74; 4-saved by the book, 96; 5-roll-back toy, 114; 6-summer breezes, 136; 7-designing a complex machine, 159; 8-behavior of air, 189, 9-classifying matter, 210; 10-placing elements into a periodic table, 233; 11-water softening, 243; 12-qualitative analysis scheme, 283; 13-minerals in garden soil, 311; 14-naming organic compounds, 329; 15-solution viscosity, 357; 16-identifying precipitates, 382; 17-making natural indicators, 405; 18-playing music, 434; 19-wavelengths, 456; 20-mirror images, 480; 21-electric circuits, 512; 22-use of diodes, 535; 23-nuclear weapons research, 558; 24-solar energy, 580
product, 366
program, computer, **535**
projectiles, 86–87; *illus.*, 86, 87
propanoic acid, 390
property, 16; chemical, 204–206; physical, 202–203; *illus.*, 203, 205; *inv.*, 207
protein, 328, 331
proton, 218
pulley, 150; *illus.*, 146, 150; *inv.*, 147

Q

qualitative analysis scheme, 283
quark, 218

R

radiation, 439–448; gamma rays, 446, 448; **infrared, 444–445;** microwave, 444; **nuclear, 546–547;** radio waves, 442–444; **of thermal energy, 122–124;** ultraviolet, 445–446; **visible, 445;** X ray, 446, 448; *illus.*, 122, 123; *inv.*, 127
radiation counters, 553; *illus.*, 553
radiation detectors, 552
radiation protection, *inv.*, 554
radiator, 128–129; *illus.*, 128
radioactive decay, 541, 546–550; *illus.*, 547; *inv.*, 548; *table*, 549
radioactive elements, 541–542; *table*, 549
radioactivity, 541–545
radio transmission, 533; *illus.*, 533
radio waves, 442–444
radium, 272–273, 542
radon, 293; *table*, 293
radon detection and reduction, 7, 9; *illus.*, 7, 8
rare earth elements, 279
reactant, 366
reaction, thermonuclear, 557–558. *See also* Chemical reaction
real image, 467, 471–472; *illus.*, 467, 472
recording engineer, 426
rectifier, 529
reflecting telescope, 474–475; *illus.*, 475
reflection, 455, 465–469; total internal, **481–482**
refracting telescope, 474; *illus.*, 475
refraction, 455–457, 471–472; *illus.*, 456, 457, 458, 471, 472
refrigerator, 187–188; *illus.*, 188
reinforcement, 430–431

renewable energy sources, 570–576
research chemist, 395
resistance, 501–503; calculating, **503;** *illus.,* 502
resistance arm, 148
resistance force, 143–144
reverberation, 432
Richards, Ellen Swallow, 355
rockets, 95–96
Roentgen, W. K., 446
room temperature, 37
Ross, Mary G., 180
rubidium 267, 268, 269
rust, *illus.,* 370
rust protection, 204
Rutherford, Ernest, 216
R-value, 124–125; *table,* 124

S

safety, 39–41; *table,* symbols, 40
salt, and neutralization, **397, 399.** *See also* sodium chloride
saponification, 404
satellite, motion of, 88
saturated hydrocarbon, 319
saturated solutions, 356–357
scale drawings, 478
scanning tunneling microscope (STM), 219
science: applied, **16;** physical, **16–17;** and technology, **15–16**
science textbook editor, 196
scientific literature, evaluating, 567
scientific methods, 8–10, 17–18
scientific model, 10
screw, 154; *illus.,* 154
selenium, 301–302; *table,* 302
semiconductor, 295, 529–530; *illus.,* 529
series circuit, 505, 508–509; *illus.,* 506
shape-memory alloys, 282
SI, 26; *table,* prefixes, 26
signal, 530
significant digits, 27–28
silica, 308–309
silicates, 308
silicon, 307–310, 529–530; *illus.,* 308, 309; *table,* 306
silicon carbide, *illus.,* 247
silicon dioxide, 307, 308–309
silicone, 309
silicon nitride, 310
silver, 277; *table,* 277
silver chloride, *illus.,* 373
simple machines, 143–154
single displacement reaction, 371
single lens reflex camera, 477
skills: asking the right question, 178, carbon-14 dating, 551; classifying, 312; comparing densities, 36; designing an experiment, 348; determining cause and effect, 131; determining constants and variables, 160; drawing conclusions, 447; evaluating scientific literature, 567; graphing, 46; identifying variables and constants, 20; inferring, 6; interpreting diagrams, 423; making models, 325; making scale drawings, 478; measuring volume, 34; observing, 6; predicting, 223; separating a mixture, 205; solving a problem, 13; solving a word problem, 64; study skills, 89; understanding statistics, 504; using a calculator, 109; using flow charts, 284; using indicators, 398; writing balanced chemical equations 376; writing chemical formulas, 256
slingshot effect, 112
soap, 404–405; *inv.,* 406
sodium, 269
sodium chloride, 241, 242–243, 247, 350; *illus.,* 247, 351, 352; *inv.,* acid-base titration, 402; solubility in water, 358
sodium hydroxide, 390–391
solar energy, 130, **570–571;** *inv.,* 573
solar heating system, 130; *illus.,* 129, 130
solar-powered automobiles, 568
solid, 170; amorphous, 171; and heat, 173; melting point of, 184; particles in, 170–171; sublimation of, **185;** *illus.,* 170, 171, 173, 185
solubility, 353–354; *table,* 353
solute, 344
solution, 198, 343–360; aqueous, 344; concentration of, 354–355; as conductor, 351–352; pH of, 395–397; process of, 344–345; rate of, 345–347; saturated, 356–357; standard, 400; supersaturated, 357; unsaturated, 357; *illus.,* 345, 346, 347; *inv.,* freezing and boiling a solution, 360; solubility of salt, 358; *tables,* 198, 344
solvent, 344, 349
Somerville, Mary, 124
sound, 419–434; control of, **432–434;** and Doppler effect, **425;** interference in, **430–431;** loudness of, **422, 424;** musical, **426–430;** pitch of, **424–425;** and pollution, **433–434;** reflection of, 432; velocity of, **422**
specific heat, 112; determining, **115**
spectator ion, 368
spectrum: electromagnetic, **441–442;** *illus.,* 458, 459, 460; *inv.,* of light, 454
speed: average, 56; determining, 57–58; and velocity, 56–57; *inv.,* 59
speedometer, *illus.,* 56
sports medicine technician, 61
standard, 26
standard solution, 400
starch, 331, 332
states of matter, 169–170; changes of, 172, **184–188;** and kinetic theory of matter, **170–171;** and thermal expansion, **173–174;** *inv.,* change of state, 172
static electricity, 493–495; *illus.,* 494; *inv.,* 495
statistics, 504
steam turbine, 135; *illus.,* 134
steel, 283; *illus.,* 280; *table,* 282
stereo microscope, *illus.,* 476
strontium, 271–272
structural formula, 319
study skills, 89
stunt car driver, 80
sublimation, 185
subscript, 240
substance, 195–196
substituted hydrocarbon, 323; *illus.,* 323
sucrose, 332
sugar, 331–332, 352; *illus.,* 352
sulfur, 300–301; *illus.,* 300, 301; *table,* 302
sulfuric acid, 388–389; *illus.,* 388, 389
superconductors, 498
supercooled liquid, 308
supernova, 545

supersaturated solution, 357; *illus.*, 357
suspension, 198; *illus.*, 198; *table*, 198
symbols, of elements, 215–216; *table*, 216
synthesis, 370
synthesis reaction, 370
synthetic elements, 542

T

tangram, 19
technical writer, 12
technology, 15–16; ceramics, 307; cool stove, 123; enzymes, 375; etching with acids, 388; fiber-reinforced plastics, 318; focusing a camera with sound, 420; gypsum, 250; knuckleball, 182; labeling and safety, 39; liquid crystal displays, 483; particle colliders, 90; perpetual motion toys, 522; photographic film, 443; radon detection and reduction, 7, 8; rust protection, 204; scanning tunnelling microscope, 219; **science and technology, 15;** shape-memory alloys, 282; slingshot effect, 112; smart cars, 68; solar-powered automobiles, 568; superconductors, 498; supernova, 545; toilet, 345
telephoto lens, 477
telescope, 474–475; *illus.*, 475
television transmission, 533–534
tellurium, 302; *table*, 302
temperature: measurement of, 37–38, 112–114; and **thermal energy, 110**
terminal velocity, 83; *illus.*, 83
textiles, *inv.*, 330
theory, 9–10
thermal energy, 108–116, 121–138; measuring changes in, 113–114; preventing loss of, 124–127; and **temperature, 110; transfer of, 121–126,** and 138; *illus.*, 108, 111; *inv.*, 116; *table*, R-values, 124
thermal expansion, 173–174; *illus.*, 173
thermal pollution, 136–137
thermography, 126; *illus.*, 126
thermometer, *illus.*, 110
thermonuclear energy, 579–580
thermonuclear reaction, 557–558
Thompson, Benjamin, 101
Thompson, J. J., 216
tidal energy, 574; *illus.*, 574
tin, 280, 310; isotopes of, 222; *illus.*, 310; *table*, 306
Tinoco, Ignacio, Jr., 445
titration, 400–401; *inv.*, 402
toilet, flushing mechanism of, 345
tone quality, 429
total internal reflection, 481–482; *illus.*, 482
transformer, 527–528; *illus.*, 527
transistor, 530; *illus.*, 530
transition element, 231, **273–279;** properties of, **273–274;** *illus.*, 273, 274, 275, 277, 278; *inv.*, 276; *tables*, 274, 277, 278
translucent material, 449
transparent material, 449
transverse wave, 416; *illus.*, 421; *inv.*, 440
travertine, *illus.*, 271
triatomic, 300
trough, 415
turbine, 135; *illus.*, 134
Tyndall effect, 200; *inv.*, 201

U

ultrasound, 421
ultraviolet radiation, 445–446; *illus.*, 445, 446
unit: derived, 33; of energy, **102;** of force, **80;** of frequency, **416;** of length, **29–30;** of mass, **31;** of measurement, **25–26;** of power, **158;** of pressure, **175;** of time, **37;** of volume, **32;** *illus.*, 26; *table*, 26
unsaturated hydrocarbon, 320
unsaturated solution, 357
uranium, 541

V

vaporization, heat of, 186
variable: dependent, **18;** determining, 160; identifying, **20;** independent, **18**
velocity: horizontal, 86–87; of sound, 422; and speed, 56–57; terminal, 83; vertical, 87; of wave; 417; *inv.*, 84
vertical velocity, 87
vinegar, 197–198, 326; *illus.*, 349
virtual image, 466, 469; *illus.*, 466, 469
viscosity, 171, 356; *illus.*, 171
visible radiation, 445
vision: color, **449;** and lenses, **473–474**
vitamin, 332–333
volt, 501
voltage, 501
voltmeter, 521
volume, measurement of, **32–33,** 34; *illus.*, 33

W

Walker, John, 16
water: boiling point of, 37, 38; composition of, 195, 196, 240; electrolysis of, **208;** freezing point of, 37, 38; melting point of, **185;** as solvent, **349;** *illus.*, 240
water treatment technician, 366
watt, 158
wave, 415–419; characteristics of, **415–416;** compressional, **420–421,** 440; frequency of, **416,** 418, 419; radio, 442–444; transverse, 416, 440; velocity of, **417;** *illus.*, 416; *inv.*, 418, 440
wavelength, 416; *illus.*, 417
weak force, 245–256
wedge, 154; *illus.*, 154
weight, and gravity, 70–71
weightlessness, 90–91 *illus.*, 90, 91
wet cell, 499–500; *illus.*, 499, 500
wheel and axle, 151–152; illus., 151
wide-angle lens, 477
wind energy, 572, 574
wind turbines, 572; *illus.*, 572
word problem, solving, 64
work, 103; calculating, 104; and energy transfer, 103–104; and heat, 111, 130–137; *illus.*, 107; *inv.*, 107, 116

X

xenon, 293; *table*, 293
X ray, 446, 448; *illus.*, 448

Y

Young, Thomas, 457, 459–460
yttrium, 279

Z

zinc, 277; *table*, 278

PHOTO CREDITS

2–3, Brian Parker/Science Photo Library/Photo Researchers, (insets, l-r) file photo, file photo, George Matchneer, file photo; **4,** S. Schwartzenburg, courtesy of San Francisco Exploratorium; **7,** courtesy of American Electric Power; **8,** Doug Martin; **9,** Tom Pantages; **12,** Ted Rice; **15**(l) Lennart Nilsson/Boehringer Ingelheim, (r) courtesy IBM; 16(l) David Falconer/Frazier Photolibrary, (r) Lynn McAfee/FPG; **17,** Doug Martin; **24,** Tim Courlas; **26**(t) Nat'l. Bureau of Standards, (b) from "Nonferrous Metals", Beijing; **31,** Doug Martin; **32,** Tim Courlas; **33,** Hickson-Bender; **35,** Doug Martin; **37**(t) Allen Zak, (b) Nat'l. Bureau of Standards; **41,** Cobalt Productions; **50,** Tom McGuire; **52–53,** P. Aventurier/Gamma-Liaison, (insets, l-r) Library of Congress, Ann Rowan Picture Library, Library of Congress; **54,** Frank Jensen/The Stock Solution; **56**(t) Tim Courlas, (b) courtesy of Ford Motor Company; **62,** Tim Courlas; **65,** courtesy of General Motors; **66,** Mindy Paderewsky; **67,** Patrick Grace/Photo Researchers; **68,** courtesy of ETAK; **69**(l) H.M. DeCruyenaere, (r) H. Armstrong Roberts; **70,** Reprinted by permission from "Nature", Vol. 311, No. 5983, cover copyright © 1984 Macmillian Journals Ltd.; **78,** Tim Courlas; **80,** Cameramann International; **81,** H.M. DeCruyenaere; **82,** Kodansha; **83**(t) Dwight R. Kuhn/Bruce Coleman, Inc., (b) courtesy of General Motors; **84,87,** Kodansha; **88,** David Madison/Bruce Coleman, Inc.; **90**(l) H.M. DeCruyenaere, (r) NASA; **91,** NASA; **92,** Cobalt Productions; **93,** file photo; **95,** Hickson-Bender; **100,** Duane Elliott/Four Wheeler Magazine; **102,** Francois Gohier/Photo Researchers; **103,** Cobalt Productions; **105,** Tim Courlas; **108,** file photo; **110,** Hickson-Bender; **113,** file photo; **120,** O. Brown, R. Evans & J. Brown, University of Miami/RSMAS; **122,** Hickson-Bender; **123,** courtesy of Gas Research Institute; **125,** Hickson-Bender; **126,** AIRSCAN™ Thermogram by Daedalus Enterprises, Inc.; **128,** Cobalt Productions; **129,** Keith Philpott; **132,** courtesy of Ford Motor Company; **134**(l) courtesy of Burndy Library, (r) Dick Luria/FPG; **135,** Tim Courlas; **136,** Geri Murphy; **137,** Alan Benoit; **142,** Susan Marquart; **146**(l) Tim Courlas, (r) Ted Rice; **147,** Hickson-Bender; **148,** Allen Zak; **149**(l) David Madison/Bruce Coleman, Inc., (c) Tim Courlas, (r) Walter Grogan/Spectra-Action, Inc.; **150,** Doug Martin; **151,** Larry Hamill; **152,** Cobalt Productions; **154**(l) Cobalt Productions, (r) Hickson-Bender; **155,** Doug Martin; **156,** Tim Courlas; **158**(l) Cobalt Productions, (r) Pictures Unlimited; **164,** courtesy of Van Geld, Inc.; **166–167,** file photo, (insets, l-r) NASA, Library of Congress, North Wind Picture Archives, North Wind Picture Archives; **168,** Latent Image; **170**(l) Bob Firth, (c) Gerard Photography, (r) Larry Hamill; **171,** Larry Hamill; **173**(t) Cobalt Productions, (b) Tim Courlas; **174,** Doug Martin; **177,** Hickson-Bender; **180,** H. Armstrong Roberts; **181,** Ed Robinson/Tom Stack & Associates; **182,** Ted Rice; **183,** courtesy of Beech Aircraft Corporation; **185**(l) Cobalt Productions, (r) Gerard Photography; **187,** John Elk III; **194,** R. Thomas/FPG; **196,** Ted Rice; **197,** Pat Lanza Field/Bruce Coleman, Inc.; **198,** Tim Courlas; **200**(l) Cobalt Productions, (r) Michael J. Pettypool/Uniphoto; **203**(t) Cobalt Productions, (b) Gerard Photography; **205,** (t) Hickson Bender, (bl) Roz Joseph/Light Images, (br) Dan McGarrah/Light Images; **208,** Tom Stack/Tom Stack & Associates; **214,** Tim Çourlas; **216,** file photo; **218,** Tersch; **219,** Larry Hamill; **222,** Cobalt Productions; **226**(t) Sovfoto/Eastfoto, (b) Linda Young; **230**(t) Tim Courlas, (b) Hickson-Bender; **238,** Dan McCoy from Rainbow; **242,** courtesy of Morton Salt Div. of Morton/Norwich; **245,** Chip Clark/Smithsonian Institution; **246**(t) Gary Milburn/Tom Stack & Associates, (b) Doug Martin; **247**(t) Pat Lynch/Photo Researchers, (b) Hickson-Bender; **248,** Doug Martin; **250,253,** Hickson-Bender; **255,** Tim Courlas; **260,** Kevin Fitzsimmons; **262–263,** John Shaw, (insets, l-r) courtesy of Franklin Institute, John Hancock Mutual Life Insurance Company, courtesy of Neils Bohr Library, Library of Congress; **264,** Runk/Schoenberger from Grant Heilman; **267,** Lester V. Bergman & Associates; **268,** Doug Martin; **269**(t) Eric Hoffhines, (b) Linda Young; **270,** Tim Courlas; **271**(tl) Hickson-Bender, (tc) Eric Hoffhines, (tr) Larry Hamill, (b) Roger K. Burnard; **272,** Eric Hoffhines; **273,** Tim Courlas; **274**(t) Jim Brady and Kathy Bendo, (b) Linda Young; **275**(t) Doug Martin, (b) David C. Rentz/Bruce Coleman, Inc.; **277**(t) Linda Young, (b) Dan McCoy from Rainbow; **278**(t) Linda Young, (b) Ad Image; **280,** Cameramann International; **281,** Manfred P. Kage/Peter Arnold, Inc.; **288,** Glen Thomas Brown/The Stock Solution; **290**(t) The Bettman Archive, (b) Doug Martin; **291,** Larry Hamill; **292**(t) Ruth Dixon, (b) Tim Courlas; **293,** Argonne National Laboratory; **294,** Eric Hoffhines; **295,** E.R. Degginger; **296**(t) Carolina Biological Supply, (b) Eric Hoffhines; **297**(t) Tim Courlas, (b) Hickson-Bender; **299**(t) Young/Hoffhines, (b) Elaine Comer-Shay; **300**(t) Rich Brommer, (b) JPL; 301, Frank S. Balthis; **302,** Linda Young; **305**(tl) Doug Martin, (tr) Tom Stack/Tom Stack & Associates, (bl) Cobalt Productions, (br) L. Jacobs/H. Armstrong Roberts; **306,** Linda Young; **307,** Stewart/FPG; **308,** D. Briskin/Tom Stack & Associates; **309**(tl) Wendler/FPG, (tc) Hickson-Bender, (tr) Cobalt Productions, (b) William E. Ferguson; **310,** USDA; **311,** Breck P. Kent; **317,** Tim Courlas; **319,** Doug Martin; **323,** Allen Zak; **324,** H. Carroll/FPG; **326,** Pictures Unlimited; **329,** Gerard Photography; **331,** NIH/Science Source; **334,** Tim Courlas; **338,** Ted Rice; **339,** Voigt/Zefa/H. Armstrong Roberts; **340–341,** Wesley Bocxe/Photo Researchers, (insets, l-r) file photo, file photo, Mark Twain Memorial, Hartford, CT, courtesy Neils Bohr Library; **342,** G. Abrens/H. Armstrong Roberts; **346,** Greg Miller; **347,** Tim Courlas; **349,** Hickson-Bender; **350,** Tim Courlas; **351,** Alexander for EPA Documerica; **353,** Doug Martin; **354,** Cobalt Productions; **357,** Doug Martin; **364,** Tim Courlas; **366**(t) Cobalt Productions, (b) Doug Martin; **367**(l) Metropolitan Museum of Art © 1988, (r) courtesy Burndy Library; **368,** H. Armstrong Roberts; **370,** Doug Martin; **371,** Tim Courlas; **373,** Doug Martin; **375,** AC Spark Plug Div. of General Motors; **377,** Russ Lappa; **379,** Tim Courlas; **381,** H. Armstrong Roberts; **386,** Doris Brookes/Unicorn Stock Photos; **388,** Doug Martin; **389,** Cobalt Productions; **391,** Tim Courlas; **393,** file photo; **395**(t) B.W. Photography, (b) Hickson-Bender; **396**(l) Tom Stack/Tom Stack & Associates, (r) Chip Clark; **397,** Chip Clark; **399,** H. Armstrong Roberts; **400,403,** Tim Courlas; **412–413,** Melvin L. Prueitt, Motion Picture/Video Production, Los Alamos National Laboratory, (insets, l-r) file photo, file photo, The Bettman Archive, © 1988 Masterson Stock; **422,** Department of the Air Force; **429,** Pan-Asian Photo News/Black Star; **430,** Doug Martin; **432,** D.R. Goff/courtesy of CAPA; **433**(l) Pierer/Zefa/H. Armstrong Roberts, (r) Allsport/Woodfin Camp & Associates; **434,** Doug Martin; **438,** Ruth Dixon; **442,** Doug Martin; **444,** Steve Solum/Bruce Coleman, Inc.; **445,** Ultra-Violet Electric Co.; **448**(l) Carroll H. Weiss, (r) D. Davidson/Tom Stack & Associates; **449,** Doug Martin; **451,** Cobalt Productions; **453,** Larry Hamill; **455,** Education Development Center, Inc.; **456,** Steve Allan Bissell; **457**(l) Eastman Kodak Company, (r) Larry Hamill; **458**(t) George Anderson, (b) U.S. Corp of Engineers; **459**(t,bl) Kodansha, (br) Hickson-Bender; **460,** Doug Martin; **464,** Sinclair Stammers/Science Photo Library; **466,** Tim Courlas; **469**(t) Latent Image, (b) Allen Zak; **470,** B.W. Photography; **471,** David Parker/Photo Researchers; **475,** courtesy of Perkin-Elmer Corp.; **476,** Daemmrich/Uniphoto; **477,480,** Cobalt Productions; **481,** Bill Pierce from Rainbow; **482**(t) George Anderson, (b) file photo; **489,** Rich Brommer; **490–491,** NASA-JPL, (insets, l-r) Ernst Haas/Magnum, Larry Hamill, UPI/Bettman Newsphotos, NASA; **492,** T.J. Florian from Rainbow; **494,** Cobalt Productions; **497,** Hickson-Bender; **501,** Craig Kramer; **506,** Tim Courlas; **510**(t) Gerard Photography, (b) Pictures Unlimited; **511,** Pictures Unlimited; **516,** FPG; **518**(t) Tim Courlas, (c,b) Bell Telephone Laboratories; **519,** Tom Pantages; **521,** Cobalt Productions; **522,** Gerard Photography; **523,** courtesy of Black & Decker; **526,** Brian Parker/Tom Stack & Associates; **530,** Tom Stack/Tom Stack & Associates; **532**(t) Thomas Russell, (b) Cobalt Productions; **535,** Dr. Arthur Lesk/Science Photo Library; **536,** Gerard Photography; **540,** Anglo-Australian Observatory; **543,** Ted Rice; **544**(l) Dan McCoy from Rainbow, (r) Phototake; **552,** Craig Kramer; **556**(t) Hickson-Bender, (bl) California Institute of Technology, Carnegie Institute of Washington, (br) NASA; **557,** © 1978 Doug Wilson/Black Star; **562,** Jim Caccavo; **565,** Ron Sherman/Bruce Coleman, Inc.; **564**(t) Gerard Photography, (2nd down) Tim Courlas, (3rd down) Cobalt Productions, (4th down) American Petroleum Institute, (5th down) Cobalt Productions, (b) Asphalt Institute; **570,** courtesy of Boston Edison; **571,** Frank S. Balthis; **572,** Kim Steele/Wheeler Pictures; **574**(t) Cameramann International, (b) N. DeVore III/Bruce Coleman, Inc.; **577,** David Frazier; **579,** UK Atomic Energy Authority; **585,** Y. Arthus-Bartrand/Peter Arnold, Inc.; **589**(l) Hickson-Bender, (r) David M. Dennis.

3 4 5 6 7 8 9 10 11 12 13 14 15—98 97 96 95 94 93 92 91 90 89